85
Janbo   85 1/15 2c

CALCULUS
A FIRST COURSE

THE McGRAW-HILL RYERSON
MATHEMATICS PROGRAM

LIFE MATH 1
LIFE MATH 2
LIFE MATH 3

INTERMEDIATE MATHEMATICS 1
INTERMEDIATE MATHEMATICS 2
INTERMEDIATE MATHEMATICS 3

TEACHER'S EDITION FOR:
INTERMEDIATE MATHEMATICS 1
INTERMEDIATE MATHEMATICS 2
INTERMEDIATE MATHEMATICS 3

BLACKLINE MASTERS FOR:
INTERMEDIATE MATHEMATICS 1
INTERMEDIATE MATHEMATICS 2

APPLIED MATHEMATICS 9
APPLIED MATHEMATICS 10
APPLIED MATHEMATICS 11
APPLIED MATHEMATICS 12

TEACHER'S EDITION FOR:
APPLIED MATHEMATICS 9

TEACHER'S GUIDES FOR:
AM 10
AM 11
AM 12

FOUNDATIONS OF MATHEMATICS 9
FOUNDATIONS OF MATHEMATICS 10
FOUNDATIONS OF MATHEMATICS 11
FOUNDATIONS OF MATHEMATICS 12

TEACHER'S EDITION FOR:
FOUNDATIONS OF MATHEMATICS 9

TEACHER'S GUIDE FOR:
FM 10
FM 11
FM 12

FINITE MATHEMATICS
ALGEBRA AND GEOMETRY
CALCULUS: A FIRST COURSE

CALCULUS
A FIRST COURSE

James Stewart, Ph.D.
Professor of Mathematics, McMaster University

Thomas M.K. Davison, Ph.D.
Professor of Mathematics, McMaster University

Bryan Ferroni, B.Sc.
Sir Allan MacNab Secondary School, Hamilton

Consultants
John Carter, M.Sc.
Department Head, North Toronto Collegiate Institute, Toronto

O. Michael G. Hamilton, M.Sc.
Department Head, Ridley College, St. Catharines

James Laxton, M.Sc.
Delta Secondary School, Hamilton

M. Patricia Lenz, M.Sc.
Department Head, St. John's College, Brantford

McGraw-Hill Ryerson Limited

Toronto   Montreal   New York   Auckland   Bogotá   Cairo   Caracas   Hamburg   Lisbon
London   Madrid   Mexico   Milan   New Delhi   Paris   San Juan
São Paulo   Singapore   Sydney   Tokyo

CALCULUS: A First Course

ISBN 0-07-549601-1

17 BP 02 01

Printed and bound in Canada

Cover and Text Design by Daniel Kewley

Technical Illustrations by Pat Code and Sam Graphics, Inc.

Photo by Don Ford

Canadian Cataloguing in Publication Data

Stewart, James
    Calculus : a first course

(The McGraw-Hill Ryerson mathematics program)
ISBN 0-07-549601-1

1. Calculus.   I. Davison, Thomas M. K.
II. Ferroni, Bryan.   III. Title.   IV. Series.

QA303.S87 1989   515   C89-093342-1

TABLE
OF
CONTENTS

3 APPLICATIONS OF DERIVATIVES 117

4 EXTREME VALUES 161

5 CURVE SKETCHING 203

PREFACE

This textbook on Calculus is part of a three-volume series, also including books on Finite Mathematics and Algebra and Geometry, for courses that represent the culmination of a high school mathematics program.

APPLICATIONS

Most students need the motivation of realistic applications to learn calculus. We have selected a diverse range of applications from the physical, social, and engineering sciences, as well as from mathematics itself. Included are the following:

- We show how derivatives occur as the slope of a tangent, the velocity of a car, the linear density of a wire, the rate of growth of an animal or bacteria population, the rate of change of temperature, the rate of flow of water, the rate of spread of an epidemic, the rate of reaction in chemistry, and the marginal cost and marginal profit in economics.
- We show how to minimize the cost of laying cable across a river, the cost of fencing a field, and the average cost of producing a commodity. We show how to maximize revenue or profit if cost and demand functions are known.
- We explain the radiocarbon dating of ancient objects.
- We show how Newton's Law of Cooling can be used to find the temperature of a 900°C rod of steel after it has been cooled by forced air.
- We solve a differential equation to find the number of fish in a lake at a given time.

PROBLEM SOLVING EMPHASIS

Our educational philosophy has been strongly influenced by the books of George Polya and the lectures of both Polya and Gabor Szego at Stanford University. They consistently introduced a topic by relating it to something concrete or familiar. In this spirit, we have tried to motivate new topics by relating mathematical concepts to the students' experiences.

The influence of Polya's work on problem solving can be seen throughout the book. The Review and Preview to Chapter 3 gives an introduction to some of the problem-solving strategies that he has explained at greater length in his books *How to Solve It*, *Mathematical Discovery*, and *Mathematics and Plausible Reasoning*. When these strategies occur in examples, we highlight their use with margin captions.

In addition to the graded exercise sets, we have included special problems, called PROBLEMS PLUS, that require a higher level of problem-solving skill.

ILLUSTRATIONS/ANSWERS

We have included an unusually large amount of art in order to convey the notion of change that is basic to calculus. The answer section alone contains 384 diagrams, many of them answers to the curve-sketching questions. All answers are given at the end of the text. Complete solutions to every question are available in the *Solutions Manual*.

FOUNDERS OF CALCULUS

We have included biographies of five mathematicians who played a major role in the invention and advancement of calculus: Sir Isaac Newton, Gottfried Leibniz, Pierre Fermat, the Bernoulli family, and Leonhard Euler. We believe that an account of the historical development of calculus helps to make the subject come alive.

ACKNOWLEDGMENTS

In addition to the reviewers listed earlier and our consultant John Carter, who attended all our authors' meetings, we wish to thank our teaching colleagues for their valuable advice, the editorial and production staff at McGraw-Hill Ryerson for a superb job, and those close to us who understandingly put up with the long hours that we devoted to this project.

James Stewart
Thomas M.K. Davison
Bryan Ferroni

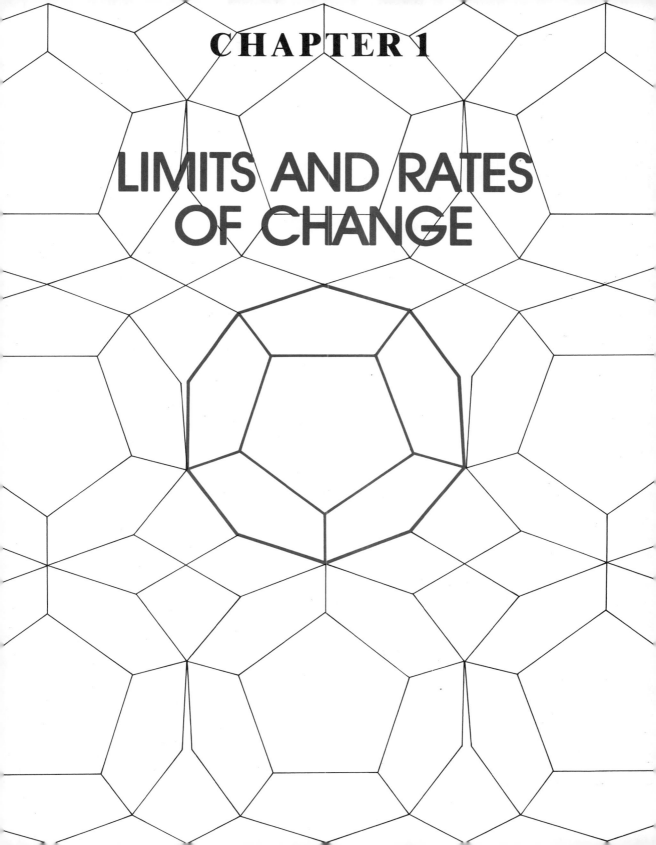

CHAPTER 1

LIMITS AND RATES OF CHANGE

REVIEW AND PREVIEW TO CHAPTER 1

Factoring

Example 1   Factor $x^2 - 3x - 18$.

Solution   The two integers that add to give -3 and multiply to give -18 are -6 and 3. Therefore

$$x^2 - 3x - 18 = (x - 6)(x + 3)$$

Some special polynomials can be factored using the following formulas.

$a^2 - b^2 = (a - b)(a + b)$	(difference of squares)
$a^3 - b^3 = (a - b)(a^2 + ab + b^2)$	(difference of cubes)
$a^3 + b^3 = (a + b)(a^2 - ab + b^2)$	(sum of cubes)

Example 2   Factor.   (a) $x^3 + 27$ (b) $2x^4 - 18x^2$

Solution   (a) Using the formula for a sum of cubes with $a = x$ and $b = 3$, we have

$$x^3 + 27 = x^3 + 3^3 = (x + 3)(x^2 - 3x + 9)$$

(b) $2x^4 - 18x^2 = 2x^2(x^2 - 9)$ (common factor)
$= 2x^2(x - 3)(x + 3)$ (difference of squares)

The Factor Theorem

A polynomial $P(x)$ has $x - b$ as a factor if and only if $P(b) = 0$.

Example 3   Factor $P(x) = 2x^3 - 5x^2 - 4x + 3$.

Solution
$$P(1) = 2(1)^3 - 5(1)^2 - 4(1) + 3 = -4 \neq 0$$
$$P(-1) = 2(-1)^3 - 5(-1)^2 - 4(-1) + 3 = 0$$

Therefore, by the Factor Theorem, $x + 1$ is a factor. We find another factor by long division:

$$
\begin{array}{r}
2x^2 - 7x + 3 \\
x + 1 \overline{)\smash{2x^3 - 5x^2 - 4x + 3}} \\
2x^3 + 2x^2 \\
\hline
-7x^2 - 4x \\
-7x^2 - 7x \\
\hline
3x + 3 \\
3x + 3 \\
\hline
\end{array}
$$

Thus we have

$$
\begin{aligned}
P(x) &= 2x^3 - 5x^2 - 4x + 3 \\
&= (x + 1)(2x^2 - 7x + 3) \\
&= (x + 1)(2x - 1)(x - 3)
\end{aligned}
$$

When factoring expressions that involve fractional or negative exponents, we use the Laws of Exponents.

Example 4   Factor $2x^{\frac{3}{2}} + 4x^{\frac{1}{2}} - 6x^{-\frac{1}{2}}$.

Solution   The term with the smallest exponent is $-6x^{-\frac{1}{2}}$ and we use $2x^{-\frac{1}{2}}$ as a common factor.

$$
\begin{aligned}
2x^{\frac{3}{2}} + 4x^{\frac{1}{2}} - 6x^{-\frac{1}{2}} &= 2x^{-\frac{1}{2}}(x^2 + 2x - 3) \\
&= 2x^{-\frac{1}{2}}(x - 1)(x + 3)
\end{aligned}
$$

EXERCISE 1

1. Factor.
   (a) $x^2 - x - 2$ (b) $x^2 - 9x + 14$
   (c) $x^2 + 7x + 12$ (d) $2x^2 - x - 1$
   (e) $5x^2 + 13x + 6$ (f) $6y^2 - 11y + 3$
   (g) $t^3 + 2t^2 - 3t$ (h) $3x^4 + 7x^3 + 2x^2$

2. Factor.
   (a) $4x^2 - 25$ (b) $x^3 - 1$
   (c) $t^3 + 64$ (d) $y^3 - 9y$
   (e) $8c^3 - 27d^3$ (f) $x^6 + 8$
   (g) $x^4 - 16$ (h) $r^8 - 1$

3. Factor.
   (a) $x^3 - x^2 - 16x + 16$ (b) $x^3 - 7x + 6$
   (c) $x^3 + 5x^2 - 2x - 24$ (d) $x^3 + 2x^2 - 11x - 12$
   (e) $4x^3 + 12x^2 + 5x - 6$ (f) $x^4 - 3x^3 - 7x^2 + 27x - 18$

4. Factor.
   (a) $x^{\frac{5}{2}} - x^{\frac{1}{2}}$ (b) $x + 5 + 6x^{-1}$
   (c) $x^{\frac{3}{2}} + 2x^{\frac{1}{2}} - 8x^{-\frac{1}{2}}$ (d) $2x^{\frac{7}{2}} - 2x^{\frac{1}{2}}$
   (e) $1 + 2x^{-1} + x^{-2}$ (f) $(x^2 + 1)^{\frac{1}{2}} + 3(x^2 + 1)^{-\frac{1}{2}}$

Rationalizing

To rationalize a numerator or denominator that contains an expression such as

$$\sqrt{a} - \sqrt{b}$$

we multiply both the numerator and the denominator by the **conjugate radical**

$$\sqrt{a} + \sqrt{b}$$

Then we can take advantage of the formula for a difference of squares:

$$(\sqrt{a} - \sqrt{b})(\sqrt{a} + \sqrt{b}) = (\sqrt{a})^2 - (\sqrt{b})^2 = a - b$$

Example   Rationalize the numerator in the expression

$$\frac{\sqrt{x + 4} - 2}{x}$$

Solution   We multiply the numerator and the denominator by the conjugate radical $\sqrt{x + 4} + 2$:

$$\frac{\sqrt{x + 4} - 2}{x} = \left(\frac{\sqrt{x + 4} - 2}{x}\right)\left(\frac{\sqrt{x + 4} + 2}{\sqrt{x + 4} + 2}\right)$$

Do not expand the denominator.

$$= \frac{(x + 4) - 4}{x(\sqrt{x + 4} + 2)}$$

$$= \frac{x}{x(\sqrt{x + 4} + 2)} \quad (x \neq 0)$$

$$= \frac{1}{\sqrt{x + 4} + 2}$$

EXERCISE 2

1. Rationalize the numerator.

(a) $\dfrac{\sqrt{x} - 3}{x - 9}$

(b) $\dfrac{\dfrac{1}{\sqrt{x}} - 1}{x - 1}$

(c) $\dfrac{x\sqrt{x} - 8}{x - 4}$

(d) $\dfrac{\sqrt{2 + h} + \sqrt{2 - h}}{h}$

(e) $\sqrt{x^2 + 3x + 4} - x$

(f) $\sqrt{x^2 + x} - \sqrt{x^2 - x}$

2. Rationalize the denominator.

(a) $\dfrac{1}{\sqrt{x + 1} - 1}$

(b) $\dfrac{4}{\sqrt{x + 2} + \sqrt{x}}$

(c) $\dfrac{x}{\sqrt{x^2 + 1} + x}$

(d) $\dfrac{x^2}{\sqrt{x + 1} - \sqrt{x - 1}}$

INTRODUCTION

In this first chapter, we show how the idea of a limit arises when we try to find a tangent to a curve. After developing the properties of limits of functions, we use them to compute tangents, velocities, and other rates of change. Then we investigate another type of limit, the limit of a sequence, and show how it is used to find the sum of an infinite series.

1.1 LINEAR FUNCTIONS AND THE TANGENT PROBLEM

A **linear function** is a function f of the form

$$f(x) = mx + b, \; m \text{ and } b \text{ constants}$$

It is called linear because its graph has the equation $y = mx + b$, which we recognize as the equation of a line with slope m and y-intercept b.

Recall that the **slope** of a nonvertical line that passes through the points $P_1(x_1, y_1)$ and $P_2(x_2, y_2)$ is defined by

$$m = \frac{\Delta y}{\Delta x} = \frac{y_2 - y_1}{x_2 - x_1}$$

Since the slope is the ratio of the change in y to the change in x, it can be interpreted as the **rate of change of y with respect to x**.

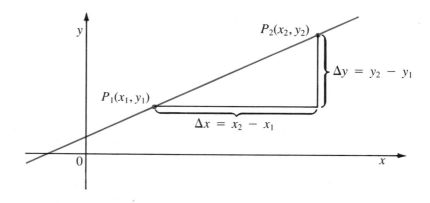

The following figure shows several lines labelled with their slopes. Notice that lines with positive slope slant upward to the right, whereas lines with negative slope slant downward to the right. Notice also that the steepest lines are the ones where the absolute value of the slope is the largest, and a horizontal line has slope zero. The slope of a vertical line is not defined.

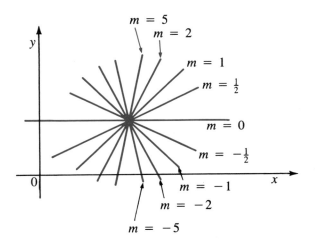

Example 1 Find a linear function whose graph passes through the points $(-1, -1)$ and $(2, 5)$.

Solution The slope of the graph is

$$m = \frac{5 - (-1)}{2 - (-1)} = \frac{6}{3} = 2$$

We find the equation of the line using the point-slope form.

$$y - y_1 = m(x - x_1)$$
$$y - 5 = 2(x - 2)$$

or $$y = 2x + 1$$

The function is given by

$$f(x) = 2x + 1$$

The fact that the rate of change of y with respect to x is 2 means that y increases twice as fast as x.

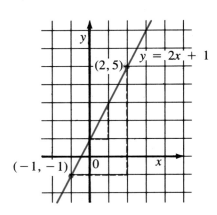

Example 2   A linear function is given by $y = 6 - 5x$. If x increases by 2, how does y change?

Solution   The rate of change is

$$\frac{\Delta y}{\Delta x} = \text{slope} = -5$$

and we are given that $\Delta x = 2$. Thus

$$\Delta y = (-5)\Delta x = (-5)(2) = -10$$

and so y decreases by 10.

The Tangent Problem

The word *tangent* comes from the Latin word *tangens*, which means touching. For a simple curve, such as a circle, a tangent is a line that intersects the circle once and only once. But for more complicated curves this definition is not good enough. The figure below shows a point P on a curve C and two lines l and t passing through P. The line l intersects C only once, but it does not look like a tangent. On the other hand, the line t looks like a tangent but it intersects C twice.

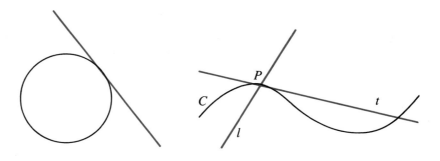

We look at the problem of finding a tangent line to a specific curve, $y = x^2$, in the following example.

Example 3   Find the equation of a tangent line to the parabola $y = x^2$ at the point $P(1, 1)$.

Solution   We will be able to find the equation of the tangent line t as soon as we know its slope m. The difficulty is that we know only one point, P, on t, whereas we need two points to compute the slope. But we can compute an approximation to m by choosing a nearby point $Q(x, y)$ on the parabola (as in the diagram) and computing the slope m_{PQ} of the line PQ, which is called a *secant line*.

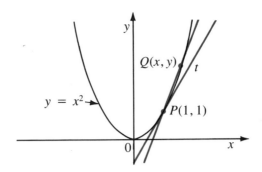

We choose $x \ne 1$ so that $Q \ne P$. Then

$$m_{PQ} = \frac{y - 1}{x - 1}$$

But since Q lies on the parabola we have $y = x^2$, so

$$m_{PQ} = \frac{x^2 - 1}{x - 1}$$

For instance, for the point $Q(1.1, 1.21)$ we have

$$m_{PQ} = \frac{1.21 - 1}{1.1 - 1} = \frac{0.21}{0.1} = 2.1$$

The following tables give the values of m_{PQ} for several values of x close to 1.

Approaching 1 From the Right			Approaching 1 From the Left	
$x > 1$	m_{PQ}		$x < 1$	m_{PQ}
2	3		0	1
1.5	2.5		0.5	1.5
1.1	2.1		0.9	1.9
1.01	2.01		0.99	1.99
1.001	2.001		0.999	1.999

The closer Q is to P, the closer x is to 1, and, it appears, the closer m_{PQ} is to 2.

This suggests that the slope of the tangent line t should be $m = 2$. We say that the slope of the tangent line is the *limit* of the slopes of the secant lines, and we express this symbolically by writing

$$\lim_{Q \to P} m_{PQ} = m$$

and

$$\lim_{x \to 1} \frac{x^2 - 1}{x - 1} = 2$$

Since the tangent line passes through $P(1, 1)$ and has slope 2, we use the point-slope form of the equation of a line to write the equation of the tangent as

$$y - 1 = 2(x - 1) \quad \text{or} \quad y = 2x - 1$$

Example 3 shows that in order to solve tangent problems we must be able to find limits. After studying methods for computing limits in the next two sections we will return to the problem of finding tangent lines to general curves in Section 1.4.

EXERCISE 1.1

A **1.** State the slopes of the given linear functions.
   (a) $y = 4x$ (b) $y = 3x - 5$
   (c) $f(x) = \frac{1}{3}x - 2$ (d) $f(x) = 2 - 3x$
   (e) $f(x) = \frac{1}{2}(1 - x)$ (f) $x + 2y = 3$

B **2.** Find an equation of the line that passes through the points $(-3, 5)$ and $(4, -5)$.

3. Find a linear function whose graph passes through the points $(-4, -2)$ and $(2, 10)$.

4. A linear function is given by $y = 16 + 3x$. How does y change
   (a) if x increases by 4?   (b) if x decreases by 2?

5. A linear function is given by $y = \dfrac{1 - x}{2}$. How does y change
   (a) if x increases by 6?   (b) if x decreases by 4?

6. A car travels at a constant speed and covers 140 km in 4 h. If s represents distance travelled (in kilometres) and t represents time elapsed (in hours), express s as a function of t and draw its graph. What does the slope of the line represent?

7. The point $P(1, 3)$ lies on the curve $y = 2x + x^2$.
   (a) If Q is the point $(x, 2x + x^2)$, find the slope of the secant line PQ for the following values of x:

         (i) 2 (ii) 1.5 (iii) 1.1 (iv) 1.01 (v) 1.001

         (vi) 0 (vii) 0.5 (viii) 0.9 (ix) 0.99 (x) 0.999

   (a) Using the results of part (a), guess the value of the slope of the tangent line to the curve at $P(1, 3)$.
   (c) Using the slope from part (b), find the equation of the tangent line to the curve at $P(1, 3)$.
   (d) Sketch the curve, two of the secant lines, and the tangent line.

8. The point $P(2, 0)$ lies on the curve $y = -x^2 + 6x - 8$.

    (a) If Q is the point $(x, -x^2 + 6x - 8)$, find the slope of the secant line PQ for the following values of x:

            (i) 3   (ii) 2.5 (iii) 2.1 (iv) 2.01
            (v) 1   (vi) 1.5 (vii) 1.9 (viii) 1.99

    (a) Using the results of part (a), guess the value of the slope of the tangent line to the curve at $P(2, 0)$.

    (c) Using the slope from part (b), find the equation of the tangent line to the curve at $P(2, 0)$.

    (d) Sketch the curve, two of the secant lines, and the tangent line.

9. The point $P(1, \frac{1}{4})$ lies on the curve $y = \frac{1}{4}x^3$.

    (a) If Q is the point $(x, \frac{1}{4}x^3)$, find the slope of the secant line PQ for the following values of x:

            (i) 2   (ii) 1.5 (iii) 1.1 (iv) 1.01 (v) 1.001
            (vi) 0   (vii) 0.5 (viii) 0.9 (ix) 0.99 (x) 0.999

    (b) Using the results of part (a), guess the value of the slope of the tangent line to the curve at $P(1, \frac{1}{4})$.

    (c) Using the slope from part (b), find the equation of the tangent line to the curve at $P(1, \frac{1}{4})$.

    (d) Sketch the curve, two of the secant lines, and the tangent line.

10. The point $P(0.5, 2)$ lies on the curve $y = \frac{1}{x}$.

    (a) If Q is the point $(x, \frac{1}{x})$, use your calculator to find approximate values of the slope of the secant line PQ for the following values of x:

            (i) 2   (ii) 1   (iii) 0.9   (iv) 0.8   (v) 0.7
            (vi) 0.6 (vii) 0.55 (viii) 0.51   (ix) 0.45   (x) 0.49

    (b) Using the results of part (a), guess the value of the slope of the tangent line to the curve at $P(0.5, 2)$.

    (c) Using the slope from part (b), find the equation of the tangent line to the curve at $P(0.5, 2)$.

    (d) Sketch the curve, two of the secant lines, and the tangent line.

C 11. As dry air moves upward, it expands and in so doing cools at a rate of about 1°C for each 100 m rise, up to about 12 km.

    (a) If the ground temperature is 20°C, find an expression for the temperature T as a function of the height h.

    (b) Sketch the graph of T. What does the slope represent?

12. The monthly cost of owning a car depends on the number of kilometres driven. Judy Weyman found that in May it cost her $500 to drive 800 km and in June it cost her $650 to drive 1400 km.

    (a) Express the monthly cost C as a function of distance driven d, assuming that a linear function is a suitable model.

(b) Use this function to predict the cost of driving 2000 km per month.

(c) What does the slope of the function represent?

(d) What is the monthly cost if she does not drive her car at all? Is it reasonable?

(e) Why is a linear function a suitable model in this situation?

1.2 THE LIMIT OF A FUNCTION

We saw in the first section how limits arise in trying to find a tangent line to a curve. Later in this chapter we will see that limits also arise in computing velocities and other rates of change. In fact, limits are basic to all of calculus and so in this section we look at limits in general and methods for calculating them.

We begin by investigating the behaviour of the function

$$f(x) = \frac{x - 3}{x^2 - 4x + 3}$$

when x is near 3. The following table gives values of $f(x)$ for values of x approaching 3 (but not equal to 3).

$x < 3$	$f(x)$		$x > 3$	$f(x)$
2.5	0.666 667		3.5	0.400 000
2.9	0.526 316		3.1	0.476 190
2.99	0.502 513		3.01	0.497 512
2.999	0.500 250		3.001	0.499 750
2.9999	0.500 025		3.0001	0.499 975

The open circle at $\left(3, \frac{1}{2}\right)$ indicates that the function is not defined when $x = 3$.

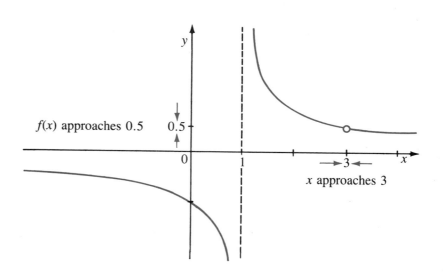

$f(x)$ approaches 0.5

x approaches 3

From the table and the graph of f, we see that when x is close to 3 (on either side of 3), $f(x)$ is close to 0.5. In fact, it appears that we can make the values of $f(x)$ as close as we like to 0.5 by taking x close enough to 3. We express this by saying

"the limit of $\dfrac{x-3}{x^2-4x+3}$ as x approaches 3 is equal to $\frac{1}{2}$"

and by writing

$$\lim_{x \to 3} \frac{x-3}{x^2-4x+3} = \frac{1}{2}$$

In general, we have the following definition of the limit of a function.

We write $\quad \lim_{x \to a} f(x) = L$

and say

"the limit of $f(x)$, as x approaches a, equals L"

if we can make the values of $f(x)$ arbitrarily close to L (as close to L as we like) by taking x to be sufficiently close to a, but not equal to a.

Roughly speaking, this says that the values of $f(x)$ become closer and closer to the number L as x gets closer and closer to the number a (from either side of a) but $x \neq a$.

Notice the phrase "but $x \neq a$" in the definition of a limit. This means that in finding the limit of $f(x)$ as x approaches a, we need never consider $x = a$. In fact, $f(x)$ need not even be defined when $x = a$. (The function f considered before the definition is not defined at $x = 3$.) The only thing that matters is how f is defined *near a*.

Example 1   Find $\lim_{x \to 5} (x^2 + 2x - 3)$.

Solution   It seems clear that when x is close to 5, x^2 is close to 25 and $2x$ is close to 10. Thus it appears that

$$\lim_{x \to 5} (x^2 + 2x - 3) = 25 + 10 - 3 = 32$$

In Example 1 we arrived at the answer by intuitive reasoning, but it is also possible to find the limit using the following properties of limits. These properties are proved in more advanced courses in calculus using a precise definition of a limit. Notice that they apply only in situations where the limits exist. See Example 8 and Question 12 in Exercise 1.2 for examples in which limits do not exist.

Properties of Limits

Suppose that the limits

$$\lim_{x \to a} f(x) \quad \text{and} \quad \lim_{x \to a} g(x)$$

both exist and let c be a constant. Then

1. $\lim_{x \to a} [f(x) + g(x)] = \lim_{x \to a} f(x) + \lim_{x \to a} g(x)$

2. $\lim_{x \to a} [f(x) - g(x)] = \lim_{x \to a} f(x) - \lim_{x \to a} g(x)$

3. $\lim_{x \to a} [cf(x)] = c \lim_{x \to a} f(x)$

4. $\lim_{x \to a} [f(x)g(x)] = \lim_{x \to a} f(x) \lim_{x \to a} g(x)$

5. $\lim_{x \to a} \dfrac{f(x)}{g(x)} = \dfrac{\lim_{x \to a} f(x)}{\lim_{x \to a} g(x)}$ if $\lim_{x \to a} g(x) \neq 0$

6. $\lim_{x \to a} [f(x)]^n = \left[\lim_{x \to a} f(x) \right]^n$ if n is a positive integer

7. $\lim_{x \to a} \sqrt[n]{f(x)} = \sqrt[n]{\lim_{x \to a} f(x)}$ if the root on the right side exists

These seven properties of limits can be stated verbally as follows.

1. The limit of a sum is the sum of the limits.
2. The limit of a difference is the difference of the limits.
3. The limit of a constant times a function is the constant times the limit of the function.
4. The limit of a product is the product of the limits.
5. The limit of a quotient is the quotient of the limits (if the limit of the denominator is not 0).
6. The limit of a power is the power of the limit.
7. The limit of a root is the root of the limit (if the root exists).

If we start with the basic limits

$$\lim_{x \to a} x = a \qquad \lim_{x \to a} c = c \qquad (c \text{ is a constant})$$

then from Properties 6 and 7 we deduce the following:

$$\lim_{x \to a} x^n = a^n \qquad \lim_{x \to a} \sqrt[n]{x} = \sqrt[n]{a} \qquad (\text{if } \sqrt[n]{a} \text{ exists})$$

Using these limits, together with the seven properties of limits, we can compute limits of more complicated functions. First we return to the limit of Example 1.

Example 2   Find $\lim\limits_{x \to 5} (x^2 + 2x - 3)$ using the properties of limits.

Solution

$$\begin{aligned} \lim\limits_{x \to 5} (x^2 + 2x - 3) &= \lim\limits_{x \to 5} x^2 + \lim\limits_{x \to 5} 2x - \lim\limits_{x \to 5} 3 \quad \text{(Properties 1 and 2)} \\ &= \lim\limits_{x \to 5} x^2 + 2 \lim\limits_{x \to 5} x - \lim\limits_{x \to 5} 3 \quad \text{(Property 3)} \\ &= 5^2 + 2(5) - 3 \\ &= 32 \end{aligned}$$

Example 3   Evaluate using the properties of limits.

(a) $\lim\limits_{x \to 1} \dfrac{x^4 - 5x^2 + 1}{x + 2}$ (b) $\lim\limits_{x \to 3} \sqrt{x^2 + x}$

Solution   (a)

$$\begin{aligned} \lim\limits_{x \to 1} \dfrac{x^4 - 5x^2 + 1}{x + 2} &= \dfrac{\lim\limits_{x \to 1} (x^4 - 5x^2 + 1)}{\lim\limits_{x \to 1} (x + 2)} \quad \text{(Property 5)} \\ &= \dfrac{\lim\limits_{x \to 1} x^4 - 5 \lim\limits_{x \to 1} x^2 + \lim\limits_{x \to 1} 1}{\lim\limits_{x \to 1} x + \lim\limits_{x \to 1} 2} \quad \begin{array}{l}\text{(Properties 2,}\\\text{3, and 1)}\end{array} \\ &= \dfrac{1^4 - 5(1)^2 + 1}{1 + 2} \\ &= -1 \end{aligned}$$

(b) $\begin{aligned}[t] \lim\limits_{x \to 3} \sqrt{x^2 + x} &= \sqrt{\lim\limits_{x \to 3} (x^2 + x)} \quad \text{(Property 7)} \\ &= \sqrt{\lim\limits_{x \to 3} x^2 + \lim\limits_{x \to 3} x} \quad \text{(Property 1)} \\ &= \sqrt{3^2 + 3} \\ &= \sqrt{12} \\ &= 2\sqrt{3} \end{aligned}$

Notice that if we let

$$f(x) = \dfrac{x^4 - 5x^2 + 1}{x + 2}$$

then

$$f(1) = \dfrac{1^4 - 5(1)^2 + 1}{1 + 2} = -1$$

and so we would have got the right answer in Example 3(a) by substituting 1 for x:

$$\lim_{x \to 1} f(x) = f(1)$$

Similarly, direct substitution provides the correct answer in Example 3(b):

$$\text{If } g(x) = \sqrt{x^2 + x}, \text{ then } \lim_{x \to 3} g(x) = g(3).$$

Functions with this property, that is,

$$\lim_{x \to a} f(x) = f(a)$$

are called **continuous at a**. The geometric properties of such functions will be studied in the next section.

Using the properties of limits, it can be shown that many familiar functions are continuous. Recall that a **polynomial** is a function of the form

$$P(x) = a_n x^n + a_{n-1} x^{n-1} + \ldots + a_1 x + a_0$$

where $a_0, a_1, \ldots, a_n$ are constants. A **rational function** is a ratio of polynomials.

(a) Any polynomial P is continuous at every number; that is,

$$\lim_{x \to a} P(x) = P(a)$$

(b) Any rational function $f(x) = \dfrac{P(x)}{Q(x)}$, where P and Q are polynomials, is continuous at every number a such that $Q(a) \neq 0$; that is,

$$\lim_{x \to a} \frac{P(x)}{Q(x)} = \frac{P(a)}{Q(a)} \qquad Q(a) \neq 0$$

For instance, we could rework the solution to Example 2 as follows:

$$f(x) = x^2 + 2x - 3 \text{ is a polynomial, so it is continuous at 5}$$

and therefore,

$$\lim_{x \to 5} (x^2 + 2x - 3) = f(5) = 5^2 + 2(5) - 3 = 32$$

Not all limits can be evaluated by direct substitution, however, as the following examples illustrate.

Example 4   Evaluate $\displaystyle\lim_{x \to 4} \frac{x^2 - 16}{x - 4}$.

Solution   Let

$$f(x) = \frac{x^2 - 16}{x - 4}$$

We cannot find the limit by substituting $x = 4$ because $f(4)$ is not defined ($\frac{0}{0}$ is meaningless). Remember that the definition of $\displaystyle\lim_{x \to a} f(x)$ says that we consider values of x that are close to a but not equal to a. Therefore in this example we have $x \neq 4$, so we can factor the numerator as a difference of squares and write

$$\begin{aligned}
\lim_{x \to 4} \frac{x^2 - 16}{x - 4} &= \lim_{x \to 4} \frac{(x - 4)(x + 4)}{x - 4} \\
&= \lim_{x \to 4} (x + 4) \\
&= 4 + 4 \\
&= 8
\end{aligned}$$

Notice that in Example 4 we replaced the given rational function by a continuous function $[g(x) = x + 4]$ that is equal to $f(x)$ for $x \neq 4$. This is illustrated by the graph of f.

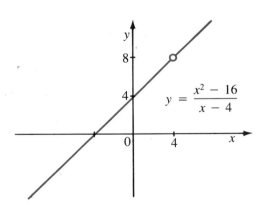

$$y = \frac{x^2 - 16}{x - 4}$$

Example 5   Find $\displaystyle\lim_{x \to 2} \frac{x^3 - 8}{x^2 - 3x + 2}$.

Solution   Notice that we cannot substitute $x = 2$ since we would obtain $\frac{0}{0}$. We replace the given rational function by a rational function that is continuous at 2. To do this, we factor the numerator by using the formula for a difference of cubes

$$a^3 - b^3 = (a - b)(a^2 + ab + b^2)$$

with $a = x$ and $b = 2$. Then

$$\lim_{x \to 2} \frac{x^3 - 8}{x^2 - 3x + 2} = \lim_{x \to 2} \frac{(x - 2)(x^2 + 2x + 4)}{(x - 2)(x - 1)}$$

$$= \lim_{x \to 2} \frac{x^2 + 2x + 4}{x - 1}$$

$$= \frac{2^2 + 2(2) + 4}{2 - 1}$$

$$= 12$$

Example 6   Find $\displaystyle\lim_{h \to 0} \frac{(2 + h)^2 - 4}{h}$.

Solution   Again we cannot compute the limit by letting $h = 0$, so we first simplify the numerator:

$$\lim_{h \to 0} \frac{(2 + h)^2 - 4}{h} = \lim_{h \to 0} \frac{(4 + 4h + h^2) - 4}{h}$$

$$= \lim_{h \to 0} \frac{4h + h^2}{h}$$

$$= \lim_{h \to 0} (4 + h)$$

$$= 4$$

Example 7   Evaluate $\displaystyle\lim_{x \to 0} \frac{\sqrt{x + 1} - 1}{x}$.

Solution   Here the algebraic simplification consists of rationalizing the numerator, that is, multiplying numerator and denominator by the conjugate radical $\sqrt{x + 1} + 1$:

$$\lim_{x \to 0} \frac{\sqrt{x + 1} - 1}{x} = \lim_{x \to 0} \left(\frac{\sqrt{x + 1} - 1}{x}\right)\left(\frac{\sqrt{x + 1} + 1}{\sqrt{x + 1} + 1}\right)$$

Do not expand the denominator.

$$= \lim_{x \to 0} \frac{(x + 1) - 1}{x(\sqrt{x + 1} + 1)}$$

$$= \lim_{x \to 0} \frac{x}{x(\sqrt{x + 1} + 1)}$$

$$= \lim_{x \to 0} \frac{1}{\sqrt{x + 1} + 1}$$

$$= \frac{\displaystyle\lim_{x \to 0} 1}{\sqrt{\displaystyle\lim_{x \to 0} (x + 1)} + \displaystyle\lim_{x \to 0} 1}$$

$$= \frac{1}{\sqrt{0 + 1} + 1}$$

$$= \frac{1}{2}$$

Example 8   Show that $\lim\limits_{x\to 0} \frac{1}{x}$ does not exist.

Solution   As x approaches 0 through positive values, $\frac{1}{x}$ becomes very large. As x approaches 0 through negative values, $\frac{1}{x}$ becomes very large negative. We see from the graph of $y = \frac{1}{x}$ that the values of y do not approach any number as x approaches 0. Therefore

$$\lim\limits_{x\to 0} \frac{1}{x} \text{ does not exist}$$

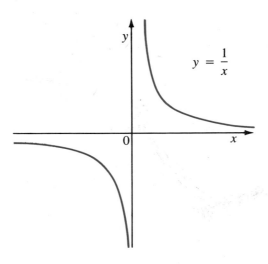

EXERCISE 1.2

A **1.**   Use the given graph of f to state the value of the limit, if it exists.

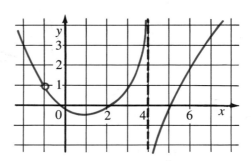

(a) $\lim\limits_{x\to 3} f(x)$ (b) $\lim\limits_{x\to 2} f(x)$ (c) $\lim\limits_{x\to -1} f(x)$ (d) $\lim\limits_{x\to 4} f(x)$

2. State the value of each limit.

(a) $\lim\limits_{x \to 2} x^3$

(b) $\lim\limits_{x \to \pi} x$

(c) $\lim\limits_{x \to 8} 3$

(d) $\lim\limits_{x \to 4} \sqrt{x}$

(e) $\lim\limits_{x \to k} x^6$

(f) $\lim\limits_{x \to 0} \pi$

 B **3.** Use the properties of limits to evaluate the following.

(a) $\lim\limits_{x \to 1} (3x - 7)$

(b) $\lim\limits_{x \to -1} (2x^2 - 5x + 3)$

(c) $\lim\limits_{x \to 2} (x^3 + x^2 - 2x - 8)$

(d) $\lim\limits_{x \to -2} (x^2 + 5x + 3)^6$

(e) $\lim\limits_{x \to 0} \dfrac{x - 1}{x + 1}$

(f) $\lim\limits_{x \to 4} \dfrac{x^2 + 2x - 3}{x^2 + 2}$

(g) $\lim\limits_{t \to 2} \dfrac{t^4 - 3t + 1}{t^2(t - 1)^3}$

(h) $\lim\limits_{u \to -4} \sqrt{u^4 + 2u^2}$

(i) $\lim\limits_{x \to 5} \sqrt[3]{x^2 + 2x - 8}$

(j) $\lim\limits_{t \to 3} \left(2t^2 + \sqrt{\dfrac{6 + t}{4 - t}}\right)$

4. Find the following limits.

(a) $\lim\limits_{x \to -2} \dfrac{x + 2}{x^2 - 4}$

(b) $\lim\limits_{x \to 1} \dfrac{x^2 - 3x + 2}{x - 1}$

(c) $\lim\limits_{x \to 3} \dfrac{x^2 - 2x - 3}{x^2 - 4x + 3}$

(d) $\lim\limits_{x \to -2} \dfrac{2x^2 + 5x + 2}{x^2 - 2x - 8}$

(e) $\lim\limits_{x \to 1} \dfrac{x^3 - 1}{x^2 - 1}$

(f) $\lim\limits_{x \to -3} \dfrac{x + 3}{x^3 + 27}$

(g) $\lim\limits_{x \to 9} \dfrac{x - 9}{\sqrt{x} - 3}$

(h) $\lim\limits_{x \to 2} \dfrac{\frac{1}{x} - \frac{1}{2}}{x - 2}$

5. Evaluate the following.

(a) $\lim\limits_{h \to 0} \dfrac{(4 + h)^3 - 64}{h}$

(b) $\lim\limits_{h \to 0} \dfrac{(h - 2)^2 - 4}{h}$

(c) $\lim\limits_{h \to 0} \dfrac{\frac{1}{1 + h} - 1}{h}$

(d) $\lim\limits_{h \to 0} \dfrac{(2 + h)^4 - 16}{h}$

(e) $\lim\limits_{h \to 0} \dfrac{\sqrt{9 + h} - 3}{h}$

(f) $\lim\limits_{h \to 0} \dfrac{\frac{1}{(2 + h)^2} - \frac{1}{4}}{h}$

6. Find the following limits, if they exist.

(a) $\lim\limits_{x \to 3} \dfrac{1}{(x - 3)^2}$

(b) $\lim\limits_{x \to -8} \dfrac{x^2 + 16x + 64}{x + 8}$

(c) $\lim\limits_{x \to 1} \dfrac{x^4 - 1}{x - 1}$

(d) $\lim\limits_{x \to -1} \dfrac{x - 1}{x^2 - 1}$

(e) $\lim\limits_{x \to 1} \dfrac{x^2 + x - 2}{x^2 - 2x + 1}$

(f) $\lim\limits_{x \to -2} \dfrac{x^2 - x - 2}{x^2 + 3x + 2}$

(g) $\lim_{x \to 3} \dfrac{x^{-2} - 3^{-2}}{x - 3}$

(h) $\lim_{x \to 4} \dfrac{\dfrac{1}{\sqrt{x}} - \dfrac{1}{2}}{x - 4}$

(i) $\lim_{x \to 1} \dfrac{x^3 - 1}{x^3 - x^2 - 4x + 4}$

(j) $\lim_{x \to 1} \dfrac{x - 1}{\sqrt{x} - x}$

7. (a) Use your calculator to evaluate $f(x) = (1 + x)^{\frac{1}{x}}$ correct to six decimal places for $x = 1, 0.1, 0.01, 0.001, 0.000\ 1, 0.000\ 01, 0.000\ 001,$ and $0.000\ 000\ 1$.

   (b) Estimate the value of the limit
   $$\lim_{x \to 0} (1 + x)^{\frac{1}{x}}$$
   to five decimal places.

8. (a) Use your calculator to evaluate $g(x) = \dfrac{2^x - 1}{x}$ correct to four decimal places for $x = 1, 0.1, 0.01, 0.001, 0.000\ 1$.

   (b) Estimate the value of the limit
   $$\lim_{h \to 0} \dfrac{2^h - 1}{h}$$
   to three decimal places.

9. Evaluate the following limits.

   (a) $\lim_{x \to 8} \dfrac{x - 8}{\sqrt[3]{x} - 2}$

   (b) $\lim_{x \to 2} \dfrac{\sqrt{6 - x} - 2}{\sqrt{3 - x} - 1}$

10. If $f(x) = 2x + 3$, show that
    $$|f(x) - 7| < 0.01 \quad \text{if} \quad |x - 2| < 0.005$$

11. How close to 1 do we have to take x so that $\dfrac{16x^2 - 1}{4x - 1}$ is within a distance of 0.001 from 5?

12. Show that $\lim_{x \to 0} \dfrac{|x|}{x}$ does not exist.

13. Find functions f and g such that $\lim_{x \to 0} [f(x) + g(x)]$ exists but $\lim_{x \to 0} f(x)$ and $\lim_{x \to 0} g(x)$ do not exist. [Hint: See Example 8.]

PROBLEMS PLUS

1. Evaluate $\lim_{x \to 1} \dfrac{\sqrt{x} - 1}{\sqrt[3]{x} - 1}$. *Hint*: Introduce a new variable $t = \sqrt[6]{x}$.

1.3 ONE-SIDED LIMITS

The functions we have considered so far have been defined by simple formulas, but there are many functions that cannot be described in this way. Here are some examples: The population of Ottawa as a function of time; the cost of a taxi ride as a function of distance; the cost of mailing a first-class letter as a function of its mass. Such functions can be given by different formulas in different parts of their domains.

Consider the function f described by

$$f(x) = \begin{cases} x^2 & \text{if } x \leqslant 1 \\ 3 - x & \text{if } x > 1 \end{cases}$$

Remember that a function is a rule. For this particular function the rule is the following: First look at the value of x. If it happens that $x \leqslant 1$, then the value of $f(x)$ is x^2. On the other hand, if $x > 1$, then the value of $f(x)$ is $3 - x$. For instance, we compute $f(0)$, $f(1)$, and $f(2)$ as follows:

Since $0 \leqslant 1$, we have $f(0) = 0^2 = 0$.
Since $1 \leqslant 1$, we have $f(1) = 1^2 = 1$.
Since $2 > 1$, we have $f(2) = 3 - 2 = 1$.

We now investigate the limiting behaviour of $f(x)$ as x approaches 1.

Approaching From the Left		Approaching From the Right	
$x < 1$	$f(x) = x^2$	$x > 1$	$f(x) = 3 - x$
0.9	0.81	1.1	1.9
0.99	0.980 1	1.01	1.99
0.999	0.998 001	1.001	1.999

We see from the tables that $f(x)$ approaches 1 as x approaches 1 from the left, but $f(x)$ approaches 2 as x approaches 1 from the right. The notation we use to indicate this is

$$\lim_{x \to 1^-} f(x) = 1 \quad \text{and} \quad \lim_{x \to 1^+} f(x) = 2$$

Notice that the ordinary two-sided limit $\lim_{x \to 1} f(x)$ does not exist because the function approaches different values from the left and right.

Further insight into this type of function is gained from its graph. We observe that if $x \leqslant 1$, then $f(x) = x^2$, so the part of the graph of f that lies to the left of $x = 1$ must coincide with the graph of the parabola $y = x^2$. If $x > 1$, then $f(x) = 3 - x$, so the part of the graph of f that lies to the right of $x = 1$ coincides with the graph of $y = 3 - x$, which is a line with slope -1. The solid circle indicates that the point is included on the graph; the open circle indicates that the point is excluded from the graph.

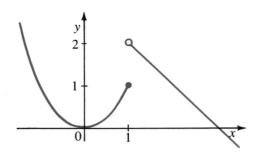

In general, we write

$$\lim_{x \to a^-} f(x) = L$$

and say

"the **left-hand limit** of $f(x)$, as x approaches a, equals L"

or "the **limit of $f(x)$ as x approaches a from the left** equals L"

if the values of $f(x)$ can be made close to L by taking x close to a with $x < a$.

Similarly, if we consider only $x > a$, we have the **right-hand limit**:

$$\lim_{x \to a^+} f(x) = L$$

If a function has different expressions to the left and right of the number a, the following theorem provides a convenient way to test whether or not $\lim_{x \to a} f(x)$ exists.

If $\lim_{x \to a^-} f(x) \neq \lim_{x \to a^+} f(x)$, then $\lim_{x \to a} f(x)$ does not exist.

If $\lim_{x \to a^-} f(x) = L = \lim_{x \to a^+} f(x)$, then $\lim_{x \to a} f(x) = L$.

When computing one-sided limits, we use the fact that the properties of limits listed in Section 1.2 also hold for one-sided limits.

Example 1 Find $\lim_{x \to 0^+} \sqrt{x}$.

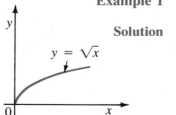

Solution Notice that the function $f(x) = \sqrt{x}$ is defined only for $x \geq 0$, so the two-sided limit $\lim_{x \to 0} \sqrt{x}$ does not make sense. If we let x approach 0 while restricting x to be positive, we see that $\sqrt{x}$ approaches 0:

$$\lim_{x \to 0^+} \sqrt{x} = \sqrt{\lim_{x \to 0^+} x} = \sqrt{0} = 0$$

Example 2   Show that $\lim\limits_{x \to 0} |x| = 0$.

Solution   Recall that

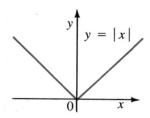

$$|x| = \begin{cases} x & \text{if } x \geq 0 \\ -x & \text{if } x < 0 \end{cases}$$

Therefore $\lim\limits_{x \to 0^+} |x| = \lim\limits_{x \to 0^+} x = 0$

and $\lim\limits_{x \to 0^-} |x| = \lim\limits_{x \to 0^-} (-x) = 0$

Since the left and right limits are equal, we have

$$\lim\limits_{x \to 0} |x| = 0$$

Example 3   The **Heaviside function** H is defined by

$$H(t) = \begin{cases} 0 & \text{if } t < 0 \\ 1 & \text{if } t \geq 0 \end{cases}$$

It is named after the electrical engineer Oliver Heaviside (1850–1925) and can be used to describe an electric current that is switched on at time $t = 0$. Evaluate, if possible,

(a) $\lim\limits_{t \to 0^-} H(t)$ (b) $\lim\limits_{t \to 0^+} H(t)$ (c) $\lim\limits_{t \to 0} H(t)$

Solution   (a) Since $H(t) = 0$ for $t < 0$, we have

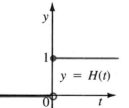

$$\lim\limits_{t \to 0^-} H(t) = \lim\limits_{t \to 0^-} 0 = 0$$

(b) Since $H(t) = 1$ for $t > 0$, we have

$$\lim\limits_{t \to 0^+} H(t) = \lim\limits_{t \to 0^+} 1 = 1$$

(c) We see that $\lim\limits_{t \to 0^-} H(t) \neq \lim\limits_{t \to 0^+} H(t)$ and so $\lim\limits_{t \to 0} H(t)$ does not exist.

Example 4   If

$$f(x) = \begin{cases} -x - 2 & \text{if } x \leq -1 \\ x & \text{if } -1 < x < 1 \\ x^2 - 2x & \text{if } x \geq 1 \end{cases}$$

determine whether or not $\lim\limits_{x \to -1} f(x)$ and $\lim\limits_{x \to 1} f(x)$ exist.

Solution   We first compute the one-sided limits. Since $f(x) = -x - 2$ for $x < -1$, we have

$$\lim_{x \to -1^-} f(x) = \lim_{x \to -1^-} (-x - 2) = -(-1) - 2 = -1$$

Since $f(x) = x$ for $-1 < x < 1$, we have

$$\lim_{x \to -1^+} f(x) = \lim_{x \to -1^+} x = -1$$

The left and right limits are equal, so

$$\lim_{x \to -1} f(x) = -1$$

Similarly, we have

$$\lim_{x \to 1^-} f(x) = \lim_{x \to 1^-} x = 1$$
$$\lim_{x \to 1^+} f(x) = \lim_{x \to 1^+} (x^2 - 2x) = 1^2 - 2(1) = -1$$

The left and right limits are different, so

$$\lim_{x \to 1} f(x) \text{ does not exist}$$

This information is shown in the graph of f.

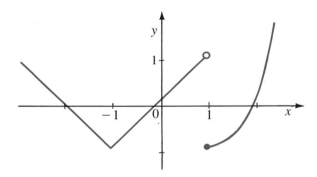

Discontinuities

We recall from Section 1.2 the definition of a continuous function.

> f is **continuous** at a number a if
> $$\lim_{x \to a} f(x) = f(a)$$

Implicitly, this requires three things if f is continuous at a.

1. $f(a)$ is defined (so a is in the domain of f)

2. $\lim\limits_{x \to a} f(x)$ exists

3. $\lim\limits_{x \to a} f(x) = f(a)$

If f is not continuous at a, we say f is **discontinuous** at a, or f has a **discontinuity** at a.

For instance, the Heaviside function in Example 3 has a discontinuity at $t = 0$ because $\lim\limits_{t \to 0} H(t)$ does not exist. Notice that there is a break in the graph of H at $t = 0$. This is typical of functions that have discontinuities. In fact, you can think of a continuous function as a function whose graph has no holes or breaks. You can draw its graph without removing your pencil from the paper. Discontinuities occur where there are breaks in the graph.

Example 5   Where are the following functions discontinuous?

(a) $f(x) = \begin{cases} x^2 + 1 & \text{if } x < 0 \\ 0 & \text{if } x = 0 \\ x^2 - 1 & \text{if } x > 0 \end{cases}$ (b) $g(x) = \begin{cases} x + 1 & \text{if } x \neq 2 \\ 1 & \text{if } x = 2 \end{cases}$

Solution   (a)   When $x < 0$, we have $f(x) = x^2 + 1$, and we know polynomials are continuous. Similarly, $f(x) = x^2 - 1$ for $x > 0$. So f is continuous when $x \neq 0$. The only possibility for a discontinuity is $x = 0$, so we try to compute $\lim\limits_{x \to 0} f(x)$.

$$\lim_{x \to 0^-} f(x) = \lim_{x \to 0^-} (x^2 + 1) = 0^2 + 1 = 1$$
$$\lim_{x \to 0^+} f(x) = \lim_{x \to 0^+} (x^2 - 1) = 0^2 - 1 = -1$$

Since the left and right limits are different, $\lim\limits_{x \to 0} f(x)$ does not exist.

Therefore f is discontinuous at 0. This can also be seen from the break in the graph of f.

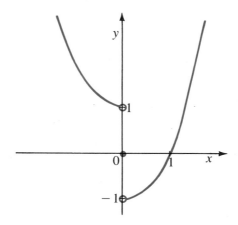

(b) The only possibility for a discontinuity is $x = 2$. Since $g(x) = x + 1$ for $x \neq 2$, we have

$$\lim_{x \to 2} g(x) = \lim_{x \to 2} (x + 1) = 2 + 1 = 3$$

But, by definition, $g(2) = 1$

So $\lim_{x \to 2} g(x) \neq g(2)$

Therefore g is discontinuous at 2.

Example 6   The cost of a long-distance night-time phone call from Pine Bay to Hester is 26¢ for the first minute and 22¢ for each additional minute (or part of a minute). There is a minimum charge of 34¢ on all calls. Draw the graph of the cost C (in dollars) of a phone call as a function of the time t (in minutes). Where are the discontinuities of this function?

Solution   From the given information, we have

$$
\begin{aligned}
C(t) &= 0.34 & &\text{if } 0 < t \leq 1 \\
C(t) &= 0.26 + 0.22 = 0.48 & &\text{if } 1 < t \leq 2 \\
C(t) &= 0.26 + 2(0.22) = 0.70 & &\text{if } 2 < t \leq 3 \\
C(t) &= 0.26 + 3(0.22) = 0.92 & &\text{if } 3 < t \leq 4
\end{aligned}
$$

and so on.

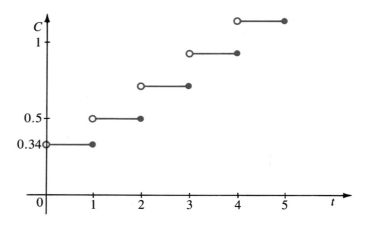

From the graph we see that there are discontinuities when $t = 1, 2, 3, \ldots$. For instance, the discontinuity at $t = 2$ occurs because

$$\lim_{t \to 2^-} C(t) = 0.48 \quad \text{and} \quad \lim_{t \to 2^+} C(t) = 0.70$$

and so $\lim_{t \to 2} C(t)$ does not exist.

The function in Example 6 is called a **step function** because of the appearance of its graph.

EXERCISE 1.3

A **1.** Use the given graph of f to state the value of the limit, if it exists.

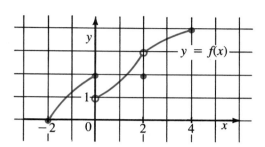

(a) $\lim\limits_{x \to -2^+} f(x)$ (b) $\lim\limits_{x \to 0^-} f(x)$ (c) $\lim\limits_{x \to 0^+} f(x)$ (d) $\lim\limits_{x \to 0} f(x)$

(e) $\lim\limits_{x \to 2^-} f(x)$ (f) $\lim\limits_{x \to 2^+} f(x)$ (g) $\lim\limits_{x \to 2} f(x)$ (h) $\lim\limits_{x \to 4^-} f(x)$

2. Use the given graph of g to state the value of the limit, if it exists.

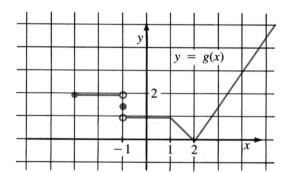

(a) $\lim\limits_{x \to -3^+} g(x)$ (b) $\lim\limits_{x \to -1^-} g(x)$ (c) $\lim\limits_{x \to -1^+} g(x)$ (d) $\lim\limits_{x \to -1} g(x)$

(e) $\lim\limits_{x \to 2^-} g(x)$ (f) $\lim\limits_{x \to 2^+} g(x)$ (g) $\lim\limits_{x \to 2} g(x)$ (h) $\lim\limits_{x \to 1} g(x)$

3. The graph of f is given. State whether f is continuous or discontinuous at each of the following numbers.

(a) -2 (b) 0   (c) 2   (d) 4   (e) 6

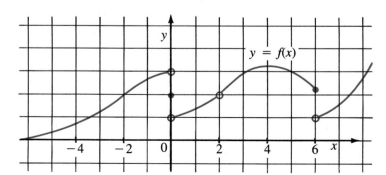

B **4.** Find the following limits, if they exist.

(a) $\displaystyle\lim_{x\to 0^+} \sqrt[4]{x}$

(b) $\displaystyle\lim_{x\to 3^+} \sqrt{x-3}$

(c) $\displaystyle\lim_{x\to 1^-} \sqrt{1-x}$

(d) $\displaystyle\lim_{x\to \frac{1}{2}^-} \sqrt[4]{1-2x}$

(e) $\displaystyle\lim_{x\to 6^+} |x-6|$

(f) $\displaystyle\lim_{x\to 6^-} |x-6|$

(g) $\displaystyle\lim_{x\to 6} |x-6|$

(h) $\displaystyle\lim_{x\to 0^+} \frac{|x|}{x}$

(i) $\displaystyle\lim_{x\to 0^-} \frac{|x|}{x}$

(j) $\displaystyle\lim_{x\to 0} \frac{|x|}{x}$

5. Let
$$f(x) = \begin{cases} -1 & \text{if } x < 0 \\ x+1 & \text{if } x \geq 0 \end{cases}$$
Find the following limits, if they exist. Then sketch the graph of f.

(a) $\displaystyle\lim_{x\to 0^-} f(x)$

(b) $\displaystyle\lim_{x\to 0^+} f(x)$

(c) $\displaystyle\lim_{x\to 0} f(x)$

6. Let
$$g(x) = \begin{cases} x^2 & \text{if } x \leq 1 \\ 2-x & \text{if } x > 1 \end{cases}$$
Find the following limits, if they exist. Then sketch the graph of g.

(a) $\displaystyle\lim_{x\to 1^-} g(x)$

(b) $\displaystyle\lim_{x\to 1^+} g(x)$

(c) $\displaystyle\lim_{x\to 1} g(x)$

7. Let
$$h(x) = \begin{cases} 1-x & \text{if } x < 0 \\ 0 & \text{if } x = 0 \\ -x-1 & \text{if } x > 0 \end{cases}$$
Find the following limits, if they exist. Then sketch the graph of h.

(a) $\displaystyle\lim_{x\to 0^-} h(x)$

(b) $\displaystyle\lim_{x\to 0^+} h(x)$

(c) $\displaystyle\lim_{x\to 0} h(x)$

8. Let
$$f(x) = \begin{cases} -1 & \text{if } x \leq -2 \\ \frac{1}{2}x & \text{if } -2 < x < 2 \\ 1 & \text{if } x \geq 2 \end{cases}$$

(a) Find the following limits.

(i) $\displaystyle\lim_{x\to -2^-} f(x)$

(ii) $\displaystyle\lim_{x\to -2^+} f(x)$

(iii) $\displaystyle\lim_{x\to 2^-} f(x)$

(iv) $\displaystyle\lim_{x\to 2^+} f(x)$

(b) Sketch the graph of f.

(c) Where is f discontinuous?

9. Let
$$f(x) = \begin{cases} (x+1)^2 & \text{if } x < -1 \\ x & \text{if } -1 \leq x \leq 1 \\ 2x - x^2 & \text{if } x > 1 \end{cases}$$

(a) Find the following limits, if they exist.

(i) $\lim_{x \to -1^-} f(x)$ (ii) $\lim_{x \to -1^+} f(x)$ (iii) $\lim_{x \to -1} f(x)$

(iv) $\lim_{x \to 1^-} f(x)$ (v) $\lim_{x \to 1^+} f(x)$ (vi) $\lim_{x \to 1} f(x)$

(b) Sketch the graph of f.

(c) Where is f discontinuous?

10. Where are the following functions discontinuous?

(a) $f(x) = \begin{cases} 2x + 3 & \text{if } x \neq 4 \\ 12 & \text{if } x = 4 \end{cases}$

(b) $f(x) = \begin{cases} 1 - x^2 & \text{if } x \leq 0 \\ x + 1 & \text{if } 0 < x \leq 1 \\ (x - 1)^2 & \text{if } x > 1 \end{cases}$

(c) $f(x) = \begin{cases} -x & \text{if } x < -1 \\ x^3 & \text{if } -1 \leq x \leq 1 \\ x & \text{if } x > 1 \end{cases}$

(d) $f(x) = \begin{cases} x & \text{if } 0 \leq x \leq 1 \\ x - 2 & 1 < x < 3 \\ x - 4 & \text{if } 3 \leq x \leq 4 \end{cases}$

11. Postal rates for a first-class letter up to 200 g are given in the following chart.

Up to and including	30 g	50 g	100 g	200 g
Mailing cost	$0.38	0.59	0.76	1.14

Draw the graph of the cost C (in dollars) of mailing a first-class letter as a function of its mass x (in grams). Where are the discontinuities of this function?

12. A taxi company charges $1.00 for the first 0.2 km (or part) and $0.10 for each additional 0.1 km (or part). Draw the graph of the cost C of a taxi ride, in dollars, as a function of the distance travelled x (in kilometres). Where are the discontinuities of this function?

C **13.** Let

$$f(x) = \begin{cases} 1 - |x| & \text{if } |x| \leq 1 \\ |x| - 1 & \text{if } 1 < |x| \leq 2 \\ (x - 3)^2 & \text{if } x > 2 \\ (x + 3)^2 & \text{if } x < -2 \end{cases}$$

Sketch the graph of f and determine any values of x at which f is discontinuous.

14. For what value of the constant c is the function

$$f(x) = \begin{cases} x + c & \text{if } x < 2 \\ cx^2 + 1 & \text{if } x \geq 2 \end{cases}$$

continuous at every number?

PROBLEMS PLUS

The *greatest integer function* is defined by $[\![x]\!]$ = the largest integer that is less than or equal to x. For instance, $[\![6]\!] = 6$, $[\![6.83]\!] = 6$, $[\![\pi]\!] = 3$, and $[\![-4.2]\!] = -5$.

(a) Sketch the graph of this function.

(b) Find $\lim\limits_{x \to 3^-} [\![x]\!]$ and $\lim\limits_{x \to 3^+} [\![x]\!]$.

(c) For what values of a does $\lim\limits_{x \to a} [\![x]\!]$ exist?

(d) For what values of a is the greatest integer function discontinuous?

(e) Sketch the graph of $g(x) = [\![2x + 1]\!]$. Where is it discontinuous?

(f) Sketch the graph of $h(x) = x - [\![x]\!]$.

1.4 USING LIMITS TO FIND TANGENTS

In Section 1.1 we found the tangent line to the parabola $y = x^2$ at the point $(1, 1)$ by computing its slope as the limit of slopes of secant lines.

In general, if a curve C has equation $y = f(x)$ and we want to find the tangent to C at the point $P(a, f(a))$, then we consider a nearby point $Q(x, f(x))$, where $x \neq a$, and compute the slope of the secant line PQ:

$$m_{PQ} = \frac{\Delta y}{\Delta x} = \frac{f(x) - f(a)}{x - a}$$

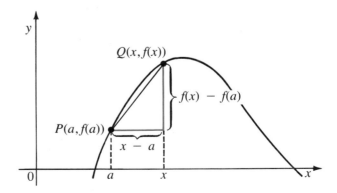

Then we let Q approach P along the curve C by letting x approach a. If m_{PQ} approaches a number m, then we define the **tangent** to be the line through P with slope m. In the notation of limits we write

$$m = \lim_{\Delta x \to 0} \frac{\Delta y}{\Delta x} = \lim_{x \to a} \frac{f(x) - f(a)}{x - a}$$ ①

This definition of the tangent amounts to saying that the tangent line is the limiting position of the sequence of secant lines PQ_1, PQ_2, PQ_3, ... in the figure below as the points Q_1, Q_2, Q_3, ... approach P along the curve.

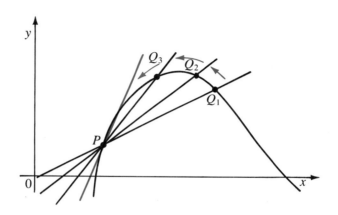

Example 1   (a) Find the slope and the equation of the tangent line to the curve $y = 2x^2 + 4x - 1$ at the point $(2, 15)$.

(b) Sketch the curve and the tangent line.

Solution   (a) We find the slope of the tangent line by using Formula 1 with $a = 2$ and $f(x) = 2x^2 + 4x - 1$:

$$m = \lim_{x \to 2} \frac{f(x) - f(2)}{x - 2}$$

$$= \lim_{x \to 2} \frac{(2x^2 + 4x - 1) - [2(2)^2 + 4(2) - 1]}{x - 2}$$

$$= \lim_{x \to 2} \frac{2x^2 + 4x - 16}{x - 2}$$

$$= \lim_{x \to 2} \frac{2(x^2 + 2x - 8)}{x - 2}$$

$$= \lim_{x \to 2} \frac{2(x - 2)(x + 4)}{x - 2}$$

$$= \lim_{x \to 2} 2(x + 4)$$

$$= 2(2 + 4)$$

$$= 12$$

$$y - y_1 = m(x - x_1)$$

The slope of the tangent line at $(2, 15)$ is 12. Using the point-slope form, we find that the equation of the tangent line is

$$y - 15 = 12(x - 2)$$

which simplifies to

$$12x - y - 9 = 0$$

(b) Recall that to graph a quadratic function we complete the square.

$$
\begin{aligned}
y &= 2x^2 + 4x - 1 \\
&= 2(x^2 + 2x) - 1 \\
&= 2[(x + 1)^2 - 1] - 1 \\
&= 2(x + 1)^2 - 3
\end{aligned}
$$

The graph is a parabola with vertex $(-1, -3)$ that opens upward.

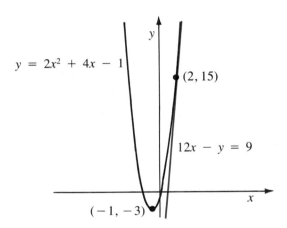

Another expression for the slope of the secant line PQ is

$$m_{PQ} = \frac{f(a + h) - f(a)}{h}$$

(The diagram illustrates the case where $h > 0$ and Q is to the right of P. If $h < 0$, however, Q would be to the left of P.) Notice that as x approaches a, h approaches 0, and so the expression for the slope of the tangent line becomes

$$m = \lim_{\Delta x \to 0} \frac{\Delta y}{\Delta x} = \lim_{h \to 0} \frac{f(a + h) - f(a)}{h}$$

②

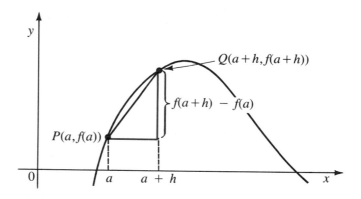

Example 2 Find the tangent line to the hyperbola $xy = 1$ at the point $\left(-2, -\frac{1}{2}\right)$.

Solution The equation of the hyperbola can be written as $y = \frac{1}{x}$. Thus, using Formula 2 with $f(x) = \frac{1}{x}$, we obtain the slope of the tangent line:

$$m = \lim_{h \to 0} \frac{f(-2 + h) - f(-2)}{h}$$

$$= \lim_{h \to 0} \frac{\dfrac{1}{-2 + h} - \dfrac{1}{-2}}{h}$$

$$= \lim_{h \to 0} \frac{\dfrac{1}{-2 + h} + \dfrac{1}{2}}{h}$$

$$= \lim_{h \to 0} \frac{\dfrac{2 + (-2 + h)}{2(-2 + h)}}{h}$$

$$= \lim_{h \to 0} \frac{h}{2(-2 + h)h}$$

$$= \lim_{h \to 0} \frac{1}{2(-2 + h)}$$

$$= \frac{1}{2(-2)}$$

$$= -\frac{1}{4}$$

The equation of the tangent line at $\left(-2, -\frac{1}{2}\right)$ is

$$y + \tfrac{1}{2} = -\tfrac{1}{4}(x + 2)$$
$$4y + 2 = -x - 2$$
$$x + 4y + 4 = 0$$

The hyperbola and the tangent line are shown in the diagram.

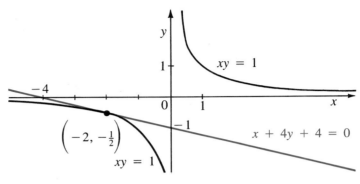

Example 3   (a) Find the tangent line to the curve $y = \sqrt{x - 2}$ at the point $(6, 2)$.

(b) Graph the curve and the tangent line.

Solution   (a) We find the slope using Formula 2 with $f(x) = \sqrt{x - 2}$.

$$m = \lim_{h \to 0} \frac{f(6 + h) - f(6)}{h}$$

$$= \lim_{h \to 0} \frac{\sqrt{(6 + h) - 2} - \sqrt{6 - 2}}{h}$$

$$= \lim_{h \to 0} \frac{\sqrt{4 + h} - 2}{h}$$

Rationalize the numerator.

$$= \lim_{h \to 0} \frac{\sqrt{4 + h} - 2}{h} \left(\frac{\sqrt{4 + h} + 2}{\sqrt{4 + h} + 2} \right)$$

$$= \lim_{h \to 0} \frac{(4 + h) - 4}{h(\sqrt{4 + h} + 2)}$$

$$= \lim_{h \to 0} \frac{h}{h(\sqrt{4 + h} + 2)}$$

$$= \lim_{h \to 0} \frac{1}{\sqrt{4 + h} + 2}$$

$$= \frac{1}{\sqrt{4 + 0} + 2}$$

$$= \frac{1}{4}$$

The equation of the tangent line at $(6, 2)$ is

$$y - 2 = \tfrac{1}{4}(x - 6)$$

$$4y - 8 = x - 6$$

$$x - 4y + 2 = 0$$

(b) We graph the curve $y = \sqrt{x - 2}$ by taking the square root function $y = \sqrt{x}$ and shifting it two units to the right.

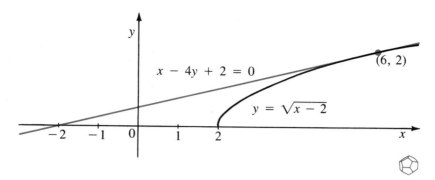

EXERCISE 1.4

B **1.** (a) Find the slope of the tangent line to the parabola $y = 2x - x^2$ at the point $(2, 0)$.
      (i) using Formula 1   (ii) using Formula 2
  (b) Find the equation of the tangent line.
  (c) Graph the parabola and the tangent line.

2. (a) Find the slope of the tangent line to the cubic curve $y = x^3$ at the point $(1, 1)$.
      (i) using Formula 1   (ii) using Formula 2
  (b) Find the equation of the tangent line.
  (c) Graph the curve and the tangent line.

3. Find the slope in Example 1 using Formula 2.

4. Find the slope in Example 2 using Formula 1.

5. Find the slope in Example 3 using Formula 1.

6. (a) Find the slope of the tangent lines to the parabola
$y = x^2 + 4x - 1$ at the points whose x-coordinates are given.
      (i) -3 (ii) -2 (iii) 0
  (b) Graph the parabola and the three tangents.

7. For each of the following curves
  (a) find the slope of the tangent at the given point,
  (b) find an equation of the tangent at the given point,
  (c) graph the curve and the tangent.
    (i) $y = 4 - x^2$ at $(-2, 0)$
    (ii) $y = x^2 - 6x + 5$ at $(2, -3)$
    (iii) $y = 1 - x^3$ at $(0, 1)$
    (iv) $y = \dfrac{1}{x - 1}$ at $\left(3, \tfrac{1}{2}\right)$
    (v) $y = \sqrt{x + 3}$ at $(6, 3)$
    (vi) $y = 2x^4$ at $(-1, 2)$

8. Find the equation of the tangent line to the graph of the given function at the given point.
   (a) $f(x) = 4 - x + 3x^2$, $(-1, 8)$
   (b) $f(x) = x^3 - x$, $(0, 0)$
   (c) $g(x) = \dfrac{2x + 1}{x - 1}$, $(2, 5)$
   (d) $g(x) = \dfrac{1}{\sqrt{x}}$, $(1, 1)$

9. (a) Find the slope of the tangent line to the parabola $y = x^2 + x + 1$ at the general point whose x-coordinate is a.
   (b) Find the slopes of the tangents to this parabola at the points whose x-coordinates are -1, $-\frac{1}{2}$, 0, $\frac{1}{2}$, 1.

C 10. (a) Find the slope of the tangent to the parabola $y = 3x^2 + 2x$ at the point whose x-coordinate is a.
   (b) At what point on the parabola is the tangent line parallel to the line $y = 10x - 2$?

11. Find the points of intersection of the parabolas $y = \frac{1}{2}x^2$ and $y = 1 - \frac{1}{2}x^2$. Show that at each of these points the tangent lines to the two parabolas are perpendicular.

1.5 VELOCITY AND OTHER RATES OF CHANGE

If a car is driven on a highway for three hours and the distance covered is 270 km, then it is easy to find the average velocity:

$$\text{average velocity} = \frac{\text{distance travelled}}{\text{time elapsed}}$$
$$= \frac{270}{3}$$
$$= 90 \text{ km/h}$$

But if you watch the speedometer of a car while travelling in city traffic, you will see that the indicator does not stay still for very long; that is, the speed of the car is not constant. We assume from watching the speedometer that the car has a definite velocity at each moment, but how is the "instantaneous" velocity defined? Before giving a general definition, let us investigate the situation of a falling ball in the following example.

Example 1 Suppose that a ball is dropped from the upper observation deck of the CN Tower, 450 m above the ground. How fast is the ball falling after 3 s?

Solution In trying to solve this problem we use the fact, discovered by Galileo almost three centuries ago, that the distance fallen by any freely falling body is proportional to the square of the time it has been falling. (This neglects air resistance.) If the distance fallen after t seconds is denoted by $s = f(t)$ and measured in metres, then Galileo's law is expressed by the equation

$$s = f(t) = 4.9t^2$$

The difficulty in finding the velocity after 3 s is that we are dealing with a single instant of time ($t = 3$) so there is no time interval involved. However, we can approximate the desired quantity by computing the average velocity over the brief time interval of a tenth of a second from $t = 3$ to $t = 3.1$:

$$\text{average velocity} = \frac{\text{distance travelled}}{\text{time elapsed}}$$
$$= \frac{\Delta s}{\Delta t}$$
$$= \frac{f(3.1) - f(3)}{0.1}$$
$$= \frac{4.9(3.1)^2 - 4.9(3)^2}{0.1}$$
$$= 29.89 \text{ m/s}$$

The following table shows the results of similar calculations of the average velocity over successively smaller time periods.

time interval	average velocity (m/s)
$3 \leqslant t \leqslant 4$	34.3
$3 \leqslant t \leqslant 3.1$	29.89
$3 \leqslant t \leqslant 3.05$	29.645
$3 \leqslant t \leqslant 3.01$	29.449
$3 \leqslant t \leqslant 3.001$	29.4049

It appears that, as we shorten the time period, the average velocity becomes closer to 29.4 m/s. Let us compute the average velocity over the general time interval $3 \leqslant t \leqslant 3 + h$:

$$\text{average velocity} = \frac{\Delta s}{\Delta t}$$

$$= \frac{f(3 + h) - f(3)}{h}$$

$$= \frac{4.9(3 + h)^2 - 4.9(3)^2}{h}$$

$$= \frac{4.9(9 + 6h + h^2 - 9)}{h}$$

$$= \frac{4.9(6h + h^2)}{h}$$

$$= 29.4 + 4.9h \quad \text{if } h \neq 0$$

If the time interval is very short, then h is small, so $4.9h$ is close to 0 and the average velocity is close to 29.4 m/s. The **instantaneous velocity** when $t = 3$ is defined to be the limiting value of these average velocities as h approaches 0. Thus, the (instantaneous) velocity after 3 s is

$$v = \lim_{h \to 0} (29.4 + 4.9h)$$
$$= 29.4 \text{ m/s}$$

Notice that we did not put $h = 0$ in the expression for the average velocity because that would have resulted in the expression $\frac{0}{0}$, which has no meaning. What we have done is to compute the instantaneous velocity as the *limit* of the average velocities as h approaches 0.

You may have the feeling that the calculations in Example 1 are very similar to those used in finding tangent lines. In fact, there is a close connection between the tangent problem and the problem of finding velocities. If we draw the graph of the distance function of the ball and we consider the points $P(3, 4.9(3)^2)$ and $Q(3 + h, 4.9(3 + h)^2)$ on the graph, then the slope of the secant line PQ is

$$m_{PQ} = \frac{4.9(3 + h)^2 - 4.9(3)^2}{h}$$

which is the same as the average velocity over the time interval $3 \leq t \leq 3 + h$ that we found in Example 1. Therefore the velocity at time t (the limit of these average velocities as h approaches 0) must be equal to the slope of the tangent line at P (the limit of the slopes of the secant lines).

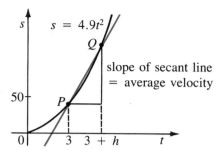

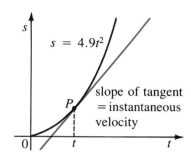

In general, suppose an object moves along a straight line according to an equation of motion $s = f(t)$, where s is the displacement (directed distance) of the object from the origin at time t. The function that describes the motion is called the **position function** of the object. In the time interval from $t = a$ to $t = a + h$, the change in position is

$$\Delta s = f(a + h) - f(a)$$

The average velocity over this time interval is

$$\frac{\Delta s}{\Delta t} = \frac{f(a + h) - f(a)}{h}$$

which is the same as the slope of the secant line PQ.

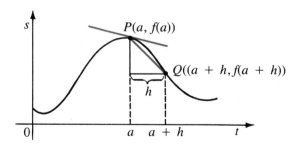

Now suppose we compute the average velocities over shorter and shorter time intervals $[a, a+h]$. In other words, we let h approach 0. As in Example 2, we define the **velocity** (or **instantaneous velocity**) $v(a)$ at time $t = a$ to be the limit of these average velocities:

> **Instantaneous Velocity**
>
> $$v(a) = \lim_{\Delta t \to 0} \frac{\Delta s}{\Delta t} = \lim_{h \to 0} \frac{f(a + h) - f(a)}{h}$$

This means that the velocity at time $t = a$ is equal to the slope of the tangent at P.

Example 2   The displacement, in metres, of a particle moving in a straight line is given by $s = t^2 + 2t$, where t is measured in seconds. Find the velocity of the particle after 3 s.

Solution   If we let $f(t) = t^2 + 2t$, then

$$
\begin{aligned}
v(3) &= \lim_{h \to 0} \frac{f(3 + h) - f(3)}{h} \\
&= \lim_{h \to 0} \frac{(3 + h)^2 + 2(3 + h) - [3^2 + 2(3)]}{h} \\
&= \lim_{h \to 0} \frac{9 + 6h + h^2 + 6 + 2h - 15}{h} \\
&= \lim_{h \to 0} \frac{8h + h^2}{h} \\
&= \lim_{h \to 0} (8 + h) = 8
\end{aligned}
$$

The velocity after 3 s is 8 m/s.

Other Rates of Change

Suppose that y is a function of x and we write $y = f(x)$. If x changes from x_1 to x_2, then the change in x is

$$\Delta x = x_2 - x_1$$

and the corresponding change in y is

$$\Delta y = f(x_2) - f(x_1)$$

The difference quotient

$$\frac{\Delta y}{\Delta x} = \frac{f(x_2) - f(x_1)}{x_2 - x_1}$$

is called the **average rate of change of y with respect to x** over the interval $x_1 \leq x \leq x_2$. By analogy with velocity, we consider the average rate of change over smaller and smaller intervals by letting x_2 approach x_1 and therefore letting Δx approach 0. The limit of these average rates of change is called the **(instantaneous) rate of change of y with respect** to x at $x = x_1$ and, as with velocity, can be interpreted as the slope of the tangent to the curve $y = f(x)$ at $P(x_1, f(x_1))$.

$$\text{Rate of change} = \lim_{\Delta x \to 0} \frac{\Delta y}{\Delta x} = \lim_{x_2 \to x_1} \frac{f(x_2) - f(x_1)}{x_2 - x_1}$$

Example 3   A thermometer is taken from a room where the temperature is 20°C to the outdoors where the temperature is 5°C. Temperature readings (T) are taken every half-minute and are shown in the following table. The time (t) is measured in minutes.

t	0.0	0.5	1.0	1.5	2.0	2.5	3.0	3.5	4.0	4.5	5.0
T	20	15	12	9.8	8.3	7.2	6.5	6.0	5.7	5.5	5.3

(a) Find the average rate of change of temperature with respect to time over the following time intervals:
   (i) $2 \leqslant t \leqslant 4$ (ii) $2 \leqslant t \leqslant 3.5$
   (iii) $2 \leqslant t \leqslant 3.0$ (iv) $2 \leqslant t \leqslant 2.5$

(b) Sketch the graph of T as a function of t and use it to estimate the instantaneous rate of change of temperature with respect to time when $t = 2$.

Solution   (a) (i)   Over the interval $2 \leqslant t \leqslant 4$ the temperature changes from $T = 8.3°$ to $T = 5.7°$, so

$$\Delta T = T(4) - T(2) = 5.7 - 8.3 = -2.6°$$

while the change in time is $\Delta t = 4 - 2 = 2$ min. Therefore the average rate of change of temperature with respect to time is

$$\frac{\Delta T}{\Delta t} = \frac{-2.6}{2} = -1.3°/\text{min}$$

The negative rate of change indicates that the temperature is decreasing.

(ii) $\dfrac{\Delta T}{\Delta t} = \dfrac{T(3.5) - T(2)}{3.5 - 2} = \dfrac{6 - 8.3}{1.5} = \dfrac{-2.3}{1.5} \doteq -1.5°/\text{min}$

(iii) $\dfrac{\Delta T}{\Delta t} = \dfrac{T(3.0) - T(2)}{3 - 2} = \dfrac{6.5 - 8.3}{1} = -1.8°/\text{min}$

(iv) $\dfrac{\Delta T}{\Delta t} = \dfrac{T(2.5) - T(2)}{2.5 - 2} = \dfrac{7.2 - 8.3}{0.5} = -2.2°/\text{min}$

(b) We plot the given data and use them to sketch a smooth curve that approximates the graph of the temperature function. Then we draw the tangent at the point P where $x = 2$ and after measuring the sides of triangle ABC, we estimate that the slope of the tangent line is

$$-\frac{BC}{AC} = -\frac{7.5}{3} = -2.5$$

So the rate of change of temperature with respect to time after two minutes is about $-2.5°$/min.

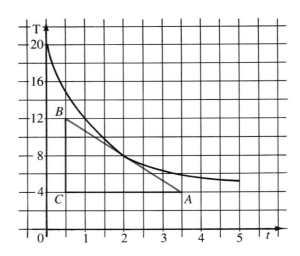

Example 4 A spherical balloon is being inflated. Find the rate of change of the volume with respect to the radius when the radius is 10 cm.

Solution If the radius of the balloon, in centimetres, is r, then the volume, in cubic centimetres, is given by

$$V(r) = \tfrac{4}{3}\pi r^3$$

When $r = 10$, the rate of change of V with respect to r is

$$\lim_{\Delta r \to 0} \frac{\Delta V}{\Delta r} = \lim_{r \to 10} \frac{V(r) - V(10)}{r - 10}$$

$$= \lim_{r \to 10} \frac{\tfrac{4}{3}\pi r^3 - \tfrac{4}{3}\pi(10)^3}{r - 10}$$

$$= \lim_{r \to 10} \tfrac{4}{3}\pi \frac{r^3 - 10^3}{r - 10}$$

$$= \lim_{r \to 10} \tfrac{4}{3}\pi \frac{(r - 10)(r^2 + 10r + 10^2)}{r - 10} \quad \text{(difference of cubes)}$$

$$= \lim_{r \to 10} \tfrac{4}{3}\pi(r^2 + 10r + 10^2)$$

$$= \tfrac{4}{3}\pi[10^2 + 10(10) + 10^2]$$

$$= 400\pi$$

$$\doteq 1260$$

The rate of change of V with respect to r is about 1260 cm³/cm.

Rates of change occur in all of the sciences. Physicists are interested in the rate of change of displacement with respect to time (called the velocity). Chemists who study a chemical reaction are interested in the rate of change in the concentration of a reactant with respect to time (called the rate of reaction). A textile manufacturer is interested in the rate of change of the cost of producing x square metres of fabric per day with respect to x (called the marginal cost). A biologist is interested in the rate of change of the population of a colony of bacteria with respect to time. All these rates of change can be interpreted as slopes of tangents. This gives added significance to the solution of the tangent problem. Whenever we solve a problem involving tangent lines, we are not just solving a problem in geometry; we are also implicitly solving a great variety of problems involving rates of change in the natural and social sciences as well as in engineering.

EXERCISE 1.5

B **1.** If a ball is thrown into the air with a velocity of 30 m/s, its height in metres after t seconds is given by $y = 30t - 4.9t^2$.
   (a) Find the average velocity for the time period beginning when $t = 2$ and lasting
      (i) 1 s   (ii) 0.5 s   (iii) 0.1 s   (iv) 0.05 s   (v) 0.01 s
   (b) Find the instantaneous velocity when $t = 2$.

2. The displacement in metres of a particle moving in a straight line is given by $s = t^2 - 4t + 3$, where t is measured in seconds.
   (a) Find the average velocity over the following time periods:
      (i) $3 \leqslant t \leqslant 5$ (ii) $3 \leqslant t \leqslant 4$
      (iii) $3 \leqslant t \leqslant 3.5$ (iv) $3 \leqslant t \leqslant 3.1$
   (b) Find the instantaneous velocity when $t = 3$.
   (c) Draw the graph of s as a function of t and draw the secant lines whose slopes are the average velocities in part (a).
   (d) Draw the tangent line whose slope is the instantaneous velocity in part (b).

3. A particle moves in a straight line with position function $s = 2t^2 + 4t - 5$, where t is measured in seconds and s in metres. Find the velocity of the particle at time $t = a$. Use this expression to find the velocities after 1 s, 2 s, and 3 s.

4. (a) Use the data of Example 3 to find the average rate of change of temperature with respect to time over the following time intervals:
      (i) $3 \leqslant t \leqslant 5$ (ii) $3 \leqslant t \leqslant 4$
      (iii) $1 \leqslant t \leqslant 3$ (iv) $2 \leqslant t \leqslant 3$
   (b) Use the graph of T to estimate the instantaneous rate of change of T with respect to t when $t = 3$.

5. The population P of a city from 1982 to 1988 is given in the following table:

Year	1982	1983	1984	1985	1986	1987	1988
P (in thousands)	211	219	229	241	255	270	286

  (a) Find the average rate of growth
      (i)   from 1984 to 1988   (ii)   from 1984 to 1987
      (iii) from 1984 to 1986   (iv) from 1984 to 1985
  (b) Estimate the instantaneous rate of growth in 1984 by measuring the slope of a tangent.

6. (a) If $y = \frac{2}{x}$, find the average rate of change of y with respect to x over the interval $3 \leqslant x \leqslant 4$. Illustrate by drawing the graph of the function and the secant line whose slope is equal to this average rate of change.

  (b) If $y = \frac{2}{x}$, find the instantaneous rate of change of y with respect to x at $x = 3$. Draw the tangent line whose slope is equal to this rate of change.

7. (a) A cubic crystal is being grown in a laboratory. Find the average rate of change of the volume of the cube with respect to its edge length x, measured in millimetres, when x changes from
      (i) 4 to 5   (ii) 4 to 4.1   (iii) 4 to 4.01
  (b) Find the instantaneous rate of change when $x = 4$.

8. If a tank holds 1000 L of water, which takes an hour to drain from the bottom of the tank, then the volume V of water remaining in the tank after t minutes is

$$V = 1000\left(1 - \frac{t}{60}\right)^2 \qquad 0 \leqslant t \leqslant 60$$

Find the rate at which the water is flowing out of the tank (the instantaneous rate of change of V with respect to t) after 10 min.

C **9.** If an arrow is shot upward on the moon with a velocity of 50 m/s, its height in metres after t seconds is given by $s = 50t - 0.83t^2$.
  (a) Find the average velocity for the time period beginning when $t = 1$ and lasting
      (i) 1 s   (ii) 0.5 s   (iii) 0.1 s   (iv) 0.05 s   (v) 0.01 s
  (b) Find the instantaneous velocity when $t = 1$.
  (c) Find the velocity after t seconds.
  (d) When will the arrow hit the moon?
  (e) With what velocity will the arrow hit the moon?

1.6 INFINITE SEQUENCES

A **sequence** is a list of numbers written in a definite order:

$$t_1, \ t_2, \ t_3, \ t_4, \ \ldots, \ t_n, \ \ldots$$

The number t_1 is called the *first term*, t_2 is the *second term*, and in general t_n is the *nth term*. We will be considering only infinite sequences, namely, those in which each term t_n has a successor t_{n+1}.

For every positive integer n there is a corresponding number t_n, so a sequence can be regarded as a function whose domain is the set of positive integers. But we usually write t_n instead of the function notation $t(n)$ for the value of the function at the number n.

Example 1   List the first five terms of the sequence defined by

$$t_n = \frac{n}{n+1}$$

and draw the graph of the sequence.

Solution   We have

$$t_1 = \tfrac{1}{2}, t_2 = \tfrac{2}{3}, t_3 = \tfrac{3}{4}, t_4 = \tfrac{4}{5}, t_5 = \tfrac{5}{6}$$

This sequence can therefore be described by indicating its initial terms as follows:

$$\tfrac{1}{2}, \tfrac{2}{3}, \tfrac{3}{4}, \tfrac{4}{5}, \tfrac{5}{6}, \ \cdots$$

The graph of this sequence is shown below.

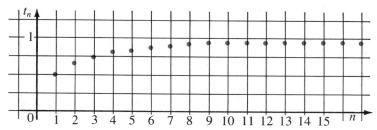

In Example 1, notice that the terms in the sequence are all less than 1 (because $n < n + 1$) but they get closer and closer to 1 as n increases. In fact, we can make the terms t_n as close as we like to 1 by making n large enough. We say the limit of this sequence is 1 and we indicate this by writing

$$\lim_{n \to \infty} \frac{n}{n + 1} = 1$$

In general we say that the sequence with general term t_n has the limit L, and we write

$$\lim_{n \to \infty} t_n = L$$

if the terms t_n are as close as we like to the number L for sufficiently large n.

Example 2   Find $\displaystyle\lim_{n \to \infty} \frac{1}{n}$.

Solution   The sequence defined by $t_n = \frac{1}{n}$ is

$$1, \frac{1}{2}, \frac{1}{3}, \frac{1}{4}, \frac{1}{5}, \frac{1}{6}, \; \cdots$$

As n becomes larger, $\frac{1}{n}$ becomes smaller. In fact, we can make $\frac{1}{n}$ as close as we like to 0 by making n sufficiently large. For instance, we have

$$\frac{1}{n} < 0.001 \quad \text{if} \quad n > \frac{1}{0.001} = 1000$$

Therefore

$$\lim_{n \to \infty} \frac{1}{n} = 0$$

The value of the limit can also be seen from the graph of the sequence.

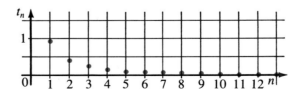

In the following example and in the exercises we make use of the result of Example 2 and the following more general fact:

$$\lim_{n \to \infty} \frac{1}{n^r} = 0 \quad \text{if } r > 0$$

In addition, we use the fact that the properties of limits stated in Section 1.2 are also valid for limits of sequences.

Example 3   Find $\displaystyle\lim_{n \to \infty} \frac{n^2 - n}{2n^2 + 1}$.

Solution   We divide the numerator and denominator by the highest power of n, namely n^2:

$$\frac{n^2 - n}{2n^2 + 1} = \frac{\dfrac{n^2 - n}{n^2}}{\dfrac{2n^2 + 1}{n^2}} = \frac{1 - \dfrac{1}{n}}{2 + \dfrac{1}{n^2}}$$

Thus
$$\lim_{n \to \infty} \frac{n^2 - n}{2n^2 + 1} = \lim_{n \to \infty} \frac{1 - \dfrac{1}{n}}{2 + \dfrac{1}{n^2}}$$

$$= \frac{\displaystyle\lim_{n \to \infty} 1 - \lim_{n \to \infty} \frac{1}{n}}{\displaystyle\lim_{n \to \infty} 2 + \lim_{n \to \infty} \frac{1}{n^2}}$$

$$= \frac{1 - 0}{2 + 0}$$

$$= \frac{1}{2}$$

Example 4   Find the following limits, if they exist.

(a) $\displaystyle\lim_{n \to \infty} (-1)^n$

(b) $\displaystyle\lim_{n \to \infty} \left(\tfrac{1}{2}\right)^n$

Solution   (a)   The terms of the sequence $t_n = (-1)^n$ are

$$-1, 1, -1, 1, -1, 1, \dots$$

As n increases, the terms do not approach any particular number. They oscillate between -1 and 1 indefinitely, as shown in the graph.

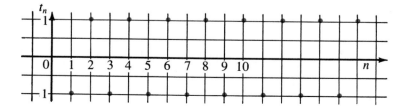

Therefore $\lim\limits_{n \to \infty} (-1)^n$ does not exist.

(b) The terms of the geometric sequence

$$t_n = \left(\frac{1}{2}\right)^n = \frac{1}{2^n}$$

are

$$\frac{1}{2}, \frac{1}{4}, \frac{1}{8}, \frac{1}{16}, \frac{1}{32}, \frac{1}{64}, \cdots$$

The denominators 2^n become large as n increases, so

$$\lim_{n \to \infty} \frac{1}{2^n} = 0$$

By the same type of reasoning as in Example 4(b) we have the following result.

> If $|r| < 1$, then $\lim\limits_{n \to \infty} r^n = 0$.

Some sequences do not have a simple defining equation but are defined recursively; that is, terms are defined by using preceding terms of the sequence as in the following example.

Example 5   The **Fibonacci sequence** is defined recursively by the equations

$$f_1 = 1, f_2 = 1, f_n = f_{n-1} + f_{n-2} \qquad (n \geq 3)$$

Find the first eight terms of the sequence.

Solution   The first two terms are given; the remaining terms are calculated by adding the two preceding terms.

$$f_1 = 1$$
$$f_2 = 1$$
$$f_3 = f_2 + f_1 = 1 + 1 = 2$$
$$f_4 = f_3 + f_2 = 2 + 1 = 3$$
$$f_5 = f_4 + f_3 = 3 + 2 = 5$$
$$f_6 = 5 + 3 = 8$$
$$f_7 = 8 + 5 = 13$$
$$f_8 = 13 + 8 = 21$$

The Fibonacci sequence arose when the 13th-century Italian mathematician known as Fibonacci solved a problem concerning the breeding of rabbits (see Question 7 in the Exercise).

The idea of a sequence having a limit is implicit in the decimal representation of real numbers. For instance, if we let t_n be the number obtained from the decimal representation of π by truncating after the nth decimal place, then

$$t_1 = 3.1$$
$$t_2 = 3.14$$
$$t_3 = 3.141$$
$$t_4 = 3.141\ 5$$
$$t_5 = 3.141\ 59$$
$$t_6 = 3.141\ 592$$

and $\quad \displaystyle\lim_{n \to \infty} t_n = \pi$

The terms in this sequence are rational approximations to π.

Zeno's Paradoxes

In the fifth century B.C. the Greek philosopher Zeno of Elea posed four problems, now known as Zeno's paradoxes. These problems were intended to challenge some of the ideas about space and time held at that time.

Zeno's second paradox concerns a race between the Greek hero Achilles and a tortoise, who was given a head start. Zeno argued that Achilles could never pass the tortoise. His argument runs this way: Suppose that Achilles starts at position a_1 and the tortoise starts at position t_1. When Achilles reaches the point $a_2 = t_1$, the tortoise is further ahead, at position t_2. When Achilles reaches $a_3 = t_2$, the tortoise is at t_3. This process continues indefinitely, so it appears that the tortoise will always be ahead! But this defies common sense.

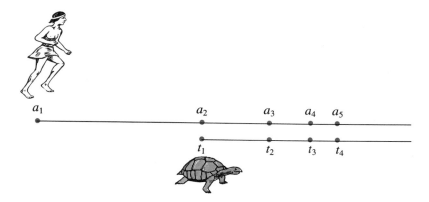

One way of explaining the paradox is through the idea of a sequence. The successive positions of Achilles $(a_1, a_2, a_3, \ldots)$ and the successive positions of the tortoise $(t_1, t_2, t_3, \ldots)$ form sequences $\{a_n\}$ and $\{t_n\}$ where $a_n < t_n$ for all n. It can be shown that both sequences have the same limit:

$$\lim_{n \to \infty} a_n = p = \lim_{n \to \infty} t_n$$

It is precisely at this point p that Achilles overtakes the tortoise.

EXERCISE 1.6

A **1.** State the limits of the following sequences, or state that the limit does not exist.

(a) $\frac{1}{3}, \frac{1}{9}, \frac{1}{27}, \frac{1}{81}, \frac{1}{243}, \ldots, \left(\frac{1}{3}\right)^n, \ldots$

(b) $5, 4\frac{1}{2}, 4\frac{1}{3}, 4\frac{1}{4}, 4\frac{1}{5}, \ldots, 4 + \frac{1}{n}, \ldots$

(c) $1, 2, 3, 4, 5, \ldots, n, \ldots$

(d) $3, 3, 3, 3, 3, \ldots, 3, \ldots$

(e) $1, 0, \frac{1}{2}, 0, \frac{1}{3}, 0, \frac{1}{4}, 0, \ldots$

(f) $5, 6\frac{1}{2}, 5\frac{2}{3}, 6\frac{1}{4}, 5\frac{4}{5}, 6\frac{1}{6}, \ldots, 6 + \dfrac{(-1)^n}{n}, \ldots$

(g) $1, \frac{1}{2}, 1, \frac{1}{3}, 1, \frac{1}{4}, 1, \frac{1}{5}, \ldots$

B **2.** List the first six terms of the following sequences.

(a) $t_n = \dfrac{n - 1}{2n - 1}$

(b) $t_n = \dfrac{2n}{n^2 + 1}$

(c) $t_n = n2^n$

(d) $t_n = \dfrac{(-1)^{n-1}}{n}$

(e) $t_1 = 1, t_n = \dfrac{1}{1 + t_{n-1}} \ (n \geq 2)$

(f) $t_1 = 1, t_2 = 2, t_n = t_{n-1} - t_{n-2} \ (n \geq 3)$

3. Find the following limits or state that the limit does not exist.

(a) $\lim_{n \to \infty} \dfrac{1}{n^2}$

(b) $\lim_{n \to \infty} \dfrac{1}{5 + n}$

(c) $\lim_{n \to \infty} \left(6 + \dfrac{1}{n^3}\right)$

(d) $\lim_{n \to \infty} \dfrac{n}{3n - 1}$

(e) $\lim_{n \to \infty} \dfrac{6n + 9}{3n - 2}$

(f) $\lim_{n \to \infty} 5n$

(g) $\lim_{n \to \infty} \dfrac{n^2 + 1}{2n^2 - 1}$

(h) $\lim_{n \to \infty} \dfrac{(n + 1)^2}{n(n + 2)}$

(i) $\lim_{n \to \infty} \dfrac{(-1)^{n+1}}{n}$

(j) $\lim_{n \to \infty} \left(-\frac{1}{4}\right)^n$

(k) $\lim\limits_{n\to\infty} \dfrac{n}{n^2 + 1}$

(l) $\lim\limits_{n\to\infty} (-1)^{n-1} n$

(m) $\lim\limits_{n\to\infty} 5^{-n}$

(n) $\lim\limits_{n\to\infty} (n^3 + n^2)$

(o) $\lim\limits_{n\to\infty} \dfrac{1 + n - 2n^2}{1 - n + n^2}$

(p) $\lim\limits_{n\to\infty} \dfrac{1}{\sqrt{n}}$

(q) $\lim\limits_{n\to\infty} \dfrac{1}{n^5}$

(r) $\lim\limits_{n\to\infty} \dfrac{1 - n^3}{1 + 2n^3}$

(s) $\lim\limits_{n\to\infty} \left(\dfrac{2}{3}\right)^n$

(t) $\lim\limits_{n\to\infty} \left(\dfrac{4}{3}\right)^n$

4. If $t_1 = 0.3$, $t_2 = 0.33$, $t_3 = 0.333$, $t_4 = 0.3333$, and so on, what is $\lim\limits_{n\to\infty} t_n$?

5. If

$$t_n = \frac{2^n}{n^2}$$

use your calculator to find t_n for $n = 1, 2, 3, 4, 5, 6, 7, 8, 9, 10$, 20, 50, and 100. Does the limit

$$\lim_{n\to\infty} \frac{2^n}{n^2}$$

exist? If so, guess its value.

6. If

$$t_n = \sqrt[n]{n}$$

use your calculator to find t_n for $n = 1, 2, 3, 4, 5, 6, 7, 8, 9, 10$, 50, 100, 500, 1000, and 10 000. Then guess the value of the limit

$$\lim_{n\to\infty} \sqrt[n]{n}$$

7. Fibonacci posed the following problem: Suppose that rabbits live forever and that every month each pair produces a new pair that becomes productive at age two months. If we start with one newborn pair, how many pairs of rabbits will there be in the nth month? Show that the answer is f_n, the nth term of the Fibonacci sequence defined in Example 5.

C **8.** Find the limit of the sequence

$$\sqrt{2},\ \sqrt{2\sqrt{2}},\ \sqrt{2\sqrt{2\sqrt{2}}},\ \sqrt{2\sqrt{2\sqrt{2\sqrt{2}}}},\ \dots$$

by expressing each term as a power of 2.

9. (a) A sequence is defined recursively by

$$t_1 = 1,\ t_n = \frac{1}{2t_{n-1} + 1} \qquad (n \geq 2)$$

Find t_2, t_3, t_4, t_5, t_6 and guess the value of $\lim\limits_{n\to\infty} t_n$.

(b) Assume that $\lim\limits_{n\to\infty} t_n = L$ exists. What is the value of $\lim\limits_{n\to\infty} t_{n-1}$? Find the value of L by taking the limit of both sides of the recursion equation.

1.7 INFINITE SERIES

Does it make sense to talk about adding infinitely many numbers? You might think this is impossible because it would take an infinite amount of time. But there are situations in which we implicitly use infinite sums. For instance, in decimal notation the symbol $0.\overline{4} = 0.444\ 444\ 444\ \dots$ means

$$\tfrac{4}{10} + \tfrac{4}{100} + \tfrac{4}{1000} + \tfrac{4}{10\ 000} + \dots$$

and so, in some sense, it must be true that

$0.\overline{4} = \tfrac{4}{9}$

$$\tfrac{4}{10} + \tfrac{4}{100} + \tfrac{4}{1000} + \tfrac{4}{10\ 000} + \dots = \tfrac{4}{9}$$

Another situation that gives rise to an infinite sum occurs in one of Zeno's paradoxes, as passed on to us by Aristotle: "A man standing in a room cannot walk to the wall. In order to do so, he would first have to go half the distance, then half the remaining distance, and then again half of what still remains. This process can always be continued and can never be ended."

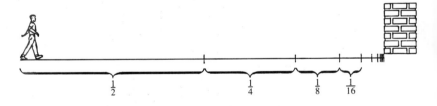

Of course we know that the man can actually reach the wall, so this suggests that perhaps the total distance can be expressed as the sum of infinitely many smaller distances as follows:

$$1 = \tfrac{1}{2} + \tfrac{1}{4} + \tfrac{1}{8} + \tfrac{1}{16} + \dots + \tfrac{1}{2^n} + \dots$$

In order to make sense of this equation, we let S_n be the sum of the first n terms of the series. Then

$$S_1 = \tfrac{1}{2} = 0.5$$

$$S_2 = \tfrac{1}{2} + \tfrac{1}{4} = 0.75$$

$$S_3 = \tfrac{1}{2} + \tfrac{1}{4} + \tfrac{1}{8} = 0.875$$

$$S_4 = \tfrac{1}{2} + \tfrac{1}{4} + \tfrac{1}{8} + \tfrac{1}{16} = 0.9375$$

$$S_5 = \tfrac{1}{2} + \tfrac{1}{4} + \tfrac{1}{8} + \tfrac{1}{16} + \tfrac{1}{32} = 0.968\ 75$$

$$S_6 = \tfrac{1}{2} + \tfrac{1}{4} + \tfrac{1}{8} + \tfrac{1}{16} + \tfrac{1}{32} + \tfrac{1}{64} = 0.984\ 375$$

$$S_7 = \tfrac{1}{2} + \tfrac{1}{4} + \tfrac{1}{8} + \tfrac{1}{16} + \tfrac{1}{32} + \tfrac{1}{64} + \tfrac{1}{128} = 0.992\ 187\ 5$$

.
.
.

$$S_{10} = \tfrac{1}{2} + \tfrac{1}{4} + \dots + \tfrac{1}{1024} \doteq 0.999\ 023\ 44$$

.
.
.

$$S_{16} = \tfrac{1}{2} + \tfrac{1}{4} + \dots + \tfrac{1}{2^{16}} \doteq 0.999\ 984\ 74$$

Notice that as we add more and more terms, the partial sums become closer and closer to 1. In fact, by making n large enough (that is, by adding sufficiently many terms of the series), we can make the partial sum S_n as close as we like to the number 1. It therefore seems reasonable to say that the sum of the infinite series is 1 and to write

$$\tfrac{1}{2} + \tfrac{1}{4} + \tfrac{1}{8} + \tfrac{1}{16} + \dots + \tfrac{1}{2^n} + \dots = 1$$

In other words, the reason the sum of the series is 1 is that

$$\lim_{n \to \infty} S_n = 1$$

We use a similar idea to determine whether or not a general series

$$t_1 + t_2 + t_3 + \dots + t_n + \dots$$

has a sum. We define the **partial sums** as follows.

$$S_1 = t_1$$
$$S_2 = t_1 + t_2$$
$$S_3 = t_1 + t_2 + t_3$$
$$S_4 = t_1 + t_2 + t_3 + t_4$$

.
.
.

$$S_n = t_1 + t_2 + t_3 + \dots + t_n$$

If the infinite sequence $S_1, S_2, \dots, S_n, \dots$ of partial sums of the series $t_1 + t_2 + t_3 + \dots + t_n + \dots$ has a limit L, then we say that the **sum** of the series is L and we write

$$t_1 + t_2 + t_3 + \dots + t_n + \dots = L$$

In sigma notation this becomes

$$\sum_{n=1}^{\infty} t_n = L$$

If a series has a sum, it is called a **convergent** series. If not, it is called **divergent**.

Example 1   Determine whether the following series are convergent or divergent.
(a) $1 + 1 + 1 + 1 + \ldots + 1 + \ldots$
(b) $1 - 1 + 1 - 1 + \ldots + (-1)^{n+1} + \ldots$

Solution   (a) $S_n = 1 + \underbrace{1 + 1 + \ldots + 1}_{n \text{ terms}} = n$

Therefore $\lim\limits_{n \to \infty} S_n = \lim\limits_{n \to \infty} n$ does not exist. It follows that the given series does not have a sum; that is, it is divergent.

(b) $S_1 = 1$
$S_2 = 1 - 1 = 0$
$S_3 = 1 - 1 + 1 = 1$
$S_4 = 1 - 1 + 1 - 1 = 0$

The sequence of partial sums is

$$1, 0, 1, 0, 1, 0, \ldots$$

which has no limit. Thus the series $1 - 1 + 1 - 1 + \ldots$ does not have a sum; that is, it is divergent.

Example 2   Find the sum of the geometric series

$$a + ar + ar^2 + \ldots + ar^{n-1} + \ldots \qquad (a \neq 0)$$

when it exists.

Solution   The nth partial sum of the geometric series is

$$S_n = a + ar + ar^2 + \ldots + ar^{n-1}$$

This is a finite geometric series with first term a and common ratio r. We recall that, for $r \neq 1$, its sum is

$$S_n = \frac{a(1 - r^n)}{1 - r}$$

TAKE CASES

Case 1: If $|r| < 1$, that is, $-1 < r < 1$, we discovered in Section 1.6 that $\lim\limits_{n \to \infty} r^n = 0$. Therefore

$$\lim_{n \to \infty} S_n = \lim_{n \to \infty} \frac{a(1 - r^n)}{1 - r}$$

$$= \frac{a(1 - 0)}{1 - r}$$

$$= \frac{a}{1 - r}$$

Thus, for $|r| < 1$, the geometric series is convergent and its sum is $\frac{a}{1 - r}$.

Case 2: If $r = 1$, the geometric series becomes

$$a + a + a + a + \dots$$

which does not have a sum. (See Example 1(a)).

Case 3: If $r = -1$, the geometric series becomes

$$a - a + a - a + \dots$$

which does not have a sum. (See Example 1(b)).

Case 4: If $|r| > 1$, then $\lim_{n \to \infty} r^n$ does not exist. Therefore $\lim_{n \to \infty} S_n$ does not exist and the geometric series does not have a sum.

We summarize the results of Example 2 as follows:

If $|r| < 1$, the infinite geometric series

$$a + ar + ar^2 + \dots + ar^{n-1} + \dots \quad (a \neq 0)$$

is convergent and has the sum

$$S = \frac{a}{1 - r}$$

If $|r| \geq 1$, the geometric series is divergent.

In sigma notation we can write

$$\sum_{n=1}^{\infty} ar^{n-1} = \frac{a}{1 - r} \qquad |r| < 1$$

Example 3 Find the sum of the series

$$16 - 12 + 9 - \tfrac{27}{4} + \tfrac{81}{16} - \dots$$

Solution   The given series is a geometric series with first term $a = 16$ and common ratio $r = -\frac{3}{4}$. Since $|r| = \frac{3}{4} < 1$, the series is convergent and its sum is

$$S = \frac{16}{1 - \left(-\frac{3}{4}\right)} = \frac{16}{\frac{7}{4}} = 16 \times \frac{4}{7} = \frac{64}{7}$$

Example 4   Express the repeating decimal $2.1\overline{35}$ as a fraction.

Solution
$$2.1\overline{35} = 2.135\,353\,535 \ldots$$
$$= 2.1 + \frac{35}{1000} + \frac{35}{100\,000} + \frac{35}{10\,000\,000} + \ldots$$

After the first term, the series is a geometric series with

$$a = \frac{35}{1000} \quad \text{and} \quad r = \frac{1}{100} = 0.01$$

Therefore

$$2.1\overline{35} = 2.1 + \frac{\frac{35}{1000}}{1 - 0.01}$$
$$= 2.1 + \frac{35}{1000(0.99)}$$
$$= \frac{21}{10} + \frac{35}{990}$$
$$= \frac{2114}{990}$$
$$= \frac{1057}{495}$$

EXERCISE 1.7

B 1.   Find the sum of each of the following series or state that the series is divergent.

(a) $1 + \frac{1}{3} + \frac{1}{9} + \frac{1}{27} + \ldots$

(b) $1 - \frac{2}{3} + \frac{4}{9} - \frac{8}{27} + \ldots$

(c) $\frac{1}{4} - \frac{5}{16} + \frac{25}{64} - \frac{125}{256} + \ldots$

(d) $3 + \frac{3}{5} + \frac{3}{25} + \frac{3}{125} + \ldots$

(e) $1 - 2 + 4 - 8 + \ldots$

(f) $60 + 40 + \frac{80}{3} + \frac{160}{9} + \ldots$

(g) $0.1 + 0.05 + 0.025 + 0.0125 + \ldots$

(h) $-3 + 3 - 3 + 3 - 3 + \ldots$

2.   Find the sum of each of the following series.

(a) $\sum_{n=1}^{\infty} 2\left(\frac{3}{4}\right)^{n-1}$

(b) $\sum_{n=1}^{\infty} \left(-\frac{2}{5}\right)^n$

3.   Express the following repeating decimals as fractions.

(a) $0.\overline{1}$

(b) $0.\overline{25}$

(c) $0.\overline{41}$

(d) $0.\overline{157}$

(e) $1.1\overline{23}$

(f) $2.3\overline{456}$

(g) $0.429\,\overline{113}$

(h) $6.814\,\overline{72}$

4. For what values of x are the following series convergent? In each case find the sum of the series for those values of x.

(a) $1 + x + x^2 + x^3 + \dots$

(b) $1 + \dfrac{x}{3} + \dfrac{x^2}{9} + \dfrac{x^3}{27} + \dots$

(c) $1 + \dfrac{1}{x} + \dfrac{1}{x^2} + \dfrac{1}{x^3} + \dots$

(d) $1 + (x - 4) + (x - 4)^2 + (x - 4)^3 + \dots$

(e) $\displaystyle\sum_{n=1}^{\infty} 2^n x^n$

5. The series

$$1 - \frac{1}{64} + \frac{1}{729} - \frac{1}{4096} + \dots + \frac{(-1)^{n-1}}{n^6} + \dots$$

is not a geometric series. Use your calculator to find the first eight partial sums of this series. Does it appear that this series is convergent? If so, estimate its sum to five decimal places.

C 6. The series

$$\frac{1}{1 \times 2} + \frac{1}{2 \times 3} + \frac{1}{3 \times 4} + \dots + \frac{1}{n(n + 1)} + \dots$$

is not a geometric series.

(a) Use your calculator to find its first 15 partial sums.

(b) Use the identity

$$\frac{1}{k(k + 1)} = \frac{1}{k} - \frac{1}{k + 1}$$

to find an expression for the nth partial sum S_n.

(c) Use part (b) to find the sum of the series.

(d) How many terms of the series would be required so that the partial sum differs from the total sum by less than 0.001?

7. A right triangle is given with $\angle A = \theta$ and $AC = 1$. CD is drawn perpendicular to AB, DE is drawn perpendicular to BC, EF is perpendicular to AB, and this process is continued indefinitely as in the figure. Find the total length of all the perpendiculars

$$CD + DE + EF + FG + \dots$$

in terms of θ.

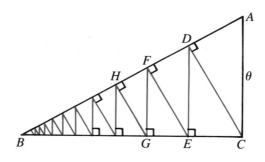

1.8   REVIEW EXERCISE

1.   Use the given graph of f to state the value of the limit, if it exists.

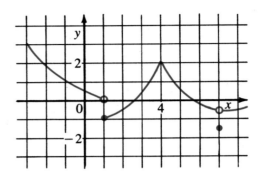

(a) $\lim\limits_{x \to -1} f(x)$

(b) $\lim\limits_{x \to 1^-} f(x)$

(c) $\lim\limits_{x \to 1^+} f(x)$

(d) $\lim\limits_{x \to 1} f(x)$

(e) $\lim\limits_{x \to -3^+} f(x)$

(f) $\lim\limits_{x \to 4^-} f(x)$

(g) $\lim\limits_{x \to 4^+} f(x)$

(h) $\lim\limits_{x \to 4} f(x)$

2.   State whether the function f, whose graph is shown in Question 1, is continuous or discontinuous at the following numbers.

(a) 1   (b) 4   (c) 7

3.   Find the following limits.

(a) $\lim\limits_{x \to 2} (3x^3 + 7x - 16)$

(b) $\lim\limits_{x \to -1} \dfrac{2x + 3}{3x + 2}$

(c) $\lim\limits_{x \to 2} \dfrac{x^2 - 2x - 8}{x^2 - 7x + 12}$

(d) $\lim\limits_{x \to 4} \dfrac{x^2 - 2x - 8}{x^2 - 7x + 12}$

(e) $\lim\limits_{x \to 5} \sqrt{\dfrac{x^2 - 25}{x - 5}}$

(f) $\lim\limits_{x \to 4} \dfrac{x - 4}{x^3 - 64}$

(g) $\lim\limits_{t \to 0} \dfrac{\sqrt{2 + t} - \sqrt{2}}{t}$

(h) $\lim\limits_{h \to 0} \dfrac{(-3 + h)^2 - 9}{h}$

4.   Find the following limits, or state that they do not exist.

(a) $\lim\limits_{x \to -1} \dfrac{x - 6}{(x + 1)^3}$

(b) $\lim\limits_{x \to 1} \dfrac{x^2 - 1}{x^2 - 7x + 6}$

(c) $\lim\limits_{h \to 0} \dfrac{\dfrac{4}{2 + h} - 2}{h}$

(d) $\lim\limits_{y \to 2} \dfrac{y^4 - 16}{y^4 + 2y^3 - y^2 - 2y}$

(e) $\lim\limits_{t \to -2^+} \sqrt[4]{8 + t^3}$

(f) $\lim\limits_{x \to 1^+} \dfrac{|x - 1|}{x - 1}$

(g) $\lim\limits_{x \to 1^-} \dfrac{|x - 1|}{x - 1}$

(h) $\lim\limits_{x \to 1} \dfrac{|x - 1|}{x - 1}$

5. Let
$$f(x) = \begin{cases} -1 - x & \text{if } x < -1 \\ x^2 & \text{if } x \geqslant -1 \end{cases}$$
   (a) Find the following limits, if they exist.
      (i) $\lim\limits_{x \to -1^-} f(x)$ (ii) $\lim\limits_{x \to -1^+} f(x)$ (iii) $\lim\limits_{x \to -1} f(x)$
   (b) Sketch the graph of f.

6. Let
$$g(x) = \begin{cases} x^3 & \text{if } x < 0 \\ x^2 & \text{if } 0 \leqslant x \leqslant 1 \\ 1 + 2x - x^2 & \text{if } x > 1 \end{cases}$$

   (a) Find the following limits, if they exist.
      (i) $\lim\limits_{x \to 0^-} g(x)$ (ii) $\lim\limits_{x \to 0^+} g(x)$ (iii) $\lim\limits_{x \to 0} g(x)$
      (iv) $\lim\limits_{x \to 1^-} g(x)$ (v) $\lim\limits_{x \to 1^+} g(x)$ (vi) $\lim\limits_{x \to 1} g(x)$
   (b) Sketch the graph of g.
   (c) Where is g discontinuous?

7. A daytime coin-paid phone call from Toronto to Montreal costs $1.95 for the first minute and $0.45 for each additional minute (or part of a minute). Draw the graph of the cost C (in dollars) of the phone call as a function of the time t (in minutes). For what values of t does this function have discontinuities?

8. The point $P(1, -2)$ lies on the curve $y = x^3 - 3x$.
   (a) If Q is the point $(x, x^3 - 3x)$, find the slope of the secant line PQ for the following values of x:
      (i) 2   (ii) 1.5   (iii) 1.1   (iv) 1.01
   (b) Find the slope of the tangent line to the curve at P.
   (c) Find an equation of the tangent line to the curve at P.
   (d) Graph the curve and the tangent line.

9. Find the equation of the tangent line to the curve $y = x^4$ at the point $(-1, 1)$.

10. If a stone is dropped off a 200 m high cliff, then its height after t seconds, and before it hits the ground, is $h = 200 - 4.9t^2$.
   (a) Find the average velocity of the stone for the following time periods.
      (i) $1 \leqslant t \leqslant 2$ (ii) $1 \leqslant t \leqslant 1.1$
   (b) Find the instantaneous velocity when $t = 1$.

11. A spherical balloon is being inflated. Find the rate of change of the surface area of the balloon with respect to the radius when the radius is 10 cm. (Use the formula $S = 4\pi r^2$, where r is the radius of a sphere and S is the surface area.)

12. Find the following limits or state that the limit does not exist.
   (a) $\lim\limits_{n \to \infty} \left(2 - \dfrac{1}{n} + \dfrac{3}{n^2} \right)$ (b) $\lim\limits_{n \to \infty} \dfrac{1 + 2n}{1 - 3n}$
   (c) $\lim\limits_{n \to \infty} (1.1)^n$ (d) $\lim\limits_{n \to \infty} \dfrac{3^n}{5^n}$

13. Find the sum of the series or state that it is divergent.

    (a) $6 - 1 + \frac{1}{6} - \frac{1}{36} + \ldots$ (b) $\frac{1}{9} + \frac{1}{3} + 1 + 3 + \ldots$

14. Express the repeating decimal $1.2\overline{45}$ as a fraction.

15. For what values of x is the series $\sum_{n=1}^{\infty} (x + 1)^n$ convergent? Find the sum of the series for those values of x.

16. A sequence is defined recursively as follows:
$$t_1 = \sqrt{3}, \quad t_{n+1} = \sqrt{3t_n} \quad (n \geq 1)$$
Find $\lim_{n \to \infty} t_n$.

1.9 CHAPTER 1 TEST

1. Find the following limits.

   (a) $\displaystyle\lim_{x \to 2} \sqrt{\dfrac{x^2 + 5}{x - 1}}$

   (b) $\displaystyle\lim_{x \to -1} \dfrac{x + 1}{x^2 - 4x - 5}$

   (c) $\displaystyle\lim_{x \to 1} \dfrac{\dfrac{1}{\sqrt{x}} - 1}{x - 1}$

2. The points $P(2, -1)$ and $Q(3, -4)$ lie on the parabola $y = -x^2 + 2x - 1$.

   (a) Find the slope of the secant line PQ.

   (b) Find the slope of the tangent line to the parabola at P.

   (c) Find the equation of the tangent line at P.

   (d) Graph the parabola, the secant line, and the tangent line.

3. Let
$$f(x) = \begin{cases} 1 - x^2 & \text{if } x \leq 0 \\ 2x - 1 & \text{if } x > 0 \end{cases}$$

   (a) Find the following limits if they exist.

   　(i) $\displaystyle\lim_{x \to 0^-} f(x)$　　(ii) $\displaystyle\lim_{x \to 0^+} f(x)$　　(iii) $\displaystyle\lim_{x \to 0} f(x)$

   (b) Sketch the graph of f.

   (c) Where is f discontinuous?

4. The displacement in metres of a particle moving in a straight line is given by $s = 5t^2 - 6t + 14$, where t is measured in seconds.

   (a) Find the average velocity over the time interval $2 \leq t \leq 3$.

   (b) Find the instantaneous velocity when $t = 2$.

5. Evaluate $\displaystyle\lim_{n \to \infty} \left(\dfrac{1}{8^n} + \dfrac{6n - 2}{2n - 3} \right)$.

6. Find the sum of the series
$$12 - 9 + \dfrac{27}{4} - \dfrac{81}{16} + \cdots$$

FOUNDERS OF CALCULUS

Sir Isaac Newton was born in the village of Woolsthorpe, England, on Christmas day in 1642, the year of Galileo's death. The signs of genius did not emerge in high school, but while he was a student at Trinity College, Cambridge, he read the works of Euclid and Descartes and these inspired him. In 1665, Cambridge was closed because of the plague and, while at home on this enforced vacation, Newton made four of his greatest discoveries: the law of gravitation, the nature of light and colour, the method of calculus, and the extended binomial theorem [the expansion of $(a + b)^n$ as an infinite series when n is not a positive integer].

The Greeks had started calculus with their calculations of areas, and mathematicians of the early seventeenth century, such as Fermat and Descartes, had furthered the subject by solving tangent problems. But Newton undertook the first systematic study of calculus. In particular, he was the first to study limits and derivatives, which he called *fluxions*.

His famous book *Principia Mathematica* of 1687 is perhaps the greatest contribution ever made to the mathematical and physical literature. In it, he applied his method of calculus to the theory of gravitation, to hydrostatics and wave motion, and to astronomical problems. He studied the action of the planets on each other, the disturbing action of the sun on the moon, and the variations of the orbit of the moon.

Newton was a professor at Cambridge University and became renowned as the most absent-minded professor of all time. He often forgot to eat meals. This absent-mindedness was a consequence of his extreme powers of concentration. When asked how he was able to solve a difficult problem, he replied: "By always thinking unto it."

Newton was knighted by Queen Anne in 1705. This was the first time that a man of science had been so honoured. When he died in 1727, he was buried in Westminster Abbey with the pomp of a king's funeral. He was very famous in his own time, even to the general public. Alexander Pope wrote

Nature and nature's laws lay hid in night,
God said, "Let Newton be," and all was light.

PROBLEMS PLUS

What is wrong with the following calculation using infinite series?

$$
\begin{aligned}
0 &= 0 + 0 + 0 + \ldots \\
&= (1 - 1) + (1 - 1) + (1 - 1) + \ldots \\
&= 1 - 1 + 1 - 1 + 1 - 1 + \ldots \\
&= 1 + (-1 + 1) + (-1 + 1) + (-1 + 1) + \ldots \\
&= 1 + 0 + 0 + 0 + \ldots \\
&= 1
\end{aligned}
$$

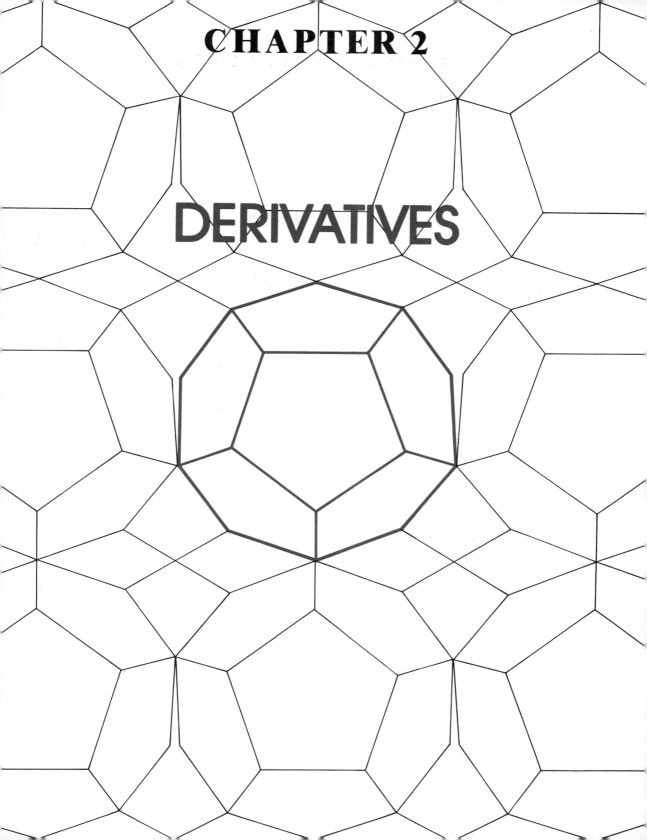

CHAPTER 2

DERIVATIVES

REVIEW AND PREVIEW TO
CHAPTER 2

The Domain of a Function

If a formula is given for $f(x)$, but the domain is not given, then the domain of f is assumed to be the set of all real values of x for which the given expression is meaningful. For example, an expression will not be meaningful when it contains a zero denominator or the square root of a negative number.

EXERCISE 1

1. Find the domains of the following functions.

    (a) $f(x) = 1 - 18x$

    (b) $g(x) = x^4 - x^2 + 15x$

    (c) $h(x) = \sqrt{x - 5}$

    (d) $F(x) = \sqrt[4]{-x}$

    (e) $G(x) = \sqrt{1 - x^2}$

    (f) $H(x) = \sqrt{x^2 - 2}$

    (g) $y = \dfrac{3 + x}{3 - x}$

    (h) $y = \dfrac{x^2}{x^2 + 4x - 5}$

    (i) $y = \dfrac{1}{\sqrt{t^2 + 5}}$

    (j) $y = \dfrac{t}{\sqrt{t^2 - 5t + 6}}$

    (k) $f(x) = \sqrt{x} + \sqrt{4 - x}$

    (l) $f(x) = \sqrt{2 - \sqrt{4 - x}}$

Composition of Functions

The **composition**, or **composite**, of f and g is the function $f \circ g$ defined by

$$(f \circ g)(x) = f(g(x))$$

Example.   If $f(x) = 2 - 3x$ and $g(x) = 5x^2 + x$, find the functions $f \circ g$ and $g \circ f$.

Solution

$$(f \circ g)(x) = f(g(x))$$
$$= f(5x^2 + x)$$
$$= 2 - 3(5x^2 + x)$$
$$= 2 - 15x^2 - 3x$$

$$(g \circ f)(x) = g(f(x))$$
$$= g(2 - 3x)$$
$$= 5(2 - 3x)^2 + (2 - 3x)$$
$$= 5(4 - 12x + 9x^2) + 2 - 3x$$
$$= 22 - 63x + 45x^2$$

EXERCISE 2

1. Find $f \circ g$, $g \circ f$, $f \circ f$, and $g \circ g$.
   (a) $f(x) = 2x - 1$, $g(x) = 4 - 3x$
   (b) $f(x) = x^2$, $g(x) = x + 1$
   (c) $f(x) = 1 - x^2$, $g(x) = 5$
   (d) $f(x) = \sqrt{x}$, $g(x) = x^2 - 4$
   (e) $f(x) = 3x - 5$, $g(x) = \dfrac{1}{x}$
   (f) $f(x) = \dfrac{1}{1 - x}$, $g(x) = \dfrac{x - 2}{x + 2}$
   (g) $f(x) = \sqrt{x}$, $g(x) = \sqrt{1 + x}$

2. Find functions f and g such that $h(x) = f(g(x))$.
   (a) $h(x) = (2x + 1)^9$ (b) $h(x) = 1 + 2x^2 + 3x^4$
   (c) $h(x) = \dfrac{1}{x^2 - 7}$ (d) $h(x) = \sqrt{6 + x}$

INTRODUCTION

One of the main concepts in calculus is the *derivative*, which is defined as a limit and arises when finding slopes of tangents and rates of change. In this chapter, we learn rules for computing derivatives so that we can apply them to curve-sketching and maximum and minimum problems in the following chapters.

2.1 DERIVATIVES

In Section 1.4 we saw that limits of the form

$$\lim_{h \to 0} \frac{f(a + h) - f(a)}{h}$$

occur as slopes of tangents and in Section 1.5 we saw that this type of limit also arises in computing velocities. In fact it occurs as a rate of change in all branches of science and engineering. Since this type of limit occurs so widely, we give it a special name and notation.

The **derivative of a function f at a number a** is

$$f'(a) = \lim_{h \to 0} \frac{f(a + h) - f(a)}{h}$$

if this limit exists.

An alternative way of writing the definition of derivative is as follows.

$$f'(a) = \lim_{x \to a} \frac{f(x) - f(a)}{x - a}$$

In fact we also used this expression in Section 1.4 to calculate slopes of tangents.

Example 1 If $f(x) = 2x^2 - 5x + 6$, find $f'(4)$, the derivative of f at 4.

Solution The calculation resembles the computation of slopes of tangents and velocities in Chapter 1. According to the definition of derivative, we have

$$f'(4) = \lim_{h \to 0} \frac{f(4 + h) - f(4)}{h}$$

$$= \lim_{h \to 0} \frac{[2(4 + h)^2 - 5(4 + h) + 6] - [2(4)^2 - 5(4) + 6]}{h}$$

$$= \lim_{h \to 0} \frac{32 + 16h + 2h^2 - 20 - 5h + 6 - 18}{h}$$

$$= \lim_{h \to 0} \frac{11h + 2h^2}{h}$$

$$= \lim_{h \to 0} (11 + 2h)$$

$$= 11$$

The derivative of f at 4 is 11.

By comparing the definition of a derivative with the definitions in Chapter 1, we have the following:

Interpretations of the Derivative

1. **As the slope of a tangent.** The tangent line to the curve $y = f(x)$ at the point $(a, f(a))$ is the line through $(a, f(a))$ with slope $f'(a)$.
2. **As a rate of change.** The (instantaneous) rate of change of $y = f(x)$ with respect to x when $x = a$ is equal to $f'(a)$. In particular, if $s = f(t)$ is the position function of a particle, then $v = f'(a)$ is the velocity of the particle at time $t = a$.

Example 2 Find the derivative of $f(x) = x^2 - 3x$ at any number a. Then use it to find the slopes of the tangents to parabola $y = x^2 - 3x$ when $x = 1$, 2, 3, 4.

Solution

$$f'(a) = \lim_{h \to 0} \frac{f(a + h) - f(a)}{h}$$

$$= \lim_{h \to 0} \frac{[(a + h)^2 - 3(a + h)] - (a^2 - 3a)}{h}$$

$$= \lim_{h \to 0} \frac{a^2 + 2ah + h^2 - 3a - 3h - a^2 + 3a}{h}$$

$$= \lim_{h \to 0} \frac{(2a - 3)h + h^2}{h}$$

$$= \lim_{h \to 0} (2a - 3 + h)$$

$$= 2a - 3$$

The derivative at a is $f'(a) = 2a - 3$.

The slopes of the tangents are obtained by putting $a = 1, 2, 3$, and 4:

$$f'(1) = 2(1) - 3 = -1 \qquad f'(2) = 2(2) - 3 = 1$$
$$f'(3) = 2(3) - 3 = 3 \qquad f'(4) = 2(4) - 3 = 5$$

The Derivative as a Function

The derivative of a function f at a is a number $f'(a)$. But if we let a vary over the domain of f, we can change our point of view and regard f' as a function.

Given a function f, the **derivative** of f is the function f' defined by

$$f'(x) = \lim_{h \to 0} \frac{f(x + h) - f(x)}{h}$$

The domain of this new function f' is the set of all numbers x for which the limit exists. Since $f(x)$ occurs in the expression for $f'(x)$, the domain of f' will always be a subset of the domain of f.

Example 3   Find the derivative of the function $f(x) = x^2$.

Solution   In computing the limit that defines $f'(x)$, we must remember that the variable is h and regard x temporarily as a constant.

$$
\begin{aligned}
f'(x) &= \lim_{h \to 0} \frac{f(x + h) - f(x)}{h} \\
&= \lim_{h \to 0} \frac{(x + h)^2 - x^2}{h} \\
&= \lim_{h \to 0} \frac{x^2 + 2xh + h^2 - x^2}{h} \\
&= \lim_{h \to 0} \frac{2xh + h^2}{h} \\
&= \lim_{h \to 0} (2x + h) \\
&= 2x
\end{aligned}
$$

The derivative is the function f' given by $f'(x) = 2x$.

Notice that in Example 3 the domains of f and f' are both R, the set of all real numbers. The next example shows that the domain of f' can be smaller than the domain of f.

Example 4 If $f(x) = \sqrt{x + 2}$, find f' and state the domains of f and f'.

Solution
$$f'(x) = \lim_{h \to 0} \frac{f(x + h) - f(x)}{h}$$

Rationalize the numerator.

$$= \lim_{h \to 0} \frac{\sqrt{x + h + 2} - \sqrt{x + 2}}{h}$$

$$= \lim_{h \to 0} \frac{\sqrt{x + h + 2} - \sqrt{x + 2}}{h} \left(\frac{\sqrt{x + h + 2} + \sqrt{x + 2}}{\sqrt{x + h + 2} + \sqrt{x + 2}}\right)$$

$$= \lim_{h \to 0} \frac{(x + h + 2) - (x + 2)}{h(\sqrt{x + h + 2} + \sqrt{x + 2})}$$

$$= \lim_{h \to 0} \frac{h}{h(\sqrt{x + h + 2} + \sqrt{x + 2})}$$

$$= \lim_{h \to 0} \frac{1}{\sqrt{x + h + 2} + \sqrt{x + 2}}$$

$$= \frac{1}{\sqrt{x + 2} + \sqrt{x + 2}}$$

$$= \frac{1}{2\sqrt{x + 2}}$$

The domain of f is $\{x \mid x + 2 \geqslant 0\} = \{x \mid x \geqslant -2\}$.
The domain of f' is $\{x \mid x + 2 > 0\} = \{x \mid x > -2\}$.

Example 5 Find f' if $f(x) = \dfrac{x + 1}{3x - 2}$.

Solution
$$f'(x) = \lim_{h \to 0} \frac{f(x + h) - f(x)}{h}$$

$$= \lim_{h \to 0} \frac{\dfrac{(x + h) + 1}{3(x + h) - 2} - \dfrac{x + 1}{3x - 2}}{h}$$

$$= \lim_{h \to 0} \frac{\dfrac{(x + h + 1)(3x - 2) - (x + 1)(3x + 3h - 2)}{(3x + 3h - 2)(3x - 2)}}{h}$$

$$= \lim_{h \to 0} \frac{(x + h + 1)(3x - 2) - (x + 1)(3x + 3h - 2)}{h(3x + 3h - 2)(3x - 2)}$$

$$= \lim_{h \to 0} \frac{(3x^2 + 3xh + 3x - 2x - 2h - 2) - (3x^2 + 3xh - 2x + 3x + 3h - 2)}{h(3x + 3h - 2)(3x - 2)}$$

$$= \lim_{h \to 0} \frac{-5h}{h(3x + 3h - 2)(3x - 2)}$$

$$= \lim_{h \to 0} \frac{-5}{(3x + 3h - 2)(3x - 2)}$$

$$= \frac{-5}{(3x - 2)^2}$$

We know that the value of the derivative of f at x, $f'(x)$, can be interpreted geometrically as the slope of the tangent line to the graph of f at the point $(x, f(x))$. This enables us to give a rough sketch of the graph of f' if we already have the graph of f.

Example 6   Use the given graph of f to sketch the graph of f'.

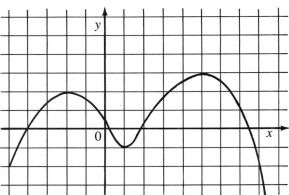

Solution

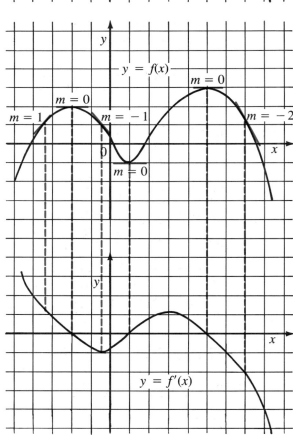

We estimate the slopes of the tangents at various points on the curve $y = f(x)$. These give the values of f' and we plot them directly beneath the graph of f. In particular, we get the x-intercepts of f' from the fact that horizontal lines have slope 0.

Other Notations

Another notation for the derivative was introduced by the German mathematician Gottfried Leibniz:

If $y = f(x)$, we write $\dfrac{dy}{dx} = f'(x)$.

In this notation, the results of Examples 3, 4, and 5 can be expressed as follows.

If $y = x^2$, then $\dfrac{dy}{dx} = 2x$.

If $y = \sqrt{x + 2}$, then $\dfrac{dy}{dx} = \dfrac{1}{2\sqrt{x + 2}}$.

If $y = \dfrac{x + 1}{3x - 2}$, then $\dfrac{dy}{dx} = -\dfrac{5}{(3x - 2)^2}$.

Leibniz used this notation as a reminder of the procedure for finding a derivative:

$$\frac{dy}{dx} = \lim_{\Delta x \to 0} \frac{\Delta y}{\Delta x}$$

For now, the symbol $\dfrac{dy}{dx}$ should not be regarded as a ratio; it is just a synonym for $f'(x)$. The Leibniz notation has the advantage that both the independent variable x and the dependent variable y are indicated. For instance, if the displacement s of a particle is given as function of the time t, then the velocity is expressed as

$$v = \frac{ds}{dt}$$

A slight variation of the Leibniz notation occurs when we think of the process of finding the derivative of a function as an operation, called **differentiation**, which is performed on f to produce a new function f'. Then we write

$$\frac{dy}{dx} = \frac{d}{dx} f(x)$$

and think of $\dfrac{d}{dx}$ as a differentiation operator. Thus we could write

$$\frac{d}{dx}(x^2) = 2x \quad \text{and} \quad \frac{d}{dx}\sqrt{x + 2} = \frac{1}{2\sqrt{x + 2}}$$

Sometimes the symbols D or D_x are also used as differentiation operators. Thus we have the following notations for the derivative of $y = f(x)$:

$$f'(x) = y' = \frac{dy}{dx} = \frac{d}{dx}f(x) = Df(x) = D_xy$$

If we want to indicate the value of a derivative $\dfrac{dy}{dx}$ in Leibniz notation at a specific number a, we use the notation

$$\frac{dy}{dx}\bigg]_{x=a} \quad \text{or} \quad \frac{dy}{dx}\bigg|_{x=a}$$

which is a synonym for $f'(a)$.

Differentiable Functions

A function f is said to be **differentiable** at a if $f'(a)$ exists. It is called **differentiable on an interval** if it is differentiable at every number in the interval. In Example 3 we saw that $f(x) = x^2$ is differentiable on R and in Example 4 we found that $f(x) = \sqrt{x + 2}$ is differentiable for $x > -2$.

Example 7 Show that the function $f(x) = |x|$ is not differentiable at 0.

Solution We must show that $f'(0)$ does not exist. Now

$$f'(0) = \lim_{h\to 0}\frac{f(0 + h) - f(0)}{h} = \lim_{h\to 0}\frac{f(h) - 0}{h} = \lim_{h\to 0}\frac{|h|}{h}$$

To show that this limit does not exist we compute the right and left limits separately. Since $|h| = h$ if $h > 0$, we have

$$\lim_{h\to 0^+}\frac{|h|}{h} = \lim_{h\to 0^+}\frac{h}{h} = \lim_{h\to 0^+}1 = 1$$

Since $|h| = -h$ if $h < 0$, we have

$$\lim_{h\to 0^-}\frac{|h|}{h} = \lim_{h\to 0^-}\frac{-h}{h} = \lim_{h\to 0^-}(-1) = -1$$

These one-sided limits are different, so $f'(0)$ does not exist. Therefore f is not differentiable at 0.

The geometric significance of Example 7 can be seen from the graph of $f(x) = |x|$ in the figure. The curve does not have a tangent line at $(0, 0)$. In general, functions whose graphs have "corners" or "kinks" are not differentiable there.

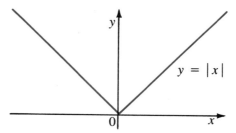

$y = |x|$

EXERCISE 2.1

A **1.** Each of the following limits represents the derivative of some function f at some number a. State f and a in each case.

(a) $\lim\limits_{h \to 0} \dfrac{(3 + h)^2 - 3^2}{h}$

(b) $\lim\limits_{h \to 0} \dfrac{(2 + h)^3 - 8}{h}$

(c) $\lim\limits_{h \to 0} \dfrac{\sqrt{4 + h} - 2}{h}$

(d) $\lim\limits_{h \to 0} \dfrac{[(1 + h)^4 + 3(1 + h)] - 4}{h}$

(e) $\lim\limits_{h \to 0} \dfrac{2^{1+h} - 2}{h}$

(f) $\lim\limits_{x \to 1} \dfrac{x^5 - 1}{x - 1}$

2. The graph of f is given. Match it with the graph of its derivative.

(a)

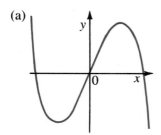

(b)

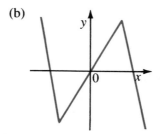

(c)

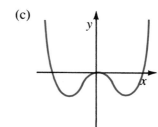

(i)

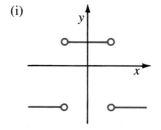

(ii)

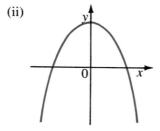

(iii)

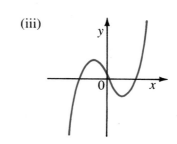

3. At what values of x are the functions not differentiable?

(a)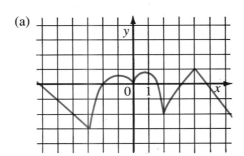

(b)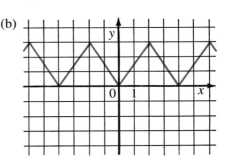

B 4. If $f(x) = x^2 + 7x$, find $f'(3)$.

5. If $g(x) = 15 - 3x^2$, find $g'(-1)$.

6. If $f(x) = \frac{1}{x}$, find $f'(3)$ and use it to find the equation of the tangent to the curve $y = \frac{1}{x}$ at the point $\left(3, \frac{1}{3}\right)$.

7. If $f(x) = x^3$, find $f'(a)$ and use it to find the slopes of the tangent lines to the cubic curve $y = x^3$ at the points $(-1, -1)$, $(0, 0)$, $(1, 1)$ and $(2, 8)$. Illustrate by sketching the curve and these tangents.

8. Find $f'(a)$ for each of the following functions.
  (a) $f(x) = 7x - x^2$
  (b) $f(x) = 2x^3 + 5$
  (c) $f(x) = \dfrac{1 + 2x}{1 + x}$
  (d) $f(x) = \sqrt{x}$

9. The position function of a particle moving along a line is given by $s = f(t) = 5t^2 - 2t + 6$, where t is measured in seconds and s in metres. Find $f'(a)$ and use it to find the velocity of the particle after 1 s, 2 s, and 3 s.

10. Find the derivative $f'(x)$ of each function.
  (a) $f(x) = 3x^2 + 2x - 4$
  (b) $f(x) = x^2 - x^3$
  (c) $f(x) = x^4$
  (d) $f(x) = \dfrac{x}{5x - 1}$

11. Find the derivative of each function. Find the domains of both the function and its derivative.
  (a) $f(x) = \sqrt{2x - 1}$
  (b) $g(x) = \dfrac{1}{\sqrt{x}}$
  (c) $F(x) = \dfrac{3 - 2x}{4 + x}$
  (d) $f(t) = \dfrac{2}{t^2 - 1}$

12. Find the derivative $\dfrac{dy}{dx}$.

    (a) $y = 7 - 3x$ (b) $y = 3x^3 + 2x$

    (c) $y = x + \dfrac{1}{x}$ (d) $y = \dfrac{1}{x^2}$

13. Use the given graph of f to sketch the graph of f'.

(a) 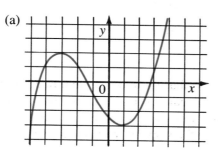   (b)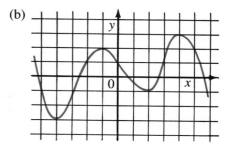

C **14.** (a) Sketch the graph of the cube root function $f(x) = \sqrt[3]{x}$.

    (b) Show that f is not differentiable at 0.

    (c) If $a \neq 0$, find $f'(a)$.

15. (a) Show that the function $f(x) = x^{\frac{2}{3}}$ is not differentiable at 0.

    (b) Sketch the curve $y = x^{\frac{2}{3}}$.

16. A function f is defined by the following conditions:

$$f(x) = |x| \text{ if } -1 \leqslant x \leqslant 1$$
$$f(x + 2) = f(x) \text{ for all values of } x$$

    (a) Sketch the graph of f.

    (b) For what values of x is f not differentiable?

2.2 THE POWER RULE

It would be time-consuming and tedious if we always had to compute derivatives directly from the definition of a derivative, as we did in the preceding section. Fortunately, there are several rules that greatly simplify the task of differentiation.

The first rule tells us how to find the derivative of a constant function.

Constant Rule

If f is a constant function, $f(x) = c$, then $f'(x) = 0$.

In Leibniz notation: $\dfrac{d}{dx}(c) = 0$

Proof

$$f'(x) = \lim_{h \to 0} \frac{f(x + h) - f(x)}{h}$$

$$= \lim_{h \to 0} \frac{c - c}{h}$$

$$= \lim_{h \to 0} 0$$

$$= 0$$

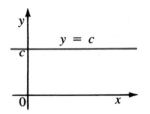

The figure illustrates the constant rule geometrically. The graph of a constant function $f(x) = c$ is the horizontal line $y = c$; the tangent line at any point on this line is the line itself. Since a horizontal line has slope 0, the slope of the tangent line is 0.

Example 1 (a) If $f(x) = 7$, then $f'(x) = 0$.

(b) If $y = \pi$, then $y' = 0$.

(c) $\dfrac{d}{dx}(-4.5) = 0$

The next rule gives a formula for differentiating the power function $f(x) = x^n$. We have already computed derivatives of special cases of the power function. In Example 3 of Section 2.1 we showed that

$$\frac{d}{dx} x^2 = 2x$$

Then in the exercises of that section you were asked to show that

$$\frac{d}{dx} x^3 = 3x^2 \quad \text{and} \quad \frac{d}{dx} x^4 = 4x^3$$

Therefore it seems reasonable to make the guess that $\dfrac{d}{dx}(x^n) = nx^{n-1}$. In fact, this is true and is called the Power Rule.

Power Rule

If $f(x) = x^n$, where n is a positive integer, then

$$f'(x) = nx^{n-1}$$

In Leibniz notation: $\qquad \dfrac{d}{dx} x^n = nx^{n-1}$

Proof

We use the formula

$$x^n - a^n = (x - a)(x^{n-1} + x^{n-2} a + \ldots + xa^{n-2} + a^{n-1})$$

which can be verified by multiplying out the right side and cancelling all but two of the terms. (See the Appendix.) Thus we have

$$f'(a) = \lim_{x \to a} \frac{f(x) - f(a)}{x - a}$$

$$= \lim_{x \to a} \frac{x^n - a^n}{x - a}$$

$$= \lim_{x \to a} \frac{(x - a)(x^{n-1} + x^{n-2}a + \ldots + xa^{n-2} + a^{n-1})}{x - a}$$

$$= \lim_{x \to a} (x^{n-1} + x^{n-2}a + \ldots + xa^{n-2} + a^{n-1})$$

$$= a^{n-1} + a^{n-2}a + \ldots + aa^{n-2} + a^{n-1}$$

$$= na^{n-1}$$

Replacing a by x, we have $f'(x) = nx^{n-1}$.

Another proof, using the Binomial Theorem, is given in the Appendix.

Example 2   (a)   If $f(x) = x^7$, then $f'(x) = 7x^6$.

(b)   If $y = x^{100}$, then $y' = 100x^{99}$.

(c)   If $y = t^5$, then $\dfrac{dy}{dt} = 5t^4$.

(d) $\dfrac{d}{du}(u^9) = 9u^8$

Example 3   Find the equation of the tangent line to the curve $y = x^6$ at the point $(-2, 64)$.

Solution   The curve is the graph of the function $f(x) = x^6$ and we know that the slope of the tangent line at $(-2, 64)$ is the derivative $f'(-2)$. From the Power Rule,

we have $f'(x) = 6x^5$

so $f'(-2) = 6(-2)^5 = -192$

Therefore the equation of the tangent line at $(-2, 64)$ is

$$y - 64 = -192(x + 2)$$

or $192x + y + 320 = 0$

Although we have proved the Power Rule when the exponent n is a positive integer, it turns out that it is true for any real number n. We will prove this fact in Chapter 8, but in the meantime we use it in the examples and exercises.

General Power Rule

If n is any real number, then

$$\frac{d}{dx}(x^n) = nx^{n-1}$$

Example 4 Differentiate: (a) $f(x) = \dfrac{1}{x^3}$ (b) $y = \sqrt{x}$

Solution   (a) We use a negative exponent to rewrite the function as

$$f(x) = \frac{1}{x^3} = x^{-3}$$

Then the Power Rule gives

$$f'(x) = (-3)x^{-3-1} = -3x^{-4} = -\frac{3}{x^4}$$

(b) Here we use a fractional exponent:

$$y = \sqrt{x} = x^{\frac{1}{2}}$$
$$\frac{dy}{dx} = \tfrac{1}{2}x^{\frac{1}{2}-1} = \tfrac{1}{2}x^{-\frac{1}{2}} = \frac{1}{2\sqrt{x}}$$

The next rule says that *the derivative of a constant times a function is the constant times the derivative of the function.*

Constant Multiple Rule

If $g(x) = cf(x)$, then $g'(x) = cf'(x)$.

In Leibniz notation: $\dfrac{d}{dx}[cf(x)] = c\dfrac{d}{dx}f(x)$

Proof

$$g'(x) = \lim_{h \to 0} \frac{g(x + h) - g(x)}{h}$$

$$= \lim_{h \to 0} \frac{cf(x + h) - cf(x)}{h}$$

$$= \lim_{h \to 0} c\left[\frac{f(x + h) - f(x)}{h}\right]$$

$$= c \lim_{h \to 0} \frac{f(x + h) - f(x)}{h} \qquad \text{(by Property 3 of limits)}$$

$$= cf'(x)$$

Example 5   Differentiate: (a) $f(x) = 8x^3$ (b) $y = 6x^{\frac{8}{3}}$

Solution   (a) $f(x) = 8x^3$

$$f'(x) = 8 \frac{d}{dx}(x^3) = 8(3x^2) = 24x^2$$

(b) $y = 6x^{\frac{8}{3}}$

$$\frac{dy}{dx} = 6 \frac{d}{dx} x^{\frac{8}{3}} = 6\left(\frac{8}{3} x^{\frac{8}{3} - 1}\right) = 6\left(\frac{8}{3} x^{\frac{5}{3}}\right) = 16x^{\frac{5}{3}}$$

Example 6   At what points on the hyperbola $xy = 12$ is the tangent line parallel to the line $3x + y = 0$?

Solution   Since $xy = 12$ can be written as $y = \dfrac{12}{x}$, we have

$$\frac{dy}{dx} = 12 \frac{d}{dx}(x^{-1}) = 12(-x^{-2}) = -\frac{12}{x^2}$$

Let the x-coordinate of a required point be a. Then the slope of the tangent line at that point is

$$-\frac{12}{a^2}$$

This tangent line will be parallel to the line $3x + y = 0$, or $y = -3x$, if it has the same slope, that is, -3. Equating slopes we get

$$-\frac{12}{a^2} = -3 \quad \text{or} \quad a^2 = 4 \quad \text{or} \quad a = \pm 2$$

Therefore the required points are $(2, 6)$ and $(-2, -6)$. The hyperbola and the tangents are shown in the figure.

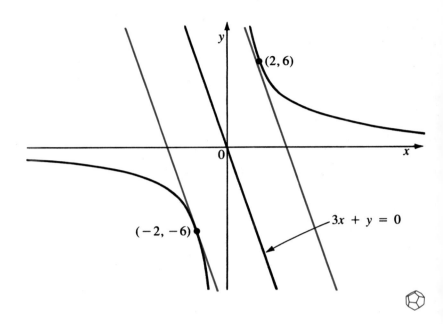

Example 7 A ball is dropped from the upper observation deck of the CN Tower. How fast is the ball falling after 3 s?

Solution We solved this problem in Example 1 of Section 1.5, but now we can give a simpler solution using the rules of differentiation. The distance fallen, in metres, after t seconds is

$$s = 4.9t^2$$

and we know that the derivative of this function is the velocity of the ball. Since

$$\frac{ds}{dt} = 4.9 \frac{d}{dt}(t^2) = 4.9(2t) = 9.8t$$

we have

$$\left. \frac{ds}{dt} \right]_{t=3} = 9.8(3) = 29.4$$

The velocity after 3 s is 29.4 m/s.

EXERCISE 2.2

A **1.** State the derivative of each function.

(a) $f(x) = 32$

(b) $f(x) = x^4$

(c) $y = x^{12}$

(d) $y = -3.724$

(e) $f(x) = x$

(f) $f(x) = x^\pi$

(g) $f(x) = x^{43}$

(h) $f(x) = 2^5$

(i) $g(x) = x^{-2}$

(j) $g(x) = x^{\frac{3}{2}}$

B **2.** Differentiate.

(a) $f(x) = 8x^{12}$

(b) $f(x) = -3x^9$

(c) $f(t) = 3t^{\frac{4}{3}}$

(d) $g(t) = 8t^{-\frac{3}{4}}$

(e) $y = \dfrac{1}{x^4}$

(f) $y = \dfrac{2}{x^2}$

(g) $g(t) = (2t)^3$

(h) $h(y) = \left(\dfrac{y}{3}\right)^2$

(i) $f(x) = \sqrt[3]{x}$

(j) $f(x) = \sqrt[3]{x^2}$

(k) $y = \dfrac{1}{\sqrt{x}}$

(l) $y = \dfrac{3}{\sqrt[4]{x}}$

(m) $y = \sqrt{3}x^{\sqrt{2}}$

(n) $y = (x^3)^4$

3. Find the slope of the tangent line to the graph of the given function at the point whose x-coordinate is given.

(a) $f(x) = 2x^3$, $x = \frac{1}{3}$

(b) $f(x) = x^{1.4}$, $x = 1$

(c) $g(x) = x^{-3}$, $x = -1$

(d) $g(x) = \sqrt[5]{x}$, $x = 32$

(e) $y = \sqrt{x^3}$, $x = 8$

(f) $y = \dfrac{6}{x}$, $x = -3$

4. Find the equation of the tangent line to the curve at the given point.

(a) $y = x^5$, $(2, 32)$

(b) $y = 2\sqrt{x}$, $(9, 6)$

(c) $xy = 1$, $\left(5, \frac{1}{5}\right)$

(d) $y = \sqrt[3]{x}$, $(-8, -2)$

5. Use the definition of derivative to show that

$$\text{if } f(x) = \frac{1}{x}, \text{ then } f'(x) = -\frac{1}{x^2}$$

(This proves the Power Rule for the case $n = -1$.)

6. Use the definition of derivative to show that

$$\text{if } f(x) = \sqrt{x}, \text{ then } f'(x) = \frac{1}{2\sqrt{x}}$$

(This proves the Power Rule for the case $n = \frac{1}{2}$.)

7. At what point on the parabola $y = 3x^2$ is the slope of the tangent line equal to 24?

8. Find the point on the curve $y = x\sqrt{x}$ where the tangent line is parallel to the line $6x - y = 4$.

9. At what point on the curve $y = -2x^4$ is the tangent line perpendicular to the line $x - y + 1 = 0$?

10. Find the points on the curve $y = 1 - \dfrac{1}{x}$ where the tangent line is perpendicular to the line $y = 1 - 4x$.

C **11.** Draw a diagram to show that there are two tangent lines to the parabola $y = x^2$ that pass through the point $(0, -5)$. Find the coordinates of the points where these tangent lines meet the parabola.

12. A manufacturer of cartridges for stereo systems has designed a stylus with a parabolic cross-section as shown in the figure. The equation of the parabola is $y = 8x^2$, where x and y are measured in millimetres. If the stylus sits in a record groove whose sides make an angle of θ with the horizontal direction, where $\tan \theta = 2.5$, find the points of contact P and Q of the stylus with the groove.

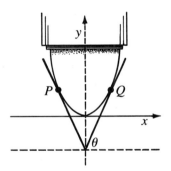

2.3 THE SUM AND DIFFERENCE RULES

The Sum Rule gives a simple rule for finding the derivative of a sum of two functions if we know the derivatives of the two functions. It says that *the derivative of a sum is the sum of the derivatives*.

Sum Rule

If both f and g are differentiable, then so is $f + g$ and

$$(f + g)' = f' + g'$$

In Leibniz notation:

$$\frac{d}{dx}[f(x) + g(x)] = \frac{d}{dx}f(x) + \frac{d}{dx}g(x)$$

Proof

Let $F = f + g$, that is, $F(x) = (f + g)(x) = f(x) + g(x)$. Then

$$F'(x) = \lim_{h \to 0} \frac{F(x + h) - F(x)}{h}$$

$$= \lim_{h \to 0} \frac{[f(x + h) + g(x + h)] - [f(x) + g(x)]}{h}$$

$$= \lim_{h \to 0} \left[\frac{f(x + h) - f(x)}{h} + \frac{g(x + h) - g(x)}{h} \right] \qquad \text{(by rearranging terms)}$$

$$= \lim_{h \to 0} \frac{f(x + h) - f(x)}{h} + \lim_{h \to 0} \frac{g(x + h) - g(x)}{h} \qquad \text{(by Property 1 of limits)}$$

$$= f'(x) + g'(x)$$

This shows that $(f + g)' = f' + g'$.

The Sum Rule can be extended to a sum of any number of functions. For instance, using the rule twice we get

$$(f + g + h)' = [(f + g) + h]'$$
$$= (f + g)' + h'$$
$$= f' + g' + h'$$

The corresponding rule for differences says that *the derivative of a difference is the difference of the derivatives*. It is proved in a similar way.

Difference Rule

$$(f - g)' = f' - g'$$

Example 1 Find the derivatives of the following functions.

(a) $f(x) = 2x^4 + \sqrt{x}$ (b) $g(x) = 6x^4 - 5x^3 - 2x + 17$

Solution We combine the sum and difference rules with the power rule and the constant multiple rule.

(a) $f'(x) = \dfrac{d}{dx}(2x^4 + \sqrt{x})$

$$= 2\frac{d}{dx}x^4 + \frac{d}{dx}x^{\frac{1}{2}}$$

$$= 2(4x^3) + \tfrac{1}{2}x^{-\frac{1}{2}}$$

$$= 8x^3 + \frac{1}{2\sqrt{x}}$$

(b) $\dfrac{d}{dx} g(x) = \dfrac{d}{dx} (6x^4 - 5x^3 - 2x + 17)$

$= 6\dfrac{d}{dx} x^4 - 5\dfrac{d}{dx} x^3 - 2\dfrac{d}{dx} x + \dfrac{d}{dx} 17$

$= 6(4x^3) - 5(3x^2) - 2(1) + 0$

$= 24x^3 - 15x^2 - 2$

With practice, it is possible to use these rules mentally and simply write down the answer.

Example 2   Differentiate $y = \left(x - \dfrac{2}{\sqrt{x}} \right)^2$.

Solution   We first simplify the function.

$$y = \left(x - \dfrac{2}{\sqrt{x}} \right)^2$$

$$= x^2 - 2x\left(\dfrac{2}{\sqrt{x}} \right) + \left(\dfrac{2}{\sqrt{x}} \right)^2$$

$$= x^2 - 4\sqrt{x} + \dfrac{4}{x}$$

$$= x^2 - 4x^{\frac{1}{2}} + 4x^{-1}$$

Now it is easy to differentiate each term.

$$y' = 2x - 4\left(\tfrac{1}{2}x^{-\frac{1}{2}} \right) + 4(-1)x^{-2}$$

$$= 2x - \dfrac{2}{\sqrt{x}} - \dfrac{4}{x^2}$$

Example 3   Find the equations of both lines that pass through the point $P(2, 9)$ and are tangent to the parabola $y = 2x - x^2$. Sketch the parabola and the tangents.

Solution   We are not given the coordinates of the points where the tangents touch the parabola. So we let the x-coordinate of such a point be a. Then the point is $Q(a, 2a - a^2)$. We determine the values of a by expressing the slope of the tangent line PQ in two ways. Using the formula for slope, we have

$$m_{PQ} = \dfrac{2a - a^2 - 9}{a - 2}$$

But, on the other hand, we know that the slope of the tangent at Q is $f'(a)$, where $f(x) = 2x - x^2$. The differentiation rules give

$$f'(x) = 2 - 2x$$

so the equation $m_{PQ} = f'(a)$ becomes

$$\frac{2a - a^2 - 9}{a - 2} = 2 - 2a$$

$$2a - a^2 - 9 = (2 - 2a)(a - 2)$$

$$2a - a^2 - 9 = -2a^2 + 6a - 4$$

$$a^2 - 4a - 5 = 0$$

$$(a - 5)(a + 1) = 0$$

$$a = 5, -1$$

Also

$$f(5) = 2(5) - 5^2 = -15$$

$$f(-1) = 2(-1) - (-1)^2 = -3$$

The points of contact are $(5, -15)$ and $(-1, -3)$ and the slopes of the tangents at these points are $f'(5) = -8$ and $f'(-1) = 4$. The equations of the tangents at these points are

$$y + 15 = -8(x - 5) \qquad \text{and} \qquad y + 3 = 4(x + 1)$$

or $\qquad 8x + y - 25 = 0 \qquad \text{and} \qquad 4x - y + 1 = 0$

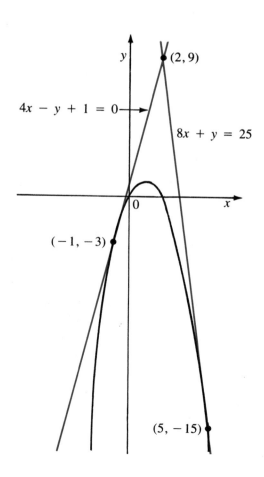

EXERCISE 2.3

B 1. Differentiate the following functions.

(a) $f(x) = x^2 + 4x$

(b) $f(x) = 3x^5 - 6x^4 + 2$

(c) $g(x) = x^{10} + 25x^5 - 50$

(d) $g(x) = x^2 - \dfrac{2}{x^2}$

(e) $h(x) = \sqrt{x} - 5x^4$

(f) $h(x) = (x - 1)(x + 6)$

(g) $y = \dfrac{x + 1}{\sqrt{x}}$

(h) $y = t^5 - 6t^{-5}$

(i) $f(t) = (1 + t)^3$

(j) $F(x) = \sqrt{x} + \sqrt[3]{x} + \sqrt[4]{x}$

(k) $u(t) = a + \dfrac{b}{t} + \dfrac{c}{t^2}$

(l) $v(r) = \sqrt{r}(2 + 3r)$

2. Find $f'(x)$ and state the domains of f and f'.

(a) $f(x) = 1 + x + \frac{1}{2}x^2 + \frac{1}{3}x^3 + \frac{1}{4}x^4$

(b) $f(x) = 4x - \sqrt[4]{x}$

(c) $f(x) = x + \dfrac{\sqrt{10}}{x^5}$

(d) $f(x) = \sqrt{x} + \dfrac{2}{\sqrt{x}}$

3. Find the equation of the tangent line to the curve at the given point.

(a) $y = x^3 - x^2 + x - 1$, $(1, 0)$

(b) $y = 7\sqrt{x} - 3x$, $(1, 4)$

(c) $y = x + \dfrac{6}{x}$, $(2, 5)$

(d) $y = (x^2 + 1)^2$, $(-1, 4)$

4. If a ball is thrown upward with a velocity of 40 m/s, its height in metres after t seconds is
$$h = 40t - 5t^2$$
Find the velocity of the ball after 2 s, 4 s, and 5 s.

5. The displacement in metres of a particle moving in a straight line is given by $s = 8t^2 - 5t + 6$, where t is measured in seconds. Find the velocity of the particle after 1 s, 2 s, and 5 s.

6. At what point on the curve $y = x^4 - 25x + 2$ is the tangent parallel to the line $7x - y = 2$?

7. At what points does the curve $y = x^3 + 3x^2 - 24x + 1$ have a horizontal tangent?

8. Show that the curve $y = 10x^3 + 4x + 2$ has no tangent lines with slope 3.

9. Find the equations of both lines that pass through the origin and are tangent to the parabola $y = 1 + x^2$.

10. Find the equations of the tangent lines to the parabola $y = x^2 + x$ that pass through the point $(2, -3)$. Sketch the curve and the tangents.

11. Find the x-coordinates of the points on the hyperbola $xy = 1$ where the tangents from the point $(1, -1)$ intersect the curve.

C **12.** Let

$$f(x) = \begin{cases} 2x + 3 & \text{if } x < -1 \\ x^2 & \text{if } -1 \le x \le 1 \\ 3 - 2x & \text{if } x > 1 \end{cases}$$

  (a) Where is f differentiable?
  (b) Find an expression for f' and sketch the graphs of f and f'.

13. (a) Sketch the graph of $f(x) = |x^2 - 4|$.
  (b) For what values of x is f not differentiable?
  (c) Find a formula for f' and sketch its graph.

PROBLEMS PLUS

Suppose that the tangent line at a point P on the curve $y = x^3$ intersects the curve again at a point Q. Show that the slope of the tangent at Q is four times the slope of the tangent at P.

2.4 THE PRODUCT RULE

In this section we develop a formula for the derivative of a product of two functions. It is tempting to guess, as Leibniz did three centuries ago, that the derivative of a product is the product of the derivatives. We can see, however, that this guess is wrong by looking at a particular example. Let

$$f(x) = x \qquad\qquad g(x) = x^2$$
Then $\quad f'(x) = 1 \qquad\qquad g'(x) = 2x$
so $\qquad\qquad f'(x)g'(x) = 2x$

But $(fg)(x) = f(x)g(x) = x(x^2) = x^3$, so

$$(fg)'(x) = 3x^2$$

Thus, in general,

$$(fg)' \ne f'g'$$

The correct formula is called the Product Rule and was discovered by Leibniz (soon after his false start).

Product Rule

If both f and g are differentiable, then so is fg and

$$(fg)' = fg' + f'g$$

In Leibniz notation: $\dfrac{d}{dx}[f(x)g(x)] = f(x)\dfrac{d}{dx}g(x) + g(x)\dfrac{d}{dx}f(x)$

In words, the Product Rule says that *the derivative of a product of two functions is the first function times the derivative of the second function plus the second function times the derivative of the first function.*

Proof

Let $F = fg$, that is, $F(x) = (fg)(x) = f(x)g(x)$. Then

$$F'(x) = \lim_{h \to 0} \frac{F(x+h) - F(x)}{h}$$

$$= \lim_{h \to 0} \frac{f(x+h)g(x+h) - f(x)g(x)}{h}$$

To evaluate this limit we would like to separate the functions f and g, as in the proof of the Sum Rule. To achieve this separation, we add and subtract the term $f(x+h)g(x)$ in the numerator. This allows us to factor as follows:

$$F'(x) = \lim_{h \to 0} \frac{f(x+h)g(x+h) - f(x+h)g(x) + f(x+h)g(x) - f(x)g(x)}{h}$$

$$= \lim_{h \to 0} \left[f(x+h)\frac{g(x+h) - g(x)}{h} + g(x)\frac{f(x+h) - f(x)}{h} \right]$$

$$= \lim_{h \to 0} f(x+h) \lim_{h \to 0} \frac{g(x+h) - g(x)}{h} + \lim_{h \to 0} g(x) \lim_{h \to 0} \frac{f(x+h) - f(x)}{h}$$

$$= f(x)g'(x) + g(x)f'(x)$$

Notice that

$$\lim_{h \to 0} g(x) = g(x)$$

since $g(x)$ is a constant with respect to h. The reason that

$$\lim_{h \to 0} f(x+h) = f(x)$$

is that f is continuous. (Differentiable functions are continuous. See the Appendix.)

Example 1   Find $\dfrac{dy}{dx}$ if $y = (2x^3 + 5)(3x^2 - x)$.

Solution   According to the Product Rule, we have

$$\frac{dy}{dx} = (2x^3 + 5)\frac{d}{dx}(3x^2 - x) + (3x^2 - x)\frac{d}{dx}(2x^3 + 5)$$
$$= (2x^3 + 5)(6x - 1) + (3x^2 - x)(6x^2)$$

If desired, this expression could be simplified as follows:

$$\frac{dy}{dx} = 12x^4 - 2x^3 + 30x - 5 + 18x^4 - 6x^3$$
$$= 30x^4 - 8x^3 + 30x - 5$$

Example 2   Differentiate $f(x) = \sqrt{x}(2 - 3x)$ and simplify.

Solution $f'(x) = \sqrt{x}\dfrac{d}{dx}(2 - 3x) + (2 - 3x)\dfrac{d}{dx}\sqrt{x}$

$$= \sqrt{x}(-3) + (2 - 3x)\left(\frac{1}{2\sqrt{x}}\right)$$

$$= -3\sqrt{x} + \frac{1}{\sqrt{x}} - \frac{3}{2}\sqrt{x}$$

$$= \frac{1}{\sqrt{x}} - \frac{9}{2}\sqrt{x}$$

Notice that we do not actually need the Product Rule to differentiate the functions in Examples 1 and 2. We could have multiplied the factors and proceeded as in Section 2.2. (In fact this is often easier.) But we will later meet functions such as $y = x^2 2^x$ for which the Product Rule must be used.

Example 3   Find the slope of the tangent to the graph of the function $f(x) = (3x^2 + 2)(2x^3 - 1)$ at the point $(1, 5)$.

Solution   The Product Rule gives

$$f'(x) = (3x^2 + 2)\frac{d}{dx}(2x^3 - 1) + (2x^3 - 1)\frac{d}{dx}(3x^2 + 2)$$
$$= (3x^2 + 2)(6x^2) + (2x^3 - 1)(6x)$$

There is no need to simplify before substituting $x = 1$.

$$f'(1) = (5)(6) + (1)(6) = 36$$

The slope of the tangent line at $(1, 5)$ is 36.

EXERCISE 2.4

B **1.** Use the Product Rule to find the derivative. Do not simplify your answer.

(a) $f(x) = (2x - 1)(x^2 + 1)$ (b) $f(x) = x(3x - 8)$

(c) $y = x^2(1 + x - 3x^2)$ (d) $y = (x^3 + x^2 + 1)(x^2 + 2)$

(e) $f(t) = (t^4 + t^2 - 1)(t^2 - 2)$ (f) $f(t) = \sqrt[3]{t}(1 - t)$

(g) $F(y) = \sqrt{y}(y - 2\sqrt{y} + 2)$ (h) $G(y) = (y - y^2)(2y - y^{\frac{4}{3}})$

2. Use the Product Rule to differentiate each function. Simplify your answer.

(a) $y = x^3(x^2 + 2x + 3)$ (b) $y = x^{-2}(x^3 - 3x^2 + 6)$

(c) $f(x) = (1 - x^2)(2 - x^3)$ (d) $f(x) = (3x^3 + 4)(1 - 2x^3)$

(e) $f(t) = (6 + t^{-2})(8t^{10} - 5t^3)$ (f) $f(t) = (at + b)(ct^2 - d)$

(g) $g(u) = \sqrt{u}(2 - u^2 + 5u^4)$ (h) $g(v) = (v - \sqrt{v})(v^2 + \sqrt{v})$

3. Find the slope of the tangent to the given curve at the point whose x-coordinate is given.

(a) $y = (1 - 2x)(3x - 4)$, $x = 2$

(b) $y = (1 - x + x^2)(x - 2)$, $x = 1$

(c) $y = x^4(4x^3 + 2)$, $x = -1$

(d) $y = (1 + x - 2x^2)(3x^3 + x - 1)$, $x = 1$

(e) $y = x^{-5}(1 + x^{-1})$, $x = 1$

(f) $y = (2 - 3\sqrt{x})(4 - \sqrt{x})$, $x = 4$

4. If $f(x) = (6x^4 - 3x^2 + 1)(2 - x^3)$, find $f'(1)$ by two methods:

(a) by using the Product Rule;

(b) by expanding $f(x)$ first.

5. Find the equation of the tangent line to the curve $y = (2 - \sqrt{x})(1 + \sqrt{x} + 3x)$ at the point $(1, 5)$.

6. If $f(2) = 3$, $f'(2) = 5$, $g(2) = -1$, and $g'(2) = -4$, find $(fg)'(2)$.

7. If f is a differentiable function, find expressions for the derivatives of the following functions.

(a) $g(x) = xf(x)$ (b) $h(x) = \sqrt{x}f(x)$ (c) $F(x) = x^2f(x)$

8. (a) Use the Product Rule with $g = f$ to show that if f is differentiable, then

$$\frac{d}{dx}[f(x)]^2 = 2f(x)f'(x)$$

(b) Use part (a) to differentiate $y = (2 + 5x - x^3)^2$.

C **9.** (a) Use the Product Rule twice to show that if f, g, and h are differentiable, then

$$(fgh)' = f'gh + fg'h + fgh'$$

(b) Use part (a) to differentiate $y = \sqrt{x}(3x + 5)(6x^2 - 5x + 1)$.

10. (a) Taking $f = g = h$ in Question 9, show that

$$\frac{d}{dx}[f(x)]^3 = 3[f(x)]^2f'(x)$$

(b) Use part (a) to differentiate $y = (1 + x^3 + x^6)^3$.

11. Use the Principle of Mathematical Induction and the Product Rule to prove the Power Rule

$$\frac{d}{dx} x^n = nx^{n-1}$$

when n is a positive integer.

2.5 THE QUOTIENT RULE

In this section we present a formula for the derivative of a quotient of two functions. In particular, this will enable us to differentiate any rational function (ratio of two polynomials) such as

$$F(x) = \frac{x^2 + 2x - 3}{x^3 + 1}$$

Quotient Rule

If both f and g are differentiable, then so is the quotient
$$F(x) = \frac{f(x)}{g(x)} \text{ and}$$

$$F'(x) = \frac{g(x)f'(x) - f(x)g'(x)}{[g(x)]^2}$$

The Quotient Rule can be proved by a method similar to the one used in proving the Product Rule. But if we make the assumption that F is differentiable, then we can use the following simpler method.

Proof Since

$$F(x) = \frac{f(x)}{g(x)}$$

we have

$$f(x) = F(x)g(x)$$

So, by the Product Rule,

$$f'(x) = F(x)g'(x) + F'(x)g(x)$$

Now we solve for $F'(x)$:

$$F'(x)g(x) = f'(x) - F(x)g'(x)$$
$$= f'(x) - \frac{f(x)}{g(x)} g'(x)$$
$$F'(x) = \frac{f'(x) - \frac{f(x)}{g(x)} g'(x)}{g(x)}$$
$$= \frac{g(x)f'(x) - f(x)g'(x)}{[g(x)]^2}$$

In Leibniz notation, the Quotient Rule can be written as follows:

$$\frac{d}{dx}\left(\frac{f(x)}{g(x)}\right) = \frac{g(x)\dfrac{d}{dx}f(x) - f(x)\dfrac{d}{dx}g(x)}{[g(x)]^2}$$

We must be careful to remember the order of the terms in this formula because of the minus sign in the numerator. In words, the Quotient Rule says that *the derivative of a quotient is the denominator times the derivative of the numerator minus the numerator times the derivative of the denominator, all divided by the square of the denominator*.

Example 1   Differentiate $F(x) = \dfrac{x^2 + 2x - 3}{x^3 + 1}$.

Solution   By the Quotient Rule, we have

$$F'(x) = \frac{(x^3 + 1)\dfrac{d}{dx}(x^2 + 2x - 3) - (x^2 + 2x - 3)\dfrac{d}{dx}(x^3 + 1)}{(x^3 + 1)^2}$$
$$= \frac{(x^3 + 1)(2x + 2) - (x^2 + 2x - 3)(3x^2)}{(x^3 + 1)^2}$$
$$= \frac{(2x^4 + 2x^3 + 2x + 2) - (3x^4 + 6x^3 - 9x^2)}{(x^3 + 1)^2}$$
$$= \frac{-x^4 - 4x^3 + 9x^2 + 2x + 2}{(x^3 + 1)^2}$$

After using the Quotient Rule, it is usually worthwhile to simplify the resulting expression.

Example 2   Find $\dfrac{dy}{dx}$ if $y = \dfrac{\sqrt{x}}{1 + 2x}$.

Solution

$$\frac{dy}{dx} = \frac{(1 + 2x)\dfrac{d}{dx}\sqrt{x} - \sqrt{x}\dfrac{d}{dx}(1 + 2x)}{(1 + 2x)^2}$$

$$= \frac{(1 + 2x)\dfrac{1}{2\sqrt{x}} - \sqrt{x}(2)}{(1 + 2x)^2}$$

Now we multiply the numerator and denominator by $2\sqrt{x}$:

$$\frac{dy}{dx} = \frac{1 + 2x - (2\sqrt{x})(2\sqrt{x})}{2\sqrt{x}(1 + 2x)^2} = \frac{1 - 2x}{2\sqrt{x}(1 + 2x)^2}$$

EXERCISE 2.5

B **1.** Differentiate.

(a) $f(x) = \dfrac{x - 1}{x + 1}$

(b) $f(x) = \dfrac{2x - 1}{x^2 + 1}$

(c) $g(x) = \dfrac{x}{x^2 + 2x - 1}$

(d) $g(x) = \dfrac{x^3 - 1}{x^2 + x + 1}$

(e) $y = \dfrac{\sqrt{x}}{x^2 + 1}$

(f) $y = \dfrac{\sqrt{x} + 2}{\sqrt{x} - 2}$

(g) $f(t) = \dfrac{2t + 1}{t^2 - 3t + 4}$

(h) $g(t) = \dfrac{2t^2 + 3t + 1}{t - 1}$

(i) $f(x) = \dfrac{1}{x^4 - x^2 + 1}$

(j) $f(x) = \dfrac{ax + b}{cx + d}$

(k) $f(x) = \dfrac{x^6}{x^5 - 10}$

(l) $f(x) = \dfrac{1 - \dfrac{1}{x}}{x + 1}$

2. Find the domain of f and compute its derivative.

(a) $f(x) = \dfrac{2 + x}{1 - 2x}$

(b) $f(x) = \dfrac{x}{x^2 - 1}$

(c) $f(x) = \dfrac{1}{(x + 1)(2x - 3)}$

(d) $f(x) = \dfrac{2x + 1}{x^2 + 2x - 3}$

(e) $f(x) = \dfrac{x^2 + 2x}{x^4 - 1}$

(f) $f(x) = \dfrac{x^2}{\sqrt{x} - 3}$

3. Find an equation of the tangent line to the curve at the given point.

(a) $y = \dfrac{x}{x - 2}$, $(4, 2)$ (b) $y = \dfrac{1 + 3x}{2 - 3x}$, $(1, -4)$

(c) $y = \dfrac{1}{x^2 + 1}$, $\left(-2, \frac{1}{5}\right)$ (d) $y = \dfrac{x^3 - 1}{1 + 2x^2}$, $(1, 0)$

4. If $f(2) = 3$, $f'(2) = 5$, $g(2) = -1$, and $g'(2) = -4$, find $\left(\dfrac{f}{g}\right)'(2)$.

5. Show that there are no tangents to the curve $y = \dfrac{x + 2}{3x + 4}$ with positive slope.

6. At what points on the curve $y = \dfrac{x^2}{2x + 5}$ is the tangent line horizontal?

7. Find the points on the curve $y = \dfrac{x}{x - 1}$ where the tangent line is parallel to the line $x + 4y = 1$.

8. If f is a differentiable function, find expressions for the derivatives of the following functions.

(a) $y = \dfrac{1}{f(x)}$ (b) $y = \dfrac{f(x)}{x}$ (c) $y = \dfrac{x}{f(x)}$

C **9.** In Section 2.2 we proved the Power Rule for positive integer exponents. Use the Quotient Rule to deduce the Power Rule for the case of negative integer exponents; that is, prove that

$$\frac{d}{dx}(x^{-n}) = -nx^{-n-1}$$

when n is a positive integer.

2.6 THE CHAIN RULE

Although we have learned to differentiate a variety of functions, our differentiation rules still do not enable us to find the derivative of the function

$$F(x) = \sqrt{2x^2 + 3}$$

Notice that F is a composite function; it can be built up from simpler functions. If we let

$$y = f(u) = \sqrt{u} \quad \text{and} \quad u = g(x) = 2x^2 + 3$$

then $f(g(x)) = f(2x^2 + 3) = \sqrt{2x^2 + 3} = F(x)$

that is, $F = f \circ g$. The Chain Rule tells us how to compute the derivative of a composite function $F = f \circ g$ in terms of the derivatives of f and g.

If we interpret derivatives as rates of change, then we can guess what the rule says. Regard $\frac{du}{dx}$ as the rate of change of u with respect to x, $\frac{dy}{du}$ as the rate of change of y with respect to u, and $\frac{dy}{dx}$ as the rate of change of y with respect to x. If u changes twice as fast as x and y changes three times as fast as u, then it seems reasonable that y changes six times as fast as x, and so we expect that

$$\frac{dy}{dx} = \frac{dy}{du}\frac{du}{dx}$$

The Chain Rule

If the derivatives $g'(x)$ and $f'(g(x))$ both exist and $F = f \circ g$ is the composite function defined by $F(x) = f(g(x))$, then $F'(x)$ exists and is given by the product $F'(x) = f'(g(x))g'(x)$; that is

$$\frac{d}{dx}f(g(x)) = f'(g(x))\ g'(x) \tag{1}$$

Thus the Chain Rule says that we differentiate a composite function $f(g(x))$ by working from the outside to the inside. We first differentiate the outer function f, but we evaluate it at the inner function $g(x)$. Then we multiply by the derivative of the inner function g.

The Chain Rule in Leibniz Notation

If $y = f(u)$, where $u = g(x)$, and f and g are differentiable, then y is a differentiable function of x and

$$\frac{dy}{dx} = \frac{dy}{du}\frac{du}{dx} \tag{2}$$

Equation 2 is easy to remember because if $\frac{dy}{du}$ and $\frac{du}{dx}$ were quotients, then we could cancel the du's. Remember, however, that du has not been defined and $\frac{du}{dx}$ should not be thought of as an actual quotient.

To indicate why the Chain Rule is true we use increment notation. If x changes by an amount Δx, then u changes by an amount

$$\Delta u = g(x + \Delta x) - g(x)$$

and the corresponding change in y is

$$\Delta y = f(u + \Delta u) - f(u)$$

If we assume that $\Delta u \neq 0$ whenever Δx is small and $\Delta x \neq 0$, then we can write

$$\frac{dy}{dx} = \lim_{\Delta x \to 0} \frac{\Delta y}{\Delta x} \qquad \text{(definition of derivative)}$$

$$= \lim_{\Delta x \to 0} \frac{\Delta y}{\Delta u} \frac{\Delta u}{\Delta x} \qquad \text{(multiply and divide by } \Delta u\text{)}$$

$$= \lim_{\Delta x \to 0} \frac{\Delta y}{\Delta u} \lim_{\Delta x \to 0} \frac{\Delta u}{\Delta x} \qquad \text{(Property 4 of limits)}$$

$$= \lim_{\Delta u \to 0} \frac{\Delta y}{\Delta u} \lim_{\Delta x \to 0} \frac{\Delta u}{\Delta x} \qquad (\Delta u \to 0 \text{ as } \Delta x \to 0 \text{ since } g \text{ is continuous})$$

$$= \frac{dy}{du} \frac{du}{dx}$$

Our assumption about Δu is true for most functions g, but there are some functions for which it is false. A proof of the Chain Rule that is valid for all differentiable functions is given in more advanced courses.

Example 1 Find $F'(x)$ if $F(x) = \sqrt{2x^2 + 3}$.

Solution 1 At the beginning of this section we expressed F as $F(x) = f(g(x))$, where the outer function is $f(u) = \sqrt{u}$ and the inner function is $g(x) = 2x^2 + 3$. Since

$$f'(u) = \tfrac{1}{2}u^{-\frac{1}{2}} = \frac{1}{2\sqrt{u}} \quad \text{and} \quad g'(x) = 4x$$

Equation 1 gives

$$F'(x) = f'(g(x))g'(x)$$

$$= \frac{1}{2\sqrt{2x^2 + 3}} (4x)$$

$$= \frac{2x}{\sqrt{2x^2 + 3}}$$

Solution 2 If $u = 2x^2 + 3$ and $y = \sqrt{u}$, then Equation 2 gives

$$\frac{dy}{dx} = \frac{dy}{du} \frac{du}{dx}$$

$$= \frac{1}{2\sqrt{u}} (4x)$$

$$= \frac{1}{2\sqrt{2x^2 + 3}} (4x)$$

$$= \frac{2x}{\sqrt{2x^2 + 3}}$$

Example 2   If $y = u^{10} + u^5 + 2$, where $u = 1 - 3x^2$, find $\dfrac{dy}{dx}\Big]_{x=1}$.

Solution   Using the Chain Rule with Leibniz notation, we have

$$\frac{dy}{dx} = \frac{dy}{du}\frac{du}{dx} = (10u^9 + 5u^4)(-6x)$$

It is not necessary to write this expression entirely in terms of x. We note that when $x = 1$ we have $u = 1 - 3(1)^2 = -2$ and so

$$\frac{dy}{dx}\Big]_{x=1} = [10(-2)^9 + 5(-2)^4][(-6)(1)] = (-5040)(-6) = 30\ 240$$

An important special case of the Chain Rule occurs when the outer function f is a power function. Suppose that $y = f(u) = u^n$, where $u = g(x)$. If we use the Power Rule and then the Chain Rule, we get

$$\frac{dy}{dx} = \frac{dy}{du}\frac{du}{dx} = nu^{n-1}\frac{du}{dx} = n[g(x)]^{n-1}g'(x)$$

Power Rule Combined with Chain Rule

If n is any real number and $u = g(x)$ is differentiable, then

$$\frac{d}{dx}(u^n) = nu^{n-1}\frac{du}{dx}$$

or

$$\frac{d}{dx}[g(x)]^n = n[g(x)]^{n-1}g'(x)$$

Special cases of this rule ($n = 2$ and 3) were developed in Exercise 2.4 using the Product Rule.

Example 3   If $y = (x^2 - x + 2)^8$, find $\dfrac{dy}{dx}$.

Solution   Taking $u = g(x) = x^2 - x + 2$ and $n = 8$, we have

$$\frac{dy}{dx} = 8(x^2 - x + 2)^7 \frac{d}{dx}(x^2 - x + 2)$$
$$= 8(x^2 - x + 2)^7(2x - 1)$$

Example 4 Find $f'(x)$ if $f(x) = \dfrac{1}{\sqrt[3]{1 - x^4}}$.

Solution First we write the function in the form

$$f(x) = (1 - x^4)^{-\frac{1}{3}}$$

Then we have

$$f'(x) = -\tfrac{1}{3}(1 - x^4)^{-\frac{4}{3}} \dfrac{d}{dx}(1 - x^4)$$

$$= -\dfrac{1}{3(1 - x^4)^{\frac{4}{3}}}(-4x^3)$$

$$= \dfrac{4x^3}{3(1 - x^4)^{\frac{4}{3}}}$$

Example 5 Differentiate $s = \left(\dfrac{2t - 1}{t + 2}\right)^6$.

Solution Here we combine the Power Rule, Chain Rule, and Quotient Rule:

$$\dfrac{ds}{dt} = 6\left(\dfrac{2t - 1}{t + 2}\right)^5 \dfrac{d}{dt}\left(\dfrac{2t - 1}{t + 2}\right)$$

$$= 6\left(\dfrac{2t - 1}{t + 2}\right)^5 \dfrac{(t + 2)(2) - (2t - 1)(1)}{(t + 2)^2}$$

$$= 6\left(\dfrac{2t - 1}{t + 2}\right)^5 \dfrac{5}{(t + 2)^2}$$

$$= \dfrac{30(2t - 1)^5}{(t + 2)^7}$$

Example 6 Find the derivative of the function $f(x) = (x^2 + 1)^3(2 - 3x)^4$.

Solution We use the Product Rule before using the Chain Rule:

$$f'(x) = (x^2 + 1)^3 \dfrac{d}{dx}(2 - 3x)^4 + (2 - 3x)^4 \dfrac{d}{dx}(x^2 + 1)^3$$

$$= (x^2 + 1)^3(4)(2 - 3x)^3(-3) + (2 - 3x)^4(3)(x^2 + 1)^2(2x)$$

$$= -12(x^2 + 1)^3(2 - 3x)^3 + 6x(2 - 3x)^4(x^2 + 1)^2$$

We will see in Chapter 4 that, for some purposes, it is useful to solve an equation of the form $f'(x) = 0$ and this is made easier by writing $f'(x)$ in factored form. For this reason it is usually preferable to simplify the derivative using common factors as follows.

$$f'(x) = -6(x^2 + 1)^2(2 - 3x)^3[2(x^2 + 1) - x(2 - 3x)]$$

$$= -6(x^2 + 1)^2(2 - 3x)^3(5x^2 - 2x + 2)$$

Example 7   If h is a differentiable function find the derivatives of the following functions.

(a) $F(x) = [h(x)]^3$ (b) $G(x) = h(x^3)$

Solution   (a) Here h is the inner function and the outer function is $y = u^3$, so, by the Chain Rule,

$$F'(x) = \frac{d}{dx} [h(x)]^3 = 3[h(x)]^2 h'(x)$$

(b) Here h is the outer function and the inner function is $y = x^3$, so the Chain Rule gives

$$G'(x) = \frac{d}{dx} h(x^3) = h'(x^3) \frac{d}{dx} (x^3) = 3x^2 h'(x^3)$$

In the next example the Chain Rule is used twice.

Example 8   Find y' if $y = \sqrt{x + \sqrt{x^2 + 1}}$.

Solution

$$y = [x + (x^2 + 1)^{\frac{1}{2}}]^{\frac{1}{2}}$$

$$y' = \frac{1}{2}[x + (x^2 + 1)^{\frac{1}{2}}]^{-\frac{1}{2}} \frac{d}{dx} [x + (x^2 + 1)^{\frac{1}{2}}]$$

$$= \frac{1}{2\sqrt{x + \sqrt{x^2 + 1}}} [1 + \frac{1}{2}(x^2 + 1)^{-\frac{1}{2}} \frac{d}{dx} (x^2 + 1)]$$

$$= \frac{1}{2\sqrt{x + \sqrt{x^2 + 1}}} \left[1 + \frac{1}{2\sqrt{x^2 + 1}} (2x)\right]$$

$$= \frac{1}{2\sqrt{x + \sqrt{x^2 + 1}}} \left[1 + \frac{x}{\sqrt{x^2 + 1}}\right]$$

This expression could be further simplified as follows:

$$y' = \frac{1}{2\sqrt{x + \sqrt{x^2 + 1}}} \left[\frac{\sqrt{x^2 + 1} + x}{\sqrt{x^2 + 1}}\right]$$

$$= \frac{\sqrt{x + \sqrt{x^2 + 1}}}{2\sqrt{x^2 + 1}}$$

Now that we discussed all the rules that are necessary to differentiate any algebraic function, we list them here for your convenience. It is wise to memorize them.

Differentiation Rules

Constant Rule: $\dfrac{d}{dx}(c) = 0$

Constant Multiple Rule: $\dfrac{d}{dx}[cf(x)] = c\dfrac{d}{dx}f(x)$

Sum Rule: $\dfrac{d}{dx}[f(x) + g(x)] = \dfrac{d}{dx}f(x) + \dfrac{d}{dx}g(x)$

Difference Rule: $\dfrac{d}{dx}[f(x) - g(x)] = \dfrac{d}{dx}f(x) - \dfrac{d}{dx}g(x)$

Product Rule: $\dfrac{d}{dx}[f(x)g(x)] = f(x)\dfrac{d}{dx}g(x) + g(x)\dfrac{d}{dx}f(x)$

Quotient Rule: $\dfrac{d}{dx}\left[\dfrac{f(x)}{g(x)}\right] = \dfrac{g(x)\dfrac{d}{dx}f(x) - f(x)\dfrac{d}{dx}g(x)}{[g(x)]^2}$

Chain Rule: $\dfrac{d}{dx}[f(g(x))] = f'(g(x))\dfrac{d}{dx}g(x)$

Power Rule: $\dfrac{d}{dx}(x^n) = nx^{n-1}$

Power and Chain Rules: $\dfrac{d}{dx}[g(x)]^n = n[g(x)]^{n-1}g'(x)$

PROBLEMS PLUS

Graph the function $f(x) = |x - 2| + |x - 5|$. Where is f discontinuous? Where is it not differentiable?

EXERCISE 2.6

B **1.** Find the derivatives of the following functions.

(a) $F(x) = (5 - 3x)^7$

(b) $F(x) = (2x^2 + 1)^{20}$

(c) $G(x) = (x^3 + x^2 - 2)^{\frac{3}{4}}$

(d) $G(x) = \sqrt{x^4 - x + 1}$

(e) $y = \sqrt[4]{x^2 + x}$

(f) $y = (1 + 3x + 4x^2)^{-3}$

(g) $y = \dfrac{1}{(x^3 + 2x^2 + 1)^2}$

(h) $y = \dfrac{4}{\sqrt{9 - x^2}}$

(i) $y = (1 + 2\sqrt{x})^6$

(j) $y = \sqrt{x + \sqrt{x}}$

(k) $y = x - \sqrt[5]{1 + x^5 - 6x^{10}}$

(l) $y = x^2 + (x^2 - 1)^5$

2. If $y = u^4 + 5u^2$, where $u = x^5 + 2x^2 + 1$, find $\dfrac{dy}{dx}$. Leave your answer in terms of u and x.

3. Find $\dfrac{dy}{dx}\bigg]_{x=4}$ if $y = u^2 - 2u^5$ and $u = x - \sqrt{x}$.

4. Find $\dfrac{dy}{dt}\bigg]_{t=1}$ if $y = \sqrt{1 + r^2}$ and $r = \dfrac{t + 1}{2t + 1}$.

5. Find $\dfrac{ds}{dt}\bigg]_{t=4}$ if $s = v + \dfrac{50}{v}$ and $v = 3t - \sqrt{t}$.

6. Differentiate:

   (a) $F(x) = x\sqrt{x^2 + 1}$ (b) $F(x) = (2x + 1)(4x - 1)^5$

   (c) $G(x) = (x^2 - 1)^4(2 - 3x)$

   (d) $G(x) = (x^4 - x + 1)^2(x^2 - 2)^3$

   (e) $F(x) = \dfrac{x}{\sqrt{2x + 3}}$ (f) $f(t) = \dfrac{(1 + 2t)^5}{(3t^2 - 5)^2}$

   (g) $g(x) = \left(\dfrac{x + 2}{x - 2}\right)^3$ (h) $h(t) = \left(\dfrac{t^2 + 1}{t + 1}\right)^{10}$

   (i) $y = \sqrt{\dfrac{x^2 - 1}{x^2 + 1}}$ (j) $y = \dfrac{(2x + 3)^3}{\sqrt{4x - 7}}$

   (k) $y = 3\sqrt{x}(2x + 1)^5 + \sqrt{4x - 3}$

   (l) $y = \sqrt{1 + \sqrt[3]{x}}$

   (m) $y = (t + \sqrt[3]{t + t^2})^{20}$ (n) $y = \sqrt{x + \sqrt{x + \sqrt{x}}}$

7. Find the equation of the tangent line to the curve $y = (x^2 - 3)^8$ at the point $(2, 1)$.

8. Find the equation of the tangent line to the curve $y = \dfrac{1}{\sqrt{20 - x^4}}$ at the point $\left(2, \frac{1}{2}\right)$.

9. If $F(x) = f(g(x))$, where $g(2) = 4$, $g'(2) = 3$, and $f'(4) = 5$, find $F'(2)$.

10. If $G(x) = h(p(x))$, where $h(5) = 1$, $h'(5) = 2$, $h'(1) = 3$, $p(1) = 5$, and $p'(1) = 7$, find $G'(1)$.

C 11. If f is a differentiable function, find expressions for the derivatives of the following functions.

   (a) $F(x) = f(x^4)$ (b) $G(x) = [f(x)]^4$

   (c) $H(x) = f(\sqrt{x})$ (d) $P(x) = \sqrt{f(x)}$

   (e) $y = f(f(x))$ (f) $y = \sqrt{1 + [f(x)]^2}$

   (g) $y = [f(x^2)]^2$ (h) $y = f([f(x)]^3)$

12. (a) Use the Chain Rule and the fact that $|x| = \sqrt{x^2}$ to show that
$$\frac{d}{dx}|x| = \frac{x}{|x|}$$

   (b) Sketch the graphs of the function $f(x) = |x|$ and its derivative.

   (c) Use the result of part (a) to differentiate the function $g(x) = x|x|$.

2.7 IMPLICIT DIFFERENTIATION

So far we have described functions by expressing one variable explicitly in terms of another variable; for example,

$$y = x^2 \quad \text{or} \quad y = \frac{\sqrt{4 - x^2}}{x + 1}$$

or, in general, $y = f(x)$. But other functions are defined implicitly by a relation between x and y such as

$$x^2 + y^2 = 25$$

In this case it is possible to solve the equation for y to get $y = \pm\sqrt{25 - x^2}$ and so two functions defined by the implicit equations are

$$f(x) = \sqrt{25 - x^2} \quad \text{and} \quad g(x) = -\sqrt{25 - x^2}$$

The graphs of f and g are the upper and lower semicircles of the circle $x^2 + y^2 = 25$.

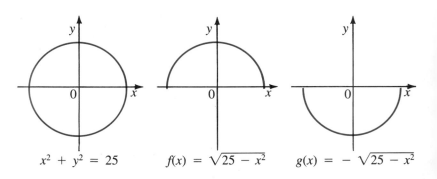

$$x^2 + y^2 = 25 \qquad f(x) = \sqrt{25 - x^2} \qquad g(x) = -\sqrt{25 - x^2}$$

Thus we could find the slope of the tangent line to the circle $x^2 + y^2 = 25$ at the point $(-4, 3)$ by differentiating the function $f(x) = \sqrt{25 - x^2}$ and substituting $x = -4$. An easier method, called **implicit differentiation**, is illustrated in the following example. In using this method, we differentiate both sides of the equation with respect to x and then we solve the resulting equation for y'.

Example 1   (a) If $x^2 + y^2 = 25$, find $\dfrac{dy}{dx}$.

(b) Find the equation of the tangent line to the circle $x^2 + y^2 = 25$ at the point $(-4, 3)$.

Solution   (a) We differentiate both sides of the equation $x^2 + y^2 = 25$ with respect to x:

$$\frac{d}{dx}(x^2 + y^2) = \frac{d}{dx}(25)$$

$$\frac{d}{dx}(x^2) + \frac{d}{dx}(y^2) = 0 \qquad\qquad ①$$

To differentiate y^2 we use the Chain Rule and keep in mind that y is a function of x:

$$\frac{d}{dx}(y^2) = \frac{d}{dy}(y^2)\frac{dy}{dx} = 2y\frac{dy}{dx}$$

So, from Equation 1, we have

$$2x + 2y\frac{dy}{dx} = 0$$

Now we solve this equation for the required derivative:

$$\frac{dy}{dx} = -\frac{x}{y}$$

(b) The expression for the derivative in part (a) involves both x and y, but this is not a disadvantage. At the point $(-4, 3)$ we have $x = -4$ and $y = 3$, so

$$\frac{dy}{dx} = -\frac{(-4)}{3} = \frac{4}{3}$$

This is the slope of the tangent at $(-4, 3)$, so the equation is

$$y - 3 = \tfrac{4}{3}(x + 4)$$

or $\quad 4x - 3y + 25 = 0$

We have seen that the problem in Example 1 could be solved either by implicit differentiation or by first solving the given equation for y. In the next example, however, it is impossible to solve the equation for y as an explicit function of x. Here the method of implicit differentiation is not just the most convenient method for finding y'; it is the *only* method.

Example 2   (a) Find $\dfrac{dy}{dx}$ if $2x^5 + x^4y + y^5 = 36$.

(b) Find the slope of the tangent to the curve $2x^5 + x^4y + y^5 = 36$ at the point $(1, 2)$.

Solution   (a) In differentiating the second term we have to regard y as a function of x and so we use the Product Rule:

$$\frac{d}{dx}(x^4y) = x^4\frac{d}{dx}(y) + y\frac{d}{dx}(x^4) = x^4\frac{dy}{dx} + (4x^3)y$$

In differentiating the third term we use the Chain Rule:

$$\frac{d}{dx}(y^5) = \frac{d}{dy}(y^5)\frac{dy}{dx} = 5y^4\frac{dy}{dx}$$

Thus differentiating both sides of the given equation, we have

$$10x^4 + x^4\frac{dy}{dx} + 4x^3y + 5y^4\frac{dy}{dx} = 0$$

Then, solving for $\dfrac{dy}{dx}$, we get

$$\frac{dy}{dx} = -\frac{4x^3y + 10x^4}{x^4 + 5y^4}$$

(b) When $x = 1$ and $y = 2$,

$$\frac{dy}{dx} = -\frac{4(1)^3(2) + 10(1)^4}{1^4 + 5(2)^4} = -\frac{18}{81} = -\frac{2}{9}$$

The slope of the tangent line at $(1, 2)$ is $-\frac{2}{9}$.

Example 3   Find y' if $x^2 + \sqrt{y} = x^2y^3 + 5$.

Solution   Differentiate both sides with respect to x:

$$2x + \frac{d}{dy}(\sqrt{y})\frac{dy}{dx} = x^2\frac{d}{dx}(y^3) + y^3\frac{d}{dx}(x^2)$$

$$2x + \frac{1}{2\sqrt{y}}y' = x^2(3y^2)y' + 2xy^3$$

$$2x - 2xy^3 = 3x^2y^2y' - \frac{1}{2\sqrt{y}}y'$$

$$y' = \frac{2x(1 - y^3)}{3x^2y^2 - \dfrac{1}{2\sqrt{y}}}$$

EXERCISE 2.7

B **1.** Use implicit differentiation to find $\dfrac{dy}{dx}$.

(a) $x^2 - y^2 = 1$ (b) $x^3 + y^3 = 6$
(c) $xy = 4$ (d) $x^2 + xy + y^2 = 1$
(e) $x^3 + y^3 = 6xy$ (f) $2xy^2 - y^3 = x^2$

(g) $\sqrt{x} + \sqrt{y} = 1$ (h) $\dfrac{2x}{x + y} = y$

2. Find the slope of the tangent line to the curve at the given point.
(a) $x^2 + 4y^2 = 5$, $(1, -1)$ (b) $x^4 + y^4 = 17$, $(2, 1)$
(c) $x^2 + x^3y^2 - y^3 = 13$, $(1, -2)$
(d) $y^2 = 2xy - 3$, $(2, 3)$

(e) $\sqrt{x + y} + \sqrt{xy} = 4$, $(2, 2)$ (f) $\dfrac{1}{x} + \dfrac{1}{y} = 1$, $\left(\frac{3}{2}, 3\right)$

3. Find the equation of the tangent line to the curve at the given point.
(a) $2x^2 - y^2 = 1$, $(-1, -1)$ (b) $x^3 + y^3 = 9$, $(2, 1)$
(c) $y^5 + x^2y^3 = 10$, $(-3, 1)$ (d) $(x + y)^3 = x^3 + y^3$, $(-1, 1)$

4. (a) Use implicit differentiation to find the slope of the tangent line to the ellipse $9x^2 + 4y^2 = 36$ at the point $\left(\sqrt{2}, \frac{3}{2}\sqrt{2}\right)$.
(b) Find the slope in part (a) by first solving for y explicitly as a function of x.
(c) Find the equation of the tangent line.
(d) Sketch the ellipse and the tangent line.

5. (a) Find an equation of the tangent line to the circle $x^2 + y^2 + 2x - 4y - 20 = 0$ at the point $(2, -2)$.
(b) Sketch the circle and the tangent line.

6. The curve with equation $2(x^2 + y^2)^2 = 25(x^2 - y^2)$ is called a *lemniscate* and is shown in the figure.
(a) Find y'.
(b) Find the equation of the tangent line to the lemniscate at the point $(-3, 1)$.
(c) Find the points on the lemniscate where the tangent line is horizontal.

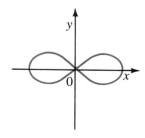

7. The curve with equation $x^{\frac{2}{3}} + y^{\frac{2}{3}} = 1$ is called an *astroid* and is shown in the figure.
   (a) Find y'.
   (b) Find the equation of the tangent line to the astroid at the point $\left(\dfrac{1}{8}, \dfrac{3\sqrt{3}}{8}\right)$.
   (c) Find the points on the astroid where the tangent line has slope 1.

8. Use implicit differentiation to show that an equation of the tangent line to the ellipse
$$\frac{x^2}{a^2} + \frac{y^2}{b^2} = 1$$
at the point (x_0, y_0) is
$$\frac{x_0 x}{a^2} + \frac{y_0 y}{b^2} = 1$$

C 9. Suppose f is a function such that $x[f(x)]^3 + x^2 f(x) = 3$ and $f(2) = 1$. Find $f'(2)$.

10. Use implicit differentiation to show that any tangent line at a point P to a circle with centre C is perpendicular to the radius CP.

11. Use implicit differentiation to show that, whenever a hyperbola with equation $x^2 - y^2 = k$ intersects a hyperbola with equation $xy = c$, the tangent lines at the points of intersection are perpendicular.

2.8 HIGHER DERIVATIVES

Since the derivative of a function f is itself a function f', we can take its derivative $(f')'$. The result is a function called the **second derivative** of f and denoted by f''.

If $y = f(x)$ and we use Leibniz notation, then
$$f''(x) = \frac{d}{dx}\left(\frac{dy}{dx}\right)$$

and we abbreviate this as
$$\frac{d^2 y}{dx^2}$$

If we use D-notation, the symbol D^2 indicates that the operation of differentiation is performed twice. Thus we have the following notations for the second derivative:
$$y'' = f''(x) = \frac{d^2 y}{dx^2} = D^2 f(x) = D_x^2 f(x)$$

Example 1   Find $\dfrac{d^2y}{dx^2}$ if $y = x^6$.

Solution
$$\frac{dy}{dx} = 6x^5$$
$$\frac{d^2y}{dx^2} = \frac{d}{dx}\left(\frac{dy}{dx}\right) = \frac{d}{dx}(6x^5) = 30x^4$$

Example 2   Find the second derivative of $f(x) = 5x^2 + \sqrt{x}$.

Solution
$$f(x) = 5x^2 + x^{\frac{1}{2}}$$
$$f'(x) = 10x + \tfrac{1}{2}x^{-\frac{1}{2}}$$
$$f''(x) = 10 + \left(\tfrac{1}{2}\right)\left(-\tfrac{1}{2}\right)x^{-\frac{3}{2}} = 10 - \tfrac{1}{4}x^{-\frac{3}{2}}$$

Example 3   Find $f''(1)$ if $f(x) = (2 - x^2)^{10}$.

Solution
$$f'(x) = 10(2 - x^2)^9(-2x) = -20x(2 - x^2)^9$$
$$f''(x) = (-20x)9(2 - x^2)^8(-2x) - 20(2 - x^2)^9$$
$$= 360x^2(2 - x^2)^8 - 20(2 - x^2)^9$$
$$f''(1) = (360)(1)^2(1)^8 - 20(1)^9 = 340$$

Since the first derivative of a function can be interpreted either as the slope of a tangent line or as a rate of change, the second derivative can be interpreted as the rate of change of the slope of the tangent line. This idea will be pursued in Chapter 5 where the second derivative gives valuable information about the shape of the graph. Another application occurs in Chapter 3 where the second derivative of a position function represents acceleration.

Higher derivatives can also be defined. The **third derivative** is the derivative of the second derivative: $f''' = (f'')'$. Other notations are as follows:

$$y''' = f'''(x) = \frac{d^3y}{dx^3} = D^3 f(x) = D_x^3 f(x)$$

Beyond the third derivative we usually do not use the prime notation. For instance, the fourth derivative is denoted by $f^{(4)}$ instead of f''''. In general the **nth derivative** of f is denoted by $f^{(n)}$ and is obtained by differentiating n times. We write

$$y^{(n)}(x) = f^{(n)} = \frac{d^n y}{dx^n} = D^n f(x) = D_x^n f(x)$$

Example 4   Find the first five derivatives of $y = x^4 + 2x^3 - 5x^2 + 3x - 6$.

Solution
$$y' = 4x^3 + 6x^2 - 10x + 3$$
$$y'' = 12x^2 + 12x - 10$$
$$y''' = 24x + 12$$
$$y^{(4)} = 24$$
$$y^{(5)} = 0$$

Example 5   If $x^3 + y^3 = 5$, use implicit differentiaton to find y''.

Solution   Differentiating the equation with respect to x, we get

$$3x^2 + 3y^2 y' = 0$$

Solving for y', we have

$$y' = -\frac{x^2}{y^2} \tag{1}$$

To find y'' we differentiate this expression using the Quotient Rule and remembering that y is a function of x:

$$y'' = \frac{d}{dx}\left(-\frac{x^2}{y^2}\right)$$
$$= -\frac{y^2 \dfrac{d}{dx}(x^2) - x^2 \dfrac{d}{dx}(y^2)}{(y^2)^2}$$
$$= -\frac{y^2(2x) - x^2(2yy')}{y^4}$$

Now we substitute Equation 1 into this expression and obtain

$$y'' = -\frac{2xy^2 - 2x^2 y\left(-\dfrac{x^2}{y^2}\right)}{y^4}$$
$$= -\frac{2xy^2 + \dfrac{2x^4}{y}}{y^4}$$
$$= -\frac{2xy^3 + 2x^4}{y^5} \qquad \text{(multiply numerator and denominator by } y\text{)}$$
$$= -\frac{2x(y^3 + x^3)}{y^5}$$

But the values of x and y must satisfy the original equation $x^3 + y^3 = 5$ and so the expression simplifies as follows:

$$y'' = -\frac{2x(5)}{y^5} = -\frac{10x}{y^5}$$

EXERCISE 2.8

B **1.** Find the first and second derivatives of the given functions.
   (a) $f(x) = x^5 - 4x^2 + 1$
   (b) $g(x) = 7x^4 + 12x^3 - 4x + 8$

   (c) $f(t) = 2t - \dfrac{1}{t+1}$
   (d) $g(t) = \dfrac{4}{\sqrt{t}}$

   (e) $y = (2x + 1)^8$
   (f) $y = t^3 + \dfrac{1}{t^3}$

   (g) $y = \sqrt{x^2 + 1}$
   (h) $y = \dfrac{t}{t-1}$

2. Find the third derivative.

   (a) $f(x) = 1 - 12x + 4x^2 - x^3$ (b) $f(x) = \dfrac{1}{x^5}$

   (c) $y = \dfrac{3}{(4-x)^2}$
   (d) $y = \sqrt{1 + 2x}$

3. Find the first six derivatives of the function
   $y = x^5 + x^4 + x^3 + x^2 + x + 1$.

4. If $f(x) = \sqrt{1 + x^3}$, find $f''(2)$.

5. If $g(x) = \dfrac{1}{\sqrt{3x + 4}}$, find $g'''(4)$.

6. If $f(x) = x^n$, find $f^{(n)}(x)$.

7. Find y'' by implicit differentiation.
   (a) $x^4 + y^4 = 1$ (b) $x^2 - y^2 = 1$ (c) $x^3 + y^3 = 6xy$

8. Find a quadratic function f such that $f(3) = 33$, $f'(3) = 22$, and $f''(3) = 8$.

C **9.** Suppose that $f(x) = g(x)h(x)$.
   (a) Express f'' in terms of g, g', g'', h, h', h''.
   (b) Find a similar expression for f'''.

10. (a) If $f(x) = |x^2 - 1|$, find f' and f'' and state their domains.
   (b) Sketch the graphs of f, f', and f''.

2.9 REVIEW EXERCISE

1. Find $f'(x)$ from first principles, that is, directly from the definition of a derivative.

    (a) $f(x) = 1 - 2x + 3x^2$ (b) $f(x) = x^3 + 4x$

    (c) $f(x) = \dfrac{x}{1 - x}$ (d) $f(x) = \sqrt{2x + 1}$

2. The limit
    $$\lim_{h \to 0} \frac{(1 + h)^4 - 1}{h}$$
    is equal to $f'(a)$ for some function f and some number a. State the value of a and give a formula for the function f.

3. Use the given graph of f to sketch the graph of f'.

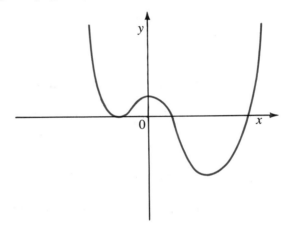

4. Differentiate the given functions.

    (a) $y = 12x^3 + 8x - 1$ (b) $y = 2x^{\pi + 1}$

    (c) $y = 2x - \dfrac{3}{x}$ (d) $y = \sqrt[5]{x^6}$

    (e) $y = \sqrt{x}(5 - \sqrt{x})$ (f) $y = \dfrac{x^2 - 2x}{\sqrt{x}}$

    (g) $y = \dfrac{2x - 1}{1 + 3x}$ (h) $y = (2x^3 - 1)^7$

    (i) $f(x) = (x^2 + x)\sqrt{1 - x^2}$ (j) $g(x) = \dfrac{3x^2 + 1}{2 - x}$

    (k) $h(x) = \dfrac{1}{\sqrt[3]{2x^4 - 1}}$ (l) $F(x) = (x^4 + 1)^3(1 - 2x)$

    (m) $f(t) = \dfrac{t}{\sqrt{1 + 2t}}$ (n) $g(t) = \left(\dfrac{t + 1}{t + 2}\right)^4$

(o) $R(u) = \sqrt[4]{u + 1} - \dfrac{2}{u^2}$ (p) $S(v) = \sqrt{v - (v^2 - 8)^5}$

(q) $M(z) = \sqrt{\dfrac{1 + z}{1 + z^2}}$ (r) $F(y) = \dfrac{1}{2 + \dfrac{3}{y}}$

5. Find f' and state the domains of f and f'.

   (a) $f(x) = \dfrac{2x - 1}{x^2 - 5}$ (b) $f(x) = \sqrt{x^2 - x - 6}$

6. Find $\left[\dfrac{dy}{dx}\right]_{x=1}$ if $y = u^2 - u^3 + 2u^4$ and $u = \dfrac{x}{2x - 1}$.

7. Find $\dfrac{dy}{dx}$.

   (a) $x^4 + y^4 = 1$ (b) $x^2 - x^2y + y^2 = 1$
   (c) $2x^2y^2 = x^3 + y^3$ (d) $y\sqrt{x - 1} + x\sqrt{y - 1} = xy$

8. Find y''.

   (a) $y = 4x^5 - \tfrac{1}{2}x^4 + 3x^2$ (b) $y = \sqrt{3x + 1}$

   (c) $y = \dfrac{t - 1}{t + 1}$ (d) $x^2 + y^2 = 16$

9. Find the equation of the tangent line to the curve at the given point.

   (a) $y = x^2 - 2x + 5, (-1, 8)$ (b) $y = \dfrac{2}{1 - x}, (2, -2)$

   (c) $y = \dfrac{1}{\sqrt{x^5}}, \left(2, \dfrac{1}{4\sqrt{2}}\right)$ (d) $y = x\sqrt{x^2 + 5}, (-2, -6)$

   (e) $(x - 1)^2 + (y + 2)^2 = 25, (-2, 2)$
   (f) $x^3 + y^3 = 9xy, (2, 4)$

10. If a ball is dropped from the top of the CN Tower, 550 m above the ground, then its height in metres after t seconds is $h = 550 - 5t^2$. Find the velocity of the ball after 1 s, 2 s, and 5 s.

11. Find the point on the parabola $y = 2x^2 - 3x + 6$ where the tangent line is parallel to the line $7x + y = 1$.

12. Find the points on the curve $y = \dfrac{1}{2x - 1}$ where the tangent line is perpendicular to the line $x - 2y = 1$.

13. Find the equations of both lines that pass through the point $(2, -3)$ and are tangent to the parabola $y = x^2 + x$.

14. Suppose $f(3) = 4, f'(3) = -1, f'(6) = 5, g(3) = 6$, and $g'(3) = 2$. Find

    (a) $(fg)'(3)$ (b) $\left(\dfrac{f}{g}\right)'(3)$ (c) $(f \circ g)'(3)$

15. If g is a differentiable function, find expressions for f' in terms of g'.

(a) $f(x) = x^2 g(x)$

(b) $f(x) = \dfrac{g(x)}{\sqrt{x}}$

(c) $f(x) = g\left(\dfrac{1}{x}\right)$

(d) $f(x) = \sqrt{g(\sqrt{x})}$

16. If g is a differentiable function and $f(x) = g(g(x))$, find an expression for $f''(x)$.

17. Let

$$f(x) = \begin{cases} 2x - x^2 & \text{if } x \leq 0 \\ 2x & \text{if } 0 < x \leq 1 \\ x + 1 & \text{if } x \geq 1 \end{cases}$$

(a) Where is f not differentiable?

(b) Find an expression for $f'(x)$ and sketch the graphs of f and f'.

PROBLEMS PLUS

Draw a diagram to show that there are two lines tangent to both of the parabolas $y = -x^2$ and $y = 4 + x^2$. Find the coordinates of the four points at which these tangents touch the parabolas.

2.10   CHAPTER 2 TEST

1. (a) Give the definition of the derivative $f'(x)$ as a limit.
   (b) Use your definition in part (a) to find the derivatives of the following functions:

   (i) $f(x) = x^2 - 7x + 4$ (ii) $f(x) = \dfrac{1}{2x + 1}$

2. Find each derivative.
   (a) $f(x) = \sqrt[3]{x^2}$
   (b) $f(x) = \dfrac{x^2 + 3}{2x - 1}$
   (c) $f(x) = (x^2 - 1)^4(2x + 1)^3$
   (d) $f(x) = (x + \sqrt{x^4 - 2x + 1})^7$

3. A curve is given by the equation $3xy = x^3 + y^3$.
   (a) Find $\dfrac{dy}{dx}$.
   (b) Find the equation of the tangent line to the curve at the point $\left(\dfrac{2}{3}, \dfrac{4}{3}\right)$.

4. Find y''' if $y = \dfrac{1}{(3 - 2x)^2}$.

5. Find the point on the curve $y = \sqrt{2x - 1}$ where the tangent line is parallel to the line $x - 3y = 16$.

6. If f is a differentiable function, find expressions for the derivatives of the following functions.
   (a) $g(x) = f(x^6)$
   (b) $h(x) = [f(x)]^6$
   (c) $F(x) = \dfrac{x^2}{f(x)}$

FOUNDERS OF CALCULUS

Gottfried Wilhelm Leibniz (1646–1716) was born in Leipzig, Germany, entered the university there at age fifteen, and earned his bachelor's degree at age seventeen. He studied logic, philosophy, mathematics, and law, and he is sometimes considered the last scholar to achieve universal knowledge. At the age of twenty he received his doctorate in law. Although he was offered a professorship, he declined and entered the diplomatic service. As a governmental representative, he travelled widely and on visits to Paris and London became interested in research in calculus.

The main contribution of Leibniz to mathematics was his development of calculus, which was published in 1684. His theory and notation were quite different from those of Newton, but they led to the same results. Today we often use the notation of Leibniz: $\dfrac{dy}{dx}$ for a derivative, dx for a differential, and $\int y\,dx$ for an integral. (See Chapter 11.)

It is often said that calculus was invented independently by Newton and Leibniz. However, integral calculus (the problem of areas) goes back to the ancient Greeks in about 500 B.C., and differential calculus (stemming from the problem of tangents) was started by Fermat and others in the 1630s. Newton's teacher at Cambridge, Isaac Barrow, saw the connection between the two branches of calculus. What Newton and Leibniz did was to exploit this connection and organize calculus into a systematic and powerful method.

Unfortunately, a dispute arose between the followers of Newton and the followers of Leibniz as to who had discovered the method of calculus first. Later, Newton and Leibniz themselves were drawn into the priority controversy. It seems clear now that Newton had invented the method first but Leibniz arrived at his results independently and was the first to publish the method. In spite of the controversy, Leibniz fully recognized Newton's genius. Leibniz said, "Taking mathematics from the beginning of the world to the time of Newton, what he has done is much the better half."

CHAPTER 3

APPLICATIONS OF DERIVATIVES

REVIEW AND PREVIEW TO
CHAPTER 3

Problem Solving

There are no hard and fast rules that will ensure success in solving problems. However, it is possible to outline some general steps in the problem-solving process and to give some principles that may be useful in the solution of certain problems. These steps and principles are just common sense made explicit. They have been adapted from George Polya's book *How to Solve It*.

1. **UNDERSTAND THE PROBLEM.** The first step is to read the problem and make sure that it is clearly understood. Ask yourself the following questions:

What is the unknown?
What are the given quantities?
What are the given conditions?

For many problems it is useful to

draw a diagram

and identify the given and required quantities on the diagram.

Usually it is necessary to

introduce suitable notation.

In choosing symbols for the unknown quantities we often use letters such as a, b, c, ..., m, n, ..., x, y, but in some cases it helps to use initials as suggestive symbols, for instance, V for volume, t for time.

2. **THINK OF A PLAN.** Find a connection between the given information and the unknown that will enable you to calculate the unknown. If you do not see a connection immediately, the following ideas may be helpful in devising a plan.

(a) *Try to recognize something familiar.* Relate the given situation to previous knowledge. Look at the unknown and try to recall a more familiar problem having a similar unknown.

(b) *Try to recognize patterns.* Some problems are solved by recognizing that some kind of pattern is occurring. The pattern could be geometric, or numeric, or algebraic. If you can see regularity or repetition in a problem, then you might be able to guess what the continuing pattern is and then prove it.

(c) *Use analogy.* Try to think of an analogous problem, that is, a similar problem, a related problem, but one that is easier than the original problem. If you can solve the similar, simpler problem, then it might give you the clues you need to solve the original, more difficult problem. For instance, if a problem involves very large numbers, you could first try a similar problem with smaller numbers. Or if the problem is in three-dimensional geometry, you could look for a similar problem in two-dimensional geometry. Or if the problem you start with is a general one, you could first try a special case.

(d) *Introduce something extra.* It may sometimes be necessary to introduce something new, an auxiliary aid, to help make the connection between the given and the unknown. For instance, in geometry the auxiliary aid could be a new line drawn in a diagram. In algebra it could be a new unknown that is related to the original unknown.

(e) *Take cases.* You may sometimes have to split a problem into several cases and give a different argument for each of the cases. We used this strategy in dealing with absolute value and other functions in Section 1.3 and in connection with geometric series in Example 2 in Section 1.7.

(f) *Work backwards.* Sometimes it is useful to imagine that your problem is solved and work backwards, step by step, till you arrive at the given data. Then you may be able to reverse your steps and thereby construct a solution to the original problem.

(g) *Use indirect reasoning.* Sometimes it is appropriate to attack a problem indirectly. For instance, in a counting argument it might be best to count the total number of objects and subtract the number of objects that do *not* have the required property. Another example of indirect reasoning is *proof by contradiction* in which we assume that the desired conclusion is false and eventually arrive at a contradiction.

3.   **CARRY OUT THE PLAN.** In Step 2 a plan was devised. In carrying out that plan we have to check each stage of the plan and write the details that prove that each stage is correct.

4.   **LOOK BACK.** Having completed our solution, it is wise to look back over it, partly to see if there are errors in the solution and partly to see if there is an easier way to solve the problem. Another reason for looking back is that it will familiarize us with the method of solution and this may be useful for solving a future problem. Descartes said, "Every problem that I solved became a rule which I then used to solve other problems."

Example   Express the hypotenuse h of a right triangle in terms of its area A and its perimeter P.

Solution   Let us first sort out the information by identifying the unknown quantity and the data.

UNDERSTAND THE PROBLEM

Unknown: h

Given quantities: A, P

It helps to draw a diagram and we do so.

DRAW A DIAGRAM

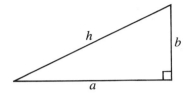

CONNECT THE GIVEN WITH THE UNKNOWN

In order to connect the given quantities to the unknown, we introduce two extra variables a and b, which are the lengths of the other two sides of the triangle. This enables us to express the given condition, which is that the triangle is right-angled, by the Pythagorean Theorem:

$$h^2 = a^2 + b^2$$

The other connections among the variables come by writing expressions for the area and perimeter:

$$A = \tfrac{1}{2}ab \qquad P = a + b + h$$

Since A and P are given, notice that we now have three equations in the three unknowns a, b, and h:

$$h^2 = a^2 + b^2 \qquad ①$$
$$A = \tfrac{1}{2}ab \qquad ②$$
$$P = a + b + h \qquad ③$$

Although we have the correct number of equations, they are not easy to solve in a straightforward fashion. But if we use the problem-solving strategy of trying to recognize something familiar, then we can solve these equations by an easier method. Look at the right sides of Equations 1, 2, and 3. Do these expressions remind you of anything familiar? Notice that they contain the ingredients of a familiar formula:

RELATE TO THE FAMILIAR

$$(a + b)^2 = a^2 + 2ab + b^2$$

Using this idea, we express $(a + b)^2$ in two ways. From Equations 1 and 2 we have

$$(a + b)^2 = (a^2 + b^2) + 2ab = h^2 + 4A$$

From Equation 3 we have

$$(a + b)^2 = (P - h)^2 = P^2 - 2Ph + h^2$$

Thus, $h^2 + 4A = P^2 - 2Ph + h^2$

$$2Ph = P^2 - 4A$$

$$h = \frac{P^2 - 4A}{2P}$$

This is the required expression.

EXERCISE 1

1. Solve the equation $\big|\,|3x + 1| - x\,\big| = 2$.
2. Use your calculator to evaluate

$$\frac{\sqrt{2} + \sqrt{6}}{\sqrt{2} + \sqrt{3}}$$

The answer looks very simple. Show that the calculated value is correct.

3. A man drives from home to work at a speed of 80 km/h. The return trip from work to home is covered at the more leisurely pace of 50 km/h. What is the average speed for the round trip?

4. In a right triangle, the hypotenuse has length 5 cm and another side has length 3 cm. What is the length of the altitude that is perpendicular to the hypotenuse?

5. A car with tires having radius 33 cm was driven on a trip and the odometer indicated that the distance travelled was 640 km. Two weeks later, with snow tires installed, the odometer indicated that the distance for the return trip over the same route was 625 km. Find the radius of the snow tires.

6. Bob and Jim, next-door neighbours, use hoses from both houses to fill Bob's swimming pool. They know it takes eighteen hours using both hoses. They also know that Bob's hose, used alone, can fill the pool in six hours less than Jim's hose. How much time is required by each hose alone?

INTRODUCTION

Now that we know how to calculate derivatives, we use them in this chapter to compute velocity, acceleration, and other rates of change in the natural and social sciences. Another application of derivatives occurs when we use them in Newton's method for finding approximate solutions of equations.

3.1 VELOCITY

We have already defined and computed velocities in Sections 1.5 and 2.1, but now we can compute them more easily with the aid of the differentiation formulas that were developed in Chapter 2.

Suppose that an object moves along a straight line. (Think of a ball being thrown vertically upward or a car being driven along a road or a stone being dropped from a cliff.) The position function is $s = f(t)$, where s is the displacement (directed distance) of the object from the origin at time t. Recall that the (instantaneous) velocity of the object at time t is defined as the limit of average velocities over shorter and shorter time intervals:

$$v = f'(t) = \lim_{h \to 0} \frac{f(t + h) - f(t)}{h}$$

Thus, the velocity is the derivative of the position function and in Leibniz notation we write

$$v = \frac{ds}{dt}$$

Example 1   If a stone is dropped from a cliff that is 122.5 m high, then its height in metres after t seconds is $h = 122.5 - 4.9t^2$ (until it hits the ground).
(a) Find its velocity after 1 s and 2 s.
(b) When will the stone hit the ground?
(c) With what velocity will it hit the ground?

Solution   (a) The position function is $h = 122.5 - 4.9t^2$, so the velocity at time t is

$$\frac{dh}{dt} = -9.8t$$

Thus, the velocity after 1 s is

$$\frac{dh}{dt}\bigg]_{t=1} = -9.8(1) = -9.8 \text{ m/s}$$

and after 2 s it is

$$\left.\frac{dh}{dt}\right]_{t=2} = -9.8(2) = -19.6 \text{ m/s}$$

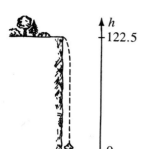

h
122.5

0

(b) The stone will hit the ground when the height is 0, that is,

$$h(t) = 122.5 - 4.9t^2 = 0$$
$$t^2 = \frac{122.5}{4.9} = 25$$

Since $t > 0$, we have $t = 5$. So the stone hits the ground after 5 s.

(c) The stone hits the ground with velocity

$$h'(5) = -9.8(5) = -49 \text{ m/s}$$

Example 2 The position of a particle moving on a line is given by the equation

$$s = f(t) = 2t^3 - 21t^2 + 60t, \ t \geqslant 0$$

where t is measured in seconds and s in metres.
(a) What is the velocity after 3 s and after 6 s?
(b) When is the particle at rest?
(c) When is the particle moving in the positive direction?
(d) Find the total distance travelled by the particle during the first 6 s.

Solution (a) The velocity after t seconds is

$$v = f'(t) = 6t^2 - 42t + 60$$

so the velocity after 3 s is

$$f'(3) = 6(3)^2 - 42(3) + 60 = -12 \text{ m/s}$$

and after 6 s it is

$$f'(6) = 6(6)^2 - 42(6) + 60 = 24 \text{ m/s}$$

(b) The particle is at rest when $v(t) = 0$, that is,

$$6t^2 - 42t + 60 = 0$$
$$t^2 - 7t + 10 = 0$$
$$(t - 2)(t - 5) = 0$$
$$t = 2 \quad \text{or} \quad t = 5$$

Thus, the particle is at rest when $t = 2$ s and when $t = 5$ s.

(c) The particle moves in the positive direction when $v(t) > 0$, that is,

$$t^2 - 7t + 10 = (t - 2)(t - 5) > 0$$

This inequality is true when both factors are positive ($t > 5$) or when both factors are negative ($t < 2$). Thus the particle moves in the positive direction in the time intervals $0 \leqslant t < 2$ and $t > 5$. It moves in the negative direction when $2 < t < 5$.

The motion of the particle is illustrated schematically in the following figure.

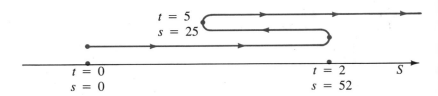

(d) The distance travelled in the first 2 s is

$$|f(2) - f(0)| = |52 - 0| = 52 \text{ m}$$

From $t = 2$ to $t = 5$ the distance travelled is

$$|f(5) - f(2)| = |25 - 52| = 27 \text{ m}$$

From $t = 5$ to $t = 6$ the distance travelled is

$$|f(6) - f(5)| = |36 - 25| = 11 \text{ m}$$

The total distance is

$$52 + 27 + 11 = 90 \text{ m}$$

EXERCISE 3.1

A **1.** The graph shows the position function of a car.

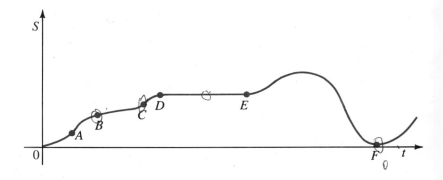

(a) What was the initial velocity of the car?
(b) Was the car going faster at B or at C?
(c) Was the car slowing down or speeding up at A, B, and C?
(d) What happened between D and E?
(e) What happened at F?

B 2. The position functions give s (in metres) as a function of t (in seconds). Find the velocity as a function of time and the velocities after 2 s and 4 s.

(a) $s = 5 + 12t$

(b) $s = 8t^2 - 24t + 5$

(c) $s = t^3 - 6t^2$

(d) $s = \dfrac{5t}{1 + t}$

3. If a stone is thrown downward with a speed of 15 m/s from a cliff that is 80 m high, its height in metres after t seconds is $h = 80 - 15t - 4.9t^2$. Find the velocity after 1 s and after 2 s.

4. If a ball is thrown directly upward with an initial velocity of 24.5 m/s, then its height after t seconds, in metres, is
$$h = 24.5t - 4.9t^2$$
(a) Find the velocity after 1 s, 2 s, 3 s, and 4 s.
(b) When does the ball reach its maximum height?
(c) What is its maximum height?
(d) When does it hit the ground?
(e) With what velocity does it hit the ground?

5. The distance travelled by a car is given by $s = 160t^2 + 20t$, where t is measured in hours and s in kilometres. When did the velocity reach 100 km/h?

6. The position function of a particle is $s = t^3 - 3t^2 - 5t,\ t \geqslant 0$, where t is measured in seconds and s in metres. When does the particle reach a velocity of 4 m/s?

7. The position of a particle is given by
$$s = t^2 - 4t + 4,\ t \geqslant 0$$
where s is measured in metres and t in seconds.
(a) Find the velocity after 1 s and 3 s.
(b) When is the particle at rest?
(c) When is the particle moving in the positive direction?
(d) Draw a diagram to illustrate the motion of the particle.

8. The motion of a particle is described by the position function
$$s = t^3 - 15t^2 + 63t,\ t \geqslant 0$$
where t is measured in metres and s in seconds.
(a) When is the particle at rest?
(b) When is the particle moving in the positive direction?
(c) Draw a diagram to illustrate the motion of the particle.
(d) Find the total distance travelled in the first 10 s.

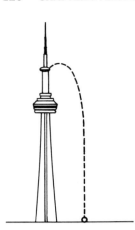

9. If a ball is thrown upward with a velocity of 10 m/s from the upper observation deck of the CN Tower, 450 m above the ground, then the distance, in metres, of the ball above ground level after t seconds is

$$s = 450 + 10t - 5t^2$$

(a) When does the ball reach its maximum height?

(b) Use the quadratic formula to find how long it takes for the ball to reach the ground.

(c) Find the approximate velocity with which the ball strikes the ground.

3.2 ACCELERATION

If an object moves along a straight line, its **acceleration** is the rate of change of velocity with respect to time. Therefore, the acceleration $a(t)$ at time t is the derivative of the velocity function:

$$a(t) = v'(t) = \frac{dv}{dt}$$

Since the velocity is the derivative of the position function $s = f(t)$, it follows that the acceleration is the second derivative of the position function:

$$a(t) = v'(t) = f''(t)$$

or, in Leibniz notation,

$$a = \frac{dv}{dt} = \frac{d^2s}{dt^2}$$

If s is measured in metres and t in seconds, then the units for acceleration are metres/second², or m/s².

Example 1   The position function of a particle is given by $s = t^3 + 2t^2 + 2t$, where s is measured in metres and t in seconds.

(a) Find the velocity and acceleration as a function of time.

(b) Find the acceleration at 3 s.

Solution   (a) The velocity is

$$v = \frac{ds}{dt} = 3t^2 + 4t + 2$$

and the acceleration is

$$a = \frac{dv}{dt} = 6t + 4$$

(b) After 3 s the acceleration is

$$a = 6(3) + 4 = 22 \text{ m/s}^2$$

Example 2 If a ball is thrown directly upward with an initial velocity of 24.5 m/s, then its distance above the ground in metres after t seconds is

$$s = 24.5t - 4.9t^2$$

(until it hits the ground). Find the acceleration of the ball.

Solution
$$s = 24.5t - 4.9t^2$$
$$\frac{ds}{dt} = 24.5 - 9.8t$$
$$a = \frac{d^2s}{dt^2} = -9.8$$

The acceleration is -9.8 m/s².

Notice that the acceleration in Example 2 is constant, and is called the *acceleration due to gravity*. The fact that it is negative means that the ball slows down as it rises and speeds up as it falls.

In general, a negative acceleration

$$a = \frac{dv}{dt} < 0$$

indicates that the velocity is decreasing (as at point A in the figure). This follows from the fact that the acceleration is the slope of the tangent to the graph of the velocity function. Likewise, a positive acceleration

$$a = \frac{dv}{dt} > 0$$

means that the velocity is increasing (as at B).

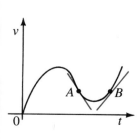

EXERCISE 3.2

A **1.**

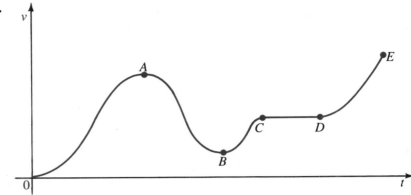

The graph of a velocity function is shown. State whether the acceleration is positive, zero, or negative

(a) from O to A,
(b) from A to B,
(c) from B to C,
(d) from C to D,
(e) from D to E.

2.

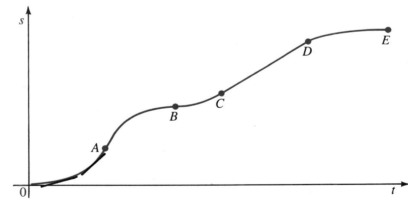

The graph of a position function is shown.
(a) For the part of the graph from O to A, use slopes of tangents to decide whether the velocity is increasing or decreasing. Is the acceleration positive or negative?
(b) State whether the acceleration is positive, zero, or negative
   (i) from A to B
   (ii) from B to C
   (iii) from C to D
   (iv) from D to E

B **3.** The position functions give the displacement s as a function of the time t. Find the velocity and acceleration as functions of t.

    (a) $s = 12 + 30t$ (b) $s = 16t^2 + 5t - 10$

    (c) $s = t^3 + 5t^2 + t + 1$ (d) $s = \sqrt{t^2 + t}$

4. The position functions give s (in metres) as a function of t (in seconds). Find the acceleration at 4 s.

    (a) $s = 100 - 15t - 4.9t^2$ (b) $s = t^3 - t^2$

    (c) $s = t^3 - 2t^2 + 3t - 5$ (d) $s = \dfrac{5t}{1 + t}$

5. A position function is given by $s = s_0 + v_0 t + \frac{1}{2}gt^2$, where s_0, v_0, and g are constants. Find

    (a) the initial position

    (b) the initial velocity

    (c) the acceleration

6. The position function of a particle is $s = t^3 - 12t$, $t \geq 0$, where s is measured in metres and t is measured in seconds. Find the acceleration at the instant when the velocity is 0.

7. A particle moves according to the equation of motion $s = t^3 - 9t^2 + 18t$, where s is measured in metres and t is measured in seconds.

    (a) When is the acceleration 0?

    (b) Find the displacement and velocity at that time.

8. The position function of a particle is $s = t^4 - 12t^3 + 30t^2 + 5t$, $t \geq 0$. When is the acceleration positive and when is it negative?

9. A car is travelling at 72 km/h and the brakes are fully applied, producing a constant deceleration of 12 m/s^2.

    (a) Verify that the velocity function $v(t) = -12t + 20$, where t is measured in seconds, gives this deceleration and initial velocity.

    (b) How long does it take for the car to come to a complete stop?

3.3 RATES OF CHANGE IN THE NATURAL SCIENCES

Recall from Section 2.1 that a derivative can be interpreted as a rate of change. In this section, we use derivatives to find rates of change in physics, biology, and chemistry.

First we recall from Section 1.5 the basic ideas behind rates of change. If y is a quantity that depends on another quantity x, we can write y as a function of x: $y = f(x)$. If x changes from x_1 to x_2, then the change in x is

$$\Delta x = x_2 - x_1$$

and the corresponding change in y is

$$\Delta y = f(x_2) - f(x_1)$$

The **(instantaneous) rate of change** of y with respect to x at x_1 is the limit of the average rate of change as x_2 approaches x_1:

$$\text{rate of change} = \lim_{\Delta x \to 0} \frac{\Delta y}{\Delta x} = \lim_{x_2 \to x_1} \frac{f(x_2) - f(x_1)}{x_2 - x_1} = f'(x_1)$$

Example 1   A spherical balloon is being inflated. Find the rate of change of the volume with respect to the radius when the radius is 10 cm.

Solution   We solved this problem as Example 4 in Section 1.5, but now we can use our differentiation formulas.

If the radius of the balloon, in centimetres, is r, then the volume V, in cubic centimetres, is given by

$$V(r) = \tfrac{4}{3}\pi r^3$$

Therefore $V'(r) = \tfrac{4}{3}\pi(3r^2) = 4\pi r^2$

and so the rate of change of V with respect to r when $r = 10$ cm is

$$V'(10) = 4\pi(10)^2 = 400\pi \text{ cm}^3/\text{cm}$$

Applications to Physics

We have already considered velocity (the rate of change of displacement with respect to time) in Section 3.1 and acceleration (the rate of change of velocity with respect to time) in Section 3.2. Other occurrences in physics include current (the rate of flow of charge), power (the rate at which work is done), temperature gradient (the rate of change of temperature with respect to position), and rate of heat flow. In what follows, we discuss in detail the linear density of a wire.

If a rod or piece of wire is homogeneous, then its *linear density* is uniform and is defined as mass per unit length:

$$\rho = \frac{m}{L}$$

If the mass m is measured in kilograms and the length L in metres, then the linear density ρ is measured in kilograms per metre. If the rod is not homogeneous, let $m = f(x)$ be its mass measured from its left end to a point x as shown in the figure.

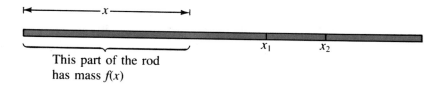

This part of the rod
has mass $f(x)$

The mass of the part of the rod that lies between $x = x_1$ and $x = x_2$ is $\Delta m = f(x_2) - f(x_1)$, so the average density of that part of the rod is

$$\text{average density} = \frac{\Delta m}{\Delta x} = \frac{f(x_2) - f(x_1)}{x_2 - x_1}$$

If we now let $\Delta x \to 0$ (that is, $x_2 \to x_1$), we are computing the average density over a smaller and smaller interval. The **linear density** ρ at x_1 is the limit of these average densities as $\Delta x \to 0$; that is, the linear density is the rate of change of mass with respect to length. Symbolically, we can write

$$\rho = \lim_{\Delta x \to 0} \frac{\Delta m}{\Delta x} = \frac{dm}{dx}$$

Thus, the linear density of the rod is the derivative of mass with respect to length.

Example 2 The mass of the left-hand x metres of a rod is $f(x) = x^2$ kilograms.
(a) Find the average density of the part of the rod given by $2 \leqslant x \leqslant 2.3$.
(b) Find the linear density at $x = 2$.

Solution (a) The average density for $2 \leqslant x \leqslant 2.3$ is

$$\frac{\Delta m}{\Delta x} = \frac{f(2.3) - f(2)}{2.3 - 2} = \frac{(2.3)^2 - 2^2}{0.3} = 4.3 \text{ kg/m}$$

(b) The linear density at $x = 2$ is

$$\rho = \frac{dm}{dx}\bigg]_{x=2} = 2x]_{x=2} = 4 \text{ kg/m}$$

Applications to Biology

If $n = f(t)$ is the number of individuals in a bacteria or animal population at time t, then the change in the population size between the times $t = t_1$ and $t = t_2$ is $\Delta n = f(t_2) - f(t_1)$. Over the time period $t_1 \leqslant t \leqslant t_2$ we have

$$\text{average rate of growth} = \frac{\Delta n}{\Delta t} = \frac{f(t_2) - f(t_1)}{t_2 - t_1}$$

The **(instantaneous) rate of growth** is the rate of change of the population size with respect to time:

$$\text{growth rate} = \lim_{\Delta t \to 0} \frac{\Delta n}{\Delta t} = \frac{dn}{dt}$$

Thus, the rate of growth is the derivative of the population function. Strictly speaking, this is not quite accurate because the actual graph of a population function $n = f(t)$ would be a step function that is discontinuous whenever a birth or death occurs and therefore not differentiable. However, for a large population, we can replace the graph by a smooth approximating curve as in the following figure.

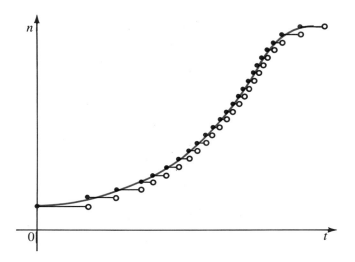

In Chapter 8, we will use the exponential function to construct models for population growth, and at that time we will be able to compute growth rates for exponentially increasing populations. The model for a population function in the next example is more appropriate for a slowly growing bacteria colony.

Example 3   The population of a bacteria culture after t hours is given by $n = 500 + 200t + 12t^2$. Find the rate of growth after 5 h.

Solution   The rate of growth is

$$\frac{dn}{dt} = 200 + 24t$$

After 5 h it is

$$\left.\frac{dn}{dt}\right]_{t=5} = 200 + 24(5) = 320 \text{ bacteria/h}$$

Another occurrence of rates of change in biology is given in Exercise 3.3 as Question 9.

Applications to Chemistry

The *concentration* of a substance A is the number of moles (6.022×10^{23} molecules) per litre and is denoted by $[A]$. During a chemical reaction the concentration will vary and so $[A]$ is a function of time. During a time interval $t_1 \leqslant t \leqslant t_2$, the average rate of reaction of a reactant A is

The minus sign is used to make the rate of reaction positive.

$$\frac{\Delta[A]}{\Delta t} = -\frac{[A](t_2) - [A](t_1)}{t_2 - t_1}$$

and the (**instantaneous**) **rate of reaction** is the rate of change of concentration with respect to time:

$$\text{rate of reaction} = -\lim_{\Delta t \to 0} \frac{\Delta[A]}{\Delta t} = -\frac{d[A]}{dt}$$

Since the rate of reaction is the derivative of the concentration function, chemists often determine the rate of reaction by measuring the slope of a tangent (see Question 8 in Exercise 3.3).

Another application of rates of change in chemistry is described in Question 7.

EXERCISE 3.3

1. Find the rate of change of the volume of a cube with respect to its edge length x when $x = 4$.

2. Find the rate of change of the area of a circle with respect to its radius r when $r = 5$ cm.

3. If a tank holds 1000 L of water, which takes an hour to drain from the bottom of the tank, then the volume V of water remaining in the tank after t minutes is

$$V = 1000\left(1 - \frac{t}{60}\right)^2 \quad 0 \leqslant t \leqslant 60$$

Find the rate at which the water is flowing out of the tank (the instantaneous rate of change of V with respect to t) after 10 min.

4. The mass of the part of a wire that lies between its left end and a point x metres to the right is $\sqrt{x}$ kilograms.
   (a) Find an approximate value for the average density of the part of the wire from $x = 1$ m to $x = 1.1$ m.
   (b) Find the linear density when $x = 1$ m.

5. The mass of the left x centimetres of a string is $x + \frac{1}{2}x^2$ grams. Find the linear density when $x = 6$ cm.

6. The population of a bacteria colony after t hours is given by $n = 1000 + 180t + 25t^2 + 3t^3$. Find the growth rate after 3 h.

7. The volume V of a substance kept at constant temperature will depend on the pressure P. The **isothermal compressibility** β is defined by

$$\beta = -\frac{1}{V}\frac{dV}{dP}$$

and measures how fast, per unit volume, the volume of the substance decreases as the pressure increases at constant temperature.

The volume V (in cubic metres) of a sample of air at 25°C was related to the pressure P (in kilopascals) by the equation

$$V = \frac{5.3}{P}$$

Find the compressibility when the pressure is 40 kPa.

8. The concentrations of dinitrogen pentoxide, N_2O_5, in the reaction
$$2N_2O_5 \rightarrow 4NO_2 + O_2$$
were measured at one-minute intervals as in the table below.

time (min)	0	1	2	3	4
$[N_2O_5]$	0.160	0.113	0.080	0.056	0.040

Draw the graph of $[N_2O_5]$ as function of time and use it to estimate the rate of reaction after two minutes.

9. When blood flows through a blood vessel, such as a vein or artery, we can assume that the blood vessel has the shape of a cylindrical tube with radius R and length L. Because of friction at the walls of the tube, the velocity v of the blood is greatest along the central axis of the tube and decreases as the distance r from the axis increases until v becomes 0 at the wall (see the figure).

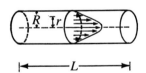

The relationship between v and r is given by the *Law of Laminar Flow* discovered by the French physician Poiseuille in 1840. This states that

$$v = \frac{P}{4\eta L}(R^2 - r^2)$$

where η is the viscosity of the blood and P is the pressure difference between the ends of the tube. If P and L are constant, then v is a function of r. In a typical human artery, the values are $\eta = 0.027$, $R = 0.008$ cm, $L = 2$ cm, and $P = 4000$ dynes/cm^2. Find the rate of change of v with respect to r (which is called the **velocity gradient**) when $r = 0.005$ cm.

3.4 RATES OF CHANGE IN THE SOCIAL SCIENCES

Although calculus has been applied to the natural sciences for centuries, it has only been recently that the social sciences, such as psychology, sociology, urban geography, and economics, have been making use of calculus.

Psychologists interested in learning theory study the so-called learning curve, which graphs the performance level $P(t)$ of someone learning a skill as a function of the training time t. Of particular interest is the rate at which performance improves as time passes, that is, the derivative $P'(t)$.

Sociologists use calculus to analyze the spread of rumours (or innovations or fads or fashions). If $f(t)$ is the fraction of the population that knows a rumour by time t, then the derivative $f'(t)$ represents the rate of spread of the rumour.

These applications to psychology and sociology will be explored in Chapter 8. In this section, we examine rates of change in business and economics.

If it costs a company $C(x)$ to produce x units of a certain commodity, then the function C is called a **cost function**. If the number of items produced is increased from x_1 to x_2, the additional cost is $\Delta C = C(x_2) - C(x_1)$ and the average rate of change of the cost is

$$\frac{\Delta C}{\Delta x} = \frac{C(x_2) - C(x_1)}{x_2 - x_1} = \frac{C(x_1 + \Delta x) - C(x_1)}{\Delta x}$$

The limit of this quantity as $\Delta x \to 0$, that is, the instantaneous rate of change of cost with respect to the number of items produced, is called the **marginal cost** by economists:

$$\text{marginal cost} = \lim_{\Delta x \to 0} \frac{\Delta C}{\Delta x} = \frac{dC}{dx}$$

Since x can usually take on only integer values, it may not make literal sense to let Δx approach 0, but we can always replace $C(x)$ by a smooth approximating function as we did for growth functions in Section 3.3.

Thus, the marginal cost is the derivative of the cost function. To see how to interpret the rate of change in this situation, we recall the definition of a derivative at $x = n$:

$$C'(n) = \lim_{h \to 0} \frac{C(n + h) - C(n)}{h}$$

Taking $h = 1$ and n large, we see that

$$C'(n) \doteq C(n + 1) - C(n)$$

Therefore, the marginal cost of producing n units is approximately equal to the cost of producing one more unit, the $(n + 1)$st unit.

It is often appropriate to represent a cost function by a polynomial

$$C(x) = a + bx + cx^2 + dx^3$$

where a represents the fixed cost (rent, heat, maintenance) and the other terms represent the cost of raw materials, labour, and so on. (The cost of raw materials may be proportional to x, but labour costs might depend partly on higher powers of x because of overtime costs and inefficiencies involved in large-scale operations.)

Example 1 Quinton Mills is a large producer of flour. Management estimates that the cost (in dollars) of producing x 5-kg bags of flour is

$$C(x) = 140\ 000 + 0.43x + 0.000\ 001x^2$$

(a) Find the marginal cost at a production level of $x = 1000$ bags.
(b) Find the actual cost of producing the 1001st bag.

Solution (a) The marginal cost function is

$$C'(x) = 0.43 + 0.000\ 002x$$

The marginal cost when $x = 1000$ is

$$C'(1000) = 0.43 + (0.000\ 002)(1000) = \$0.432/\text{bag}$$

(b) The cost of producing the 1001st bag is

$$C(1001) - C(1000) = [140\ 000 + (0.43)(1001) + (0.000\ 001)(1001)^2]$$
$$- [140\ 000 + (0.43)(1000) + (0.000\ 001)(1000)^2]$$
$$= \$0.432\ 001$$

Of course a businessman is interested not only in costs but also in revenue and profit. Let $p(x)$ be the price per unit that a company can charge if it sells x units. Then p is called the **demand function** (or **price function**). If x units are sold and the price per unit is $p(x)$, then the total revenue is

$$R(x) = xp(x)$$

and R is called the **revenue function**. The derivative R' of the revenue function is called the **marginal revenue function** and is the rate of change of revenue with respect to the number of units sold.

Example 2 Howard's Hamburgers has taken a market survey and has found that the yearly demand for their hamburgers is given by

$$p = \frac{800\ 000 - x}{200\ 000} \qquad (p \text{ in dollars})$$

(a) Graph the demand function.

(b) What is the demand for hamburgers corresponding to prices of $0.00, $0.50, $1.00, $1.50, $2.00, $2.50, $3.00, $3.50, $4.00?

(c) Find the marginal revenue when $x = 300\ 000$.

Solution (a) Notice from the graph that, unsurprisingly, more hamburgers are sold as the price decreases.

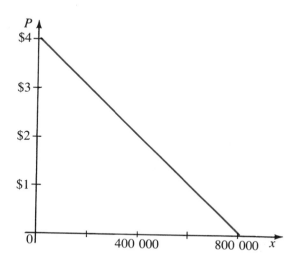

(b) The table shows the demand at the given prices.

p	0	$0.50	$1.00	$1.50	$2.00	$2.50	$3.00	$3.50	$4.00
x	800 000	700 000	600 000	500 000	400 000	300 000	200 000	100 000	0

(c) The revenue function is

$$R(x) = xp(x) = x\left(\frac{800\ 000 - x}{200\ 000}\right) = \frac{1}{200\ 000}(800\ 000x - x^2)$$

So the marginal revenue function is

$$R'(x) = \frac{1}{200\ 000}(800\ 000 - 2x)$$

When $x = 300\ 000$ the marginal revenue is

$$R'(300\ 000) = \frac{1}{200\ 000}(800\ 000 - 600\ 000) = \$1/\text{hamburger}$$

In Example 2(c), the marginal revenue of $1 per hamburger is the rate at which revenue is increasing with respect to increase in sales. It represents the approximate additional income to the company per additional item sold.

In general, if x units of a commodity are sold, the total profit is obtained by subtracting the cost from the revenue:

$$P(x) = R(x) - C(x)$$

and P is called the **profit function**. The **marginal profit** function is P', the derivative of the profit function.

Example 3 Howard's Hamburgers estimates that the cost, in dollars, of making x hamburgers is

$$C(x) = 125\ 000 + 0.42x$$

Using the demand function from Example 2, find the profit and the marginal profit when (a) $x = 300\ 000$, (b) $x = 400\ 000$.

Solution From Example 2, the revenue function is

$$R(x) = \frac{1}{200\ 000}(800\ 000x - x^2)$$

and so the profit function is

$$P(x) = R(x) - C(x)$$
$$= \frac{1}{200\ 000}(800\ 000x - x^2) - (125\ 000 + 0.42x)$$
$$= -\frac{x^2}{200\ 000} + 3.58x - 125\ 000$$

The marginal profit function is

$$P'(x) = -\frac{x}{100\ 000} + 3.58$$

(a) When $x = 300\ 000$, the profit is

$$P(300\ 000) = -\frac{(300\ 000)^2}{200\ 000} + (3.58)(300\ 000) - 125\ 000$$
$$= \$499\ 000$$

and the marginal profit is

$$P'(300\ 000) = -\frac{300\ 000}{100\ 000} + 3.58 = \$0.58/\text{hamburger}$$

(b) When $x = 400\ 000$, the profit is

$$P(400\ 000) = -\frac{(400\ 000)^2}{200\ 000} + (3.58)(400\ 000) - 125\ 000$$
$$= \$507\ 000$$

and the marginal profit is

$$P'(400\ 000) = -\frac{400\ 000}{100\ 000} + 3.58 = -\$0.42/\text{hamburger}$$

In Example 3(a), the marginal profit of $0.58/hamburger represents the approximate additional income per additional hamburger sold when 300 000 hamburgers have been sold. The negative marginal profit in part (b) shows that, when 400 000 hamburgers have been sold, additional sales will increase revenue but decrease profits. In Section 4.5 we will see how to choose x so as to maximize profits.

EXERCISE 3.4

1. A company determines that the cost, in dollars, of producing x items is
$$C(x) = 55\ 000 + 23x + 0.012x^2$$
   (a) Find the marginal cost function.
   (b) Find the marginal cost at a production level of 100 items.
   (c) Find the cost of producing the 101st item.

2. The cost in dollars for the production of x units of a commodity is
$$C(x) = 1500 + \frac{x}{10} + \frac{x^2}{1000}$$
   (a) Find the marginal cost function.
   (b) Find the marginal cost at a production level of 800 units.
   (c) Find the cost of producing the 801st unit.

3. A manufacturer determines that the revenue derived from selling x units of one of their products is $R(x) = 8000x - 0.02x^3$.
   (a) Find the marginal revenue function.
   (b) Find the marginal revenue when 300 units are sold.
   (c) Compare this to the actual gain in revenue when the 301st unit is sold.

4. The Manchester Pen Company estimates that the cost of manufacturing x pens is
$$C(x) = 23\ 000 + 0.24x + 0.0001x^2$$
   and the revenue is
$$R(x) = 0.98x - 0.0002x^2$$
   (a) Find the profit function.
   (b) Find the marginal profit function.
   (c) Find the marginal profit when 1000 pens are sold.
   (d) Compare this to the actual increase when the 1001st pen is sold.

5. Sue's Submarines has determined that the monthly demand for their submarines is given by

$$p = \frac{30\ 000 - x}{10\ 000}$$

and the cost of making x submarines is

$$C(x) = 6000 + 0.8x$$

(a) Graph the demand function.
(b) Fill in the following table to illustrate the demand at the given prices.

p	0	$0.50	$1.00	$1.50	$2.00	$2.50	$3.00
x							

(c) Find the revenue function.
(d) Find the marginal revenue function.
(e) Find the marginal revenue when $x = 1000$.
(f) Find the profit function.
(g) Find the marginal profit function.
(h) Find the marginal profit when $x = 10\ 000$.

6. A company estimates that its production costs, in dollars, for x items is

$$C(x) = 82\ 000 + 23x + 0.001x^2$$

and the demand function for this product is given by

$$p = 100 - 0.01x$$

(a) Find the marginal cost function.
(b) Find the marginal revenue function.
(c) Find the marginal profit function.
(d) Find the marginal profit at a production level of 50 items.

3.5 RELATED RATES

In a related rates problem, we are given the rate of change of one quantity and we are asked to find the rate of change of a related quantity. To do this, we find an equation that relates the two quantities and use the Chain Rule to differentiate both sides of the equation with respect to time.

Example 1 A spherical snowball is melting in such a way that its volume is decreasing at a rate of 1 cm³/min. At what rate is the radius decreasing when the radius is 5 cm?

Solution Let V be the volume of the snowball and r its radius. Then V and r are related by the equation

$$V = \tfrac{4}{3}\pi r^3 \tag{1}$$

We are given the rate of change of V:

$$\frac{dV}{dt} = -1 \ \text{cm}^3/\text{min}$$

The minus sign is used because the volume is decreasing.

We are asked to find $\frac{dr}{dt}$ when $r = 5$. Using the Chain Rule to differentiate Equation 1 with respect to time, we have

$$\frac{dV}{dt} = \frac{dV}{dr}\frac{dr}{dt} = 4\pi r^2 \frac{dr}{dt}$$

so

$$\frac{dr}{dt} = \frac{1}{4\pi r^2}\frac{dV}{dt}$$

Now we put $r = 5$ and $\frac{dV}{dt} = -1$ in this equation and we get

$$\frac{dr}{dt} = \frac{1}{4\pi(5)^2}(-1) = -\frac{1}{100\pi}$$

The radius of the snowball is decreasing at a rate of $\frac{1}{100\pi} \doteq 0.003$ cm/min.

Example 2 A water tank is built in the shape of a circular cone with height 5 m and diameter 6 m at the top. Water is being pumped into the tank at a rate of 1.6 m³/min. Find the rate at which the water level is rising when the water is 2 m deep.

Solution First we sketch the cone.

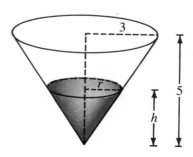

Let V be the volume of the water and let r and h be the radius of the surface and the height at time t, where t is measured in minutes. We are given the rate of increase of V, that is,

$$\frac{dV}{dt} = 1.6 \text{ m}^3/\text{min}$$

and we are asked to find $\dfrac{dh}{dt}$ when $h = 2$ m.

The quantities V and h are related by the equation

$$V = \tfrac{1}{3}\pi r^2 h$$

but we have to express V as a function of h alone. To eliminate r we look for a relationship between r and h. We use the similar triangles in the figure to write

$$\frac{r}{h} = \frac{3}{5}$$

Thus $r = \tfrac{3}{5}h$ and we have

$$V = \frac{1}{3}\pi\left(\frac{3}{5}h\right)^2 h = \frac{3\pi}{25}h^3$$

Differentiating both sides with respect to t, we have

$$\frac{dV}{dt} = \frac{3\pi}{25}(3h^2)\frac{dh}{dt} = \frac{9\pi}{25}h^2\frac{dh}{dt}$$

$$\frac{dh}{dt} = \frac{25}{9\pi}\frac{1}{h^2}\frac{dV}{dt}$$

When $h = 2$ and $\dfrac{dV}{dt} = 1.6$, we have

$$\frac{dh}{dt} = \frac{25}{9\pi}\frac{1}{2^2}(1.6) = \frac{10}{9\pi}$$

The water level is rising at a rate of $\dfrac{10}{9\pi} \doteq 0.4$ m/min.

In solving related rates problems it is useful to recall some of the problem-solving principles from the Review and Preview to this chapter and adapt them to the present situation:

1. Read the problem carefully until you understand it.
2. Draw a diagram if possible.

3. Introduce notation. Assign symbols to all quantities that are functions of time.
4. Express the given information and the required rate in terms of derivatives.
5. Write an equation that relates the various quantities of the problem. If necessary, use the geometry of the situation to eliminate one of the variables by substitution (as in Example 2).
6. Use the Chain Rule to differentiate both sides of the equation with respect to t.
7. Substitute the given information into the resulting equation and solve for the unknown rate.

A common error is to substitute the given numerical information (for quantities that vary with time) at too early a stage. This should only be done *after* the differentiation. (Step 7 follows Step 6.) For instance, in Example 2 we dealt with general values of h until we finally substituted $h = 2$ at the last stage. (If we had put $h = 2$ earlier, we would have got $\dfrac{dV}{dt} = 0$, which is clearly wrong.)

The remaining two examples further illustrate this strategy.

Example 3   A spotlight on the ground shines on a wall 10 m away. A man 2 m tall walks from the spotlight toward the wall at a speed of 1.2 m/s. How fast is his shadow on the wall decreasing when he is 3 m from the wall?

Solution

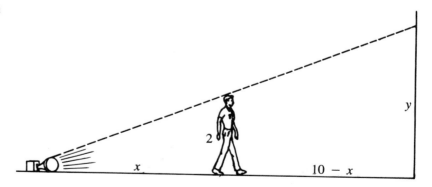

As in the figure, let x be the distance from the light to the man and let y be the height of his shadow, in metres.

We are given that $\dfrac{dx}{dt} = 1.2$ m/s, and we wish to find $\dfrac{dy}{dt}$ when $10 - x = 3$ m, that is, $x = 7$ m.

To relate y to x we use similar triangles:

$$\frac{y}{10} = \frac{2}{x}$$

Thus, $\quad y = \dfrac{20}{x}$

and so, $\quad \dfrac{dy}{dt} = -\dfrac{20}{x^2}\dfrac{dx}{dt}$

When $x = 7$ and $\dfrac{dx}{dt} = 1.2$, we have

$$\frac{dy}{dt} = -\frac{20}{7^2}(1.2) = -\frac{24}{49}$$

The shadow is decreasing at a rate of $\dfrac{24}{49}$ m/s.

Example 4

A man starts walking north at a speed of 1.5 m/s and a woman starts at the same point P at the same time walking west at a speed of 2 m/s. At what rate is the distance between the man and the woman increasing one minute later?

Solution

At any given time t after they start, let x be the distance travelled by the man, y be the distance travelled by the woman, and z be the distance between them. We are given that

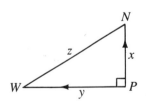

$$\frac{dx}{dt} = 1.5 \text{ m/s} \quad \text{and} \quad \frac{dy}{dt} = 2 \text{ m/s}$$

and we are required to find $\dfrac{dz}{dt}$ when $t = 60$.

The equation that relates x, y, and z is given by the Pythagorean Theorem:

$$z^2 = x^2 + y^2 \qquad \text{①}$$

Differentiating with respect to t, we get

$$2z\frac{dz}{dt} = 2x\frac{dx}{dt} + 2y\frac{dy}{dt}$$

$$\frac{dz}{dt} = \frac{1}{z}\left(x\frac{dx}{dt} + y\frac{dy}{dt}\right) \qquad \text{②}$$

When $t = 60$, we have $x = 90$ m and $y = 120$ m, so Equation 1 gives

$$z = \sqrt{90^2 + 120^2} = 150 \text{ m}$$

Putting these values in Equation 2, we have

$$\frac{dz}{dt} = \frac{1}{150}[90(1.5) + 120(2)] = 2.5$$

The distance between the man and the woman is increasing at a rate of 2.5 m/s.

EXERCISE 3.5

1. If $xy^2 = 12$ and $\frac{dy}{dt} = 6$, find $\frac{dx}{dt}$ when $y = 2$.

2. If $x^3 + y^3 = 9$ and $\frac{dx}{dt} = 4$, find $\frac{dy}{dt}$ when $x = 2$.

3. How fast is the area of a square increasing when the side is 3 m in length and growing at a rate of 0.8 m/min?

4. How fast is the edge length of a cube increasing when the volume of the cube is increasing at a rate of 144 cm³/s and the edge length is 4 cm?

5. A stone is dropped into a lake, creating a circular ripple that travels outward at a speed of 25 cm/s. Find the rate at which the area within the circle is increasing after 4 s.

6. A spherical balloon is being inflated so that the volume is increasing at a rate of 8 m³/min. How fast is the radius of the balloon increasing when the diameter is 2 m?

7. A snowball melts so that its surface area decreases at a rate of 0.5 cm²/min. Find the rate at which the radius decreases when the radius is 4 cm.

8. The side of an equilateral triangle decreases at the rate of 2 cm/s. At what rate is the area decreasing when the area is 100 cm²?

9. The area of a triangle is increasing at a rate of 4 cm²/min and its base is increasing at a rate of 1 cm/min. At what rate is the altitude of the triangle increasing when the altitude is 20 cm and the area is 80 cm²?

10. A man 2 m tall walks away from a lamppost whose light is 5 m above the ground. If he walks at a speed of 1.5 m/s, at what rate is his shadow growing when he is 10 m from the lamppost?

11. A ladder 4 m long rests against a vertical wall. If the bottom of the ladder slides away from the wall at a speed of 30 cm/s, how quickly is the top of the ladder sliding down the wall when the bottom of the ladder is 2 m from the wall?

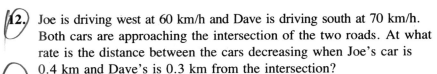

12. Joe is driving west at 60 km/h and Dave is driving south at 70 km/h. Both cars are approaching the intersection of the two roads. At what rate is the distance between the cars decreasing when Joe's car is 0.4 km and Dave's is 0.3 km from the intersection?

13. At 1:00 p.m. ship A was 80 km south of ship B. Ship A is sailing north at 30 km/h and ship B is sailing east at 40 km/h. How fast is the distance between them changing at 3:00 p.m.?

14. A waterskier skis over the ramp shown in the figure at a speed of 12 m/s. How fast is she rising as she leaves the ramp?

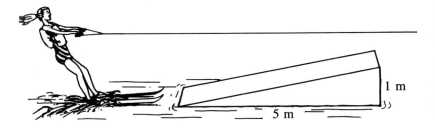

15. A plane flies horizontally with a speed of 600 km/h at an altitude of 10 km and passes directly over the town of Quinton. Find the rate at which the distance from the plane to Quinton is increasing when it is 20 km away from Quinton.

16. A water trough is 10 m long and a cross-section has the shape of an isosceles triangle that is 1 m across at the top and is 50 cm high. The trough is being filled with water at a rate of 0.4 m³/min. How fast will the water level rise when the water is 40 cm deep?

17. Sand is being dumped from a conveyor belt at a rate of 1.2 m³/min and forms a pile in the shape of a cone whose base diameter and height are always equal. How fast is the height of the pile growing when the pile is 3 m high?

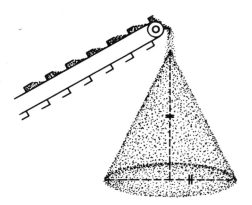

3.6 NEWTON'S METHOD

A quadratic equation $ax^2 + bx + c = 0$ can be solved either by factoring or by using the quadratic formula. For a cubic equation $ax^3 + bx^2 + cx + d = 0$ there is also a formula, but it is so complicated that it is seldom used. Likewise, the formula for the solutions of a fourth-degree equation is extremely difficult and there is no formula at all for equations of degrees higher than four. Using **Newton's method**, however, we can find *approximations* to the solutions of such equations.

Suppose we want to solve an equation of the form $f(x) = 0$, where f is a differentiable function. Let r be a **solution**, or **root**, of the equation; that is, $f(r) = 0$. Our aim is to find a good approximation to r. The idea behind Newton's method is seen in the figure, where r is shown as the x-intercept of the graph of f.

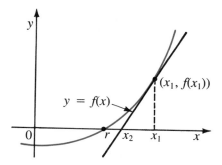

We start with a first approximation x_1 to r, obtained by guessing, or by numerical experimentation, or by roughly sketching the graph of f. We draw the tangent line to the graph of f at the point $(x_1, f(x_1))$. Let x_2 be the x-intercept of this tangent line. It appears from the figure that if x_1 is close to r, then x_2 is even closer to r and so we use it as the second approximation to r.

To express x_2 in terms of x_1, we first write the equation of the tangent line in slope-point form:

$$y - f(x_1) = f'(x_1)(x - x_1)$$

Since the x-intercept is x_2, we put $y = 0$ and $x = x_2$ in this equation:

$$0 - f(x_1) = f'(x_1)(x_2 - x_1)$$

If $f'(x_1) \neq 0$, we can solve for x_2:

$$x_2 = x_1 - \frac{f(x_1)}{f'(x_1)} \qquad \textcircled{1}$$

If we repeat this procedure with x_1 replaced by x_2, we get a third approximation x_3 given by

$$x_3 = x_2 - \frac{f(x_2)}{f'(x_2)}$$

In fact, if we repeat the procedure indefinitely, we get a sequence of approximations x_1, x_2, x_3, x_4, ... as shown in the following diagram. If, as we hope, these numbers become closer and closer to the desired root r, then, in the notation of Section 1.6, we can write

$$\lim_{n \to \infty} x_n = r$$

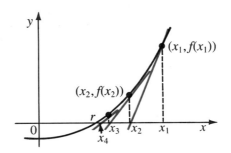

Newton's Method

If x_1 is a first approximation to a root of the equation $f(x) = 0$, then successive approximations are given by

$$x_{n+1} = x_n - \frac{f(x_n)}{f'(x_n)}, \quad n = 1, 2, 3, \ldots$$

if $f'(x_n) \neq 0$.

②

Example 1   Starting with $x_1 = 1$, find the third approximation x_3 to the root of the equation $x^3 + x - 1 = 0$.

Solution   Applying Newton's method with

$$f(x) = x^3 + x - 1$$
and $\qquad f'(x) = 3x^2 + 1$

we have $\qquad x_2 = x_1 - \dfrac{f(x_1)}{f'(x_1)}$

$$= x_1 - \frac{x_1^3 + x_1 - 1}{3x_1^2 + 1}$$

$$= 1 - \frac{1^3 + 1 - 1}{3(1)^2 + 1}$$

$$= \tfrac{3}{4}$$

Then, using this value to get the next approximation, we have

$$x_3 = x_2 - \frac{f(x_2)}{f'(x_2)}$$

$$= \frac{3}{4} - \frac{f\left(\frac{3}{4}\right)}{f'\left(\frac{3}{4}\right)}$$

$$= \frac{3}{4} - \frac{\frac{27}{64} - \frac{1}{4}}{\frac{27}{16} + 1}$$

$$= \frac{59}{86}$$

The third approximation is $\frac{59}{86} \doteq 0.6860$.

If we wish to find a root correct to six decimal places, say, we use Formula 2 for $n = 1, 2, 3, \ldots$ and we stop when successive approximations x_n and x_{n+1} agree to six decimal places.

The procedure in going from stage n to stage $n + 1$ is the same for all values of n, and we call Formula 2 a **recursion formula**. As a result, it is especially convenient to use a computer or a programmable calculator when using Newton's method.

Example 2 Use Newton's method to find $\sqrt[4]{13}$ correct to four decimal places.

Solution Notice that finding $\sqrt[4]{13}$ is equivalent to finding the positive root of the equation

$$x^4 - 13 = 0$$

Therefore we take $f(x) = x^4 - 13$ in Newton's method, so $f'(x) = 4x^3$ and Equation 2 becomes

$$x_{n+1} = x_n - \frac{f(x_n)}{f'(x_n)} = x_n - \frac{x_n^4 - 13}{4x_n^3} \qquad ③$$

If we take $x_1 = 2$ as our initial approximation and we put $n = 1$ in Equation 3, we get

$$x_2 = 2 - \frac{2^4 - 13}{4(2)^3} = 1.906\ 250$$

With this value of x_2, Equation 3 gives

$$x_3 \doteq 1.898\ 872$$

Repeating this procedure using a calculator, we obtain

$$x_4 \doteq 1.898\ 829$$
$$x_5 \doteq 1.898\ 829$$

These values agree to six decimal places, so we conclude that

$$\sqrt[4]{13} \doteq 1.898\ 829$$

correct to six decimal places.

If we had used a different positive initial value for x_1 in Example 2, we would have arrived at the same approximation for $\sqrt[4]{13}$, though more steps might be required. For instance, if the initial guess is $x_1 = 5$, then we get

$$x_2 \doteq 3.776\ 000$$
$$x_3 \doteq 2.892\ 365$$
$$x_4 \doteq 2.303\ 589$$
$$x_5 \doteq 1.993\ 561$$
$$x_6 \doteq 1.905\ 370$$
$$x_7 \doteq 1.898\ 863$$
$$x_8 \doteq 1.898\ 829$$
$$x_9 \doteq 1.898\ 829$$

Example 3   Find the coordinates of the point of intersection of the curves $y = x^5$ and $y = x^2 + 1$ correct to six decimal places.

Solution   First notice that the x-coordinate of the point of intersection satisfies

$$x^5 = x^2 + 1$$

so it is a root of the equation

$$x^5 - x^2 - 1 = 0$$

and we can employ Newton's method with $f(x) = x^5 - x^2 - 1$ and $f'(x) = 5x^4 - 2x$.

To find a first approximation x_1 we sketch the curves $y = x^5$ and $y = x^2 + 1$. It appears that the curves intersect when x is slightly larger than 1, so we take $x_1 = 1$.

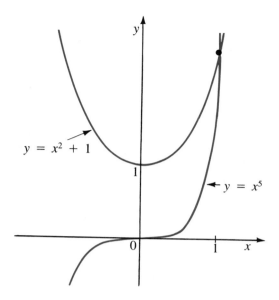

$y = x^2 + 1$

$y = x^5$

Newton's method gives

$$x_{n+1} = x_n - \frac{f(x_n)}{f'(x_n)} = x_n - \frac{x_n^5 - x_n^2 - 1}{5x_n^4 - 2x_n}$$

So we have, successively,

$$x_2 \doteq 1.333\ 333$$
$$x_3 \doteq 1.223\ 997$$
$$x_4 \doteq 1.195\ 608$$
$$x_5 \doteq 1.193\ 865$$
$$x_6 \doteq 1.193\ 859$$
$$x_7 \doteq 1.193\ 859$$

The y-coordinate of the point of intersection can be approximated using either of the equations $y = x^5$ or $y = x^2 + 1$. Correct to six decimal places, the point of intersection is

$$(1.193\ 859,\ 2.425\ 300)$$

Finally, we note that care should be taken to ensure a reasonable first approximation x_1. If x_1 is not chosen close enough to r, it could happen that x_2 is a worse approximation than x_1. (See the diagram below and Question 3(a) in Exercise 3.6.)

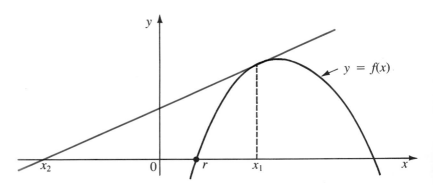

EXERCISE 3.6

1. Start with $x_1 = 0$ and use Newton's method to find the second approximation x_2 to the root of the equation $x^3 + 2x + 1 = 0$.

2. Find the second and third approximations to the root of the equation $x^3 + x^2 + 1 = 0$ using Newton's method and taking $x_1 = -1$.

3. (a) Use Newton's method with $x_1 = 2$ to find the root of the equation $x^3 - x - 2 = 0$ correct to six decimal places.
   (b) Solve the equation in part (a) using $x_1 = 1$ as the initial approximation.
   (c) Solve the equation in part (a) using $x_1 = 0.57$. Sketch the graph of $f(x) = x^3 - x - 2$ to show why x_2 is such a poor approximation.

4. Use Newton's method to approximate the root of the equation in the given interval correct to six decimal places.
   (a) $x^4 - x^2 + x - 5 = 0, 1 < x < 2$
   (b) $x^3 - x^2 + 2x = 9, 2 < x < 3$
   (c) $x^6 = \sqrt{x + 7}, 1 < x < 2$

5. Use Newton's method to find all roots of the equation correct to six decimal places.
   (a) $x^3 - 5x + 1 = 0$ (b) $x^5 = 4x^2 - 1$

6. (a) Apply Newton's method to derive the following square-root algorithm (used by the ancient Babylonians to compute $\sqrt{a}$):
   $$x_{n+1} = \tfrac{1}{2}\left(x_n + \frac{a}{x_n}\right)$$
   (b) Use part (a) to compute $\sqrt{17.2}$ correct to six decimal places.

7. Use Newton's method to approximate the following numbers correct to six decimal places.
   (a) $\sqrt[5]{28}$ (b) $\sqrt[8]{1.23}$

8. Sketch the following pairs of curves and find the coordinates of their point of intersection correct to six decimal places.
   (a) $y = x^3, y = x + 1$ (b) $y = x^2 + 1, xy = 1$

COMPUTER APPLICATION

Newton's method for solving equations is well suited to computer implementation. We present a pseudocode (the logic of the algorithm) for Newton's method, together with a computer program in BASIC. This program relates to Example 3 in Section 3.6.

Pseudocode

```
define the function
define the derivative
establish a first root
loop through calculations of successive
  approximations
    calculate next approximation using
     Newton's formula
    check for desired accuracy
    reset the variables in preparation
     for the next pass through the loop
continue looping until desired accuracy
  reached
print out the root of the equation
```

A BASIC version

```
DEF function(x)=X^5-X^2-1
DEF derivative(x)=5*X^4-2*X
PRINT ``enter a first approximation for
  the root...'';
INPUT xn

DO
  LET xnext=xn-funtion(xn)/
    derivative(xn)
  LET difference=abs(xn-xnext)
  LET xn=xnext
LOOP until difference<0.00000001
PRINT ``correct to 8 decimal places, the
  root is ...'';
PRINT using ``#########'' : xnext

END
```

The Output

```
enter a first approximation for the root
  ...? 1
correct to 8 decimal places, the root is
  ... 1.19385911
```

3.7 REVIEW EXERCISE

1. The position function of a particle is given by $s = 2t^3 + 4t^2 - t$, where s is measured in metres and t in seconds.
   (a) Find the velocity and acceleration as functions of t.
   (b) Find the velocity and acceleration after 4 s.

2. The motion of a particle is described by the position function
   $$s = t^3 - 12t^2 + 45t + 3, \; t \geq 0$$
   where t is measured in seconds and s in metres.
   (a) When is the particle at rest?
   (b) When is the velocity positive and when is it negative?
   (c) When is the acceleration positive and when is it negative?
   (d) Find the velocity when the acceleration is 0.
   (e) Draw a diagram to illustrate the motion of the particle.
   (f) Find the total distance travelled in the first 8 s.

3. If a ball is thrown upward on the moon with a velocity of 65 m/s, its height in metres after t seconds is
   $$h = 65t - 0.83t^2$$
   (a) Find the velocity of the ball after 1 s.
   (b) Find the acceleration of the ball after 1 s.
   (c) When will the ball hit the moon?
   (d) With what velocity will it hit the moon?

4. Find the rate of change of the area of a square with respect to the length L of a side when $L = 5$.

5. The mass of a length of wire from its left end to a point x metres to the right is $\left(2 + x + \frac{1}{2}x^2\right)$ kilograms.
   (a) Find the average density of the part of the wire from $x = 2$ m to $x = 2.1$ m.
   (b) Find the linear density when $x = 2$ m.

6. A company estimates that the cost, in dollars, of manufacturing x units of their product is $C(x) = 19\,000 + 16.2x + 0.06x^2$.
   (a) Find the marginal cost function.
   (b) Find the marginal cost at a production level of 200 units.
   (c) Find the cost of manufacturing the 201st item.

7. Pasquale's Pizza makes only one size of pizza and has determined that the cost of making x pizzas is
   $$C(x) = 12\,500 + 1.08x$$
   The monthly demand for their pizzas is given by
   $$p = \frac{20\,000 - x}{1000}$$
   (a) Find the marginal cost function.
   (b) Find the revenue function.
   (c) Find the marginal revenue function.
   (d) Find the profit function.

(e) Find the marginal profit function.

(f) Find the marginal profit when $x = 8000$.

8. A rectangle is expanding so that its length is always twice its width. The perimeter of the rectangle is increasing at a rate of 6 cm/min. Find the rate of increase of the area of the rectangle when the perimeter is 40 cm.

9. Boyle's Law states that when a sample of gas is compressed at a constant temperature, the pressure P and volume V satisfy the equation $PV = C$, where C is a constant. At a certain instant, the volume is 480 cm³, the pressure is 160 kPa, and the pressure is increasing at a rate of 15 kPa/min. At what rate is the volume decreasing at this instant?

10. At 9 a.m. ship A is 50 km east of ship B. Ship A is sailing north at 40 km/h and ship B is sailing south at 30 km/h. How fast is the distance between them changing at noon?

11. Use Newton's method with initial approximation $x_1 = 1$ to find the second approximation x_2 to the root of the equation $x^4 + x - 1 = 0$ that lies between 0 and 1.

12. Use Newton's method to find all the roots of the equation $x^3 - x^2 + 1 = 0$ correct to six decimal places.

13. (a) Sketch the curves $y = x^6$ and $y = 3 - 2x$ using the same axes.

(b) Find the coordinates of the points of intersection of these curves correct to six decimal places.

3.8 CHAPTER 3 TEST

1. The position function of a particle is given by
$$s = t^3 - 6t^2 + 9t + 1, t \geqslant 0$$
where t is measured in seconds and s in metres.
   (a) Find the velocity after 4 s.
   (b) Find the acceleration after 4 s.
   (c) When is the particle at rest?
   (d) When is the particle moving in the positive direction?
   (e) Find the velocity when the acceleration is 0.
   (f) Find the total distance travelled in the first 4 s.

2. A manufacturer of CD players estimates that the cost of making x machines is
$$C(x) = 87\ 000 + 122x$$
and the demand function is given by
$$p = \frac{600\ 000 - x}{1000}$$
   (a) Find the marginal cost function.
   (b) Find the revenue function.
   (c) Find the marginal revenue function.
   (d) Find the profit function.
   (e) Find the marginal profit function.

3. A paper cup has the shape of a cone with height 8 cm and radius 3 cm at the top. Water is poured into the cup at a rate of 2 cm³/s. How fast is the water level rising when the water level is 6 cm deep?

4. Find the root of the equation $x^5 = x + 2$ correct to six decimal places.

CUMULATIVE REVIEW FOR CHAPTERS 1 TO 3

1. Find each limit.

   (a) $\displaystyle\lim_{x \to 2} \frac{2x^2 + 1}{3x^2 - 4}$

   (b) $\displaystyle\lim_{x \to 2} \frac{x^2 - 3x + 2}{x^2 - 4}$

   (c) $\displaystyle\lim_{x \to -1} \frac{x^2 + 2x + 1}{x^3 + 1}$

   (d) $\displaystyle\lim_{h \to 0} \frac{(2 + h)^3 - 8}{h}$

   (e) $\displaystyle\lim_{h \to 0} \frac{\frac{1}{(3 + h)^2} - \frac{1}{9}}{h}$

   (f) $\displaystyle\lim_{x \to -2} \frac{x^2 - x - 6}{2x^2 + 5x + 2}$

   (g) $\displaystyle\lim_{x \to 2^+} \sqrt{x^2 - x - 2}$

   (h) $\displaystyle\lim_{x \to -5^-} \frac{2x + 10}{|x + 5|}$

2. Let

$$f(x) = \begin{cases} -x - 2 & \text{if } x < -2 \\ 1 - x^2 & \text{if } -2 \leqslant x \leqslant 2 \\ x - 5 & \text{if } x > 2 \end{cases}$$

   (a) Find the following limits, if they exist.

   (i) $\displaystyle\lim_{x \to -2^-} f(x)$

   (ii) $\displaystyle\lim_{x \to -2^+} f(x)$

   (iii) $\displaystyle\lim_{x \to -2} f(x)$

   (iv) $\displaystyle\lim_{x \to 2^-} f(x)$

   (v) $\displaystyle\lim_{x \to 2^+} f(x)$

   (vi) $\displaystyle\lim_{x \to 2} f(x)$

   (b) Sketch the graph of f.

   (c) Where is f discontinuous?

   (d) Where is f not differentiable?

3. Find the following limits.

   (a) $\displaystyle\lim_{n \to \infty} \frac{1 - 2n^3}{n + n^3}$

   (b) $\displaystyle\lim_{n \to \infty} 3^{-n}$

4. Find the sum of the series or state that it is divergent.

   (a) $2 - 3 + \dfrac{9}{4} - \dfrac{27}{8} + \ldots$

   (b) $3 + 2 + \dfrac{4}{3} + \dfrac{8}{9} + \dfrac{16}{27} + \ldots$

5. (a) If $f(x) = 6 - 5x + 3x^2$, find $f'(x)$ directly from the definition of a derivative.

   (b) Find the equation of the tangent line to the parabola $y = 6 - 5x + 3x^2$ at the point where $x = 1$.

6. Find the derivative of the function $g(x) = \sqrt{3 - x}$ directly from the definition.

7. Differentiate.

   (a) $f(x) = 12x^5 - \frac{1}{2}x^4 - 4x$

   (b) $f(x) = \dfrac{6}{x^2}$

   (c) $g(x) = \sqrt[3]{x}\left(2x + \dfrac{1}{x}\right)$

   (d) $g(x) = \dfrac{x^2}{2x - 3}$

   (e) $f(t) = \sqrt{2t - t^3}$

   (f) $f(y) = \left(\dfrac{2 - y}{1 + 2y}\right)^4$

(g) $y = (3x + 5)(x^3 - 1)^3$

(h) $y = \dfrac{1}{\sqrt[5]{x^5 + 1}}$

(i) $y = \dfrac{\sqrt{x} - x}{x^2}$

(j) $y = \sqrt{\dfrac{x}{1 + x^2}}$

8. If $f(x) = \dfrac{1}{\sqrt{x^2 - 1}}$, find $f'(x)$ and state the domains of both f and f'.

9. Find $\dfrac{dy}{dx}$ if $x^4 + 2x^2y^3 + y^2 = 21$.

10. Find y' and y''.

(a) $y = \dfrac{x + 1}{x + 2}$

(b) $x^2 - y^3 = 7$

11. Find the equation of the tangent line to the curve at the given point.

(a) $y = \dfrac{2}{1 + x^2}$, $(1, 1)$

(b) $x^2 - y^2 = 3$, $(-2, -1)$

12. Find the equation of both tangent lines to the curve $y = x^3 - x$ that are parallel to the line $22x - 2y + 1 = 0$.

13. Suppose that $f(2) = -3, f'(2) = 10, f'(4) = 6, g(2) = 4$, and $g'(2) = 1$. Evaluate

(a) $(fg)'(2)$

(b) $\left(\dfrac{f}{g}\right)'(2)$

(c) $(f \circ g)'(2)$

14. If f is a differentiable function, find an expression for $F'(x)$ in terms of $f'(x)$.

(a) $F(x) = f(x^5)$

(b) $F(x) = [f(x)]^5$

(c) $F(x) = x^5f(x)$

(d) $F(x) = \sqrt{\dfrac{f(x)}{x}}$

15. If a ball is thrown downward from a 120 m high cliff with an initial speed of 18 m/s, then its height after t seconds, before it hits the ground, is
$$h = 120 - 18t - 4.9t^2$$
(a) Find the average velocity of the stone for the following time periods.

      (i) $2 \leqslant t \leqslant 3$ (ii) $2 \leqslant t \leqslant 2.1$ (iii) $2 \leqslant t \leqslant 2.01$

(b) Find the velocity after 2 s.

(c) Find the acceleration after 2 s.

16. The motion of a particle is described by the position function
$$s = t^3 - 6t^2 + 9t + 5, \; t \geqslant 0$$
where s is measured in metres and t in seconds.

(a) Find the velocity after 2 s and 4 s.

(b) Find the acceleration after 2 s and 4 s.

(c) When is the particle at rest?

(d) When is the velocity positive and when is it negative?
(e) When is the acceleration positive and when is it negative?
(f) Find the total distance travelled in the first 5 s.

17. A spherical balloon is being inflated.
   (a) Find the rate of change of the volume with respect to the radius when the radius is 0.5 m.
   (b) If the volume of the balloon is increasing at a rate of 10 m³/min, how fast is the radius increasing when the radius is 3 m?

18. A boat is pulled into a dock by a rope attached to the bow of the boat and passing through a pulley on the dock that is 1 m higher than the bow of the boat. If the rope is pulled in at rate of 0.8 m/s, how fast does the boat approach the dock when it is 10 m from the dock?

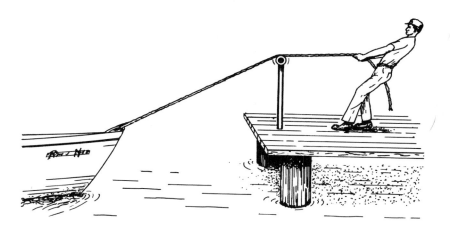

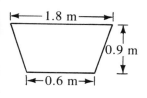

19. A water trough is 6 m long and has a cross-section in the shape of an isosceles trapezoid with dimensions as shown in the diagram. Water is being pumped into the trough at a rate of 0.5 m³/min. How fast is the water level rising when it is 0.5 m deep?

20. Use Newton's method to find the root of the equation $x^3 = 2x + 5$ correct to six decimal places.

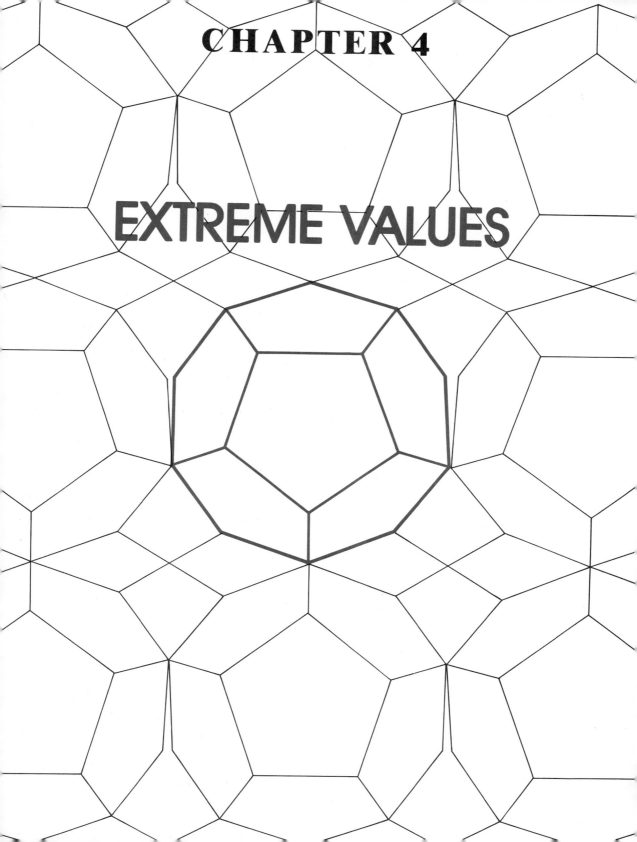

CHAPTER 4

EXTREME VALUES

REVIEW AND PREVIEW TO
CHAPTER 4

Intervals

There are certain sets of real numbers, called **intervals**, that occur frequently in calculus and correspond geometrically to line segments. For example, if $a < b$, the **open interval** from a to b consists of all numbers between a and b and is denoted by the symbol (a, b). Using set-builder notation, we can write

$$(a, b) = \{x \mid a < x < b\}$$

Notice that the endpoints of the interval—namely, a and b—are excluded. This is indicated by the parentheses ( ) and the open circles in the figure. The **closed interval** from a to b is the set

$$[a, b] = \{x \mid a \leq x \leq b\}$$

Here, the endpoints of the interval are included. This is indicated by the square brackets [ ] and the solid circles in the figure.

The open interval (a, b) The closed interval $[a, b]$

We also need to consider infinite intervals such as

$$(a, \infty) = \{x \mid x > a\}$$

This does not mean that ∞ ("infinity") is a number. The notation (a, ∞) stands for the set of all numbers that are greater than a, so the symbol ∞ simply indicates that the interval extends indefinitely far in the positive direction.

The following table lists the nine possible types of intervals. When these intervals are discussed, it will always be assumed that $a < b$.

Notation	Set Description	Picture
(a, b)	$\{x \mid a < x < b\}$	
$[a, b]$	$\{x \mid a \leqslant x \leqslant b\}$	
$[a, b)$	$\{x \mid a \leqslant x < b\}$	
$(a, b]$	$\{x \mid a < x \leqslant b\}$	
(a, ∞)	$\{x \mid x > a\}$	
$[a, \infty)$	$\{x \mid x \geqslant a\}$	
$(-\infty, b)$	$\{x \mid x < b\}$	
$(-\infty, b]$	$\{x \mid x \leqslant b\}$	
$(-\infty, \infty)$	R (set of all real numbers)	

Example Express the following intervals in terms of inequalities and graph the intervals:

(a) $\left[\frac{1}{2}, 4\right]$, (b) $[-2, 1)$, (c) $(-4, \infty)$.

Solution (a) $\left[\frac{1}{2}, 4\right] = \{x \mid \frac{1}{2} \leqslant x \leqslant 4\}$

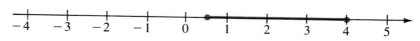

(b) $[-2, 1) = \{x \mid -2 \leqslant x < 1\}$

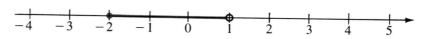

(c) $(-4, \infty) = \{x \mid x > -4\}$

EXERCISE 1

1. Express the interval in terms of inequalities and graph the interval.
   (a) $(-2, 6)$ (b) $[-3, -2)$
   (c) $(1, 4]$ (d) $[-2, 1.5]$
   (e) $[3, \infty)$ (f) $(-\infty, 2)$
   (g) $(-\infty, 1]$ (h) $\left(-\frac{3}{2}, \infty\right)$

2. Express the inequality in interval notation and graph the corresponding interval.
   (a) $x < 2$ (b) $0 < x < 3$
   (c) $-1 \leqslant x < 2$ (d) $x > 1$
   (e) $-1 \leqslant x \leqslant 3$ (f) $x \leqslant -1$

Inequalities

Rules for Inequalities

1.   If $a < b$, then $a + c < b + c$.
2.   If $a < b$ and $c < d$, then $a + c < b + d$.
3.   If $a < b$ and $c > 0$, then $ac < bc$.
4.   If $a < b$ and $c < 0$, then $ac > bc$.
5.   If $0 < a < b$, then $\dfrac{1}{a} > \dfrac{1}{b}$.

These rules also apply to any of the other order relations $>$, $\leq$, and $\geq$. Rule 1 says that we can add (or subtract) any number to (or from) both sides of an inequality and Rule 2 says that two inequalities can be added. However, we have to be careful with multiplication. Rule 3 says that we can multiply (or divide) both sides of an inequality by a *positive* number, but Rule 4 says that *if we multiply both sides of an inequality by a negative number, then we reverse the direction of the inequality*. For example, if we take the inequality $3 < 5$ and multiply by 2, we get $6 < 10$, but if we multiply by -2, we get $-6 > -10$. Finally, Rule 5 says that if we take reciprocals, then we reverse the direction of an inequality (provided the numbers are positive).

Example 1   Solve the inequality $1 + x < 6x - 4$.

Solution

$$1 + x < 6x - 4$$
$$5 + x < 6x \qquad \text{(Rule 1, } c = 4)$$
$$5 < 5x \qquad \text{(Rule 1, } c = -x)$$
$$1 < x \qquad \text{(Rule 3, } c = \tfrac{1}{5})$$

In interval notation, the solution of the inequality is $(1, \infty)$.

Example 2   Solve $x^2 + 2x > 0$.

Solution 1   For a quadratic inequality we first factor:

$$x^2 + 2x = x(x + 2)$$

The product of two factors is positive when both factors are positive or both are negative, so there are two cases to consider.

TAKE CASES

Case 1: *both positive*

$$x > 0 \quad \text{and} \quad x + 2 > 0$$
$$x > 0 \quad \text{and} \quad x > -2$$

The intersection of these two intervals is $x > 0$.

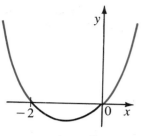

$y = x(x + 2)$
$y > 0$ when
$x < -2$ or $x > 0$

Case 2: *both negative.*

$$x < 0 \quad \text{and} \quad x + 2 < 0$$
$$x < 0 \quad \text{and} \quad x < -2$$

The intersection of these two intervals is $x < -2$.
Thus, the solution set of the given inequality is

$$\{x \mid x > 0 \text{ or } x < -2\} = (-\infty, -2) \cup (0, \infty)$$

Solution 2 We know that the corresponding equation $x(x + 2) = 0$ has the solutions 0 and -2. These numbers divide the number line into three intervals

$$(\infty, -2) \qquad (-2, 0) \qquad (0, \infty)$$

On each of these intervals we determine the signs of the factors. For instance,

$$x < -2 \implies x + 2 < 0$$

Then we record these signs in the following chart and deduce the sign of the product.

Interval	x	$x + 2$	$x(x + 2)$
$x < -2$	−	−	+
$-2 < x < 0$	−	+	−
$x > 0$	+	+	+

We read from the chart that $x(x + 2)$ is positive when $x < -2$ or $x > 0$. Thus, the solution of the given inequality is

$$\{x \mid x > 0 \text{ or } x < -2\} = (-\infty, -2) \cup (0, \infty)$$

When more than two factors are involved in an inequality, the method of Solution 1 of Example 2 is cumbersome, so we use the chart method.

Example 3 (a) Solve the inequality $(x + 1)(x - 2)(x - 3) < 0$.
(b) Solve the inequality $(x + 1)(x - 2)(x - 3) > 0$.

Solution We combine parts (a) and (b) by making a chart as in Solution 2 of Example 2:

Interval	$x + 1$	$x - 2$	$x - 3$	$(x + 1)(x - 2)(x - 3)$
$x < -1$	−	−	−	−
$-1 < x < 2$	+	−	−	+
$2 < x < 3$	+	+	−	−
$x > 3$	+	+	+	+

We read from the chart that $(x + 1)(x - 2)(x - 3)$ is negative when $x < -1$ or $2 < x < 3$. Thus, the solution of the inequality $(x + 1)(x - 2)(x - 3) < 0$ is

$$\{x \mid x < -1 \text{ or } 2 < x < 3\} = (-\infty, -1) \cup (2, 3)$$

and is shown in the following figure.

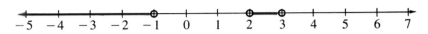

Similarly, the solution of the inequality $(x + 1)(x - 2)(x - 3) > 0$ is

$$\{x \mid -1 < x < 2 \text{ or } x > 3\} = (-1, 2) \cup (3, \infty)$$

Another method for obtaining the information in the charts in Examples 2 and 3 is to use test values. For instance in Example 3, if we use the test value $x = 1$ for the interval $(-1, 2)$, then substitution in $(x + 1)(x - 2)(x - 3)$ gives

$$(2)(-1)(-2) = 4$$

or, schematically,

$$(+)(-)(-) = +$$

The function $f(x) = (x + 1)(x - 2)(x - 3)$ does not change sign within any of the intervals, so we conclude that it is positive on the interval $(-1, 2)$.

EXERCISE 2

1. Solve the inequality.
   (a) $3x + 7 > 0$ (b) $18 - 4x < 0$
   (c) $17 - 2x \geqslant 13$ (d) $2x + 1 < 5x - 11$
   (e) $2x - 1 < 19$ (f) $x^2 - 7x + 6 > 0$
   (g) $12 - x - x^2 > 0$ (h) $x^2 < 3x$
   (i) $x^2 - 9 > 0$ (j) $x^2 \leqslant 5$
   (k) $(x + 1)(2x + 1)(x - 6) > 0$ (l) $x^3 + 3x^2 - 10x < 0$
   (m) $x^3 + 3x^2 - 4 < 0$ (n) $x^3 + 2x^2 - 9x - 18 > 0$
   (o) $x^3 - 8 \geqslant 0$ (p) $x^9 + x > 0$

2. Solve the inequality.
   (a) $\dfrac{2x + 1}{x^2 + 1} > 0$ (b) $\dfrac{x + 2}{x - 3} > 0$
   (c) $\dfrac{x^2 + x}{(x - 1)^3} < 0$ (d) $\dfrac{5x}{(x^2 - 1)^2} < 0$

INTRODUCTION

In this chapter, we use our knowledge of derivatives to find maximum and minimum values of functions. Then we apply this skill to practical problems that require us to maximize an area or a volume or to minimize a cost or, in general, to find the best possible outcome of a situation.

4.1 INCREASING AND DECREASING FUNCTIONS

Interval notation was introduced in the Review and Preview to this chapter.

One of the most useful things to know about a function is where its graph rises and where it falls. The graph of f, shown in the figure below, falls from A to B, rises from B to C, and falls again from C to D. We say that f is *decreasing* on the interval $(1, 3)$, *increasing* on $(3, 6)$, and decreasing on $(6, 8)$. Notice that for any two numbers x_1 and x_2 between 3 and 6 with $x_1 < x_2$, we have $f(x_1) < f(x_2)$.

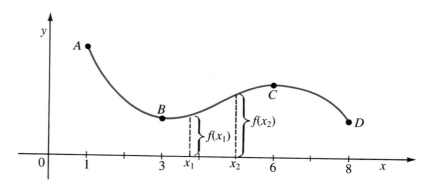

In general, a function f is called **increasing on an interval I** if

$$f(x_1) < f(x_2) \qquad \text{whenever } x_1 < x_2 \text{ in I}$$

It is called **decreasing on I** if

$$f(x_1) > f(x_2) \qquad \text{whenever } x_1 < x_2 \text{ in I}$$

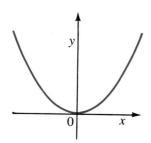

For instance, you can see from the graph of the function $f(x) = x^2$ that f is decreasing on $(-\infty, 0)$ and increasing on $(0, \infty)$.

To see how the derivative of a function can tell us where a function is increasing or decreasing, look at the following diagram. When $f'(x) > 0$, the tangents have positive slope; that is, the tangents slope upward to the right. Thus, it appears that a positive derivative indicates an increasing function. When $f'(x) < 0$, the tangents slope downward to the right and f is decreasing. These facts are proved in more advanced courses.

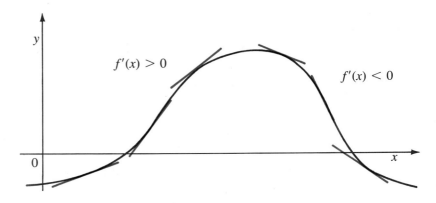

Test for Increasing or Decreasing Functions

1. If $f'(x) > 0$ for all x in an interval I, then f is increasing on I.
2. If $f'(x) < 0$ for all x in I, then f is decreasing on I.

Example 1   Find the intervals on which the function $f(x) = 1 - 5x + 4x^2$ is increasing and decreasing.

Solution   First we find the derivative:

$$f'(x) = -5 + 8x$$

The function f will be increasing when

$$-5 + 8x > 0$$
$$8x > 5$$
$$x > \tfrac{5}{8}$$

Thus, f is increasing on the interval $\left(\tfrac{5}{8}, \infty\right)$. Similarly,

$$-5 + 8x < 0 \quad \text{when} \quad x < \tfrac{5}{8}$$

So f is decreasing on the interval $\left(-\infty, \tfrac{5}{8}\right)$.

Since the function in Example 1 is quadratic, its graph is a parabola and is shown in the figure.

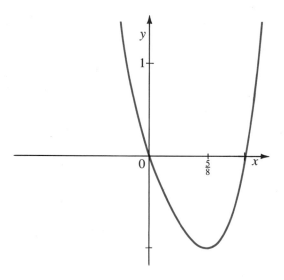

Example 2 Where is the function $y = x^3 + 6x^2 + 9x + 2$ increasing?

Solution We compute y' and factor it:

$$y' = 3x^2 + 12x + 9$$
$$= 3(x^2 + 4x + 3)$$
$$= 3(x + 1)(x + 3)$$

The function will be increasing when $y' > 0$, so we have to solve the quadratic inequality

$$(x + 1)(x + 3) > 0$$

We observe that the product is 0 when $x = -1$ or -3. These numbers divide the line into three intervals $(-\infty, -3)$, $(-3, -1)$, and $(-1, \infty)$, on each of which the product keeps a constant sign as in the following chart. The last column of the chart gives the conclusion based on the Test for Increasing and Decreasing Functions.

Interval	$x + 1$	$x + 3$	$f'(x)$	f
$x < -3$	$-$	$-$	$+$	increasing on $(-\infty, -3)$
$-3 < x < -1$	$-$	$+$	$-$	decreasing on $(-3, -1)$
$x > -1$	$+$	$+$	$+$	increasing on $(-1, \infty)$

Another method of solving the quadratic inequality in Example 2 is to take cases as in Solution 1 of Example 2 in the Review and Preview to this chapter. A third method would be to graph the parabola $y = (x + 1)(x + 3)$ and observe that it lies above the x-axis when $x < -3$ or $x > -1$. For more complicated functions, however, the chart method is usually simplest, as in the following example.

Example 3   Find the intervals of increase and decrease for the function
$$g(x) = x^4 - 4x^3 - 8x^2 - 1.$$

Solution
$$\begin{aligned} g'(x) &= 4x^3 - 12x^2 - 16x \\ &= 4x(x^2 - 3x - 4) \\ &= 4x(x + 1)(x - 4) \end{aligned}$$

This expression is 0 when $x = 0, -1$, and 4. As in Example 2, we indicate the signs of the factors and the conclusion about g in a chart.

Interval	$4x$	$x + 1$	$x - 4$	$g'(x)$	g
$x < -1$	$-$	$-$	$-$	$-$	decreasing on $(-\infty, -1)$
$-1 < x < 0$	$-$	$+$	$-$	$+$	increasing on $(-1, 0)$
$0 < x < 4$	$+$	$+$	$-$	$-$	decreasing on $(0, 4)$
$x > 4$	$+$	$+$	$+$	$+$	increasing on $(4, \infty)$

EXERCISE 4.1

A 1. State the intervals of increase or decrease for the functions whose graphs are given.

(a)
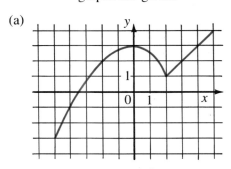

(b)
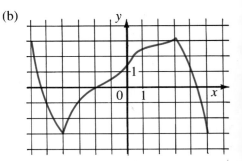

B 2. Find the intervals on which the following functions are increasing.
(a) $f(x) = 12 + x - x^2$ (b) $f(x) = x^4$
(c) $g(x) = x^3 - 3x + 2$ (d) $g(x) = 2x^3 - 3x^2$
(e) $y = 3x^4 + 4x^3 - 12x^2 + 7$ (f) $y = x^5 + 8x^3 + x$

3. Find the intervals on which the following functions are decreasing.
(a) $f(x) = x^2 + x^3$
(b) $g(x) = 2x^3 - 3x^2 - 36x + 62$
(c) $h(x) = (1 - x^2)^2$
(d) $F(x) = 4x + x^4$

4. Find the intervals of increase and decrease for the following functions.

(a) $f(x) = 3x^2 - 18x + 1$

(b) $f(x) = 2x^3 - 9x^2 - 60x + 82$

(c) $g(x) = x^4 - 2x^2 + 16$

(d) $g(x) = 3x^4 - 16x^3 + 6x^2 + 72x + 8$

(e) $h(x) = x^3(x - 1)^4$

(f) $h(x) = \dfrac{x - 1}{x + 1}$

(g) $y = x\sqrt{4 - x}$

(h) $y = (x^2 - 9)^{\frac{2}{3}}$

C **5.** Where is the function $y = 12x^5 + 15x^4 - 20x^3 + 27$ decreasing?

4.2 MAXIMUM AND MINIMUM VALUES

The graph of a function f is shown. Notice that the highest point on the graph is $(7, 6)$ and so the largest value taken on by the function is $f(7) = 6$. We say that f has an *absolute maximum* at 7 and the maximum value is $f(7) = 6$. The lowest point on the graph is $(2, 1)$, so the smallest value of the function is $f(2) = 1$. We say that f has an *absolute minimum* at 2 and the minimum value is $f(2) = 1$.

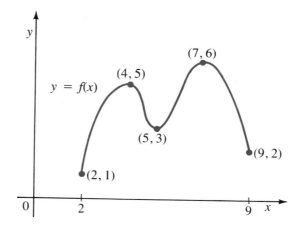

In general, a function f has an **absolute maximum** at c if $f(c) \geqslant f(x)$ for all x in the domain of f, and the number $f(c)$ is called the **maximum value** of f. The function has an **absolute minimum** at c if $f(c) \leqslant f(x)$ for all x in the domain, and the number $f(c)$ is called the **minimum value** of f. The **extreme values** of f are the maximum and minimum values.

Notice that if we restrict our attention to the interval $(2, 5)$, then the largest value is $f(4) = 5$. For that reason, we say that $f(4) = 5$ is a *local maximum value* of f. Likewise $f(5) = 3$ is called a *local minimum value* because it is the smallest value of f if we consider values of x that are near 5 [for instance, values of x in the interval $(4, 7)$].

In general, a function f has a **local maximum** (also called a **relative maximum**) at c if $f(c) \geqslant f(x)$ when x is close to c (on both sides of c). Similarly, f has a **local minimum** (or **relative minimum**) at c if $f(c) \leqslant f(x)$ when x is close to c.

Example 1   If $f(x) = x^2$, then $f(x) \geqslant f(0)$ for all x since $x^2 \geqslant 0$. So $f(0) = 0$ is the absolute (and local) minimum value. But this function has no maximum value.

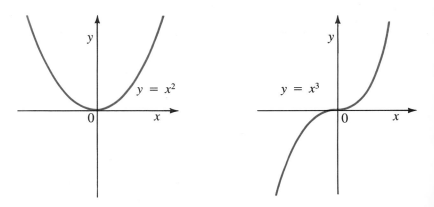

Example 2   We see from the graph of the function $f(x) = x^3$ that it has no absolute, or local, maximum or minimum value.

Example 3   The function $f(x) = 1 - x^2$, $0 \leqslant x < 1$, has maximum value $f(0) = 1$, but it has no minimum value. It takes on values very close to 0, but it never actually attains the value 0.

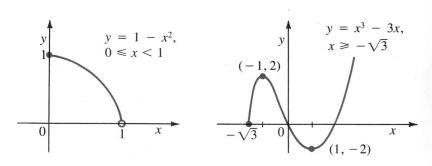

Example 4 The graph of the function

$$f(x) = x^3 - 3x, \qquad x \geq -\sqrt{3}$$

shows the following:

$f(-1) = 2$ is a local maximum

$f(1) = -2$ is a local and absolute minimum

f has no absolute maximum

We see from these examples that a function need not possess maximum and minimum values. But it can be proved that any continuous function defined on a closed interval $[a, b]$ has both an absolute maximum value and an absolute minimum value.

If we do not already know what the graph of a function looks like, how can we find the maximum and minimum values? Looking at the graph of f in the figure, we see that f has local maximum values when $x = a$, c, and e. It appears that the tangent lines at $(a, f(a))$ and $(c, f(c))$ are horizontal and so the slopes are $f'(a) = 0$ and $f'(c) = 0$. At $(e, f(e))$ there is no tangent line (since there is a corner) and so $f'(e)$ does not exist; that is, f is not differentiable at e.

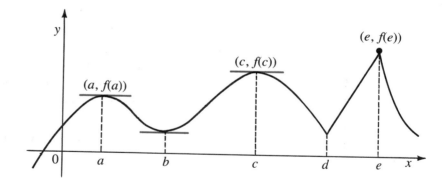

Similarly, it appears that f has a local minimum value at b, where $f'(b) = 0$, and at d, where $f'(d)$ does not exist. These facts can be proved generally and are known as Fermat's Theorem after the French mathematician Pierre Fermat (1601–1665).

See the biography of Fermat at the end of this chapter

Fermat's Theorem

If f has a local maximum or minimum at c, then either $f'(c) = 0$ or $f'(c)$ does not exist.

We must be careful when using Fermat's Theorem. If $f'(c) = 0$, it does not automatically follow that f has a local maximum or minimum at c. For instance, the function $f(x) = x^3$ considered in Example 2 has no maximum and yet $f'(x) = 3x^2$, so $f'(0) = 0$. The significance of the derivative being 0 is just that the tangent is horizontal.

Fermat's Theorem does say that we should at least start looking for extreme values at the numbers c for which $f'(c) = 0$ or $f'(c)$ does not exist. These numbers are called *critical numbers*.

A **critical number** of a function is a number c in the domain of f such that either $f'(c) = 0$ or $f'(c)$ does not exist.

Example 5 Find the critical numbers of the following functions.

(a) $f(x) = x^3 + 6x^2 + 9x + 2$ (b) $f(x) = |x|$

Solution (a) First we find the derivative and factor it:

$$f'(x) = 3x^2 + 12x + 9$$
$$= 3(x^2 + 4x + 3)$$
$$= 3(x + 1)(x + 3)$$

The derivative exists for all values of x, so the only critical numbers occur when $f'(x) = 0$, that is, when

$$3(x + 1)(x + 3) = 0$$
$$x = -1 \quad \text{or} \quad x = -3$$

Therefore the critical numbers are -1 and -3.

(b) We know from Example 7 in Section 2.1 that the absolute value function is not differentiable at 0; that is, $f'(0)$ does not exist. Therefore 0 is a critical number.

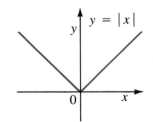

Since

$$f(x) = |x| = \begin{cases} x & \text{if } x \geq 0 \\ -x & \text{if } x < 0 \end{cases}$$

we have

$$f'(x) = \begin{cases} 1 & \text{if } x > 0 \\ -1 & \text{if } x < 0 \end{cases}$$

Thus, $f'(x)$ is never 0. The only critical number is 0.

The absolute maximum or minimum of a continuous function on a closed interval is either a local maximum or minimum, in which case it occurs at a critical number, or it occurs at an endpoint of the interval. Therefore, we have the following.

> ### Procedure for Finding the Absolute Maximum and Minimum Values of a Continuous Function on a Closed Interval [a, b].
> 1. Find the values of f at the critical numbers of f in (a, b).
> 2. Find the values of f at the endpoints; that is, evaluate $f(a)$ and $f(b)$.
> 3. The largest of the values from steps 1 and 2 is the absolute maximum value; the smallest of these values is the absolute minimum value.

Example 6   Find the absolute maximum and minimum values of the function

$$f(x) = x^3 + 6x^2 + 9x + 2, \quad -3.5 \leqslant x \leqslant 1$$

Solution   From Example 5 we know that the critical numbers of f are -1 and -3. (Notice that each of these critical numbers lies in the interval $[-3.5, 1]$.) The values of f at these numbers are

$$f(-1) = -2 \qquad f(-3) = 2$$

The values of f at the endpoints of the interval are

$$f(-3.5) = 1.125 \qquad f(1) = 18$$

Comparing these four numbers, we see that the absolute maximum value is $f(1) = 18$ and the absolute minimum value is $f(-1) = -2$.

Note that in this example the absolute maximum occurs at an endpoint, whereas the absolute minimum occurs at a critical number. (See the following graph of f).

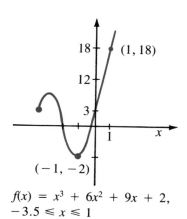

$$f(x) = x^3 + 6x^2 + 9x + 2,$$
$$-3.5 \leqslant x \leqslant 1$$

Example 7   Find the absolute maximum and minimum values of the function

$$g(x) = x^{\frac{2}{3}}(5 + x), \qquad -5 \leq x \leq 1$$

Solution   We could differentiate this function using the Product Rule, but it is perhaps simpler to rewrite the function first.

$$g(x) = x^{\frac{2}{3}}(5 + x) = 5x^{\frac{2}{3}} + x^{\frac{5}{3}}$$

$$g'(x) = \tfrac{10}{3}x^{-\frac{1}{3}} + \tfrac{5}{3}x^{\frac{2}{3}} = \frac{10 + 5x}{3x^{\frac{1}{3}}} = \frac{5(2 + x)}{3\sqrt[3]{x}}$$

This expression shows that $g'(x) = 0$ when $2 + x = 0$, that is, $x = -2$, and $g'(x)$ does not exist when $x = 0$. So the critical numbers are -2 and 0, and

$$g(0) = 0$$
$$g(-2) = (-2)^{\frac{2}{3}}(3) = 3(4^{\frac{1}{3}}) \doteq 4.8$$

At the endpoints of the given interval $[-5, 1]$ we have

$$g(-5) = 0 \qquad\qquad g(1) = 6$$

We compare these values and see that the absolute maximum value is $g(1) = 6$ and the absolute minimum is $g(0) = g(-5) = 0$.

EXERCISE 4.2

A **1.**   For the functions whose graphs are given, state
   (a)   the absolute maximum value,
   (b)   the absolute minimum value,
   (c)   the local maximum values,
   (d)   the local minimum values.

(i)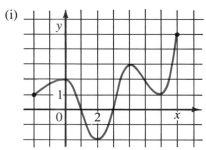

(ii)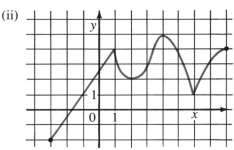

B **2.** Sketch the graph of each function and use it to state the absolute and local maximum and minimum values of the function.

(a) $f(x) = 3x - 1, x > -1$ (b) $g(x) = 3x - 1, x \geqslant -1$

(c) $f(x) = x^2 + 1$ (d) $y = x^2 + 1, -1 < x < 2$

(e) $y = x^2 + 1, -1 \leqslant x \leqslant 2$ (f) $y = 2 - x^3$

(g) $y = |x - 2| - 1$ (h) $f(x) = \begin{cases} 2 - x & \text{if } x < 1 \\ x & \text{if } x \geqslant 1 \end{cases}$

3. Find the critical numbers of the given functions.

(a) $f(x) = 17 - 6x + 12x^2$ (b) $f(x) = x^3 - 3x + 2$

(c) $g(x) = x^4 - 4x^3 - 8x^2 - 1$

(d) $g(x) = 3x^4 - 16x^3 + 6x^2 + 72x + 8$

(e) $y = 2x^3 + 3x^2 - 6x + 3$ (f) $y = x^3 + x^2 + x + 1$

(g) $y = |x + 6|$ (h) $y = \sqrt[3]{x}$

(i) $y = x - \sqrt{x}$ (j) $y = x\sqrt{x - 1}$

(k) $y = \dfrac{t}{t + 1}$ (l) $y = \dfrac{t}{t^2 + 1}$

4. Find the absolute maximum value and absolute minimum value of the function.

(a) $f(x) = 2x^2 - 8x + 1, 0 \leqslant x \leqslant 3$

(b) $f(x) = 3 + 2(x + 1)^2, -3 \leqslant x \leqslant 2$

(c) $f(x) = 2x^3 - 3x^2, -2 \leqslant x \leqslant 2$

(d) $f(x) = 2x^3 - 3x^2 - 36x + 62, -3 \leqslant x \leqslant 4$

(e) $f(x) = x^4 - 2x^2 + 16, -3 \leqslant x \leqslant 2$

(f) $f(x) = x^5 + 3x^3 + x, -1 \leqslant x \leqslant 2$

(g) $g(x) = x^2 + \dfrac{16}{x}, 1 \leqslant x \leqslant 4$

(h) $f(x) = 3x^{\frac{2}{3}} - 2x, 1 \leqslant x \leqslant 3$

(i) $f(x) = (x^2 - 9)^{\frac{2}{3}}, -6 \leqslant x \leqslant 6$

(j) $f(x) = |2x - 1| - 1, 0 \leqslant x \leqslant 2$

C **5.** Show that the function $y = x^{21} + x^{11} + 13x$ does not have a local maximum or a local minimum.

6. Find the value of k if the function $y = x^2 + kx + 72$ has a local minimum at $x = 4$.

7. Find the values of a and b if the function $y = 2x^3 + ax^2 + bx + 36$ has a local maximum when $x = -4$ and a local minimum when $x = 5$.

8. (a) Use Newton's method to find the critical numbers of the function $f(x) = 2x^5 - 5x^2 - 20x + 12$ correct to three decimal places.

(b) Find the absolute minimum value of the function $f(x) = 2x^5 - 5x^2 - 20x + 12, -1 \leqslant x \leqslant 2$, correct to two decimal places.

4.3   THE FIRST DERIVATIVE TEST

If f has a local maximum or minimum at c, then c must be a critical number of f (Fermat's Theorem), but not all critical numbers give rise to a maximum or minimum. For instance, recall that 0 is a critical number of the function $y = x^3$ but this function has no maximum or minimum. Therefore we need a test that will tell us whether or not a function has a maximum or minimum at a critical number.

One way of resolving the question is suggested by the graph in the figure below. If f is increasing just to the left of a critical number c and decreasing just to the right of c, then f has a local maximum at c. Similarly, if f is decreasing just to the left of c and increasing just to the right, then f has a local minimum at c.

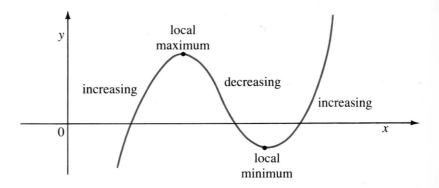

We know from Section 4.1 that f is increasing when $f'(x) > 0$ and decreasing when $f'(x) < 0$. Therefore we have the following test.

First Derivative Test

Let c be a critical number of a continuous function f.
1. If $f'(x)$ changes from positive to negative at c, then f has a local maximum at c.
2. If $f'(x)$ changes from negative to positive at c, then f has a local minimum at c.
3. If $f'(x)$ does not change sign at c, then f has no maximum or minimum at c.

The sketches in the following table illustrate how the First Derivative Test works.

Sign of $f'(x)$ to the left of c	Sign of $f'(x)$ to the right of c	Graph	$f(c)$
+	−		local maximum
−	+		local minimum
+	+		neither
−	−		neither

Example 1   Find the local maximum and minimum values of $f(x) = x^3 - 3x + 1$.

Solution   First we find the critical numbers. The derivative is

$$f'(x) = 3x^2 - 3 = 3(x^2 - 1)$$

Since $f'(x) = 0$ when $x^2 = 1$, the critical numbers are $x = \pm 1$.
Next we analyze the sign of the derivative. To see where it is positive or negative, we solve the following inequalities.

$$\sqrt{x^2} = |x|$$

$$
\begin{array}{ll}
f'(x) > 0 & f'(x) < 0 \\
x^2 - 1 > 0 & x^2 - 1 < 0 \\
x^2 > 1 & x^2 < 1 \\
|x| > 1 & |x| < 1 \\
x < -1 \text{ or } x > 1 & -1 < x < 1
\end{array}
$$

Therefore $f'(x)$ changes sign from positive to negative at -1 and from negative to positive at 1. By the First Derivative Test it follows that

$$
\begin{array}{ll}
f(-1) = 3 & \text{is a local maximum} \\
f(1) = -1 & \text{is a local minimum}
\end{array}
$$

Another method of solving Example 1 is to factor $x^2 - 1$ as $(x - 1)(x + 1)$ and use a chart.

Example 2   Find the local maximum and minimum values of
$g(x) = x^4 - 4x^3 - 8x^2 - 1$ and use this information to sketch the
graph of g.

Solution   In Example 3 in Section 4.1 we found that $g'(x) = 4x(x + 1)(x - 4)$,
so the critical numbers are 0, -1, and 4. We reproduce the chart that
gave the sign of $g'(x)$:

Interval	$4x$	$x + 1$	$x - 4$	$g'(x)$	g
$x < -1$	$-$	$-$	$-$	$-$	decreasing on $(-\infty, -1)$
$-1 < x < 0$	$-$	$+$	$-$	$+$	increasing on $(-1, 0)$
$0 < x < 4$	$+$	$+$	$-$	$-$	decreasing on $(0, 4)$
$x > 4$	$+$	$+$	$+$	$+$	increasing on $(4, \infty)$

From the chart we see immediately that $g'(x)$ changes from negative
to positive at -1, from positive to negative at 0, and from negative
to positive at 4. Therefore, by the First Derivative Test,

$$g(-1) = -4 \quad \text{is a local minimum}$$
$$g(0) = -1 \quad \text{is a local maximum}$$
$$g(4) = -129 \quad \text{is a local minimum}$$

Using this information we sketch the graph of g.

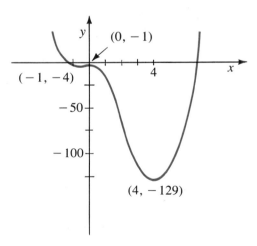

Example 3   Find the critical numbers, intervals of increase and decrease, and local
maximum and minimum values of the function $f(x) = 2x - 3x^{\frac{2}{3}}$.

Solution   The derivative is

$$f'(x) = 2 - 2x^{-\frac{1}{3}} = \frac{2(\sqrt[3]{x} - 1)}{\sqrt[3]{x}}$$

which is not defined when $x = 0$. (But note that $f(x)$ is defined everywhere.) Also $f'(x) = 0$ when $x = 1$. So the critical numbers are 0 and 1.

The intervals of increase and decrease are obtained in the following chart.

Interval	$\sqrt[3]{x}$	$\sqrt[3]{x} - 1$	$f'(x)$	f
$x < 0$	$-$	$-$	$+$	increasing on $(-\infty, 0)$
$0 < x < 1$	$+$	$-$	$-$	decreasing on $(0, 1)$
$x > 1$	$+$	$+$	$+$	increasing on $(1, \infty)$

From the chart we see that the derivative changes from positive to negative at 0 and from negative to positive at 1. Thus, by the First Derivative Test,

$$f(0) = 0 \quad \text{is a local maximum}$$
$$f(1) = -1 \quad \text{is a local minimum}$$

In certain circumstances, the First Derivative Test can be used to find an *absolute* maximum or minimum.

First Derivative Test for Absolute Extreme Values

Let c be a critical number of a continuous function f defined on an interval.
1. If $f'(x)$ is positive for all $x < c$ and $f'(x)$ is negative for all $x > c$, then $f(c)$ is the absolute maximum value.
2. If $f'(x)$ is negative for all $x < c$ and $f'(x)$ is positive for all $x > c$, then $f(c)$ is the absolute minimum value.

Example 4   Find the absolute minimum value of the function
$$f(x) = x + \frac{1}{x}, \, x > 0.$$

Solution   The derivative is

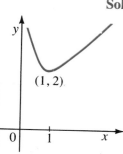

(1, 2)

$$f'(x) = 1 - \frac{1}{x^2} = \frac{x^2 - 1}{x^2}$$

Thus $f'(x) = 0$ when $x^2 = 1$, that is, $x = 1$ (since $x > 0$). Also $f'(x) > 0$ when $x^2 > 1$, that is, $x > 1$. Similarly, $f'(x) < 0$ when $0 < x < 1$.

Thus, by the First Derivative Test, the absolute minimum value of f is $f(1) = 2$. The graph of f illustrates this fact.

EXERCISE 4.3

B 1. Find the local maximum and minimum values of f.
  (a) $f(x) = 3x^2 - 4x + 13$ (b) $f(x) = x^3 - 12x - 5$
  (c) $f(x) = 2 + 5x - x^5$ (d) $f(x) = x^4 - x^3$

2. Find the critical numbers, intervals of increase and decrease, and local maximum values of the function. Then use this information to sketch the graph of f.
  (a) $f(x) = 2 + 6x - 6x^2$
  (b) $f(x) = x^3 - 9x^2 + 24x - 10$
  (c) $g(x) = 1 + 3x^2 - 2x^3$
  (d) $g(x) = 3x^4 - 16x^3 + 18x^2 + 1$
  (e) $h(x) = x^4 - 8x^2 + 6$
  (f) $h(x) = 3x^5 - 5x^3$

3. Find the local maximum and minimum values of f.

  (a) $f(x) = 2x^{\frac{2}{3}}(3 - 4x^{\frac{1}{3}})$ (b) $f(x) = \dfrac{x^2}{x^2 - 1}$

  (c) $f(x) = x\sqrt{4 - x}$ (d) $f(x) = x\sqrt{1 - x^2}$

4. Find the absolute maximum or minimum value of the function.

  (a) $f(x) = 27 + x - x^2$ (b) $f(x) = 3 - \dfrac{1}{\sqrt{x^2 + 1}}$

  (c) $g(x) = \dfrac{x^2 - 1}{x^2 + 1}$ (d) $g(x) = \dfrac{x^2 - x + 1}{x^2 + 1}, \ x \geqslant 0$

C 5. Sketch the graph of a function f that satisfies all of the following conditions.
  (a) $f(2) = 3, f(5) = 6$
  (b) $f'(2) = f'(5) = 0$
  (c) $f'(x) \geqslant 0$ for $x < 5$
  (d) $f'(x) < 0$ for $x > 5$

6. Find the local maximum and minimum values of the function f defined by
$$f(x) = \begin{cases} -x & \text{if } x < 0 \\ 2x^3 - 15x^2 + 36x & \text{if } 0 \leqslant x \leqslant 4 \\ 216 - x & \text{if } x > 4 \end{cases}$$

PROBLEMS PLUS

Find the absolute maximum value of the function
$$f(x) = \frac{1}{1 + |x|} + \frac{1}{1 + |x - 2|}$$

4.4 APPLIED MAXIMUM AND MINIMUM PROBLEMS

One of the most important applications of derivatives occurs in the solution of "optimization" problems, in which a quantity must be maximized or minimized. In this section and the next, we solve such problems as maximizing areas, volumes, and profits, and minimizing distances, times, and costs.

In solving these problems, the first step is to express the problem in mathematical language by setting up the function that is to be maximized or minimized. Then we use the methods of this chapter to find the extreme value.

Example 1   Find two positive numbers whose product is 10 000 and whose sum is a minimum.

Solution   Let x be the first number and y the second number. We wish to minimize the sum

INTRODUCE NOTATION

$$S = x + y$$

but we first express S in terms of just one variable. To eliminate one of the variables we use the given condition that the product of the numbers is 10 000:

$$xy = 10\ 000$$

Solving for y, we get

$$y = \frac{10\ 000}{x}$$

and, substituting into the equation for S, we have

$$S = x + \frac{10\ 000}{x}, x > 0$$

$$\frac{dS}{dx} = 1 - \frac{10\ 000}{x^2} = \frac{x^2 - 10\ 000}{x^2}$$

To find the critical numbers, we equate the derivative to 0:

$$\frac{x^2 - 10\ 000}{x^2} = 0$$

$$x^2 = 10\ 000$$

$$x = 100 \qquad (\text{since } x > 0)$$

Now we verify that $x = 100$ gives a minimum value for S. Since

$$\frac{dS}{dx} < 0 \text{ for } 0 < x < 100 \quad \text{and} \quad \frac{dS}{dx} > 0 \text{ for } x > 100$$

S has an absolute minimum at $x = 100$ by the First Derivative Test for Absolute Extreme Values.

When $x = 100$, we have $y = \dfrac{10\ 000}{100} = 100$. Therefore the two

numbers are both 100.

Example 2 If 2700 cm² of material is available to make a box with a square base and open top, find the largest possible volume of the box.

Solution

DRAW A DIAGRAM

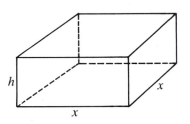

INTRODUCE NOTATION

Let x be the length of the base of the box and h its height, in centimetres. The quantity to be maximized is the volume of the box:

$$V = x^2h$$

We eliminate h by finding a relationship between x and h. To do this, we use the fact that the area of the available material is 2700 cm². Since the box is open at the top, its surface area is given by

$$\text{(area of base)} + \text{(area of four sides)} = 2700$$
$$x^2 + 4xh = 2700$$

Solving for h, we get

$$h = \frac{2700 - x^2}{4x}$$

This allows us to express V as a function of x:

$$V = x^2h = x^2\left(\frac{2700 - x^2}{4x}\right) = x\left(\frac{2700 - x^2}{4}\right)$$
$$V = 675x - \tfrac{1}{4}x^3$$

It is important to identify the domain of this function. Since x represents the base, we have $x \geqslant 0$. Also $h \geqslant 0$, so

$$2700 - x^2 \geqslant 0$$
$$x^2 \leqslant 2700$$
$$x \leqslant \sqrt{2700} = 30\sqrt{3}$$

Thus, the domain of the function V is given by $0 \leqslant x \leqslant 30\sqrt{3}$.

Now we differentiate:

$$V' = 675 - \tfrac{3}{4}x^2$$

The critical numbers occur when $V' = 0$:

$$675 - \tfrac{3}{4}x^2 = 0$$

$$\tfrac{3}{4}x^2 = 675$$

$$x^2 = \tfrac{4}{3}(675) = 900$$

$$x = 30$$

To find the absolute maximum of V on the interval $[0, 30\sqrt{3}]$, we evaluate V at the critical number and the endpoints:

$$V(30) = (675)(30) - \tfrac{1}{4}(30)^3 = 13\ 500$$
$$V(0) = 0$$
$$V(30\sqrt{3}) = (675)(30\sqrt{3}) - \tfrac{1}{4}(30\sqrt{3})^3 = 0$$

Thus, the absolute maximum volume occurs when $x = 30$ cm and the maximum volume is 13 500 cm^3.

We summarize the steps in solving applied maximum and minimum problems by adapting the problem-solving principles stated in the Review and Preview to Chapter 3 and by keeping in mind the procedures used in solving Examples 1 and 2.

1. **Understand the problem.** The first step is to read the problem carefully until it is clearly understood. Ask yourself: What is the unknown? What are the given quantities? What are the given conditions?

2. **Draw a diagram.** In most problems it is useful to draw a diagram and identify the given and required quantities on the diagram.

3. **Introduce notation.** Assign a symbol to the quantity that is to be maximized or minimized (let us call it Q for now). Also select symbols $(a, b, c, \ldots, x, y)$ for other unknown quantities and label the diagram with these symbols. It may help to use initials as suggestive variables— for example, A for area, h for height, t for time.

4. Express Q in terms of some of the other symbols from Step 3.

5. If Q has been expressed as a function of more than one variable in Step 4, use the given information to find relationships (in the form of equations) among these variables. Then use these equations to eliminate all but one of the variables in the expression for Q. Thus, Q will be given as a function of *one* variable x—say, $Q = f(x)$. Write the domain of this function.

6. Use the methods of Section 4.2 and 4.3 to find the *absolute* maximum or minimum value of f.

Example 3 Find the points on the parabola $y = 6 - x^2$ that are closest to the point $(0, 3)$.

Solution From the sketch it appears that there are two points at a minimum distance from $(0, 3)$.

DRAW A DIAGRAM

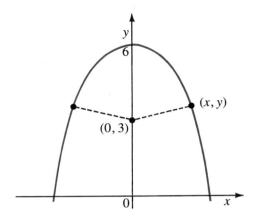

The distance d from the point $(0, 3)$ to the point (x, y) is

$$d = \sqrt{x^2 + (y - 3)^2}$$

But if (x, y) lies on the parabola, then $y = 6 - x^2$. Substituting, we get

$$d = \sqrt{x^2 + (6 - x^2 - 3)^2} = \sqrt{x^2 + (3 - x^2)^2}$$

Instead of minimizing d, we minimize the simpler expression for d^2. (Note that d is smallest when d^2 is smallest; see Question 9 in Exercise 4.4.) Therefore we need to find the critical numbers of the function

$$f(x) = x^2 + (3 - x^2)^2 = x^4 - 5x^2 + 9$$

Differentiation gives $f'(x) = 4x^3 - 10x$, so the critical numbers occur when

$$4x^3 - 10x = 0$$
$$2x(2x^2 - 5) = 0$$
$$x = 0, \ \pm\sqrt{2.5}$$

The First Derivative Test shows that $x = 0$ gives a local maximum, whereas $x = \sqrt{2.5}$ and $x = -\sqrt{2.5}$ minimize $f(x)$ and, therefore, the distance d.

When $x = \pm\sqrt{2.5}$, we have $y = 6 - 2.5 = 3.5$, so the points on the parabola closest to $(0, 3)$ are $(\sqrt{2.5}, 3.5)$ and $(-\sqrt{2.5}, 3.5)$.

Example 4   A cable television company is laying cable in an area with underground utilities. Two subdivisions are located on opposite sides of Willow Creek, which is 100 m wide. The company has to connect points P and Q with cable, where Q is on the north bank 1200 m east of P. It costs \$40/m to lay cable underground and \$80/m to lay cable underwater. What is the least expensive way to lay the cable?

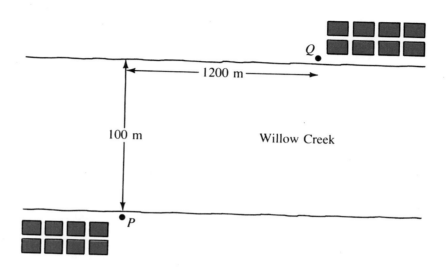

Solution   The company can lay the cable on the south shore to the point R directly opposite Q, or it can proceed east a distance x metres to a point S before laying underwater cable from S to Q.

DRAW A DIAGRAM

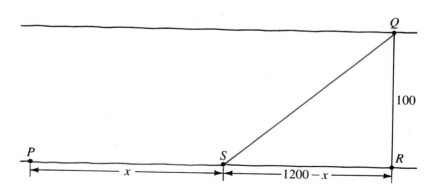

The cost of the underground portion is

$$40x$$

Since $SQ = \sqrt{100^2 + (1200 - x)^2}$

the cost of the underwater portion is

$$80SQ = 80\sqrt{100^2 + (1200 - x)^2}$$

So the total cost is

$$C(x) = 40x + 80\sqrt{100^2 + (1200 - x)^2}, \ 0 \leqslant x \leqslant 1200$$

and

$$C'(x) = 40 + \frac{40(2)(1200 - x)(-1)}{\sqrt{100^2 + (1200 - x)^2}}$$

Thus, $C'(x) = 0$ when $40 + \dfrac{40(2)(1200 - x)(-1)}{\sqrt{100^2 + (1200 - x)^2}} = 0$

$$1 - \frac{2(1200 - x)}{\sqrt{100^2 + (1200 - x)^2}} = 0$$
$$2(1200 - x) = \sqrt{100^2 + (1200 - x)^2}$$
$$4(1200 - x)^2 = 100^2 + (1200 - x)^2$$
$$3(1200 - x)^2 = 100^2$$
$$x - 1200 = \pm\frac{100}{\sqrt{3}}$$
$$x = 1200 \pm \frac{100}{\sqrt{3}} \doteq 1142 \text{ or } 1258$$

Notice that 1258 lies outside the domain of C. So we evaluate C at the critical number 1142 and at the endpoints of the interval [0, 1200]:

$$C(1142) = \$54\ 928$$
$$C(0) = \$96\ 333$$
$$C(1200) = \$56\ 000$$

The cheapest method is to lay cable underground to a point about 1142 m east of P and then to lay the remaining cable underwater.

EXERCISE 4.4

1. Find two numbers whose difference is 150 and whose product is a minimum.

2. Find two positive numbers with product 200 such that the sum of one number and twice the second number is as small as possible.

3. A rectangle has a perimeter of 100 cm. What length and width should it have so that its area is a maximum?

4. Show that a rectangle with given area has minimum perimeter when it is a square.

5. A box with a square base and open top must have a volume of 4000 cm³. Find the dimensions of the box that minimizes the amount of material used.

6. A box with an open top is to be constructed from a square piece of cardboard, 3 m wide, by cutting out a square from each of the four corners and bending up the sides, as indicated in the figure. Find the largest volume that such a box can have.

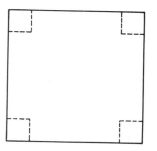
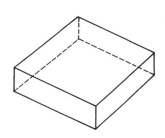

7. The lifeguard at a public beach has 400 m of rope available to lay out a rectangular restricted swimming area using the straight shoreline as one side of the rectangle.
    (a) If she wants to maximize the swimming area, what will the dimensions of the rectangle be?
    (b) To ensure the safety of swimmers, she decides that nobody should be more than 50 m from shore. What should the dimensions of the swimming area be with this added restriction?

8. A farmer wants to fence an area of 750 000 m² in a rectangular field and divide it in half with a fence parallel to one of the sides of the rectangle. How can this be done so as to minimize the cost of the fence?

9. Show that if the function $y = f(x)$ has a minimum at c, then the function $y = \sqrt{f(x)}$ also has a minimum at c.

10. Find the point on the line $y = 5x + 4$ that is closest to the origin.

11. Find the point on the parabola $2y = x^2$ that is closest to the point $(-4, 1)$.

12. A can is to be made to hold a litre of oil. Find the radius of the can that will minimize the cost of the metal to make the can. (Take $1 \text{ L} = 1000 \text{ cm}^3$.)

13. A piece of wire 40 cm long is cut into two pieces. One piece is bent into the shape of a square and the other is bent into the shape of a circle. How should the wire be cut so that the total area enclosed is
    (a) a maximum?   (b) a minimum?

14. A rectangle is inscribed in a semicircle of radius 2 cm as shown. Find the largest area of such a rectangle.

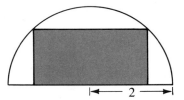

15. Solve the problem in Example 4 if it costs $120/m to lay the cable underwater.

16. A Norman window has the shape of a rectangle capped by a semicircular region as shown. If the perimeter of the window is 8 m, find the width of the window that will admit the greatest amount of light.

2x

17. A boat leaves a dock at noon and heads west at a speed of 25 km/h. Another boat heads north at 20 km/h and reaches the same dock at 1:00 p.m. When were the boats closest to each other?

18. Find the largest possible volume of a right circular cylinder that is inscribed in a sphere of radius r.

19. A 1-km racetrack is to be built with two straight sides and semicircles at the ends (as in the figure). Find the dimensions of the track that encloses the maximum area.

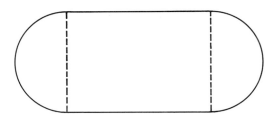

20. Painters are painting the second floor exterior wall of a building that adjoins a busy sidewalk. A corridor 2 m wide and 3 m high is built to protect pedestrians as shown in the following figure. What is the length of the shortest ladder that will reach from the ground over the corridor to the wall of the building?

3 m

2 m

4.5   EXTREME VALUE PROBLEMS IN ECONOMICS

In this section we use the techniques of this chapter to solve problems that arise in business and economics: minimizing average costs and maximizing revenues or profits.

In Section 3.4 we introduced the idea of marginal cost. Recall that if it costs a company an amount $C(x)$ to produce x units of a commodity, then the function C is called a cost function. The marginal cost function is the rate of change of C with respect to x; that is, the derivative $C'(x)$ of the cost function.

The **average cost function**

$$c(x) = \frac{C(x)}{x} \tag{1}$$

is the cost per unit when x units are produced. We want to minimize the average cost and we do so by locating the critical number of c.

Using the Quotient Rule to differentiate Equation 1 and equating the derivative to zero, we have

$$c'(x) = \frac{xC'(x) - C(x)}{x^2} = 0$$

$$xC'(x) - C(x) = 0$$

$$C'(x) = \frac{C(x)}{x} = c(x)$$

In words, this says:

> When the average cost is a minimum
> marginal cost = average cost

Example 1   The cost, in dollars, of producing x 5-kg bags of flour is

$$C(x) = 140\ 000 + 0.43x + 0.000\ 001x^2$$

(See Example 1 in Section 3.4.)
(a) Find the average cost and marginal cost of producing 100 000 bags.
(b) At what production level will the average cost be smallest, and what is this average cost?

Solution   (a) The average cost function is

$$c(x) = \frac{C(x)}{x}$$

$$= \frac{140\ 000 + 0.43x + 0.000\ 001x^2}{x}$$

$$= \frac{140\ 000}{x} + 0.43 + 0.000\ 001x$$

The average cost of producing 100 000 bags of flour is

$$c(100\ 000) = \frac{140\ 000}{100\ 000} + 0.43 + (0.000\ 001)(100\ 000)$$

$$= 1.4 + 0.43 + 0.1$$

$$= \$1.93/\text{bag}$$

The marginal cost function is

$$C'(x) = 0.43 + 0.000\ 002x$$

When $x = 100\ 000$, the marginal cost is

$$C'(100\ 000) = 0.43 + (0.000\ 002)(100\ 000)$$

$$= 0.43 + 0.2$$

$$= \$0.63$$

(b) To minimize the average cost we could equate the marginal cost and the average cost, or we could simply differentiate $c(x)$:

$$c'(x) = \frac{-140\ 000}{x^2} + 0.000\ 001 = 0$$

$$\frac{140\ 000}{x^2} = 0.000\ 001$$

$$x^2 = \frac{140\ 000}{0.000\ 001} = 14 \times 10^{10}$$

$$x = \sqrt{14} \times 10^5 \doteq 3.74 \times 10^5$$

Since $c'(x) < 0$ for $x < \sqrt{14} \times 10^5$ and $c'(x) > 0$ for $x > \sqrt{14} \times 10^5$, this value gives an absolute minimum by the First Derivative Test.

Thus, the average cost will be smallest when the production level is about 374 000 bags and this minimum average cost is

$$c(\sqrt{14} \times 10^5) \doteq \$1.18/\text{bag}$$

Recall that the demand function $p(x)$ is the price per unit that a company can charge if it sells x units. The revenue function is

$$R(x) = xp(x)$$

and the marginal revenue function is its derivative, $R'(x)$. The profit is obtained by subtracting costs from revenue:

$$P(x) = R(x) - C(x)$$

To maximize profit we look for the critical numbers of P:

$$P'(x) = R'(x) - C'(x) = 0$$
$$R'(x) = C'(x)$$

> For maximum profit
> marginal revenue = marginal cost

Example 2   In Examples 2 and 3 in Section 3.4 we considered the case of Howard's Hamburgers with yearly demand function

$$p = \frac{800\ 000 - x}{200\ 000}$$

and cost function

$$C(x) = 125\ 000 + 0.42x$$

What level of sales will maximize profits?

Solution   The revenue function is

$$R(x) = xp(x) = \frac{1}{200\ 000}(800\ 000x - x^2)$$

so the marginal revenue is

$$R'(x) = \frac{1}{200\ 000}(800\ 000 - 2x) = \frac{1}{100\ 000}(400\ 000 - x)$$

The marginal cost is

$$C'(x) = 0.42$$

Profits are maximized when marginal revenue = marginal cost.

$$R'(x) = C'(x)$$

$$\frac{1}{100\ 000}(400\ 000 - x) = 0.42$$

$$400\ 000 - x = 42\ 000$$

$$x = 358\ 000$$

Sales of 358 000 will maximize profits.

Example 3   A store has been selling 200 compact disc players a week at $350 each. A market survey indicates that for each $10 rebate offered to the buyers, the number of sets sold will increase by 20 a week.
(a) Find the demand function and the revenue function.
(b) How large a rebate should the store offer to maximize its revenue?

Solution   (a) If x is the number of CD players sold per week, then the weekly increase in sales is $x - 200$. For each increase of 20 players sold, the price is decreased by $10. So for each additional player sold the decrease in price will be $\$\frac{1}{20}10$ and the demand function is

$$p(x) = 350 - \tfrac{10}{20}(x - 200) = 450 - \tfrac{1}{2}x$$

The revenue function is

$$R(x) = xp(x) = 450x - \tfrac{1}{2}x^2$$

(b) We find the critical numbers of R by differentiating:

$$R'(x) = 450 - x$$

Thus $R'(x) = 0$ when $x = 450$. (Or use marginal revenue = marginal cost.) This value of x gives an absolute maximum by the First Derivative Test (or by observing that the graph of R is a parabola that opens downward).

The corresponding price is

$$p(450) = 450 - \tfrac{1}{2}(450) = 225$$

and the rebate is

$$350 - 225 = 125$$

To maximize revenue the store should offer a rebate of $125.

EXERCISE 4.5

B **1.** A company determines that the cost, in dollars, of producing x items is

$$C(x) = 280\ 000 + 12.5x + 0.07x^2$$

(a) Find the average cost and marginal cost of producing 1000 items.

(b) At what production level will the average cost be least?

(c) What is the minimum average cost?

2. The cost, in dollars, for the production of x units of a commodity is

$$C(x) = 6400 + \frac{x}{10} + \frac{x^2}{1000}$$

(a) Find the average cost and marginal cost at a production level of 3000 units.

(b) Find the production level that will minimize the average cost.

(c) Find the smallest average cost.

3. The Bouchard Soup Company estimates that the cost, in dollars, of making x cans of pea soup is

$$C(x) = 48\ 000 + 0.28x + 0.000\ 01x^2$$

and the revenue is

$$R(x) = 0.68x - 0.000\ 01\ x^2$$

In order to maximize profits how many cans of pea soup should be sold?

4. Sue's Submarines has found that the monthly demand for their submarines is given by

$$p = \frac{30\ 000 - x}{10\ 000}$$

and the cost of making x submarines is

$$C(x) = 6000 + 0.8x$$

What level of sales will maximize profits?

5. A baseball team plays in a stadium that holds 52 000 spectators. Average attendance at a game was 27 000 with tickets priced at $10. When ticket prices were lowered to $8, the average attendance rose to 33 000.

(a) Find the demand function, assuming that it is linear.

(b) How should the owners set ticket prices so as to maximize revenue?

6. A chain of stores has been selling a line of cameras for $50 each and has been averaging sales of 8000 cameras a month. They decide to increase the price, but their market research indicates that for each $1 increase in price, sales will fall by 100.

(a) Find the demand function.

(b) Find the price that will maximize their revenue.

7. The manager of a 120-unit apartment complex knows from experience that all units will be occupied if the rent is $400 a month. A market survey suggests that, on the average, one additional unit will remain vacant for each $10 increase in rent. What rent should she charge to maximize revenue?

8. New Horizons Travel advertises a package plan for a Florida vacation. The fare for the flight is $400/person plus $8/person for each unsold seat on the plane. The plane holds 120 passengers and the flight will be cancelled if there are fewer than 50 passengers. What number of passengers will maximize revenue?

4.6 REVIEW EXERCISE

1. For each of the following functions find the critical numbers and the intervals of increase or decrease.

(a) $f(x) = x - x^3$ (b) $f(x) = x + x^3$

(c) $f(x) = 3x^4 - 8x^3 - 6x^2 + 24x + 3$

(d) $f(x) = \dfrac{2x + 1}{2x - 1}$

(e) $f(x) = \dfrac{x^2}{x + 1}$ (f) $f(x) = 3x^{\frac{5}{3}} - 15x^{\frac{2}{3}}$

2. Find the absolute maximum value and absolute minimum value of each function.

(a) $f(x) = 4x^2 + 12x - 7, \ -2 \leqslant x \leqslant 1$

(b) $f(x) = x^3 - 27x + 32, \ -4 \leqslant x \leqslant 4$

(c) $g(x) = 3x^5 - 50x^3 + 135x, \ -2 \leqslant x \leqslant 4$

(d) $g(x) = \dfrac{1 + x}{1 - x}, \ 2 \leqslant x \leqslant 5$

3. Find the local maximum and minimum values of f.

(a) $f(x) = 7 + 72x + 3x^2 - 2x^3$

(b) $f(x) = x^4 - 72x^2 + 10$

(c) $f(x) = \sqrt{16 - x^2}$

(d) $f(x) = 12 - 2|x + 3|$

4. For the function $f(x) = x^4 - 8x^3 + 22x^2 - 24x$,
   (a) find the critical numbers,
   (b) find the intervals of increase or decrease,
   (c) find the local maximum and minimum values,
   (d) sketch the graph.

5. Find the absolute maximum value of the function
$$f(x) = \frac{1}{x^2 + x + 1}.$$

6. A printed page is to contain 60 cm² of printed material with clear margins of 5 cm on each side and 3 cm on the top and bottom. Find the minimum total area of the page.

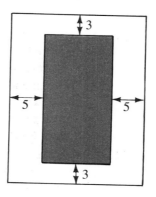

7. The illumination of an object by a light source is directly proportional to the strength of the source and inversely proportional to the square of the distance from the source. Two streetlights are 40 m apart and one is twice as strong as the other. Where is the darkest spot between the two lights?

8. Find the dimensions of the largest rectangle with sides parallel to the axes that can be inscribed in the ellipse $x^2 + 4y^2 = 4$ as shown in the figure.

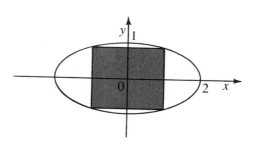

9. Two towns A and B are 5 km and 7 km, respectively, from a railroad line. The points C and D nearest to A and B on the line are 6 km apart. Where should a station be located to minimize the length of a new road from A to S to B?

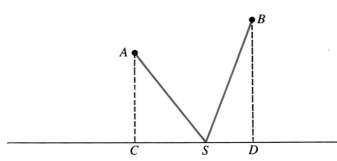

10. A company determines that the cost of making x units of a commodity is
$$C(x) = 480\,000 + 2.4x + 0.0008x^2$$
and the demand function is given by
$$p(x) = 4 - 0.001x$$
(a) What production level will minimize the average cost?
(b) What level of sales will maximize profits?

11. The manager of a 120-room resort hotel has found that, on the average, 50 rooms are booked when the price is $100 per night and 80 rooms are booked when the price is $80 per night.
(a) Find the demand function, assuming that it is linear.
(b) What price should he charge to maximize revenue?

4.7 CHAPTER 4 TEST

1. Find the interval on which the function $f(x) = \dfrac{x}{x^2 + 1}$ is increasing.

2. Find the absolute maximum and minimum values of the function
$f(x) = x^3 + 2x^2 + x - 1, \, -1 \leqslant x \leqslant 1$.

3. For the function $f(x) = x^4 - 8x^2 + 3$,
   (a) find the critical numbers,
   (b) find the intervals of increase and decrease,
   (c) find the local maximum and minimum values.

4. A box is to be built with a square base and an open top. Material for the base costs \$4/m², while material for the sides costs \$2/m². Find the dimensions of the box of maximum volume that can be built for \$1200.

5. A company estimates that the cost, in dollars, of producing x items is

$$C(x) = 16\,000 + 22.5x + 0.004x^2$$

At what production level will the average cost be lowest?

6. An apple orchard now has 80 trees planted per hectare and the average yield is 400 apples per tree. For each additional tree planted per hectare the average yield per tree is reduced by approximately four apples. How many trees per hectare will give the largest crop of apples?

FOUNDERS OF CALCULUS

Pierre Fermat (1601–1665) was not a professional mathematician. He was a French lawyer and civil servant whose hobby was mathematics. Whenever he had some spare time, he discovered and proved mathematical theorems for pure enjoyment. But he found enough spare time to invent two of the most important areas of mathematics, analytic geometry and differential calculus, as well as to contribute to the revival of two other areas, number theory and probability theory. As an amateur, Fermat never published his discoveries, though his new results circulated in manuscript form through letters. Thus, although he invented analytic geometry at the same time as Descartes, he did not receive credit for it at the time.

Laplace called Fermat "the true inventor of differential calculus" in spite of the fact that Fermat did not formulate the general idea of a derivative. What Laplace meant was that Fermat's methods in solving maximum and minimum problems and tangent problems used ideas that Newton later employed in formulating derivatives.

For example, Fermat would have solved a maximum problem in the 1630s as follows. If $f(a)$ is a maximum value, then it seems intuitively clear from a picture that f changes very slowly near a.

Thus, if E is very small, then $f(a)$ and $f(a + E)$ are approximately equal:

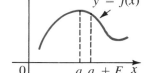

$$f(a + E) \doteq f(a) \qquad \text{or} \qquad f(a + E) - f(a) \doteq 0$$

Dividing both sides by E,

$$\frac{f(a + E) - f(a)}{E} \doteq 0$$

If f is a polynomial, we can carry out the division of E into $f(a + E) - f(a)$. Fermat then set $E = 0$ and solved the resulting equation for a. We see that, for polynomials, Fermat's method is equivalent to finding

$$\lim_{E \to 0} \frac{f(a + E) - f(a)}{E}$$

and equating it to 0. Fermat did not use limits, but essentially his method amounts to setting $f'(a) = 0$ as we would today.

PROBLEMS PLUS

Find the point P on the parabola $y = 1 - x^2$ at which the tangent line cuts from the first quadrant the triangle with the smallest area.

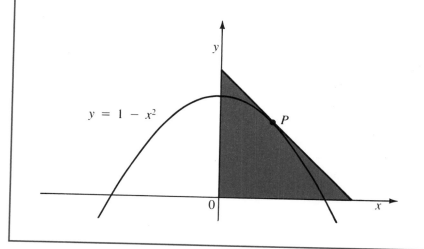

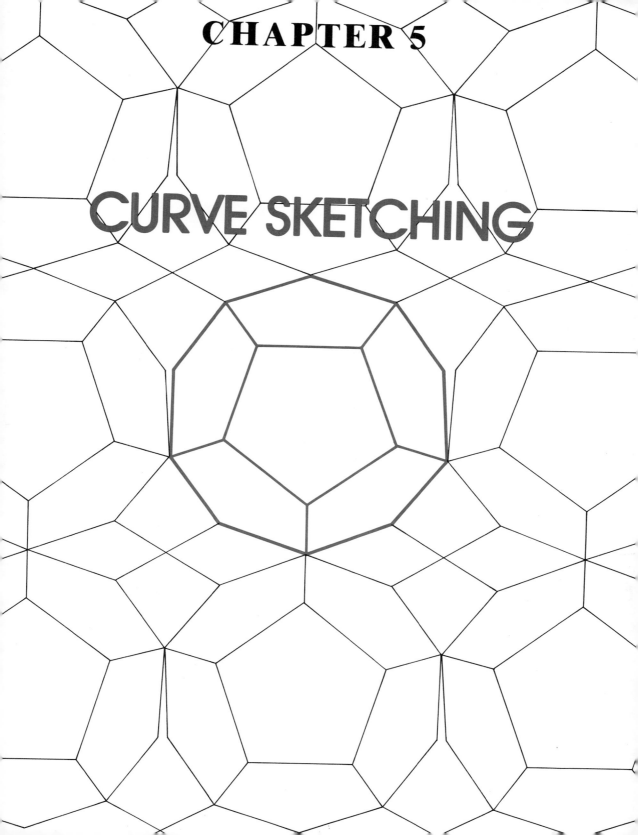

CHAPTER 5

CURVE SKETCHING

REVIEW AND PREVIEW TO
CHAPTER 5

Intercepts

To find the x-intercepts of $y = f(x)$, set $y = 0$ and solve for x.
To find the y-intercept of $y = f(x)$, set $x = 0$; the y-intercept is $f(0)$.

EXERCISE 1

1. Find the intercepts of the following curves.
   (a) $y = 25 - 4x^2$ (b) $y = 2x^2 - x - 1$
   (c) $y = \dfrac{x^2 + 2x - 3}{x^2 + 1}$ (d) $y = x^2 + x + 1$
   (e) $y = 3x^2 + 4x - 6$ (f) $y = x^3 - 3x$
   (g) $y = x^3 - x^2 - x + 1$ (h) $y = 2x^3 - 9x^2 - 18x$
   (i) $y = x^3 + 8$ (j) $y = x^4 - 16$

2. Find the intercepts of the curve $y = 9x - x^3$ and use them, together with the methods of Chapter 4, to sketch the curve.

3. Use Newton's method to find the x-intercepts of the curve $y = x^3 - 3x + 1$ correct to two decimal places.

Symmetry

An **even function** satisfies

$$f(-x) = f(x)$$

for all x in its domain. Thus, a function is even if it is unchanged when x is replaced by $-x$. The graph of an even function is symmetric about the y-axis.

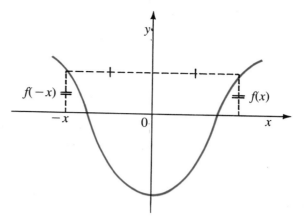

An **odd function** satisfies

$$f(-x) = -f(x)$$

for all x in its domain. The graph of an odd function is symmetric about the origin.

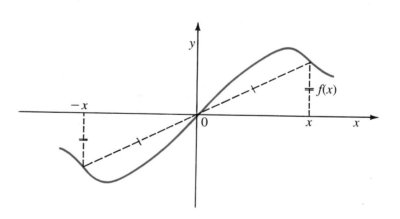

Symmetry is used to reduce the amount of work in graphing. If we have graphed an even function for $x \geqslant 0$, we just reflect in the y-axis to get the entire graph. For an odd function we just rotate through $180°$ about the origin.

Example Determine whether each function is even, or odd, or neither.

(a) $f(x) = x^6$

(b) $g(x) = x^3 + \dfrac{1}{x}$

Solution

(a) $f(-x) = (-x)^6$
$= (-1)^6 x^6$
$= x^6$
$= f(x)$
Thus f is even.

(b) $g(-x) = (-x)^3 + \dfrac{1}{-x}$

$= -x^3 - \dfrac{1}{x}$

$= -\left(x^3 + \dfrac{1}{x}\right)$

$= -g(x)$

Thus g is odd.

EXERCISE 2

1. State whether the functions of the following graphs are even, odd, or neither.

(a)

(b)

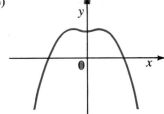

(c)

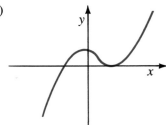

(d)

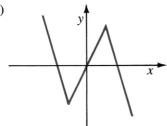

2. Determine whether the function is even, odd, or neither.

(a) $f(x) = x^2$

(b) $f(x) = x^3$

(c) $g(x) = x^2 + x^3$

(d) $g(x) = \dfrac{2}{x^4 + 1}$

(e) $h(x) = (x + x^5)^3$

(f) $h(x) = x^6(1 + x - x^2)$

(g) $y = |x|$

(h) $y = \dfrac{x^3}{x^4 + x^2 + 1}$

INTRODUCTION

In this chapter we look at further aspects of curves—vertical asymptotes, horizontal asymptotes, concavity, and inflection points. Then we use them, together with intervals of increase and decrease and maximum and minimum values, to develop a procedure for curve sketching.

5.1 VERTICAL ASYMPTOTES

Let us examine the behaviour of the function $f(x) = \dfrac{1}{x^2}$ for x close to 0.

x	$f(x) = \dfrac{1}{x^2}$
± 1	1
± 0.5	4
± 0.2	25
± 0.1	100
± 0.05	400
± 0.01	10 000
± 0.001	1 000 000

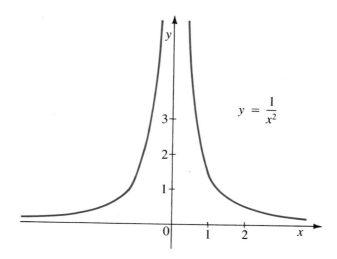

The values in the table and the graph show that the closer we take x to 0, the larger $\dfrac{1}{x^2}$ becomes. In fact, it appears that by taking x close enough to 0, we can make $f(x)$ as large as we like. We indicate this type of behaviour by writing

$$\lim_{x \to 0} \frac{1}{x^2} = \infty$$

and we say that the line $x = 0$ is a *vertical asymptote* of $y = \frac{1}{x^2}$.

Notice that f is not defined at $x = 0$, so f has a discontinuity at 0 (see Section 1.3). This type of discontinuity is called an **infinite discontinuity**.

In general, if $f(x)$ is defined on both sides of the number a, we write symbolically

$$\lim_{x \to a} f(x) = \infty$$

if the values of $f(x)$ can be made arbitrarily large (as large as we like) by taking x sufficiently close to a, but not equal to a. This type of limit is called an **infinite limit**. Roughly speaking, the values of $f(x)$ become larger and larger (or "increase without bound") as x gets closer and closer to a.

The symbol ∞ is not a number, but the expression

$$\lim_{x \to a} f(x) = \infty$$

is usually read as

"the limit of $f(x)$, as x approaches a, is infinity"

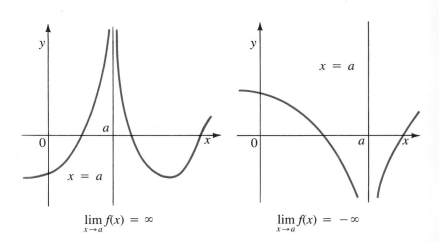

$$\lim_{x \to a} f(x) = \infty \qquad\qquad \lim_{x \to a} f(x) = -\infty$$

These figures illustrate the definition of an infinite limit and a similar type of limit, denoted by

$$\lim_{x \to a} f(x) = -\infty$$

for functions that become large negatives as x becomes close to a. Similar definitions can be given for the **one-sided infinite limits**

$$\lim_{x \to a^-} f(x) = \infty \qquad\qquad \lim_{x \to a^+} f(x) = \infty$$

$$\lim_{x \to a^-} f(x) = -\infty \qquad\qquad \lim_{x \to a^+} f(x) = -\infty$$

remembering that "$x \to a^-$" means that x approaches a from the left and "$x \to a^+$" means that x approaches a from the right. If any of these four statements is true, we say that $x = a$ is a **vertical asymptote**. Illustrations are shown in the following figures.

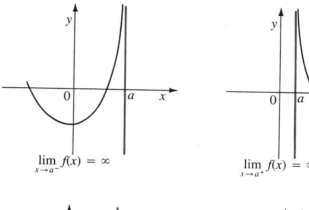

$$\lim_{x \to a^-} f(x) = \infty$$

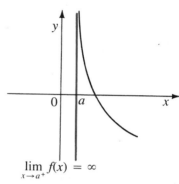

$$\lim_{x \to a^+} f(x) = \infty$$

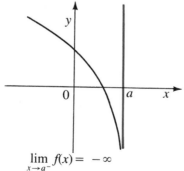

$$\lim_{x \to a^-} f(x) = -\infty$$

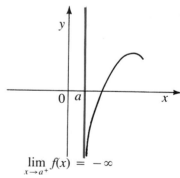

$$\lim_{x \to a^+} f(x) = -\infty$$

Example 1   Find $\displaystyle\lim_{x \to 0^+} \frac{1}{x}$ and $\displaystyle\lim_{x \to 0^-} \frac{1}{x}$.

Solution   If x is close to 0, but positive, then $\dfrac{1}{x}$ is a large positive number. For instance,

$$\frac{1}{0.01} = 100 \qquad \frac{1}{0.000\ 1} = 10\ 000 \qquad \frac{1}{0.000\ 001} = 1\ 000\ 000$$

As x approaches 0 from the right, $\dfrac{1}{x}$ becomes increasingly large. Therefore,

$$\lim_{x \to 0^+} \frac{1}{x} = \infty$$

If x is close to 0, but negative, then $\dfrac{1}{x}$ is a large negative number. Thus,

$$\lim_{x \to 0^-} \frac{1}{x} = -\infty$$

These limits can also be seen from the graph of the hyperbola $y = \dfrac{1}{x}$. The line $x = 0$ (the y-axis) is a vertical asymptote.

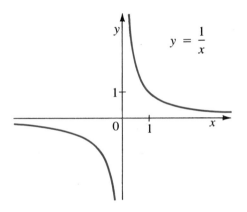

Example 2   Find $\lim\limits_{x \to 6} \left[2 - \dfrac{5}{(x-6)^2} \right]$.

Solution   If x is close to 6 (on either side of 6), $(x - 6)^2$ is a small positive number, and so

$$-\frac{5}{(x-6)^2}$$

is a large negative number. Therefore,

$$\lim_{x \to 6} \left[2 - \frac{5}{(x-6)^2} \right] = -\infty$$

To find the vertical asymptotes of a rational function, we find the values of x where the denominator is zero and compute the limits of the function from the right and left.

Example 3 (a) Find the vertical asymptotes of the function $y = \dfrac{x}{x^2 - x - 6}$.

(b) Sketch the graph near the asymptotes.

Solution (a) First we factor the denominator:

$$y = \frac{x}{(x - 3)(x + 2)}$$

Since the denominator is 0 when $x = 3$ or -2, the lines $x = 3$ and $x = -2$ are candidates for vertical asymptotes.

If x is close to 3, but $x > 3$, the denominator is close to 0 and $y > 0$ (since $x > 0$, $x - 3 > 0$, and $x + 2 > 0$). Symbolically, we could write

$$\frac{x}{(x - 3)(x + 2)} = \frac{[\text{positive}]}{[\text{small positive}][\text{positive}]} = \text{large positive}$$

Therefore,

$$\lim_{x \to 3^+} \frac{x}{(x - 3)(x + 2)} = \infty$$

If x is close to 3, but $x < 3$, we have

$$\frac{x}{(x - 3)(x + 2)} = \frac{[\text{positive}]}{[\text{small negative}][\text{positive}]} = \text{large negative}$$

and so $\lim\limits_{x \to 3^-} \dfrac{x}{(x - 3)(x + 2)} = -\infty$

Similar reasoning gives

$$\lim_{x \to -2^+} \frac{x}{(x - 3)(x + 2)} = \infty$$

and $\lim\limits_{x \to -2^-} \dfrac{x}{(x - 3)(x + 2)} = -\infty$

The vertical asymptotes are $x = 3$ and $x = -2$.

(b) Using the information from part (a), we can sketch the part of the graph that lies near the asymptotes. We will be able to complete the picture with the information from the next section.

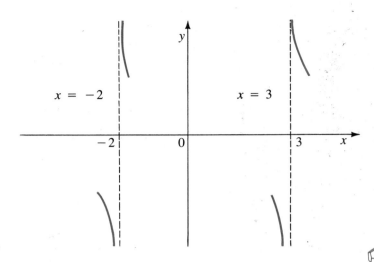

EXERCISE 5.1

A **1.** The graph of f is given.

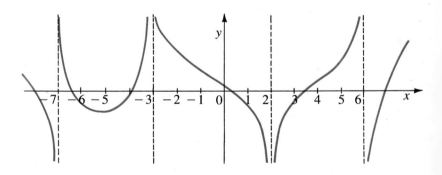

(a) State the equations of the vertical asymptotes.
(b) State the following.

   (i) $\displaystyle\lim_{x \to -7^-} f(x)$ (ii) $\displaystyle\lim_{x \to -7^+} f(x)$

   (iii) $\displaystyle\lim_{x \to -3} f(x)$ (iv) $\displaystyle\lim_{x \to 2} f(x)$

   (v) $\displaystyle\lim_{x \to 6^-} f(x)$ (vi) $\displaystyle\lim_{x \to 6^+} f(x)$

B **2.** Find each limit.

(a) $\displaystyle\lim_{x \to 8} \frac{1}{(x - 8)^2}$ (b) $\displaystyle\lim_{x \to 1^-} \frac{3}{x - 1}$

(c) $\displaystyle\lim_{x \to 1^+} \frac{3}{x - 1}$ (d) $\displaystyle\lim_{x \to -1} \frac{-2}{(x + 1)^2}$

(e) $\displaystyle\lim_{x\to 2^+}\frac{x-4}{x-2}$

(f) $\displaystyle\lim_{x\to 2^-}\frac{x-4}{x-2}$

(g) $\displaystyle\lim_{x\to -4}\left[1+\frac{2x}{(x+4)^6}\right]$

(h) $\displaystyle\lim_{x\to 3^+}\left[x+\frac{2-x}{x-3}\right]$

(i) $\displaystyle\lim_{x\to -2^+}\frac{x}{x^2-4}$

(j) $\displaystyle\lim_{x\to -2^-}\frac{x}{x^2-4}$

(k) $\displaystyle\lim_{x\to 9^+}\frac{5-x}{\sqrt{x-9}}$

(l) $\displaystyle\lim_{x\to -3^+}\frac{10}{x^2-x-12}$

3. Find the vertical asymptotes and sketch the graph near the asymptotes.

(a) $\displaystyle y=\frac{2}{x+1}$

(b) $\displaystyle y=\frac{3}{(x-6)^2}$

(c) $\displaystyle y=\frac{x}{(x+2)^2}$

(d) $\displaystyle y=\frac{1}{x^2-1}$

(e) $\displaystyle y=\frac{x}{x^2-1}$

(f) $\displaystyle y=\frac{6x^3}{x^2+4x+3}$

(g) $\displaystyle y=\frac{1}{x^2(x+1)}$

(h) $\displaystyle y=\frac{1}{x^4-4x^2}$

C **4.** Find $\displaystyle\lim_{x\to 0^+}\left(\frac{5}{x}-\frac{2}{x^2}\right)$.

5. How small do we have to take x so that $\dfrac{1}{x^4}>100\,000\,000$?

5.2 HORIZONTAL ASYMPTOTES

The table gives the values, correct to six decimal places, of the function

$$f(x)=\frac{x^2+2}{x^2+1}$$

for large values of x.

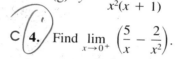

x	$f(x)=\dfrac{x^2+2}{x^2+1}$
0	2.000 000
± 1	1.500 000
± 2	1.200 000
± 3	1.100 000
± 4	1.058 824
± 5	1.038 462
± 10	1.009 901
± 50	1.000 400
± 100	1.000 100
± 1000	1.000 001

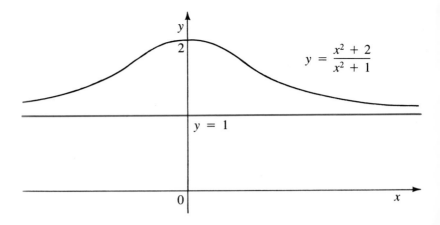

From the table and the graph we see that the values of $f(x)$ become closer and closer to 1 as x grows larger and larger. In fact, it appears that by taking x large enough, we can make $f(x)$ as close to 1 as we like. We indicate this type of behaviour by writing

$$\lim_{x \to \infty} \frac{x^2 + 2}{x^2 + 1} = 1$$

and we say that the line $y = 1$ is a *horizontal asymptote*.

Similarly, we see that, for large negative values of x, the values of $f(x)$ are close to 1. By letting x decrease through negative values without bound, we can make $f(x)$ as close as we like to 1. We express this by writing

$$\lim_{x \to -\infty} \frac{x^2 + 2}{x^2 + 1} = 1$$

In general, we define a **limit at infinity** by writing

$$\lim_{x \to \infty} f(x) = L$$

if the values of $f(x)$ can be made arbitrarily close to L by taking x sufficiently large. In other words, the values of $f(x)$ become closer and closer to L as x gets larger and larger. (Notice the similarity to the limit of a sequence in Section 1.6.)

Again the symbol ∞ is not a number, but the expression

$$\lim_{x \to \infty} f(x) = L$$

is read as

"the limit of $f(x)$, as x approaches infinity, is L"

Similarly, the notation

$$\lim_{x \to -\infty} f(x) = L$$

means that the values of $f(x)$ approach L as x becomes large negative.

The line $y = L$ is called a **horizontal asymptote** of the curve $y = f(x)$ if either

$$\lim_{x \to \infty} f(x) = L \quad \text{or} \quad \lim_{x \to -\infty} f(x) = L$$

For instance, the line $y = 1$ is a horizontal asymptote of the function f considered at the beginning of this section.

The figures show that there are many ways for a curve to approach a horizontal asymptote.

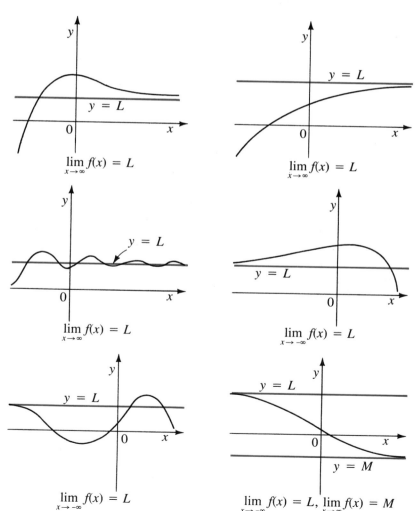

Example 1   Find $\lim\limits_{x \to \infty} \dfrac{1}{x}$ and $\lim\limits_{x \to -\infty} \dfrac{1}{x}$.

Solution   When x is large, its reciprocal $\dfrac{1}{x}$ is small. For instance,

$$\frac{1}{100} = 0.01 \qquad \frac{1}{10\ 000} = 0.0001 \qquad \frac{1}{1\ 000\ 000} = 0.000\ 001$$

In fact, by taking x large enough, we can make $\dfrac{1}{x}$ as close to 0 as we like. Therefore,

$$\lim_{x \to \infty} \frac{1}{x} = 0$$

Likewise, when x is large negative, $\dfrac{1}{x}$ is small negative, so

$$\lim_{x \to -\infty} \frac{1}{x} = 0$$

Thus, the line $y = 0$ (the x-axis) is a horizontal asymptote of the curve $y = \dfrac{1}{x}$, as illustrated by the figure.

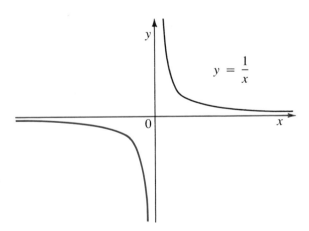

The seven properties of limits that were stated in Section 1.2 are also valid for finite limits at infinity. In particular, if we combine the results of Example 1 with Properties 6 and 7, we get the following rule.

If r is a positive rational number, then

$$\lim_{x \to \infty} \frac{1}{x^r} = 0$$

If r is a positive rational number and x^r is defined for all x, then

$$\lim_{x \to -\infty} \frac{1}{x^r} = 0$$

In the following example, we use this rule to compute a more complicated limit.

Example 2   Evaluate $\displaystyle\lim_{x \to \infty} \frac{4x^2 - x + 2}{6x^2 + 5x + 1}$.

Solution   To evaluate the limit at infinity of a rational function, we first divide the numerator and denominator by the highest power of x that occurs. (We can assume that $x \neq 0$ because we are interested only in large values of x.) In this case the highest power of x is x^2, so we proceed as follows:

$$\lim_{x \to \infty} \frac{4x^2 - x + 2}{6x^2 + 5x + 1} = \lim_{x \to \infty} \frac{\dfrac{4x^2 - x + 2}{x^2}}{\dfrac{6x^2 + 5x + 1}{x^2}}$$

$$= \lim_{x \to \infty} \frac{4 - \dfrac{1}{x} + \dfrac{2}{x^2}}{6 + \dfrac{5}{x} + \dfrac{1}{x^2}}$$

$$= \frac{\displaystyle\lim_{x \to \infty} 4 - \lim_{x \to \infty} \frac{1}{x} + 2 \lim_{x \to \infty} \left(\frac{1}{x^2}\right)}{\displaystyle\lim_{x \to \infty} 6 + 5 \lim_{x \to \infty} \frac{1}{x} + \lim_{x \to \infty} \left(\frac{1}{x^2}\right)}$$

$$= \frac{4 - 0 + 2(0)}{6 + 5(0) + 0}$$

$$= \frac{4}{6}$$

$$= \frac{2}{3}$$

Example 3 Find the horizontal and vertical asymptotes of the function

$$y = \frac{x + 1}{x - 2}$$

and sketch its graph.

Solution We find the horizontal asymptotes by computing the limit at infinity. The first step is to divide the numerator and denominator by x.

$$\lim_{x \to \infty} \frac{x + 1}{x - 2} = \lim_{x \to \infty} \frac{1 + \dfrac{1}{x}}{1 - \dfrac{2}{x}}$$

$$= \frac{\lim\limits_{x \to \infty} 1 + \lim\limits_{x \to \infty} \dfrac{1}{x}}{\lim\limits_{x \to \infty} 1 - 2 \lim\limits_{x \to \infty} \dfrac{1}{x}}$$

$$= \frac{1 + 0}{1 - 2(0)}$$

$$= 1$$

A similar calculation shows that

$$\lim_{x \to -\infty} \frac{x + 1}{x - 2} = 1$$

and so the horizontal asymptote is $y = 1$.

The denominator is 0 when $x = 2$, so we find the following limits by noting that $y > 0$ for $x > 2$ and $y < 0$ when $x < 2$ and x is close to 2.

$$\lim_{x \to 2^+} \frac{x + 1}{x - 2} = \infty \qquad \lim_{x \to 2^-} \frac{x + 1}{x - 2} = -\infty$$

Thus, the line $x = 2$ is the vertical asymptote.

We sketch the asymptotes as broken lines. Then we plot the x-intercept, -1, and the y-intercept, $-\frac{1}{2}$, and use the information from the limits to sketch the graph of the given function. [It could be verified using the derivative that the function is decreasing on each of the intervals $(-\infty, 2)$ and $(2, \infty)$.]

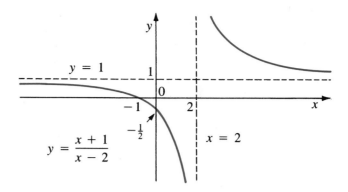

Example 4 Find the horizontal and vertical asymptotes of the function

$$y = \frac{x}{x^2 - x - 6}$$

and sketch the graph.

Solution As in Example 2, we divide numerator and denominator by x^2:

$$\lim_{x \to \infty} \frac{x}{x^2 - x - 6} = \lim_{x \to \infty} \frac{\dfrac{1}{x}}{1 - \dfrac{1}{x} - \dfrac{6}{x^2}}$$

$$= \frac{\displaystyle\lim_{x \to \infty} \frac{1}{x}}{\displaystyle\lim_{x \to \infty} 1 - \lim_{x \to \infty} \frac{1}{x} - 6\lim_{x \to \infty} \frac{1}{x^2}}$$

$$= \frac{0}{1 - 0 - 6(0)}$$

$$= 0$$

A similar calculation shows that

$$\lim_{x \to -\infty} \frac{x}{x^2 - x - 6} = 0$$

Therefore the line $y = 0$ (the x-axis) is a horizontal asymptote.

In Example 3 in Section 5.1 we found that the vertical asymptotes are $x = 3$ and $x = -2$, and we sketched the graph near these asymptotes. We now combine that information with the intercepts (both 0) and limits at infinity to sketch the complete graph. [Calculation of the derivative would confirm that $y' < 0$, so y is decreasing on the intervals $(-\infty, -2)$, $(-2, 3)$, and $(3, \infty)$.]

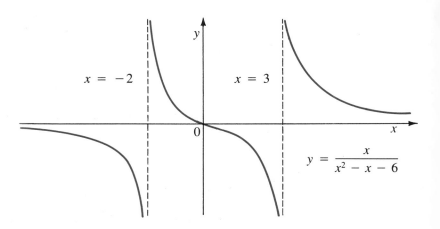

Infinite Limits at Infinity

We use the notation

$$\lim_{x \to \infty} f(x) = \infty$$

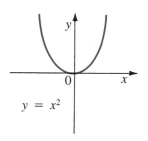

$y = x^2$

to indicate that the values of $f(x)$ become large as x becomes large. There are similar meanings for the following symbols:

$$\lim_{x \to \infty} f(x) = -\infty \qquad \lim_{x \to -\infty} f(x) = \infty \qquad \lim_{x \to -\infty} f(x) = -\infty$$

For example, we can see from the graphs of $y = x^2$ and $y = x^3$ that

$$\lim_{x \to -\infty} x^2 = \infty \qquad\qquad \lim_{x \to \infty} x^2 = \infty$$

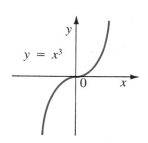

$y = x^3$

$$\lim_{x \to -\infty} x^3 = -\infty \qquad\qquad \lim_{x \to \infty} x^3 = \infty$$

For infinite limits, not all of the properties of limits hold, as we see in the next example.

Example 5   Find $\lim\limits_{x \to \infty} (x^4 - x)$.

Solution   It would be wrong to write this as a difference of limits:

$$\lim_{x \to \infty} (x^4 - x) \neq \lim_{x \to \infty} x^4 - \lim_{x \to \infty} x$$

because ∞ is not a number ($\infty - \infty$ cannot be defined).
But we can write

$$\lim_{x \to \infty} (x^4 - x) = \lim_{x \to \infty} x(x^3 - 1) = \infty$$

since x and $x^3 - 1$ both become large and therefore their product becomes large.

Using limits at infinity, together with intercepts, we can get a rough idea of the graph of a polynomial.

Example 6   Sketch the graph of $y = (x - 3)^2(x + 2)(1 - x)$ by finding its intercepts and its limits as $x \to \infty$ and $x \to -\infty$.

Solution   The y-intercept is

$$f(0) = (-3)^2(2)(1) = 18$$

To find the x-intercepts, we set

$$y = (x - 3)^2(x + 2)(1 - x) = 0$$

and find that $x = 3, -2$, or 1. Note that since $(x - 3)^2$ is positive, the function does not change sign at 3. Therefore the graph does not cross the x-axis at 3.
When x is large and positive we have

$$(x - 3)^2(x + 2)(1 - x) = [\text{large positive}][\text{large positive}][\text{large negative}]$$
$$= \text{large negative}$$

and so

$$\lim_{x \to \infty} (x - 3)^2(x + 2)(1 - x) = -\infty$$

When x is large and negative we have

$$(x - 3)^2(x + 2)(1 - x) = [\text{large positive}][\text{large negative}][\text{large positive}]$$
$$= \text{large negative}$$

and so

$$\lim_{x \to -\infty} (x - 3)^2(x + 2)(1 - x) = -\infty$$

Combining this information, we give a rough sketch of the graph.

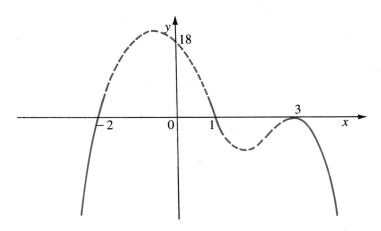

The use of derivatives would enable us to complete the picture by giving the precise location of the maximum and minimum points.

EXERCISE 5.2

A **1.** State the equations of the horizontal and vertical asymptotes.

(a)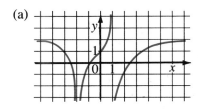

(b)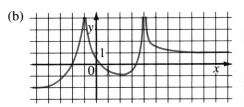

B **2.** Find the limit.

(a) $\lim\limits_{x \to \infty} \dfrac{6}{\sqrt{x}}$

(b) $\lim\limits_{x \to -\infty} 3x^{-5}$

(c) $\lim\limits_{x \to \infty} \dfrac{2x + 1}{x - 3}$

(d) $\lim\limits_{x \to -\infty} \dfrac{2x + 1}{x - 3}$

(e) $\lim\limits_{x \to \infty} \dfrac{1 - x}{3 + 5x}$

(f) $\lim\limits_{x \to -\infty} \dfrac{x^2 - x + 1}{x^2 + 3x - 2}$

(g) $\lim\limits_{x \to \infty} \dfrac{x + 3}{x^2 - 5x + 7}$

(h) $\lim\limits_{x \to \infty} \dfrac{x^2 - 1}{(x + 3)(2x + 4)}$

(i) $\displaystyle\lim_{x \to -\infty} \frac{3x^3 + x^2 - 5}{x^3 - 4x + 1}$ (j) $\displaystyle\lim_{x \to -\infty} \frac{12x^2 - 2x + 1}{3x^4 - 14x^2 + x - 3}$

3. Find the horizontal asymptotes of each curve.

    (a) $y = \dfrac{2x - 3}{5 - 4x}$ (b) $y = \dfrac{x}{x^2 + 1}$

    (c) $y = \dfrac{x^3 + 1}{x^3 - 1}$ (d) $y = 1 - \dfrac{x}{x^2 - 2}$

4. Find the horizontal and vertical asymptotes. Use them, together with intercepts, to sketch the graph.

    (a) $y = \dfrac{2}{x + 1}$ (b) $y = \dfrac{x}{x + 1}$

    (c) $y = \dfrac{4x + 5}{3 - 2x}$ (d) $y = \dfrac{1}{x^2 - 1}$

    (e) $y = \dfrac{x}{x^2 - 1}$ (f) $y = \dfrac{2x^2}{x^2 + 3x - 4}$

    (g) $y = \dfrac{x}{(x + 2)^2}$ (h) $y = \dfrac{x^2}{(x + 2)^2}$

5. Find the limit.

    (a) $\displaystyle\lim_{x \to \infty} \sqrt{x}$ (b) $\displaystyle\lim_{x \to -\infty} x^5$

    (c) $\displaystyle\lim_{x \to \infty} (x^3 - x^2)$ (d) $\displaystyle\lim_{x \to -\infty} (x^3 - x^2)$

    (e) $\displaystyle\lim_{x \to \infty} x^2(2x + 1)(x - 2)$ (f) $\displaystyle\lim_{x \to \infty} (x + 2)^4(3 - x)$

6. Find the limits as $x \to \infty$ and $x \to -\infty$. Use this information, together with intercepts, to give a rough sketch of the graph.

    (a) $y = (x + 1)(x - 2)(3 - x)$ (b) $y = x^2(x - 2)(2x + 5)$
    (c) $y = (1 - x)^2(2 - x)(5 - x)$ (d) $y = (x + 1)^3(x - 2)^4$

7. Find the horizontal asymptotes of $y = \dfrac{x}{|x| + 1}$.

C 8. Find $\displaystyle\lim_{x \to \infty} \dfrac{\sqrt{4x^2 + 1}}{2x - 3}$. [*Hint:* Divide numerator and denominator by x.]

9. Find $\displaystyle\lim_{x \to -\infty} \dfrac{3x}{\sqrt{x^2 + 6}}$. [*Hint:* Note that $\sqrt{x^2} = -x$ when $x < 0$.]

10. Find $\displaystyle\lim_{x \to \infty} (\sqrt{x^2 + 5x + 1} - x)$. [*Hint:* Rationalize.]

11. Find $\displaystyle\lim_{x \to -\infty} \dfrac{x^{10} + 6x^6 - 3}{x^5 + 2x}$. [*Hint:* Divide numerator and denominator

                  by x^5.]

12. How large do we have to take x so that $\dfrac{1}{x^2} < 0.000\ 001$?

5.3   CONCAVITY AND POINTS OF INFLECTION

The graphs of the functions f and g, shown in the diagrams, each connect point A to point B, but they bend in different directions. The graph of f lies above its tangent lines and is called *concave upward*; the graph of g lies below its tangent lines and is called *concave downward*.

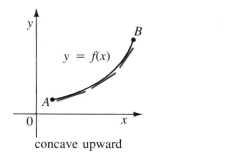
concave upward

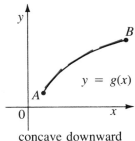
concave downward

In general, the graph of f is called **concave upward** on an interval I if it lies above all of its tangents on I. It is called **concave downward** on I if it lies below all of these tangents.

For instance, the function whose graph is shown is concave upward (abbreviated CU) on the intervals $(-4, 1)$, $(3, 6)$, and $(6, 8)$, and concave downward (CD) on $(1, 3)$ and $(8, \infty)$.

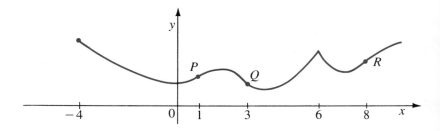

A point P on a curve is called a **point of inflection** if the curve changes from concave upward to concave downward or from concave downward to concave upward at P. For instance, the graph just considered has three points of inflection, namely, P, Q, and R. Notice that if a curve has a tangent line at a point of inflection, then the curve crosses its tangent line there.

To see how the sign of the second derivative affects the direction of concavity, we consider a function f with positive second derivative, that is, $f''(x) > 0$ on an interval I. Thus,

$$\frac{d}{dx} f'(x) > 0 \qquad \text{for } x \in I$$

We know that if a function has a positive derivative, then it is increasing, so $f'(x)$ is increasing on I. This says that the slopes of the tangent lines increase from left to right. From the figures, we see that the graph is concave upward.

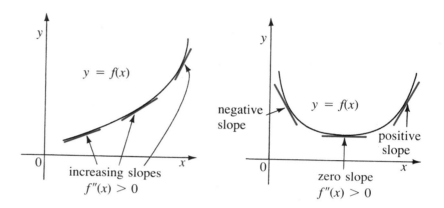

Similarly, if $f''(x) < 0$, then $f'(x)$ is decreasing, so the slopes of the tangent lines decrease. You should draw the corresponding pictures, which suggest that f is concave downward.

Test For Concavity

If $f''(x) > 0$ for all x in I, then the graph of f is concave upward on I.

If $f''(x) < 0$ for all x in I, then the graph of f is concave downward on I.

It follows from the Test for Concavity that there will be a point of inflection at any point where the second derivative changes sign.

Example 1 (a) Determine where the curve $y = x^3 - 3x^2 + 4x - 5$ is concave upward and where it is concave downward.

(b) Find the points of inflection.

(c) Use this information to sketch the curve.

Solution (a) If $f(x) = x^3 - 3x^2 + 4x - 5$

then $f'(x) = 3x^2 - 6x + 4$

and $f''(x) = 6x - 6 = 6(x - 1)$

The curve is concave upward when $f''(x) > 0$, that is,

$$6(x - 1) > 0$$
$$x - 1 > 0$$
$$x > 1$$

Also, the curve is concave downward when $f''(x) < 0$, that is, $x < 1$. Thus, the curve is concave upward on $(1, \infty)$ and concave downward on $(-\infty, 1)$.

(b) The curve changes from concave downward to concave upward when $x = 1$, so the point $(1, -3)$ is a point of inflection.

(c) We note that there is no critical number because the discriminant of the equation

$$f'(x) = 3x^2 - 6x + 4 = 0$$

is $$b^2 - 4ac = 36 - 48 < 0$$

Thus $f'(x) > 0$, so the function is always increasing and there is no maximum or minimum. This information, together with parts (a) and (b) and the y-intercept, allows us to sketch the curve. You can see that the information regarding concavity is very helpful in sketching this particular curve.

The slope of the tangent at the inflection point is $f'(1) = 1$.

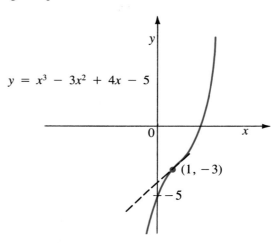

$$y = x^3 - 3x^2 + 4x - 5$$

$(1, -3)$

-5

Example 2   Discuss the curve $y = \dfrac{x}{x^2 + 1}$ with respect to concavity and points of inflection.

Solution   If $$f(x) = \frac{x}{x^2 + 1}$$

then $$f'(x) = \frac{x^2 + 1 - x(2x)}{(x^2 + 1)^2} = \frac{1 - x^2}{(x^2 + 1)^2}$$

and $$f''(x) = \frac{(1 + x^2)^2(-2x) - (1 - x^2)2(x^2 + 1)(2x)}{(x^2 + 1)^4} = \frac{2x(x^2 - 3)}{(x^2 + 1)^3}$$

Noting that the denominator of $f''(x)$ is always positive and the numerator is 0 when $x = 0$ or $x = \pm\sqrt{3}$, we analyze the concavity of f in the following chart.

Interval	$2x$	$x^2 - 3$	$f''(x)$	f
$x < -\sqrt{3}$	$-$	$+$	$-$	CD on $(-\infty, -\sqrt{3})$
$-\sqrt{3} < x < 0$	$-$	$-$	$+$	CU on $(-\sqrt{3}, 0)$
$0 < x < \sqrt{3}$	$+$	$-$	$-$	CD on $(0, \sqrt{3})$
$x > \sqrt{3}$	$+$	$+$	$+$	CU on $(\sqrt{3}, \infty)$

From the chart we also see that the direction of concavity changes when $x = -\sqrt{3}, 0$, and $\sqrt{3}$. Therefore there are three points of inflection:

$$\left(-\sqrt{3}, -\frac{\sqrt{3}}{4}\right) \qquad (0, 0) \qquad \left(\sqrt{3}, \frac{\sqrt{3}}{4}\right)$$

The following example shows that inflection points cannot be located simply by setting $f''(x) = 0$. There must be a change in the direction of concavity.

Example 3 Show that the function $f(x) = x^4$ satisfies $f''(0) = 0$ but has no inflection point.

Solution Since $f(x) = x^4$, we have $f'(x) = 4x^3$ and $f''(x) = 12x^2$, so $f''(0) = 0$. But $12x^2 > 0$ for both $x < 0$ and $x > 0$, so the direction of concavity does not change and there is no inflection point (see the diagram).

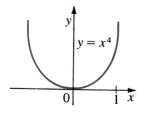

Example 4 For the function $f(x) = x^{\frac{1}{3}}(x + 3)^{\frac{2}{3}}$,
(a) find the intervals of increase and decrease,
(b) find the local maximum and minimum values,
(c) find the intervals of concavity,
(d) find the points of inflection,
(e) sketch the graph of f.

Solution (a)
$$f'(x) = \tfrac{1}{3}x^{-\frac{2}{3}}(x + 3)^{\frac{2}{3}} + x^{\frac{1}{3}}\left(\tfrac{2}{3}\right)(x + 3)^{-\frac{1}{3}}$$
$$= \frac{x + 3 + 2x}{3x^{\frac{2}{3}}(x + 3)^{\frac{1}{3}}} = \frac{x + 1}{x^{\frac{2}{3}}(x + 3)^{\frac{1}{3}}}$$

Therefore, $f'(x) = 0$ when $x = -1$ and $f'(x)$ does not exist when $x = 0$ or -3. So the critical numbers are -3, -1, and 0. We set up a chart accordingly.

Interval	$x + 1$	$x^{\frac{2}{3}}$	$(x + 3)^{\frac{1}{3}}$	$f'(x)$	f
$x < -3$	$-$	$+$	$-$	$+$	increasing on $(-\infty, -3)$
$-3 < x < -1$	$-$	$+$	$+$	$-$	decreasing on $(-3, -1)$
$-1 < x < 0$	$+$	$+$	$+$	$+$	increasing on $(-1, 0)$
$x > 0$	$+$	$+$	$+$	$+$	increasing on $(0, \infty)$

(b) From part (a) and the First Derivative Test, $f(-3) = 0$ is a local maximum and $f(-1) = -4^{\frac{1}{3}} \doteq -1.6$ is a local minimum.

(c)
$$f''(x) = \frac{x^{\frac{2}{3}}(x + 3)^{\frac{1}{3}} - (x + 1)\left[\frac{2}{3}x^{-\frac{1}{3}}(x + 3)^{\frac{1}{3}} + x^{\frac{2}{3}}\left(\frac{1}{3}\right)(x + 3)^{-\frac{2}{3}}\right]}{x^{\frac{4}{3}}(x + 3)^{\frac{2}{3}}}$$

Multiplying numerator and denominator by $x^{\frac{1}{3}}(x + 3)^{\frac{2}{3}}$, we get

$$f''(x) = \frac{x(x + 3) - (x + 1)\left[\frac{2}{3}(x + 3) + \frac{1}{3}x\right]}{x^{\frac{5}{3}}(x + 3)^{\frac{4}{3}}} = \frac{-2}{x^{\frac{5}{3}}(x + 3)^{\frac{4}{3}}}$$

Since $(x + 3)^{\frac{4}{3}} \geqslant 0$ for all x (it is a fourth power), we see that $f''(x) > 0$ when $x < 0$ ($x \neq -3$) and $f''(x) < 0$ when $x > 0$. Thus, f is concave upward on $(-\infty, -3)$ and $(-3, 0)$ and concave downward on $(0, \infty)$.

(d) Since the curve changes from concave upward to concave downward at 0, $(0, 0)$ is an inflection point.

(e) In sketching the curve, notice the shape near the intercepts. Although f is concave upward on $(-\infty, -3)$ and $(-3, 0)$, it is not concave upward on $(-\infty, 0)$. The fact that $f'(x)$ does not exist at -3 and 0 is reflected in the almost vertical shape of the curve near these points.

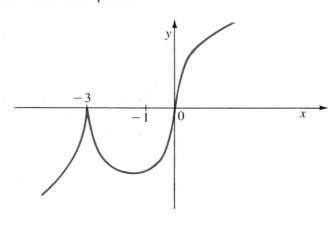

EXERCISE 5.3

A 1. (a) State the intervals on which f is concave upward or concave downward.

(b) State the coordinates of the points of inflection.

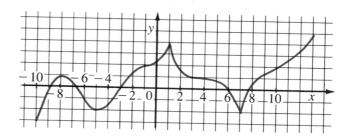

B 2. Find the intervals on which the curve is concave upward or concave downward and state the points of inflection.

(a) $y = 2 + 5x - 12x^2$

(b) $y = 6x^2 - 12x + 1$

(c) $y = 16 + 4x + x^2 - x^3$

(d) $y = 2x^3 + 24x^2 - 5x - 21$

(e) $y = x^4 - 2x^3 + x - 2$

(f) $y = x^4 - 24x^2 + x - 1$

(g) $y = \dfrac{1}{x - 1}$

(h) $y = \dfrac{x - 2}{5 - x}$

(i) $y = \dfrac{1}{x^2 + 1}$

(j) $y = \dfrac{1 - x^2}{x^3}$

(k) $y = x^{\frac{2}{3}}(5 + x)$

(l) $y = \dfrac{x^2}{\sqrt{x + 1}}$

3. For each of the following functions,

(a) find the intervals of increase or decrease,

(b) find the local maximum and minimum values,

(c) find the intervals of concavity,

(d) find the points of inflection,

(e) sketch the curve.

(i) $y = 4 - 13x - 6x^2 - x^3$

(ii) $y = x^4 - 8x^2$

(iii) $y = x\sqrt{x^2 + 4}$

(iv) $y = 3x^{\frac{2}{3}} - 2x$

C 4. For what values of the constants c and d is $(4, -7)$ a point of inflection of the cubic curve $y = x^3 + cx^2 + x + d$?

5. Show that the function $f(x) = x|x|$ has an inflection point at $(0, 0)$, but $f''(0)$ does not exist.

6. Sketch the graph of a continuous function that satisfies all of the following conditions.

(a) $f(0) = f(3) = 0, f(-1) = f(1) = -2$

(b) $f'(-1) = f'(1) = 0$

(c) $f'(x) < 0$ for $x < -1$ and for $0 < x < 1, f'(x) > 0$ for $-1 < x < 0$ and for $x > 1$

(d) $f''(x) > 0$ for $x < 3$ $(x \neq 0)$, $f''(x) < 0$ for $x > 3$

(e) $\lim\limits_{x \to \infty} f(x) = 1$, $\lim\limits_{x \to -\infty} f(x) = \infty$

7. Sketch the graph of a continuous function that satisfies all of the following conditions.

(a) $f'(x) > 0$ for $0 < x < 1$, $f'(x) < 0$ for $x > 1$

(b) $f''(x) < 0$ for $0 < x < 2$, $f''(x) > 0$ for $x > 2$

(c) $\lim\limits_{x \to \infty} f(x) = 0$

(d) $f(-x) = -f(x)$ for all x

8. Use Newton's method to find the coordinates of the inflection point of the curve $y = x^5 + 2x^3 + 6x^2 - 5x + 4$ correct to three decimal places.

9. Suppose that f is positive, concave upward, and $f''(x)$ exists on an interval I. Show that the function $g(x) = [f(x)]^2$ is also concave upward on I.

5.4 THE SECOND DERIVATIVE TEST

Another application of the second derivative in curve-sketching occurs in locating the local maximum and minimum values of a function f. We assume that $f''(x)$ exists and is continuous throughout the domain of f.

The figure shows the graph of a function f with $f''(c) > 0$ and $f'(c) = 0$. Since $f''(c) > 0$, the graph of f is concave upward near c and therefore lies above its tangent at $(c, f(c))$. But since $f'(c) = 0$, this tangent is horizontal. Therefore, f has a local minimum at c.

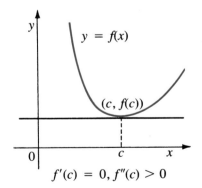

$f'(c) = 0, f''(c) > 0$

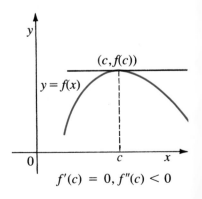

$f'(c) = 0, f''(c) < 0$

Similarly, if $f'(c) = 0$ and $f''(c) < 0$, then the graph of f is concave downward near c and therefore lies below its horizontal tangent at $(c, f(c))$. Thus, f has a local maximum at c.

> **Second Derivative Test**
>
> If $f'(c) = 0$ and $f''(c) > 0$, then f has a local minimum at c.
> If $f'(c) = 0$ and $f''(c) < 0$, then f has a local maximum at c.

Example 1   Find the local maximum and minimum values of $f(x) = x^3 - 12x + 5$.

Solution   First we find the critical numbers.

$$f'(x) = 3x^2 - 12 = 3(x^2 - 4) = 0$$
$$x^2 = 4$$
$$x = \pm 2$$

To apply the Second Derivative Test we find the second derivative:

$$f''(x) = 6x$$

Since $f'(2) = 0$ and $f''(2) = 12 > 0$,

$$f(2) = -11 \text{ is a local minimum}$$

Since $f'(-2) = 0$ and $f''(-2) = -12 < 0$,

$$f(-2) = 21 \text{ is a local maximum}$$

Example 2   Find the maximum and minimum values of $y = x^4 - 8x^3$. Use these, together with concavity and points of inflection, to sketch the curve.

Solution   If $f(x) = x^4 - 8x^3$, then

$$f'(x) = 4x^3 - 24x^2 = 4x^2(x - 6)$$
$$f''(x) = 12x^2 - 48x = 12x(x - 4)$$

To find the critical numbers we set $f'(x) = 0$ and obtain $x = 0$ and $x = 6$. Then to use the Second Derivative Test we evaluate f'' at these numbers:

$$f''(0) = 0 \qquad f''(6) = 144$$

Since $f'(6) = 0$ and $f''(6) > 0$, $f(6) = -432$ is a local minimum. Since $f''(0) = 0$, the Second Derivative Test gives no information about the critical number 0. But since the first derivative does not change sign at 0 (it is negative on both sides of 0), the First Derivative Test tells us that f has no maximum or minimum at 0.

Since $f''(x) = 12x(x - 4)$, we have $f''(x) > 0$ for $x < 0$ or $x > 4$ and $f''(x) < 0$ for $0 < x < 4$. So f is concave upward on $(-\infty, 0)$ and $(4, \infty)$ and concave downward on $(0, 4)$. The inflection points are $(0, 0)$ and $(4, -256)$.

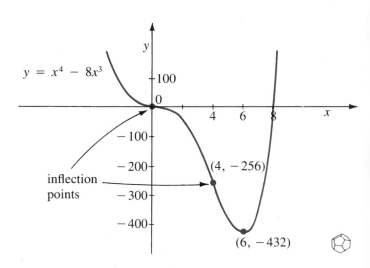

Note: Example 2 illustrates the fact that the Second Derivative Test gives no information when $f''(c) = 0$. It also fails when $f''(c)$ does not exist. For instance, in Example 4 in Section 5.3 the function has a local maximum value when $x = -3$, but $f''(-3)$ does not exist and so the Second Derivative Test does not apply. In such cases we must use the First Derivative Test. In fact, the First Derivative Test has the added advantage that we need not calculate the second derivative.

EXERCISE 5.4

B **1.** Use the Second Derivative Test to find the local maximum and minimum values of each function, wherever possible.

(a) $f(x) = 3x^2 - 4x + 13$ (b) $f(x) = 2 + 6x - 6x^2$

(c) $g(x) = 2x^3 - 48x - 17$ (d) $g(x) = 1 + 3x^2 - 2x^3$

(e) $h(x) = x^3 - 9x^2 + 24x - 10$ (f) $h(x) = x^4 - x^3$

(g) $F(x) = 3x^4 - 16x^3 + 18x^2 + 1$ (h) $F(x) = 2 + 5x - x^5$

(i) $G(x) = (1 - 3x^2 + x^3)^5$ (j) $G(x) = x^2 + \dfrac{16}{x}$

2. Use any method to find the local maximum and minimum values of each function.

(a) $f(x) = x^4 - 6x^2 + 10$ (b) $f(x) = x\sqrt{x - 1}$

(c) $g(x) = \dfrac{x}{x^2 + 9}$ (d) $g(x) = \dfrac{x}{(2x - 3)^2}$

(e) $f(t) = \dfrac{t^2}{2t + 5}$ (f) $f(t) = t + 3t^{\frac{2}{3}}$

3. Find the local maximum and minimum values of each function. Use this information, together with concavity, to sketch the curve.

(a) $y = x - x^3$ (b) $y = x^4 - 3x^3 + 3x^2 - x + 1$

(c) $y = 3x^5 - 25x^3 + 60x$ (d) $y = x\sqrt{10 + x}$

5.5   A PROCEDURE FOR CURVE SKETCHING

You may have wondered why we bother using calculus to sketch curves when we could easily use a calculator to plot points and join them with a smooth curve. The danger in this approach can be seen from the points plotted in the figures below. We might join the points to produce the curve shown in (a), but the correct graph might be as in (b).

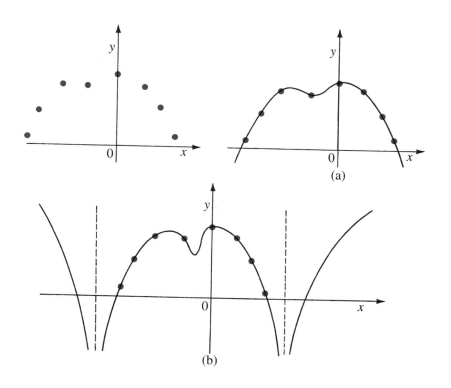

(a)

(b)

If we just plot points, we don't know when to stop. (How far should we go to the left or right?) Furthermore, it would be easy to miss such essential features as maximum or minimum values. But if we use calculus, we can be sure that all the important aspects of the curve are illustrated.

You are encouraged to use the sophisticated function-plotting software that is available. Even here, calculus is useful in choosing significant domains.

The procedure we use for sketching a curve $y = f(x)$ is to assemble the following information.

A. ***Domain.***   The first step is to find the domain of the function. (See the Review and Preview to Chapter 2.)

B. ***Intercepts.***   Next we find the x-intercepts and the y-intercept. (See the Review and Preview to this chapter.)

C. **Symmetry.** If $f(-x) = f(x)$, then f is even and its graph is symmetric about the x-axis. If $f(-x) = -f(x)$, then f is odd and its graph is symmetric about the origin. (See the Review and Preview to this chapter.)

D. **Asymptotes.**

(i) *Vertical Asymptotes.* The vertical asymptotes of a rational function can be found by equating the denominator to 0 after dividing out any common factors. If $x = a$ is a vertical asymptote, then the limits

$$\lim_{x \to a^-} f(x) \quad \text{and} \quad \lim_{x \to a^+} f(x)$$

should be identified as either ∞ or $-\infty$. (See Section 5.1.)

(ii) *Horizontal Asymptotes.* Recall from Section 5.2 that the line $y = L$ is a horizontal asymptote of the curve $y = f(x)$ if either

$$\lim_{x \to \infty} f(x) = L \quad \text{or} \quad \lim_{x \to -\infty} f(x) = L$$

E. **Intervals of Increase or Decrease.** We calculate $f'(x)$ and use the Test for Increasing or Decreasing Functions. (See Section 4.3.)

F. **Local Maximum and Minimum Values.** We find the critical numbers of f and use the First Derivative Test. (See Section 4.3.) It is also possible to use the Second Derivative Test. (See Section 5.3.)

G. **Concavity and Points of Inflection.** We calculate $f''(x)$ and use the Test for Concavity. (See Section 5.3.) Inflection points occur where the direction of concavity changes.

H. **Sketch of the Curve.** We draw the asymptotes as broken lines and sketch the portions of the curve near the asymptotes. We plot the intercepts, maximum and minimum points, and inflection points. Then we draw the curve so that it passes through these points, rising and falling according to E, with concavity according to G, and joining with the parts near the asymptotes.

Example 1   Discuss the curve $y = 3x^5 - 5x^3$ under the headings A–H.

Solution   Let $f(x) = 3x^5 - 5x^3$.

A. **Domain.**   The domain is R.

B. **Intercepts.**   The y-intercept is 0. The x-intercepts occur when $3x^5 - 5x^3 = x^3(3x^2 - 5) = 0$, so they are 0 and $\pm\sqrt{\frac{5}{3}}$.

C. **Symmetry.**   Since

$$f(-x) = 3(-x)^5 - 5(-x)^3 = -3x^5 + 5x^3 = -f(x)$$

f is an odd function. The curve is symmetric about the origin.

D. **Asymptotes.**   A polynomial has no asymptote, but it is still useful to note that

$$\lim_{x \to \infty} (3x^5 - 5x^3) = \infty \quad \text{and} \quad \lim_{x \to -\infty} (3x^5 - 5x^3) = -\infty$$

E. *Intervals of Increase or Decrease.*
$$f'(x) = 15x^4 - 15x^2 = 15x^2(x^2 - 1)$$
Thus $f'(x) > 0$ when $x^2 > 1$, that is, when $x > 1$ or $x < -1$, so f is increasing on $(-\infty, -1)$ and $(1, \infty)$. Also, $f'(x) < 0$ when $-1 < x < 1$ ($x \neq 0$), so f is decreasing on $(-1, 0)$ and $(0, 1)$.

F. *Local Maximum and Minimum Values.* By part E and the First Derivative Test, $f(-1) = 2$ is a local maximum and $f(1) = -2$ is a local minimum.

G. *Concavity and Points of Inflection.*
$$f''(x) = 60x^3 - 30x = 30x(2x^2 - 1)$$

Interval	x	$2x^2 - 1$	$f''(x)$	f
$x < -\dfrac{1}{\sqrt{2}}$	$-$	$+$	$-$	CD on $\left(-\infty, -\dfrac{1}{\sqrt{2}}\right)$
$-\dfrac{1}{\sqrt{2}} < x < 0$	$-$	$-$	$+$	CU on $\left(-\dfrac{1}{\sqrt{2}}, 0\right)$
$0 < x < \dfrac{1}{\sqrt{2}}$	$+$	$-$	$-$	CD on $\left(0, \dfrac{1}{\sqrt{2}}\right)$
$x > \dfrac{1}{\sqrt{2}}$	$+$	$+$	$+$	CU on $\left(\dfrac{1}{\sqrt{2}}, \infty\right)$

The inflection points occur when $x = 0, \pm\dfrac{1}{\sqrt{2}}$.

H. *Sketch of the Curve.* Using the information in A–G, we sketch the curve. Notice that we need only sketch it for $x \geq 0$ and use symmetry.

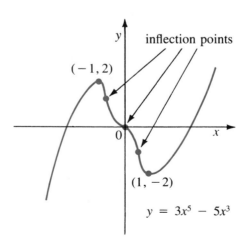

$$y = 3x^5 - 5x^3$$

Example 2 Sketch the graph of the function $f(x) = \dfrac{1}{1 + x^2}$.

Solution. A. *Domain.* The domain is R.

B. *Intercepts.* There is no x-intercept. The y-intercept is $f(0) = 1$.

C. **Symmetry.**   Since

$$f(-x) = \frac{1}{1 + (-x)^2} = \frac{1}{1 + x^2} = f(x)$$

the function is even and its graph is symmetric about the y-axis.

D. **Asymptotes.**   The denominator is never 0, so there is no vertical asymptote. To find any horizontal asymptote we compute as follows:

$$\lim_{x \to \infty} \frac{1}{1 + x^2} = \lim_{x \to \infty} \frac{\frac{1}{x^2}}{\frac{1}{x^2} + 1} = \frac{0}{0 + 1} = 0$$

Similarly, $\lim_{x \to -\infty} \dfrac{1}{1 + x^2} = 0$

So the line $y = 0$ (the x-axis) is a horizontal asymptote.

Charts are possible but not necessary in E and G

E. **Intervals of Increase or Decrease.**

$$f'(x) = -\frac{2x}{(1 + x^2)^2}$$

Since the denominator is positive, $f'(x) > 0$ when $x < 0$ and $f'(x) < 0$ when $x > 0$. Therefore f is increasing on $(-\infty, 0)$ and decreasing on $(0, \infty)$.

F. **Local Maximum and Minimum Values.**   By the First Derivative Test, $f(0) = 1$ is a local (and absolute) maximum.

G. **Concavity and Points of Inflection.**

$$f''(x) = -\frac{2(1 + x^2)^2 - (2x)2(1 + x^2)(2x)}{(1 + x^2)^4} = \frac{2(3x^2 - 1)}{(1 + x^2)^3}$$

Thus, $f''(x) > 0$ when

$$3x^2 > 1$$
$$x^2 > \tfrac{1}{3}$$
$$|x| > \frac{1}{\sqrt{3}}$$
$$x > \frac{1}{\sqrt{3}} \quad \text{or} \quad x < -\frac{1}{\sqrt{3}}$$

Thus f is concave upward on $\left(-\infty, -\dfrac{1}{\sqrt{3}}\right)$ and $\left(\dfrac{1}{\sqrt{3}}, \infty\right)$. It is concave downward on $\left(-\dfrac{1}{\sqrt{3}}, \dfrac{1}{\sqrt{3}}\right)$. The inflection points are

$$\left(-\frac{1}{\sqrt{3}}, \frac{3}{4}\right) \quad \text{and} \quad \left(\frac{1}{\sqrt{3}}, \frac{3}{4}\right)$$

H. *Sketch of the Curve.*

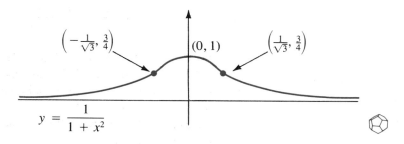

Example 3   Sketch the graph of the function $f(x) = \dfrac{x^2}{1 - x^2}$.

Solution   A. *Domain.*   The domain is $\{x \mid x^2 \neq 1\} = \{x \mid x \neq \pm 1\}$.

B. *Intercepts.*   The intercepts are both 0.

C. *Symmetry.* $f(-x) = f(x)$, so f is even and the curve is symmetric about the y-axis.

D. *Asymptotes.*

(i) Noting that $f(x) > 0$ for $-1 < x < 1$ and $f(x) < 0$ for $x > 1$ and $x < -1$, we have

$$\lim_{x \to 1^-} \frac{x^2}{1 - x^2} = \infty \qquad\qquad \lim_{x \to 1^+} \frac{x^2}{1 - x^2} = -\infty$$

$$\lim_{x \to -1^-} \frac{x^2}{1 - x^2} = -\infty \qquad\qquad \lim_{x \to -1^+} \frac{x^2}{1 - x^2} = \infty$$

So $x = 1$ and $x = -1$ are the vertical asymptotes.

(ii) $$\lim_{x \to \pm\infty} \frac{x^2}{1 - x^2} = \lim_{x \to \pm\infty} \frac{1}{\dfrac{1}{x^2} - 1} = \frac{1}{0 - 1} = -1$$

So $y = -1$ is the horizontal asymptote.

E. *Intervals of Increase or Decrease.*

$$f'(x) = \frac{(1 - x^2)(2x) - x^2(-2x)}{(1 - x^2)^2} = \frac{2x}{(1 - x^2)^2}$$

Thus $f'(x) > 0$ for $x > 0$ ($x \neq 1$) and $f'(x) < 0$ for $x < 0$ ($x \neq -1$). The function is increasing on $(0, 1)$ and $(1, \infty)$ and decreasing on $(-\infty, -1)$ and $(-1, 0)$.

F. *Local Maximum and Minimum Values.*   By the First Derivative Test, $f(0) = 0$ is a local minimum.

G. *Concavity and Points of Inflection.*

$$f''(x) = \frac{(1 - x^2)^2(2) - (2x)2(1 - x^2)(-2x)}{(1 - x^2)^4} = \frac{2 + 6x^2}{(1 - x^2)^3}$$

So $f''(x) > 0$ when $x^2 < 1$ and $f''(x) < 0$ when $x^2 > 1$. Thus, f is concave upward on $(-1, 1)$ and concave downward on $(-\infty, -1)$ and $(1, \infty)$. There is no inflection point because the numbers -1 and 1 are not in the domain.

H. *Sketch of the Curve.*   We first sketch the asymptotes and the nearby parts of the curve.

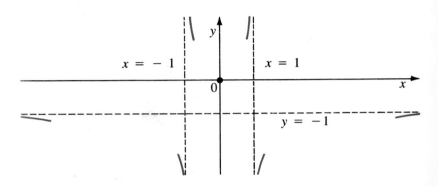

Then we use the remaining information to complete the picture.

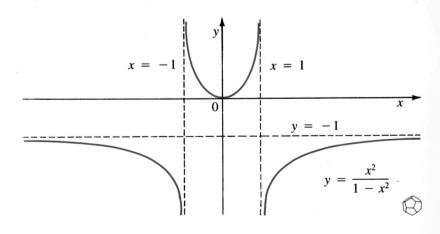

Example 4   Sketch the curve $y = x\sqrt{2 - x}$.

Solution   Let $f(x) = x\sqrt{2 - x}$.

A. **Domain.**   The domain is
$$\{x \mid 2 - x \ge 0\} = \{x \mid x \le 2\} = (-\infty, 2]$$

B. **Intercepts.**   The y-intercept is $f(0) = 0$. The x-intercepts occur when $y = 0$, so they are 0 and 2.

C. **Symmetry.**   There is no symmetry.

D. **Asymptotes.**   There is no asymptote, but
$$\lim_{x \to -\infty} x\sqrt{2 - x} = -\infty$$

E. **Intervals of Increase or Decrease.**
$$f'(x) = \sqrt{2 - x} + x\frac{-1}{2\sqrt{2 - x}}$$
$$= \frac{2(2 - x) - x}{2\sqrt{2 - x}}$$
$$= \frac{4 - 3x}{2\sqrt{2 - x}}$$

So $f'(x) > 0$ when
$$4 - 3x > 0 \quad \Leftrightarrow \quad 3x < 4 \quad \Leftrightarrow \quad x < \tfrac{4}{3}$$

and f is increasing on $\left(-\infty, \tfrac{4}{3}\right)$. Also, $f'(x) < 0$ when $x > \tfrac{4}{3}$, so f is decreasing on $\left(\tfrac{4}{3}, 2\right)$. (Remember that the domain is $(-\infty, 2)$.)

F. **Local Maximum and Minimum Values.**   By the First Derivative Test,
$$f\left(\tfrac{4}{3}\right) = \frac{4\sqrt{2}}{3\sqrt{3}} \text{ is a local (and absolute) maximum}$$

G. **Concavity and Points of Inflection.**
$$f''(x) = \frac{(2\sqrt{2 - x})(-3) - (4 - 3x)\left(-\dfrac{1}{\sqrt{2 - x}}\right)}{4(2 - x)}$$
$$= \frac{-6(2 - x) + 4 - 3x}{4(2 - x)^{\frac{3}{2}}}$$
$$= \frac{3x - 8}{4(2 - x)^{\frac{3}{2}}}$$

Note that the domain of f is $(-\infty, 2]$ and $f''(x) < 0$ on this domain. (The denominator is positive since it is a power of a square root.) Thus, f is concave downward on $(-\infty, 2)$.

H. *Sketch of the Curve.*

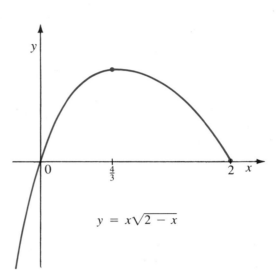

$$y = x\sqrt{2 - x}$$

EXERCISE 5.5

B   Discuss the curve in each question under the headings A. Domain; B. Intercepts; C. Symmetry; D. Asymptotes; E. Intervals of Increase or Decrease; F. Local Maximum and Minimum Values; G. Concavity and Points of Inflection; and H. Sketch of the Curve.

1. $y = 3x^5 - 10x^3 + 45x$

2. $y = (x^2 - 1)^3$

3. $y = \dfrac{x - 4}{x + 4}$

4. $y = \dfrac{x^2}{x^2 + 3}$

5. $y = \dfrac{x}{x^2 - 1}$

6. $y = \dfrac{x}{(x - 1)^2}$

7. $y = \dfrac{1}{x^3 - x}$

8. $y = \dfrac{x^2 - 1}{x^3}$

9. $y = x\sqrt{1 - x^2}$

10. $y = \dfrac{x}{\sqrt{x^2 - 4}}$

11. $y = \dfrac{\sqrt{x}}{\sqrt{x} + 1}$

12. $y = x - \sqrt[3]{x}$

**5.6 SLANT ASYMPTOTES

Consider the function

$$f(x) = x + 1 + \frac{1}{x}$$

For large values of x, $\frac{1}{x}$ is small and so the values of $f(x)$ are close to $x + 1$. This means that the graph of f is close to the graph of the line $y = x + 1$. This line is called a *slant asymptote* or an *oblique asymptote* of the graph of f.

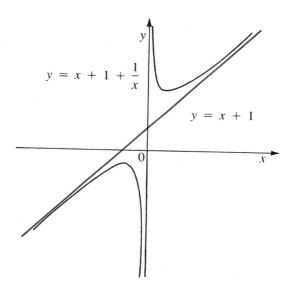

In terms of limits, we have

$$\lim_{x \to \infty} [f(x) - (x + 1)] = \lim_{x \to \infty} \left[\left(x + 1 + \frac{1}{x} \right) - (x + 1) \right]$$

$$= \lim_{x \to \infty} \frac{1}{x}$$

$$= 0$$

In general, the line $y = mx + b$ is a **slant asymptote** if the vertical distance between the curve $y = f(x)$ and the line approaches 0 as x gets large (or large negative). We can write this condition as

$$\lim_{x \to \infty} [f(x) - (mx + b)] = 0$$

or

$$\lim_{x \to -\infty} [f(x) - (mx + b)] = 0$$

For rational functions, slant asymptotes occur when the degree of the numerator is one more than the degree of the denominator. For instance, another way of writing

$$f(x) = x + 1 + \frac{1}{x} \quad \text{is} \quad f(x) = \frac{x^2 + x + 1}{x}$$

In general, for any rational function:

> The equation of a slant asymptote can be found by division.

Example 1   Find the slant asymptote of the curve $y = \dfrac{2x^3 - 3x^2 + x - 3}{x^2 + 1}$.

Solution   First we note that there will be a slant asymptote because the degree of the numerator is one more than the degree of the denominator. Long division gives

$$
\begin{array}{r}
2x \;-\; 3 \\
x^2 + 1 \overline{)\, 2x^3 - 3x^2 + x - 3 } \\
\underline{2x^3 + 2x } \\
-3x^2 - x - 3 \\
\underline{-3x^2 - 3} \\
- x
\end{array}
$$

and so

$$f(x) = \frac{2x^3 - 3x^2 + x - 3}{x^2 + 1} = 2x - 3 - \frac{x}{x^2 + 1}$$

Therefore

$$\lim_{x \to \infty} [f(x) - (2x - 3)] = \lim_{x \to \infty} \left[2x - 3 - \frac{x}{x^2 + 1} - (2x - 3) \right]$$

$$= \lim_{x \to \infty} \left[-\frac{x}{x^2 + 1} \right]$$

$$= \lim_{x \to \infty} \frac{-\dfrac{1}{x}}{1 + \dfrac{1}{x^2}}$$

$$= \frac{0}{1 + 0}$$

$$= 0$$

Thus the line $y = 2x - 3$ is the slant asymptote.

Example 2   Find the slant asymptote of the curve $y = \dfrac{1 + x - x^2}{x - 1}$, then use it to help sketch the curve.

Solution   Long division gives

$$
\begin{array}{r}
-x \\
x - 1 \overline{\smash{)}\, -x^2 + x + 1} \\
\underline{-x^2 + x} \\
1
\end{array}
$$

$$
f(x) = \frac{1 + x - x^2}{x - 1} = -x + \frac{1}{x - 1}
$$

Therefore, $\displaystyle\lim_{x \to \infty} [f(x) - (-x)] = \lim_{x \to \infty} \frac{1}{x - 1} = 0$

and so the slant asymptote is $y = -x$.

We analyze the other aspects of the curve using the headings of Section 5.5.

A. **Domain.**   The domain is $\{x \mid x \neq 1\}$.

B. **Intercepts.**   The y-intercept is $f(0) = -1$. The x-intercepts occur when

$$
x^2 - x - 1 = 0
$$
$$
x = \frac{1 \pm \sqrt{5}}{2}
$$

C. **Symmetry.**   There is no symmetry.

D. **Asymptotes.** $\displaystyle\lim_{x \to 1^+} \left(-x + \frac{1}{x - 1} \right) = \infty$

$$
\lim_{x \to 1^-} \left(-x + \frac{1}{x - 1} \right) = -\infty
$$

So $x = 1$ is a vertical asymptote. Since there is a slant asymptote, there cannot be a horizontal asymptote.

E. **Intervals of Increase or Decrease.** $f'(x) = -1 - \dfrac{1}{(x - 1)^2}$

Thus $f'(x) < 0$ for all $x \neq 1$, so f is decreasing on $(-\infty, 1)$ and $(1, \infty)$.

F. **Local Maximum and Minimum Values.**   There is no maximum or minimum.

G. **Concavity and Points of Inflection.** $f''(x) = \dfrac{2}{(x - 1)^3}$

So $f''(x) > 0$ for $x > 1$ and $f''(x) < 0$ for $x < 1$. Thus, f is concave upward on $(1, \infty)$ and concave downward on $(-\infty, 1)$. There is no inflection point.

H. *Sketch of the Curve.*

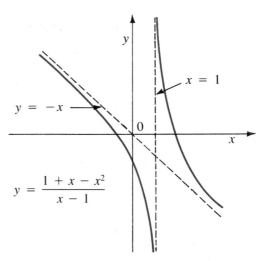

EXERCISE 5.6

B 1. Find the equation of the slant asymptote.

(a) $y = \dfrac{2x - x^2 - 1}{x}$

(b) $y = \dfrac{x^3 - 1}{x^2}$

(c) $y = \dfrac{3x^2 + 4x + 2}{x + 1}$

(d) $y = \dfrac{4x^2}{2x + 1}$

(e) $y = \dfrac{x^3 + 4x^2 + 5x + 16}{x^2 + 4}$

(f) $y = \dfrac{x + x^2 - x^4}{x^3 - 1}$

2. Find the slant asymptote of the curve. Thus, use it to help graph the curve.

(a) $y = \dfrac{x^2 + 9}{x}$

(b) $y = \dfrac{x^2 - 2x - 1}{x}$

(c) $y = \dfrac{x^3}{x^2 - 1}$

(d) $y = \dfrac{(x - 1)^3}{x^2}$

C 3. Let $f(x) = \dfrac{x^3 + 1}{x}$

Show that

$$\lim_{x \to \infty} [f(x) - x^2] = 0$$

This shows that the graph of f approaches the graph of $y = x^2$, and we say that the graph of f is *asymptotic* to the parabola $y = x^2$. Use this fact to help sketch the graph of f.

5.7 REVIEW EXERCISE

1. Find the limit.

(a) $\lim_{x \to 4^+} \dfrac{2}{4 - x}$

(b) $\lim_{x \to 4} \dfrac{6}{(x - 4)^2}$

(c) $\lim_{x \to -1^-} \dfrac{1}{(x + 1)^3}$

(d) $\lim_{x \to 5^-} \dfrac{x + 3}{x^2 - 4x - 5}$

(e) $\lim_{x \to -2} \dfrac{x}{(x + 2)^2}$

(f) $\lim_{x \to \infty} \dfrac{6 - x}{6 + 5x}$

(g) $\lim_{x \to -\infty} \dfrac{x}{x^3 - 1}$

(h) $\lim_{x \to \infty} \dfrac{4x^2 - 3x + 5}{2x^2 + 5x - 4}$

(i) $\lim_{x \to \infty} (x^4 - 2x^2)$

(j) $\lim_{x \to \infty} (\sqrt{x^2 + x} - \sqrt{x^2 - x})$

2. Find the vertical and horizontal asymptotes.

(a) $y = \dfrac{6x - 1}{1 - 2x}$

(b) $y = \dfrac{1}{x^2 + 6x + 9}$

(c) $y = \dfrac{x}{2x^2 - 5x - 3}$

(d) $y = \dfrac{x^3}{x^3 - 1}$

3. Find the intervals on which the curve is concave upward or concave downward and state the points of inflection.

(a) $y = 5x^3 + 12x^2 - 3x + 2$

(b) $y = x^4 - x^3 - 3x^2 + x - 12$

(c) $y = \dfrac{x^2}{x^2 + 4}$

(d) $y = x + \dfrac{1}{\sqrt{x}}$

4. Find the local maximum and minimum values of each function.

(a) $f(x) = x^2 - x^3$

(b) $f(x) = 2x^3 + 15x^2 - 36x$

(c) $g(x) = \dfrac{x^2}{x - 1}$

(d) $g(x) = x + \sqrt{1 - x}$

5. Discuss each curve under the headings A–H given in Section 5.5.

(a) $y = x^3 - 6x^2 + 9x$

(b) $y = x^3 - x^4$

(c) $y = \dfrac{2}{4 + x}$

(d) $y = \dfrac{1 - x^2}{1 + x^2}$

(e) $y = \dfrac{1 + x^2}{1 - x^2}$

(f) $y = x^{\frac{1}{3}}(x - 4)^{\frac{2}{3}}$

6. Sketch the graph of a function f that satisfies all the following conditions.

(a) $f(0) = 0, f'(0) = 1$

(b) $f''(x) > 0$ for $x < 0$, $f''(x) < 0$ for $x > 0$

(c) $\lim_{x \to \infty} f(x) = 2$, $\lim_{x \to -\infty} f(x) = -2$

7. Sketch the graph of a function g that satisfies the following conditions.

(a) $g(0) = 0$

(b) $g''(x) > 0$ for $x \neq 0$

(c) $\lim\limits_{x \to 0^-} g'(x) = \infty$, $\lim\limits_{x \to 0^+} g'(x) = -\infty$

(d) $\lim\limits_{x \to -\infty} g(x) = -\infty$, $\lim\limits_{x \to \infty} g(x) = \infty$

PROBLEMS PLUS

Sketch the curve $y = x + \sqrt{|x|}$

5.8   CHAPTER 5 TEST

1. Find the following limits.

   (a) $\lim\limits_{x \to \infty} \dfrac{6x^3 - 3x + 1}{2x^3 + x^2 - 5}$

   (b) $\lim\limits_{x \to -2+} \dfrac{x - 1}{x^2 - 4}$

2. Find the vertical and horizontal asymptotes of the curve
   $$y = \frac{1 - 2x}{3x + 5}.$$

3. (a) Find the intervals on which the curve $y = \dfrac{x}{(x + 1)^2}$ is concave upward or concave downward.

   (b) Find any points of inflection.

4. For the curve $y = 2 - 12x + 9x^2 - 2x^3$,

   (a) find the intervals of increase and decrease,

   (b) find the local maximum and minimum values,

   (c) find the intervals of concavity,

   (d) find any inflection points,

   (e) sketch the curve.

5. Discuss the curve $y = \dfrac{x}{x^2 - 9}$ under the following headings.

   (a) Domain

   (b) Intercepts

   (c) Symmetry

   (d) Asymptotes

   (e) Intervals of Increase or Decrease

   (f) Local Maximum and Minimum Values

   (g) Concavity and Points of Inflection

   (h) Sketch of the Curve.

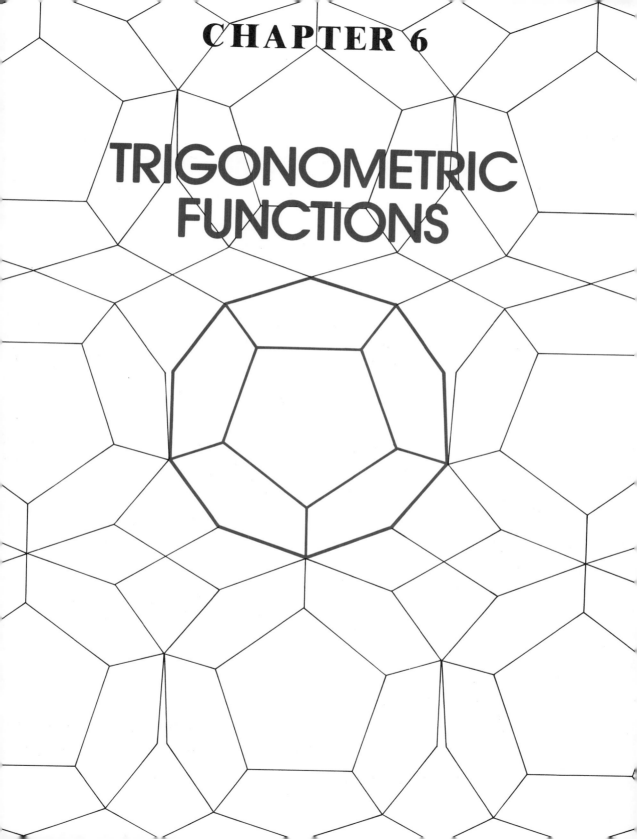

CHAPTER 6

TRIGONOMETRIC FUNCTIONS

REVIEW AND PREVIEW TO
CHAPTER 6

Angles and Arcs

The measure of an angle is an amount of rotation, where one complete revolution is divided into 360 equal parts, each of which is called a **degree**.

$$1 \text{ rev } = 360°$$

This unit of measure is seldom used in calculus. In order to simplify the formulas for the derivatives of the trigonometric functions, we use the unit of measurement called a **radian**.

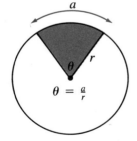

$\theta = \frac{a}{r}$

> The measure of an angle in radians is the ratio of the arc length that subtends the angle at the centre of a circle to the radius of the circle.

In the diagram the arc with length a subtends angle θ at the centre of the circle with radius r. The radian measure of angle θ is

$$\theta = \frac{a}{r}$$

$\theta = 1 \text{ rad}$

Since a and r represent lengths measured in the same units, the ratio $\frac{a}{r}$ has no unit. Thus the radian measure of angle θ is a pure number. In particular, if a is equal to r, the radian measure of θ is one.

If we let $r = 1$, we can interpret radian measure as the length of an arc on the unit circle. Now θ, the angle subtended at the centre of the unit circle by arc a, is just equal to a.

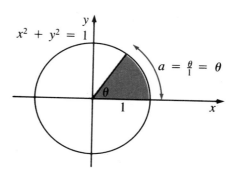

The radian measure of the angle θ subtended by an arc equal in length to the circumference of the circle is

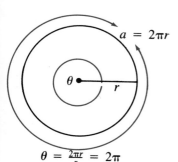

$$\theta = \frac{2\pi r}{r} = 2\pi$$

Since θ is 1 rev it has degree measure 360.

Therefore 2π rad $= 360°$

which simplifies to

$$\boxed{\pi \text{ rad} = 180°}$$

This enables us to convert any angle expressed in degrees to radians and vice versa.

Example 1   Convert 2 radians to degrees.

Solution   A simple method of conversion is presented.

Since π rad $= 180°$

$$1 \text{ rad} = \frac{180°}{\pi}$$

Therefore $2 \text{ rad} = \dfrac{2 \times 180°}{\pi} \doteq 115°$

Example 2   Convert 60° to radian measure.

Solution   Since $180° = \pi$ rad

$$1° = \frac{\pi}{180} \text{ rad}$$

so $60(1°) = 60\left(\frac{\pi}{180}\right)$ rad

Finally $60° = \frac{\pi}{3}$ rad $\doteq 1.047$ rad

EXERCISE 1

1. Calculate the degree measure of the angles having radian measures
   (a) $\frac{\pi}{6}$ (b) $\frac{-3\pi}{2}$ (c) $\frac{5\pi}{4}$ (d) 3π

   (e) 4   (f) $-\frac{3}{4}$ (g) -12

2. Calculate the radian measure of the angles whose measures are
   (a) 45°   (b) 315°   (c) $-210°$ (d) 570°
   (e) 2°   (f) $-28°$ (g) 601°

3. The radius of a circle is 10 cm. Calculate:
   (a) the arc length that determines an angle of 2.5 rad.
   (b) the angle in radians that determines an arc length of 12 cm.

4. The length of an arc of a circle is 32 cm and the angle it determines is 72°. Find the radius of the circle.

Definitions of the Trigonometric Functions

A point $P(x, y)$ in the Cartesian plane determines an angle θ as shown in the diagram. This angle θ, with one arm along the positive x-axis, is said to be in **standard position**. If we let the distance from P to the origin be r, six ratios are determined. Their names, abbreviations, and definitions are summarized in the following chart.

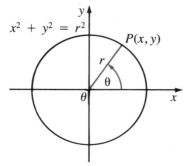

Trigonometric Ratios			
sine:	$\sin \theta = \frac{y}{r}$	cosecant:	$\csc \theta = \frac{r}{y}$
cosine:	$\cos \theta = \frac{x}{r}$	secant:	$\sec \theta = \frac{r}{x}$
tangent:	$\tan \theta = \frac{y}{x}$	cotangent:	$\cot \theta = \frac{x}{y}$

Eight relationships involving the trigonometric ratios are listed below. The proof of each is requested in Exercise 2.

Fundamental Relationships		
$\csc\theta = \dfrac{1}{\sin\theta}$ $\qquad$ $\sec\theta = \dfrac{1}{\cos\theta}$ $\qquad$ $\cot\theta = \dfrac{1}{\tan\theta}$		
$\tan\theta = \dfrac{\sin\theta}{\cos\theta}$ $\cot\theta = \dfrac{\cos\theta}{\sin\theta}$	$\sin^2\theta + \cos^2\theta = 1$ $\sec^2\theta = 1 + \tan^2\theta$ $\csc^2\theta = 1 + \cot^2\theta$

EXERCISE 2

1. $P(3, 4)$ determines an angle θ in standard position. Determine the six trigonometric ratios of angle θ.

2. $P(-2, -1)$ determines an angle θ in standard position. Determine the sine, cosine, and tangent of angle θ.

3. $P(5, -12)$ determines an angle θ in standard position. Determine the cosecant, secant, and cotangent of angle θ.

4. If $\sin\theta = \dfrac{1}{3}$, $0 \leqslant \theta \leqslant \dfrac{\pi}{2}$, find $\cos\theta$ and $\tan\theta$.

5. If $\cos\theta = -\dfrac{1}{2}$, $\dfrac{\pi}{2} \leqslant \theta \leqslant \pi$, find $\csc\theta$ and $\cot\theta$.

6. If $\tan\theta = -\dfrac{5}{3}$, $\dfrac{3\pi}{2} \leqslant \theta \leqslant 2\pi$, find $\cos\theta$ and $\csc\theta$.

7. If $\cot\theta = \dfrac{5}{12}$, $\pi \leqslant \theta \leqslant \dfrac{3\pi}{2}$, find $\sec\theta$ and $\sin\theta$.

8. If $\tan\theta = -\dfrac{4}{3}$, $\dfrac{\pi}{2} \leqslant \theta \leqslant \pi$, show that $\sin^2\theta + \cos^2\theta = 1$.

9. If $\csc\theta = 2$, $\dfrac{\pi}{2} \leqslant \theta \leqslant \pi$, show that $\dfrac{\sin\theta}{\cos\theta} = \tan\theta$.

10. If $\sin\theta = -\dfrac{1}{2}$, $\dfrac{3\pi}{2} \leqslant \theta \leqslant 2\pi$, show that $\sec^2\theta = 1 + \tan^2\theta$.

11. Use the basic definitions and the relationship $x^2 + y^2 = r^2$ to prove each of the following relationships:

    (a) $\csc\theta = \dfrac{1}{\sin\theta}$ $\qquad\qquad$ (b) $\sec\theta = \dfrac{1}{\cos\theta}$

    (c) $\cot\theta = \dfrac{1}{\tan\theta}$ $\qquad\qquad$ (d) $\tan\theta = \dfrac{\sin\theta}{\cos\theta}$

(e) $\cot \theta = \dfrac{\cos \theta}{\sin \theta}$ (f) $\sin^2 \theta + \cos^2 \theta = 1$

12. Use $\sin^2 \theta + \cos^2 \theta = 1$ to prove:
(a) $\sec^2 \theta = 1 + \tan^2 \theta$ (b) $\csc^2 \theta = 1 + \cot^2 \theta$

Graphs of the Trigonometric Functions

When we talk about the function f defined for all real numbers x by $f(x) = \sin x$, it is understood that $\sin x$ means the sine of the angle whose *radian* measure is x. A similar convention holds for the other trigonometric functions.

The graphs of the basic trigonometric functions and knowledge of their domain, range, and periodicity are useful. In Section 6.5, we use them to help us solve trigonometric equations. In Chapter 7, the graphs of the sine and cosine functions are instrumental in the development of the derivative of $f(x) = \sin x$.

$$y = \sin x$$

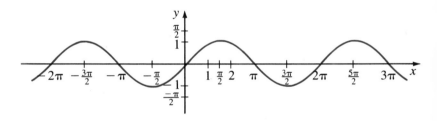

Domain $= R$
Range $= \{y \mid -1 \leqslant y \leqslant 1\}$
Period $= 2\pi$

$$y = \cos x$$

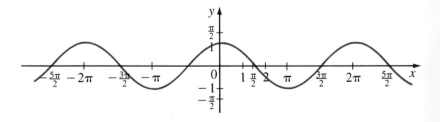

Domain $= R$
Range $= \{y \mid -1 \leqslant y \leqslant 1\}$
Period $= 2\pi$

$$y = \tan x$$

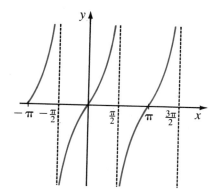

$$y = \cot x$$

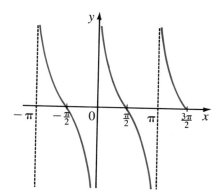

Domain $= \{x \mid x \neq (2n - 1)\frac{\pi}{2}, n \in I\}$

Range $= R$
Period $= \pi$
Vertical asymptotes:

$x = (2n - 1)\frac{\pi}{2}, n \in I$

Domain $= \{x \mid x \neq n\pi, n \in I\}$
Range $= R$
Period $= \pi$
Vertical asymptotes: $x = n\pi, n \in I$

$$y = \csc x$$

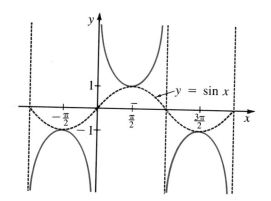

$$y = \sec x$$

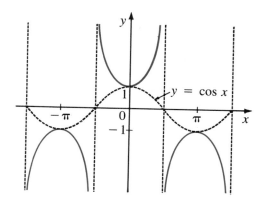

Domain $= \{x \mid x \neq n\pi, n \in I\}$
Range $= \{y \mid y \leqslant -1 \text{ or } y \geqslant 1\}$
Period $= 2\pi$
Vertical asymptotes: $x = n\pi, n \in I$

Domain $= \{x \mid x \neq (2n - 1)\frac{\pi}{2}, n \in I\}$

Range $= \{y \mid y \leqslant -1 \text{ or } y \geqslant 1\}$
Period $= 2\pi$
Vertical asymptotes: $x = (2n - 1)\frac{\pi}{2}, n \in I$

Transformations, such as translations and reflections, can reduce the amount of work in graphing functions.

Vertical and Horizontal Shifts

If $c > 0$ the graph of

$\left.\begin{array}{l} y = f(x) + c \\ y = f(x) - c \end{array}\right\}$ is the graph of $y = f(x)$ shifted c units $\left\{\begin{array}{l} \text{upward.} \\ \text{downward.} \end{array}\right.$

$\left.\begin{array}{l} y = f(x + c) \\ y = f(x - c) \end{array}\right\}$ $\left.\begin{array}{l} \text{to the left.} \\ \text{to the right.} \end{array}\right.$

Stretching and Reflecting

The graph of $y = af(x)$ is obtained from the graph of $y = f(x)$ by

stretching in the y-direction	if $a > 1$.
shrinking in the y-direction	if $0 < a < 1$.
reflection in the x-axis	if $a = -1$.
shrinking and reflecting in the x-axis	if $-1 < a < 0$.
stretching and reflecting in the x-axis	if $a < -1$.

The graph of $y = f(ax)$ is obtained from the graph of $y = f(x)$ by

shrinking in the x-direction	if $a > 1$.
stretching in the x-direction	if $0 < a < 1$.

EXERCISE 3

1. Sketch $y = \sin x$, $y = 2 \sin x$, and $y = \sin 2x$, $0 \leqslant x \leqslant 2\pi$, on the same set of axes.

2. Sketch $y = \cos x$, $y = \cos\left(x + \dfrac{\pi}{4}\right)$, and $y = \cos\left(x - \dfrac{\pi}{4}\right)$, $-2x \leqslant x \leqslant 2\pi$, on the same set of axes.

3. Sketch $y = \tan \frac{1}{2}x$ for $-2\pi \leqslant x \leqslant 2\pi$. Sketch $y = -\tan \frac{1}{2}x$ on the same set of axes over the same interval.

Trigonometric Ratios of Special Angles

The values of the trigonometric functions at $\frac{\pi}{6}, \frac{\pi}{4}$, and $\frac{\pi}{3}$ can be found from the special right triangles illustrated. In problems dealing with these angles or multiples of these angles, knowing the values can give us exact answers.

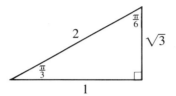
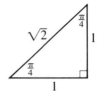

EXERCISE 4

1. Evaluate each of the following using the special triangles.

(a) $\sin \frac{\pi}{3} - \cos \frac{\pi}{6}$

(b) $\sec \frac{\pi}{6} + 2 \cot \frac{\pi}{4}$

(c) $\sin^2 30° + \cos^2 45°$

(d) $4 \sin \frac{\pi}{6} + \sec^2 \frac{\pi}{4}$

(e) $\sqrt{3} \cos 30° - \csc 45° + 3 \sin^2 45°$

(f) $\tan \frac{\pi}{3} \cos \frac{\pi}{4} \csc \frac{\pi}{3} - \sec \frac{\pi}{6} \tan \frac{\pi}{6}$

PROBLEMS PLUS

Find the number of solutions of the equation $\sin x = \frac{x}{100}$.

INTRODUCTION

In this chapter, we take a short break from our study of calculus to extend our knowledge of the trigonometric functions. Relationships that will enable us to apply the calculus to the trigonometric functions are developed. Attention is devoted to the proofs of trigonometric identities and the solution of trigonometric equations, two skills that are frequently used when the techniques of calculus are applied to problems involving the trigonometric functions.

6.1 FUNCTIONS OF RELATED VALUES

In this section, we develop formulas that express the trigonometric function of any angle in terms of the trigonometric function of an acute angle. We use reflections in the coordinate axes or the origin to develop the formulas. The following diagrams illustrate the coordinate of P', the image of $P(a, b)$ after a reflection in the y-axis, the x-axis, and the origin.

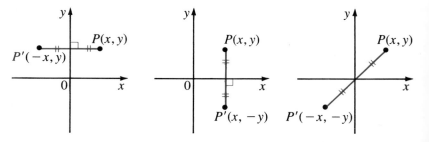

Reflection in y-axis   Reflection in x-axis   Reflection in origin

Now we express a point on the unit circle in terms of the angle it determines at the origin. $P(x, y)$ determines angle θ in the diagram.

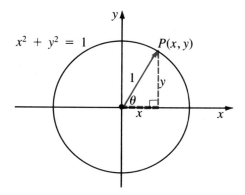

Since $\cos \theta = \dfrac{x}{1} = x$ and $\sin \theta = \dfrac{y}{1} = y$, $P(x, y)$ can be expressed as $P(\cos \theta, \sin \theta)$.

Example 1 Find the coordinates of the point on the unit circle determined by

(a) angle $\dfrac{\pi}{6}$ in standard position.

(b) angle $\pi - a$ in standard position.

Solution (a)

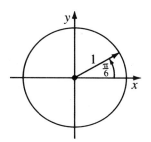

The required point is $\left(\cos \dfrac{\pi}{6}, \sin \dfrac{\pi}{6} \right) = \left(\dfrac{\sqrt{3}}{2}, \dfrac{1}{2} \right)$.

(b)

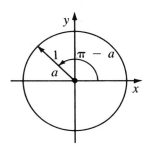

The required coordinates are $(\cos(\pi - a), \sin(\pi - a))$.

If an angle is in standard position, the acute angle between its terminal arm and the x-axis is called the **related acute angle**. In each diagram, θ has related acute angle a and can be expressed in terms of a.

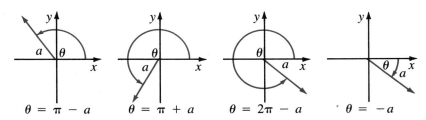

$\theta = \pi - a$ $\theta = \pi + a$ $\theta = 2\pi - a$ $\theta = -a$

We are now ready to develop the related angle formulas. In the diagram, point P on the unit circle determines acute angle a. P' is the image of P after a reflection in the y-axis. By symmetry, the acute angle between OP' and the x-axis is equal to a. Therefore P' determines the second quadrant angle $\pi - a$ having related acute angle a.

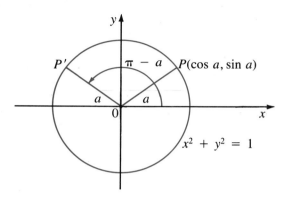

Since P' is the image of P, its coordinates are $(-\cos a, \sin a)$. Since P' determines angle $\pi - a$, its coordinates are $(\cos(\pi - a), \sin(\pi - a))$.

Therefore $\sin(\pi - a) = \sin a$

and $\cos(\pi - a) = -\cos a$

and $\tan(\pi - a) = \dfrac{\sin(\pi - a)}{\cos(\pi - a)}$

$$= \dfrac{\sin a}{-\cos a}$$

$$= -\tan a$$

$$\boxed{\begin{aligned} \sin(\pi - a) &= \sin a \\ \cos(\pi - a) &= -\cos a \\ \tan(\pi - a) &= -\tan a \end{aligned}}$$

Example 2   Find the exact value of $\sin \dfrac{2\pi}{3}$.

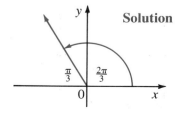

Solution   Express $\dfrac{2\pi}{3}$ in terms of its related acute angle $\dfrac{\pi}{3}$.

$$\sin \frac{2\pi}{3} = \sin\left(\pi - \frac{\pi}{3}\right) = \sin \frac{\pi}{3} = \frac{\sqrt{3}}{2}$$

Example 3 If $\tan\theta = -\dfrac{1}{\sqrt{3}}, \dfrac{\pi}{2} \leq \theta \leq \pi$, find θ.

Solution In the diagram, a is the related acute angle of second quadrant angle θ.

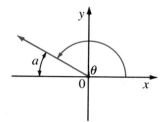

Now
$$\theta = \pi - a$$

Therefore
$$\tan(\pi - a) = -\frac{1}{\sqrt{3}}$$

Using our new formula we get

$$-\tan a = -\frac{1}{\sqrt{3}}$$

$$\tan a = \frac{1}{\sqrt{3}}$$

$$a = \frac{\pi}{6}$$

and so
$$\theta = \pi - \frac{\pi}{6} = \frac{5\pi}{6}$$

When $P(\cos a, \sin a)$ is reflected in the origin its image P' determines angle $\pi + a$ in the third quadrant with a as its related acute angle.

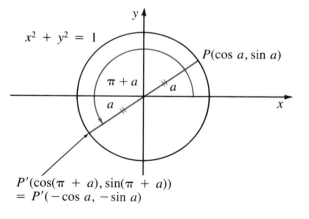

$$\sin(\pi + a) = -\sin a$$
$$\cos(\pi + a) = -\cos a$$
$$\tan(\pi + a) = \tan a$$

When P is reflected in the x-axis, the image determines angle $2\pi - a$ in the fourth quadrant. The related acute angle is a.

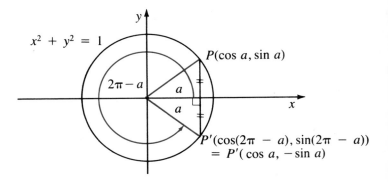

$$\sin(2\pi - a) = -\sin a$$
$$\cos(2\pi - a) = \cos a$$
$$\tan(2\pi - a) = -\tan a$$

A point on the unit circle is determined by more than one angle. When $P(\cos a, \sin a)$ is reflected in the x-axis, the image P' is not uniquely determined by the angle $2\pi - a$. In fact, all of the positive and negative angles that are coterminal with $2\pi - a$ also determine the position of P'. Let us consider the particular coterminal angle $-a$.

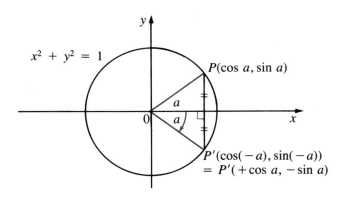

$$\sin(-a) = -\sin a$$
$$\cos(-a) = \cos a$$
$$\tan(-a) = -\tan a$$

It is important to note that, even though we developed these formulas with a as an acute angle, they are true for all values of a. The following example illustrates this fact.

Example 4   Prove that $\cos\left(\pi + \dfrac{2\pi}{3}\right) = -\cos\dfrac{2\pi}{3}$.

Solution   We manipulate the argument of each function to create one of the forms introduced in this section. We work with each side separately to achieve the same result.

$$\cos\left(\pi + \frac{2\pi}{3}\right) = \cos\frac{5\pi}{3} \qquad\qquad -\cos\frac{2\pi}{3} = -\cos\left(\pi - \frac{\pi}{3}\right)$$

$$= \cos\left(2\pi - \frac{\pi}{3}\right) \qquad\qquad = -\left(-\cos\frac{\pi}{3}\right)$$

$$= \cos\frac{\pi}{3} \qquad\qquad\qquad = \cos\frac{\pi}{3}$$

Therefore $\qquad\qquad \cos\left(\pi + \dfrac{2\pi}{3}\right) = -\cos\dfrac{2\pi}{3}$

Example 5   Prove that $\cos(\pi - b) = -\cos b$ if b is in the interval $\left(\pi, \dfrac{3\pi}{2}\right)$.

Solution   In the diagram, P is a point on the unit circle and P' is the image of P after a reflection in the y-axis.

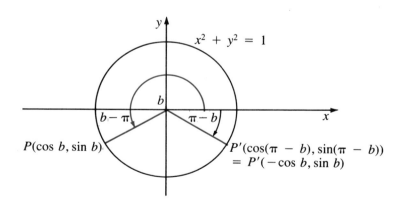

Since P' is the image of P, it has coordinates $(-\cos b, \sin b)$. But P' determines the angle $\pi - b$ and has coordinates $(\cos(\pi - b), \sin(\pi - b))$.

Therefore $\qquad \cos(\pi - b) = -\cos b$

Example 6   Find the exact value of $\sin\left(-\dfrac{3\pi}{4}\right)$.

Solution   Since $\sin(-a) = -\sin a$ for all values of a, we proceed as follows:

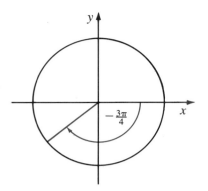

$$\sin\left(-\frac{3\pi}{4}\right) = -\sin\frac{3\pi}{4}$$

$$= -\sin\left(\pi - \frac{\pi}{4}\right)$$

$$= -\sin\frac{\pi}{4}$$

$$= -\frac{1}{\sqrt{2}}$$

The complement of the related acute angle is the *co-related acute angle*. It is the acute angle between the terminal arm of an angle in standard position and the *y*-axis. In each diagram, θ has co-related acute angle *a* and can be expressed in terms of *a*.

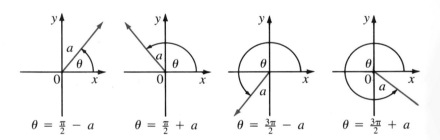

$\theta = \frac{\pi}{2} - a$ $\qquad$ $\theta = \frac{\pi}{2} + a$ $\qquad$ $\theta = \frac{3\pi}{2} - a$ $\qquad$ $\theta = \frac{3\pi}{2} + a$

Any angle can also be expressed as a function of its co-related acute angle. In the diagram, $P(\cos a, \sin a)$ determines the acute angle *a*. P' is the image of P after a reflection in the line $y = x$. Thus P' has coordinates $(\sin a, \cos a)$.

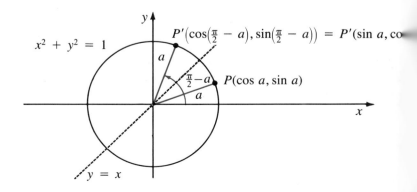

But P' determines the angle $\dfrac{\pi}{2} - a$ and has coordinates

$$\left(\cos\left(\frac{\pi}{2}-a\right), \ \sin\left(\frac{\pi}{2}-a\right)\right).$$

Therefore $\sin\left(\dfrac{\pi}{2} - a\right) = \cos a$

and $\cos\left(\dfrac{\pi}{2} - a\right) = \sin a$

Now $\tan\left(\dfrac{\pi}{2} - a\right) = \dfrac{\sin\left(\dfrac{\pi}{2} - a\right)}{\cos\left(\dfrac{\pi}{2} - a\right)}$

$$= \frac{\cos a}{\sin a}$$

$$= \cot a$$

We now reflect $P'(\sin a, \cos a)$ in the y-axis, the origin, and the x-axis to generate the rest of the co-related angle formulas.

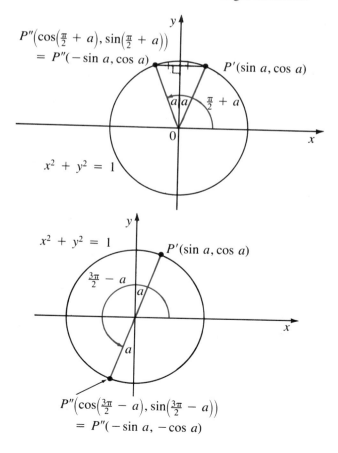

$P''\left(\cos\left(\frac{\pi}{2} + a\right), \sin\left(\frac{\pi}{2} + a\right)\right)$
$= P''(-\sin a, \cos a)$

$P'(\sin a, \cos a)$

$\frac{\pi}{2} + a$

$x^2 + y^2 = 1$

$x^2 + y^2 = 1$

$P'(\sin a, \cos a)$

$\frac{3\pi}{2} - a$

$P''\left(\cos\left(\frac{3\pi}{2} - a\right), \sin\left(\frac{3\pi}{2} - a\right)\right)$
$= P''(-\sin a, -\cos a)$

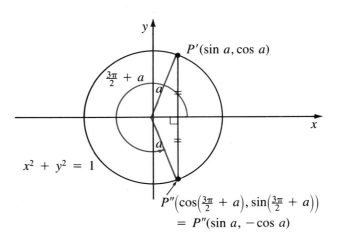

The results are summarized in the following charts.

$$\sin\left(\frac{\pi}{2} - a\right) = \cos a$$

$$\cos\left(\frac{\pi}{2} - a\right) = \sin a$$

$$\tan\left(\frac{\pi}{2} - a\right) = \cot a$$

$$\sin\left(\frac{\pi}{2} + a\right) = \cos a$$

$$\cos\left(\frac{\pi}{2} + a\right) = -\sin a$$

$$\tan\left(\frac{\pi}{2} + a\right) = -\cot a$$

$$\sin\left(\frac{3\pi}{2} - a\right) = -\cos a$$

$$\cos\left(\frac{3\pi}{2} - a\right) = -\sin a$$

$$\tan\left(\frac{3\pi}{2} - a\right) = \cot a$$

$$\sin\left(\frac{3\pi}{2} + a\right) = -\cos a$$

$$\cos\left(\frac{3\pi}{2} + a\right) = \sin a$$

$$\tan\left(\frac{3\pi}{2} + a\right) = -\cot a$$

Example 7   Express $\cos\left(-\frac{4\pi}{3}\right)$ as a function of its co-related acute angle and evaluate.

Solution   Use the identity $\cos(-a) = \cos a$ to produce a positive argument.

$$\cos\left(-\frac{4\pi}{3}\right) = \cos\frac{4\pi}{3}$$

$$= \cos\left(\frac{3\pi}{2} - \frac{\pi}{6}\right)$$

$$= -\sin\frac{\pi}{6}$$

$$= -\tfrac{1}{2}$$

Example 8 Express tan 240° as a function of its co-related acute angle and evaluate.

Solution
$$\tan 240° = \tan(270° - 30°)$$
$$= \cot 30°$$
$$= \sqrt{3}$$

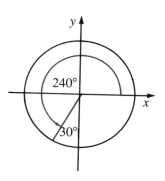

As was the case with the related angle formulas, the co-related angle formulas are true for all values of a. Example 9 illustrates this fact.

Example 9 Prove that $\cos\left(\dfrac{\pi}{2} - \dfrac{2\pi}{3}\right) = \sin\dfrac{2\pi}{3}$.

Solution We work with each side separately to achieve an identical result.

$$\cos\left(\frac{\pi}{2} - \frac{2\pi}{3}\right) = \cos\left(-\frac{\pi}{6}\right) \qquad \sin\frac{2\pi}{3} = \sin\left(\frac{\pi}{2} + \frac{\pi}{6}\right)$$
$$= \cos\frac{\pi}{6} \qquad\qquad\qquad = \cos\frac{\pi}{6}$$

Therefore $\qquad\qquad \cos\left(\dfrac{\pi}{2} - \dfrac{2\pi}{3}\right) = \sin\dfrac{2\pi}{3}$

EXERCISE 6.1

B **1.** Express each of the following as a function of its related acute angle and evaluate.

(a) $\sin\left(-\dfrac{7\pi}{6}\right)$

(b) $\cos\dfrac{15\pi}{4}$

(c) $\tan\left(-\dfrac{8\pi}{3}\right)$

(d) $\tan\dfrac{33\pi}{4}$

(e) $\sin 240°$

(f) $\cos(-135°)$

(g) $\tan 330°$

(h) $\sin 495°$

2. Express each of the following as a function of its co-related acute angle and evaluate.

   (a) $\cos \dfrac{11}{6}\pi$

   (b) $\sin\left(-\dfrac{7\pi}{6}\right)$

   (c) $\sin 120°$

   (d) $\tan\left(-\dfrac{5\pi}{3}\right)$

   (e) $\tan 510°$

   (f) $\cos(-315°)$

3. Simplify.

   (a) $\cos x + \cos(\pi - x) - \cos(\pi + x) - \cos(-x)$

   (b) $\tan x + \tan(\pi - x) + \cot\left(\dfrac{\pi}{2} - x\right) - \tan(2\pi - x)$

   (c) $\sin(\pi + x) + \cos\left(\dfrac{\pi}{2} - x\right) + \tan\left(\dfrac{\pi}{2} + x\right) + \tan\left(\dfrac{3\pi}{2} - x\right)$

   (d) $\sin\left(\dfrac{\pi}{2} + x\right) - \cos\left(\dfrac{3\pi}{2} - x\right) + \sin\left(\dfrac{3\pi}{2} - x\right)$

   (e) $\sin\left(\dfrac{\pi}{2} - x\right) + \sin(\pi - x) + \sin\left(\dfrac{3\pi}{2} - x\right) + \sin(2\pi - x)$

4. Find the cosecant, secant, and cotangent of each of the following. Express your answers in terms of cosecant, secant, or cotangent of x.

   (a) $\pi - x$ (b) $\dfrac{\pi}{2} + x$ (c) $\pi + x$ (d) $\dfrac{3\pi}{2} + x$

5. Simplify.

   (a) $\sin(x - \pi)$ (b) $\cos\left(x - \dfrac{\pi}{2}\right)$ (c) $\tan(-x - \pi)$

6. Evaluate.

   (a) $\sec\left(\pi + \dfrac{\pi}{3}\right)$

   (b) $\csc\left(\dfrac{3\pi}{2} - \dfrac{\pi}{6}\right)$

   (c) $\cot\left(\dfrac{\pi}{2} + \dfrac{\pi}{3}\right)$

   (d) $\sec\left(\dfrac{3\pi}{4}\right)$

   (e) $\csc\left(\dfrac{3\pi}{2} - \dfrac{\pi}{4}\right)$

   (f) $\cot\left(-\pi + \dfrac{\pi}{4}\right)$

7. Simplify.

   (a) $\dfrac{\cos(\pi + x)\cos\left(\dfrac{\pi}{2} + x\right)}{\cos(\pi - x)} - \dfrac{\sin\left(\dfrac{3\pi}{2} - x\right)}{\sec(\pi + x)}$

   (b) $\dfrac{\sin\left(x - \dfrac{\pi}{2}\right)}{\cos(\pi - x)} + \dfrac{\tan\left(x - \dfrac{3\pi}{2}\right)}{-\tan(\pi + x)}$

8. If $b + c = \pi$, prove that $2(1 - \sin b \sin c) = \cos^2 b + \cos^2 c$.

9. If A, B, and C are angles in a triangle prove that $\sin B = \sin(A + C)$.

10. Use a reflection to prove that $\cos\left(\dfrac{\pi}{2} - b\right) = \sin b$ if b is in the interval $\left(\dfrac{\pi}{2}, \pi\right)$.

11. Use a reflection to prove that $\sin(2\pi - b) = -\sin b$ if b is in the interval $\left(\dfrac{3\pi}{2}, 2\pi\right)$.

6.2 ADDITION AND SUBTRACTION FORMULAS

In this section we show that it is possible to express the sine and the cosine of $a + b$ and of $a - b$ in terms of sines and cosines of a and of b. Similarly, the tangent of $a + b$ and of $a - b$ can be expressed in terms of tangents of a and of b.

Subtraction Formula for Cosine

$\cos(a - b) = \cos a \cos b + \sin a \sin b$

Proof

Points A and B on the unit circle determine angles a and b respectively. We can assume that $a > b$. D is the point $(1, 0)$ and C is selected so that $\angle DOC = a - b$.

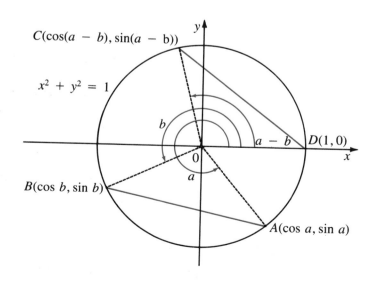

Now $\qquad \angle AOB = \angle COD = a - b$

and $\qquad OA = OB = OC = OD$

Therefore $\qquad \triangle AOB$ is congruent to $\triangle COD$

and so $\qquad AB = CD$

$$\sqrt{(\cos a - \cos b)^2 + (\sin a - \sin b)^2}$$
$$= \sqrt{[\cos(a - b) - 1]^2 + [\sin(a - b)]^2}$$
$$\cos^2 a - 2 \cos a \cos b + \cos^2 b + \sin^2 a - 2 \sin a \sin b + \sin^2 b$$
$$= \cos^2(a - b) - 2 \cos(a - b) + 1 + \sin^2(a - b)$$

We apply the identity $\sin^2 \theta + \cos^2 \theta = 1$ for $\theta = a$, $\theta = b$, and $\theta = a - b$ to obtain

$$2 - 2(\cos a \cos b + \sin a \sin b) = 2 - 2 \cos(a - b)$$
$$2(\cos a \cos b + \sin a \sin b) = 2 \cos(a - b)$$
$$\cos(a - b) = \cos a \cos b + \sin a \sin b$$

It is no longer necessary to create a diagram to develop the rest of the formulas of this section. We apply the previously established formula and results derived in Section 6.1 to establish each successive formula.

Addition Formula for Cosine

$$\cos(a + b) = \cos a \cos b - \sin a \sin b$$

Proof

Using the Subtraction Formula for Cosine, we have

$$\cos(a + b) = \cos[a - (-b)]$$
$$= \cos a \cos(-b) + \sin a \sin(-b)$$
$$= \cos a \cos b + \sin a(-\sin b)$$
$$= \cos a \cos b - \sin a \sin b$$

Addition Formula for Sine

$$\sin(a + b) = \sin a \cos b + \cos a \sin b$$

Proof

Using a co-related angle identity and the Subtraction Formula for Cosine we get

$$\sin(a + b) = \cos\left[\frac{\pi}{2} - (a + b)\right]$$

$$= \cos\left[\left(\frac{\pi}{2} - a\right) - b\right]$$

$$= \cos\left(\frac{\pi}{2} - a\right)\cos b + \sin\left(\frac{\pi}{2} - a\right)\sin b$$

$$= \sin a \cos b + \cos a \sin b$$

The proof of the following theorem is requested in Exercise 6.2.

Subtraction Formula for Sine

$$\sin(a - b) = \sin a \cos b - \cos a \sin b$$

The identity $\tan\theta = \dfrac{\sin\theta}{\cos\theta}$ is used to develop the Addition Formula for Tangent.

Addition Formula for Tangent

$$\tan(a + b) = \frac{\tan a + \tan b}{1 - \tan a \tan b}$$

In the proof that follows and in all subsequent proofs it is understood that we are dealing with values of the variables for which the trigonometric expressions are defined.

Proof

$$\tan(a + b) = \frac{\sin(a + b)}{\cos(a + b)}$$

$$= \frac{\sin a \cos b + \cos a \sin b}{\cos a \cos b - \sin a \sin b}$$

$$= \frac{\dfrac{\sin a \cos b}{\cos a \cos b} + \dfrac{\cos a \sin b}{\cos a \cos b}}{\dfrac{\cos a \cos b}{\cos a \cos b} - \dfrac{\sin a \sin b}{\cos a \cos b}}$$

$$= \frac{\dfrac{\sin a}{\cos a} + \dfrac{\sin b}{\cos b}}{1 - \dfrac{\sin a \sin b}{\cos a \cos b}}$$

$$= \frac{\tan a + \tan b}{1 - \tan a \tan b}$$

The next formula follows from the Addition Formula for Tangent. Its proof is left as an exercise.

$$
\boxed{
\begin{array}{c}
\textbf{Subtraction Formula for Tangent} \\[6pt]
\tan(a - b) = \dfrac{\tan a - \tan b}{1 + \tan a \tan b}
\end{array}
}
$$

Example 1   Find the exact value of $\sin \dfrac{\pi}{12}$.

Solution

$$
\begin{aligned}
\sin \frac{\pi}{12} &= \sin\left(\frac{\pi}{4} - \frac{\pi}{6}\right) \\[6pt]
&= \sin \frac{\pi}{4} \cos \frac{\pi}{6} - \cos \frac{\pi}{4} \sin \frac{\pi}{6} \\[6pt]
&= \frac{1}{\sqrt{2}} \times \frac{\sqrt{3}}{2} - \frac{1}{\sqrt{2}} \times \frac{1}{2} \\[6pt]
&= \frac{\sqrt{3} - 1}{2\sqrt{2}}
\end{aligned}
$$

Example 2   If $\sin a = -\dfrac{4}{5}$, $\pi \le a \le \dfrac{3\pi}{2}$ and $\cos b = -\dfrac{5}{13}$, $\dfrac{\pi}{2} \le b \le \pi$, evaluate $\tan(a + b)$.

Solution

$$
\begin{aligned}
\tan(a + b) &= \frac{\tan a + \tan b}{1 - \tan a \tan b} \\[6pt]
&= \frac{\frac{4}{3} + \left(-\frac{12}{5}\right)}{1 - \left(\frac{4}{3}\right)\left(-\frac{12}{5}\right)} \\[10pt]
&= \frac{20 - 36}{15 + 48} \\[6pt]
&= -\frac{16}{63}
\end{aligned}
$$

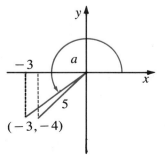

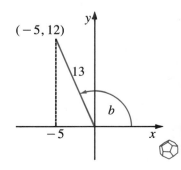

Example 3   Prove that $\sin x + \sin y = 2 \sin \dfrac{x + y}{2} \cos \dfrac{x - y}{2}$.

Solution   We know that

$$\sin(a + b) = \sin a \cos b + \cos a \sin b$$

and

$$\sin(a - b) = \sin a \cos b - \cos a \sin b$$

Adding, we get

$$\sin(a + b) + \sin(a - b) = 2 \sin a \cos b$$

Let

$$a + b = x$$
$$a - b = y$$

Therefore $2a = x + y$ and $2b = x - y$

$$a = \frac{x + y}{2} \quad \text{and} \quad b = \frac{x - y}{2}.$$

and

$$\sin(a + b) + \sin(a - b) = 2 \sin a \cos b$$

becomes

$$\sin x + \sin y = 2 \sin \frac{x + y}{2} \cos \frac{x - y}{2}$$

In Example 3 we have changed the form of a trigonometric expression from a sum into a product. It is but one of a group of formulas called the *transformation formulas*. You will encounter more of them in Exercise 6.2.

The Addition and Subtraction Formulas provide an alternative method for simplifying expressions involving related angles.

Example 4   Prove that $\cos(\pi + x) = -\cos x$.

Solution

$$\cos(\pi + x) = \cos \pi \cos x - \sin \pi \sin x$$
$$= (-1)\cos x - (0) \sin x$$
$$= -\cos x$$

Example 5   Prove that $\cos\left(\dfrac{\pi}{2} - x\right) = \sin x$.

Solution

$$\cos\left(\frac{\pi}{2} - x\right) = \cos \frac{\pi}{2} \cos x + \sin \frac{\pi}{2} \sin x$$
$$= (0) \cos x + (1) \sin x$$
$$= \sin x$$

EXERCISE 6.2

A **1.**   Express as a single trigonometric function.

(a) $\cos 2a \cos a - \sin 2a \sin a$ (b) $\cos x \cos 4x + \sin x \sin 4x$

(c) $\sin 5 \cos 2 - \cos 5 \sin 2$

(d) $\sin 2m \cos m + \cos 2m \sin m$

(e) $\dfrac{\tan 2a + \tan 3a}{1 - \tan 2a \tan 3a}$ (f) $\dfrac{\tan 7 - \tan 9}{1 + \tan 7 \tan 9}$

(g) $\cos^2 x - \sin^2 x$ (h) $\sin a \cos a + \cos a \sin a$

(i) $\dfrac{\tan x + \tan x}{1 - \tan^2 x}$ (j) $\cos^2 2 + \sin^2 2$

B 2. Evaluate using formulas developed in this section.

(a) $\sin \dfrac{11\pi}{12}$ (b) $\cos \dfrac{13\pi}{12}$

(c) $\tan\left(-\dfrac{7}{12}\pi\right)$ (d) $\tan\left(-\dfrac{5}{12}\pi\right)$

(e) $\sin 75°$ (f) $\cos(-15°)$

3. Find the value of each of the following.

(a) $\sin\left(\dfrac{\pi}{4} - \dfrac{\pi}{3}\right)$ (b) $\cos\left(-\dfrac{\pi}{6} - \dfrac{\pi}{4}\right)$ (c) $\tan\left(-\dfrac{3\pi}{4} + \dfrac{2\pi}{3}\right)$

4. If x and y are in the interval $\left(0, \dfrac{\pi}{2}\right)$ and $\sin x = \frac{3}{5}$ and $\cos y = \frac{12}{13}$, evaluate each of the following.

(a) $\sin(x - y)$ (b) $\cos(x + y)$ (c) $\tan(x + y)$

5. If x is in the interval $\left(\dfrac{\pi}{2}, \pi\right)$ and y is in the interval $\left(\pi, \dfrac{3\pi}{2}\right)$ and $\cos x = -\frac{5}{13}$ and $\tan y = \frac{4}{3}$, evaluate each of the following.

(a) $\sin(x + y)$ (b) $\cos(x - y)$ (c) $\tan(x - y)$

6. Find the exact value of each of the following.

(a) $\sin 50° \cos 20° - \cos 50° \sin 20°$

(b) $\cos \dfrac{\pi}{7} \cos \dfrac{4\pi}{21} - \sin \dfrac{\pi}{7} \sin \dfrac{4\pi}{21}$

(c) $\dfrac{\tan 7° + \tan 8°}{1 - \tan 7° \tan 8°}$

(d) $\sin \dfrac{5\pi}{36} \cos \dfrac{5\pi}{18} + \cos \dfrac{5\pi}{36} \sin \dfrac{5\pi}{18}$

7. Use the Addition Formula for Sine to prove the Subtraction Formula for Sine, namely, $\sin(a - b) = \sin a \cos b - \cos a \sin b$.

8. Use the identity $\tan \theta = \dfrac{\sin \theta}{\cos \theta}$ to prove the Subtraction Formula for Tangent, namely $\tan(a - b) = \dfrac{\tan a - \tan b}{1 + \tan a \tan b}$.

9. Use the Addition Formula for Tangent to prove the Subtraction Formula for Tangent.

10. Prove each of the following.

(a) $\sin(\pi + x) = -\sin x$ (b) $\tan(2\pi - x) = -\tan x$

(c) $\cos\left(\dfrac{3\pi}{2} + x\right) = \sin x$ (d) $\sin\left(\dfrac{3\pi}{2} - x\right) = -\cos x$

(e) $\cos\left(\dfrac{\pi}{2} + x\right) = -\sin x$ (f) $\tan\left(\dfrac{\pi}{2} + x\right) = -\cot x$

(g) $\sin(x - \pi) = -\sin x$ (h) $-\tan(-x - \pi) = \tan x$

11. Using the method developed in Example 3 of this section, prove each of the following Transformation Formulas.

(a) $\sin x - \sin y = 2 \cos \dfrac{x + y}{2} \sin \dfrac{x - y}{2}$

(b) $\cos x + \cos y = 2 \cos \dfrac{x + y}{2} \cos \dfrac{x - y}{2}$

(c) $\cos x - \cos y = -2 \sin \dfrac{x + y}{2} \sin \dfrac{x - y}{2}$

12. Express each of the following as a product and simplify.

(a) $\sin 60° + \sin 20°$

(b) $\cos 70° - \cos 110°$

(c) $\cos 40° + \cos 80°$

(d) $\sin 6x - \sin 2x$

(e) $\sin 130° - \sin 40°$

(f) $\cos 4x - \cos 2x$

13. Simplify.

(a) $\dfrac{\sin(x - 30°) + \cos(60° - x)}{\sin x}$

(b) $\dfrac{\tan\left(\dfrac{\pi}{4} - x\right) - \tan\left(\dfrac{\pi}{4} + x\right)}{\tan x}$

(c) $\dfrac{\cos 4x + \cos 3x}{\sin 4x - \sin 3x}$

14. If $\sin x = -\frac{1}{3}$, $\pi < x < \dfrac{3\pi}{2}$ and $\cos y = \frac{2}{5}$, $\dfrac{3\pi}{2} < y < 2\pi$, find the value of $\sec(x - y)$.

15. Express $\csc(x + y)$ in terms of secants and cosecants of x and y.

16. Develop a formula for $\sin(x + y + z)$. Start by rewriting it in form $\sin[(x + y) + z]$.

17. If x, y, and z are second quadrant angles and $\cos x = -\frac{1}{3}$, $\sin y = \frac{1}{4}$, and $\sin z = \frac{1}{5}$, find the value of $\cos(x + y - z)$.

C 18. If $\dfrac{\sin x}{\sin y} = \dfrac{1}{2}$ and $\dfrac{\cos x}{\cos y} = 3$ prove:

(a) $\sin(x + y) = \frac{7}{3} \sin x \cos x$

(b) $\cos(x + y) = \dfrac{7 \cos^2 x - 6}{3}$

19. If $2 \sin(x - y) = \sin(x + y)$, prove that $\tan x = 3 \tan y$.

20. If $\tan\left(\dfrac{\pi}{4} + x\right) = 3 \tan\left(\dfrac{\pi}{4} - x\right)$, find the value of $\tan x$.

21. Simplify.

(a) $\cos\left(\dfrac{3\pi}{4} + x\right) + \sin\left(\dfrac{3\pi}{4} - x\right)$

(b) $\cos\left(\dfrac{\pi}{12} - x\right) \sec \dfrac{\pi}{12} - \sin\left(\dfrac{\pi}{12} - x\right) \csc \dfrac{\pi}{12}$

(c) $\dfrac{\sin(x - y)}{\cos x \cos y} + \dfrac{\sin(z - x)}{\cos z \cos x} + \dfrac{\sin(y - z)}{\cos y \cos z}$

6.3 DOUBLE ANGLE FORMULAS

In this section we use the addition formulas for sine, cosine, and tangent to generate some frequently used trigonometric relationships.

If we start with

$$\sin(a + b) = \sin a \cos b + \cos a \sin b$$

then, setting $a = b = x$ gives

$$\sin(x + x) = \sin x \cos x + \cos x \sin x$$
$$\sin 2x = 2 \sin x \cos x$$

Double Angle Formula for Sine

$$\sin 2x = 2 \sin x \cos x$$

Example 1   If $\sin x = \dfrac{4}{5}, \dfrac{\pi}{2} < x < \pi$, find the value of $\sin 2x$.

Solution   Now $\qquad\qquad \sin 2x = 2 \sin x \cos x$

and, since $\dfrac{\pi}{2} < x < \pi$,

$$\cos x = -\tfrac{3}{5}$$

Therefore $\qquad \sin 2x = 2\left(\tfrac{4}{5}\right)\left(-\tfrac{3}{5}\right) = -\tfrac{24}{25}$

A similar development produces the Double Angle Formula for Cosine. If we start with

$$\cos(a + b) = \cos a \cos b - \sin a \sin b$$

then, letting $a = b = x$ gives

$$\cos(x + x) = \cos x \cos x - \sin x \sin x$$
$$\cos 2x = \cos^2 x - \sin^2 x$$

The identity $\sin^2 \theta + \cos^2 \theta = 1$ is applied to the original result to produce two alternative forms of the formula.

$$\cos 2x = \cos^2 x - (1 - \cos^2 x) \qquad \cos 2x = (1 - \sin^2 x) - \sin^2 x$$
$$= 2 \cos^2 x - 1 \qquad\qquad\qquad = 1 - 2 \sin^2 x$$

Double Angle Formulas for Cosine

$$\cos 2x = \cos^2 x - \sin^2 x$$
$$\cos 2x = 2 \cos^2 x - 1$$
$$\cos 2x = 1 - 2 \sin^2 x$$

The three results are equivalent, but as you gain experience working with these formulas, you will learn that one form may be superior to the others in a particular problem.

Example 2 If $\cos a = \frac{2}{3}$, find the value of $\cos 4a$.

Solution We must express $\cos 4a$ in terms of trigonometric functions of a. This is accomplished by applying the Double Angle Formula for Cosine twice.

$$
\begin{aligned}
\cos 4a &= \cos[2(2a)] \\
&= 2\cos^2 2a - 1 \\
&= 2(2\cos^2 a - 1)^2 - 1 \\
&= 2[2\left(\tfrac{2}{3}\right)^2 - 1]^2 - 1 \\
&= 2\left(-\tfrac{1}{9}\right)^2 - 1 \\
&= -\tfrac{79}{81}
\end{aligned}
$$

The application of the Double Angle Formula for Cosine in the next example should be examined carefully.

Example 3 Evaluate $\sin \dfrac{\pi}{8}$.

Solution Since

$$\cos \frac{\pi}{4} = \cos 2\left(\frac{\pi}{8}\right)$$

the Double Angle Formula gives

$$\cos \frac{\pi}{4} = 1 - 2\sin^2 \frac{\pi}{8}$$

Solve for $\sin \dfrac{\pi}{8}$:

$$\sin^2 \frac{\pi}{8} = \frac{1 - \cos \dfrac{\pi}{4}}{2}$$

Since $\sin \dfrac{\pi}{8}$ is positive,

$$\sin \frac{\pi}{8} = \sqrt{\frac{1 - \dfrac{1}{\sqrt{2}}}{2}}$$

$$= \sqrt{\frac{\sqrt{2} - 1}{2\sqrt{2}}}$$

Now we develop the Double Angle Formula for Tangent. If we start with

$$\tan(a + b) = \frac{\tan a + \tan b}{1 - \tan a \tan b}$$

then, setting $a = b = x$ gives

$$\tan(x + x) = \frac{\tan x + \tan x}{1 - \tan x \tan x}$$

Therefore

Double Angle Formula for Tangent

$$\tan 2x = \frac{2 \tan x}{1 - \tan^2 x}$$

Example 4   If $\tan x = \frac{4}{3}$, $\pi < x < \dfrac{3\pi}{2}$, find the value of $\tan \dfrac{x}{2}$.

Solution

$$\tan x = \frac{4}{3}$$

$$\tan\left[2\left(\frac{x}{2}\right)\right] = \frac{4}{3}$$

$$\frac{2 \tan \dfrac{x}{2}}{1 - \tan^2 \dfrac{x}{2}} = \frac{4}{3}$$

$$6 \tan \frac{x}{2} = 4 - 4 \tan^2 \frac{x}{2}$$

$$2 \tan^2 \frac{x}{2} + 3 \tan \frac{x}{2} - 2 = 0$$

$$\left(2 \tan \frac{x}{2} - 1\right)\left(\tan \frac{x}{2} + 2\right) = 0$$

Therefore

$$\tan \frac{x}{2} = \frac{1}{2} \quad \text{or} \quad \tan \frac{x}{2} = -2$$

Since $\pi < x < 2\pi$, we have $\dfrac{\pi}{2} < \dfrac{x}{2} < \pi$, so

$$\tan \frac{x}{2} = -2$$

EXERCISE 6.3

B **1.** Use a Double Angle Formula to rewrite each expression.
   (a) $\cos 2(2x)$ (b) $\sin 3x$ (c) $\tan 6x$
   (d) $\sin \frac{1}{2}x$ (e) $\cos \frac{2}{3}x$ (f) $\tan(-7x)$

2. Express as a single sine or cosine function.
   (a) $2 \sin 3\theta \cos 3\theta$ (b) $6 \sin \theta \cos \theta$
   (c) $\frac{1}{2} \sin \frac{\theta}{2} \cos \frac{\theta}{2}$ (d) $\cos^2 \frac{3\theta}{2} - \sin^2 \frac{3\theta}{2}$
   (e) $1 - 2 \sin^2 \frac{\theta}{4}$ (f) $2 \cos^2 \left(\frac{7}{2}\theta\right) - 1$
   (g) $8 \sin^2 2\theta - 4$ (h) $1 - 2 \sin^2\left(\frac{\pi}{4} - \frac{x}{2}\right)$

3. If $\cos \theta = -\frac{4}{5}, \frac{\pi}{2} \leqslant \theta \leqslant \pi$, find the value of $\sin 2\theta$ and $\cos 2\theta$.
   Determine the quadrant of angle 2θ.

4. If $\sin \theta = \frac{12}{13}, 0 \leqslant \theta \leqslant \frac{\pi}{2}$, evaluate $\sin 2\theta$ and $\cos 2\theta$. Determine
   the quadrant of angle 2θ.

5. If $\sin \theta = \frac{2}{3}, 0 \leqslant \theta \leqslant \frac{\pi}{2}$, find the value of $\sin 4\theta$.

6. If $\cos \theta = \frac{2}{5}, \frac{3\pi}{2} \leqslant \theta \leqslant 2\pi$, find the values of $\csc 2\theta$ and $\sec 2\theta$.

7. If $\tan a = \frac{1}{2}, 0 \leqslant a \leqslant \frac{\pi}{2}$, find the value of $\tan 2a$.

8. If $\tan a = 2, -2\pi \leqslant a \leqslant -\frac{3\pi}{2}$, evaluate $\tan 4a$.

9. Develop formulas for
   (a) $\sin 3\theta$ in terms of $\sin \theta$.   (b) $\cos 3\theta$ in terms of $\cos \theta$.
   (c) $\tan 3\theta$ in terms of $\tan \theta$.   (d) $\cos 4\theta$ in terms of $\cos \theta$.

10. Find the exact values.
   (a) $\sin 67\frac{1}{2}°$ (b) $\cos 112\frac{1}{2}°$ (c) $\tan 22.5°$
   (d) $\sin\left(-\frac{\pi}{8}\right)$ (e) $\cos \frac{\pi}{16}$ (f) $\tan 33.75°$

11. (a) Express $\sin \dfrac{\theta}{2}$ in terms of $\cos \theta$.

   (b) Express $\cos \dfrac{\theta}{2}$ in terms of $\cos \theta$.

   (c) Express $\tan \dfrac{\theta}{2}$ in terms of $\cos \theta$.

12. If $\cos x = -\dfrac{12}{13}$ and x is in the interval $\left(\pi, \dfrac{3\pi}{2}\right)$, find the following.

   (a) $\sin \dfrac{x}{2}$ (b) $\cos \dfrac{x}{2}$ (c) $\tan \dfrac{x}{2}$

13. Express $\sin 2\theta$ and $\cos 2\theta$ in terms of $\tan \theta$.

14. Express $\dfrac{\sin 2x}{1 + \cos 2x}$ in terms of $\tan x$.

15. Express $\dfrac{1 - \cos 2x}{\sin 2x}$ in terms of $\tan x$.

16. Express $\dfrac{1 - \tan^2 x}{1 + \tan^2 x}$ as a trigonometric function of $2x$.

C 17. If $\cos \theta + \sin \theta = \frac{2}{3}$, find the value of $\sin 2\theta$.

18. If $\cos \theta + \sin \theta = \dfrac{1 + \sqrt{3}}{2}$ and $\cos \theta - \sin \theta = \dfrac{1 - \sqrt{3}}{2}$ find the value of $\sin 2\theta$.

19. If $2a + b = \dfrac{\pi}{2}$, prove that $\cos a = \pm \sqrt{\dfrac{1 + \sin b}{2}}$.

20. If $\tan a = \frac{1}{5}$ and $\tan b = \frac{1}{239}$, find the value of $\tan(4a - b)$.

21. If $\sec 4\theta - \sec 2\theta = 2$, find the value of $\cos^2 \theta$, $0 < \theta < \dfrac{\pi}{2}$.

22. Simplify $\sin^2 \left(\dfrac{\pi}{8} + \dfrac{\theta}{2}\right) - \sin^2 \left(\dfrac{\pi}{8} - \dfrac{\theta}{2}\right)$.

6.4 TRIGONOMETRIC IDENTITIES

Statements of equality in mathematics generally fall into two categories. A *conditional equation* is valid for certain values of the variable or variables involved. Each of the following fall into this category.

$$3x - 2 = 7 \qquad ①$$
$$x^2 - 7x + 12 = 0 \qquad ②$$
$$2x - 3y = 6 \qquad ③$$

Equation 1 is only true for $x = 3$. Equation 2 is true for $x = 3$ or $x = 4$, but no other values of x. Equation 3 is true for an infinite number of values of x and y, but values chosen at random will generally fail to satisfy it.

The second type of equation is called an *identity*. It holds for all values of the variable or variables for which it is defined. Each of the following is an identity.

$$7x - 4x = 3x \qquad \text{④}$$
$$x^2 - 7xy + 12y^2 = (x - 3y)(x - 4y) \qquad \text{⑤}$$
$$\frac{x^2 - 9}{x + 3} = x - 3 \qquad \text{⑥}$$

Equations 4 and 5 are obviously true for all values of their respective variables. Equation 6 is undefined at $x = -3$, but is true for all other values of x.

We have encountered most of the fundamental trigonometric identities in earlier courses. Many more have been established in the first three sections of this chapter. By means of these established identities, trigonometric expressions can be transformed or simplified. They can also be used to prove other identities.

To prove an identity we may:
    (1) transform the left side to the exact form of the right side; or
    (2) transform the right side to the exact form of the left side; or
    (3) transform both sides to an identical form.

To accomplish this we may:
    (1) perform substitutions based on established identities;
    (2) employ algebraic manipulation, (factoring and creating common denominators are two of the most popular); and
    (3) use our ingenuity.

Here is the complete list of identities and formulas required to attempt Exercise 6.4.

Reciprocal Identities	Quotient Identities	Pythagorean Identities
$\csc x = \dfrac{1}{\sin x}$	$\tan x = \dfrac{\sin x}{\cos x}$	$\sin^2 x + \cos^2 x = 1$
$\sec x = \dfrac{1}{\cos x}$	$\cot x = \dfrac{\cos x}{\sin x}$	$\sec^2 x = 1 + \tan^2 x$
$\cot x = \dfrac{1}{\tan x}$		$\csc^2 x = 1 + \cot^2 x$

Addition and Subtraction Formulas	**Double Angle Formulas**

$$\sin(x + y) = \sin x \cos y + \cos x \sin y$$
$$\sin(x - y) = \sin x \cos y - \cos x \sin y$$
$$\cos(x + y) = \cos x \cos y - \sin x \sin y$$
$$\cos(x - y) = \cos x \cos y + \sin x \sin y$$
$$\tan(x + y) = \frac{\tan x + \tan y}{1 - \tan x \tan y}$$
$$\tan(x - y) = \frac{\tan x - \tan y}{1 + \tan x \tan y}$$

$$\sin 2x = 2 \sin x \cos x$$

$$\cos 2x = \cos^2 x - \sin^2 x$$
$$= 2 \cos^2 x - 1$$
$$= 1 - 2 \sin^2 x$$
$$\tan 2x = \frac{2 \tan x}{1 - \tan^2 x}$$

Related Angle Identities

$$\sin(\pi - x) = \sin x$$
$$\cos(\pi - x) = -\cos x$$
$$\tan(\pi - x) = -\tan x$$

$$\sin(2\pi - x) = -\sin x$$
$$\cos(2\pi - x) = \cos x$$
$$\tan(2\pi - x) = -\tan x$$

$$\sin(\pi + x) = -\sin x$$
$$\cos(\pi + x) = -\cos x$$
$$\tan(\pi + x) = \tan x$$

$$\sin(-x) = -\sin x$$
$$\cos(-x) = \cos x$$
$$\tan(-x) = -\tan x$$

Corelated Angle Identities

$$\sin\left(\frac{\pi}{2} - x\right) = \cos x$$
$$\cos\left(\frac{\pi}{2} - x\right) = \sin x$$
$$\tan\left(\frac{\pi}{2} - x\right) = \cot x$$

$$\sin\left(\frac{3\pi}{2} - x\right) = -\cos x$$
$$\cos\left(\frac{3\pi}{2} - x\right) = -\sin x$$
$$\tan\left(\frac{3\pi}{2} - x\right) = \cot x$$

$$\sin\left(\frac{\pi}{2} + x\right) = \cos x$$
$$\cos\left(\frac{\pi}{2} + x\right) = -\sin x$$
$$\tan\left(\frac{\pi}{2} + x\right) = -\cot x$$

$$\sin\left(\frac{3\pi}{2} + x\right) = -\cos x$$
$$\cos\left(\frac{3\pi}{2} + x\right) = \sin x$$
$$\tan\left(\frac{3\pi}{2} + x\right) = -\cot x$$

Once you know the formulas, the key to becoming adept at proving identities is perseverance. If you relish the challenge of a good puzzle, this will prove to be a particularly enjoyable section.

A list of the most common strategies used in performing substitutions is provided.

(1) Move from the complex to the simple.
(2) Express all functions in terms of sine and cosine.
(3) Look for squares and the use of the Pythagorean identities.
(4) Express all functions with the same argument.

Example 1   Prove $1 + \cos x = \dfrac{\sin^2 x}{1 - \cos x}$.

Solution   We start with the more complex right side and focus on $\sin^2 x$.

$$\frac{\sin^2 x}{1 - \cos x} = \frac{1 - \cos^2 x}{1 - \cos x}$$

$$= \frac{(1 - \cos x)(1 + \cos x)}{1 - \cos x}$$

$$= 1 + \cos x$$

Example 2   Prove $\cos(x + y)\cos(x - y) = \cos^2 x + \cos^2 y - 1$.

Solution   The left side contains two familiar factors, so let's start with it. As we move through the proof, we are constantly aware of the terms on the right side that we need to produce on the left side.

$$\cos(x + y)\cos(x - y) = (\cos x \cos y - \sin x \sin y)(\cos x \cos y + \sin x \sin y)$$
$$= \cos^2 x \cos^2 y - \sin^2 x \sin^2 y$$

Noting that $\sin^2 x$ and $\sin^2 y$ do not appear on the right side, we replace them and get

$$\cos(x + y)\cos(x - y) = \cos^2 x \cos^2 y - (1 - \cos^2 x)(1 - \cos^2 y)$$
$$= \cos^2 x \cos^2 y - (1 - \cos^2 x - \cos^2 y + \cos^2 x \cos^2 y)$$
$$= \cos^2 x \cos^2 y - 1 + \cos^2 x + \cos^2 y - \cos^2 x \cos^2 y$$
$$= \cos^2 x + \cos^2 y - 1$$

Example 3   Prove $\dfrac{\sin 2x}{1 - \cos 2x} = 2 \csc 2x - \tan x$.

Solution   We express csc and tan in terms of sin and cos. Next we note the presence of two different arguments, $2x$ and x. We work with each side separately to achieve a common result.

$$\frac{\sin 2x}{1 - \cos 2x} = \frac{2 \sin x \cos x}{1 - (1 - 2\sin^2 x)} \qquad 2 \csc 2x - \tan x = \frac{2}{\sin 2x} - \tan x$$

$$= \frac{2 \sin x \cos x}{2 \sin^2 x} \qquad\qquad\qquad = \frac{2}{2 \sin x \cos x} - \frac{\sin x}{\cos x}$$

$$= \frac{\cos x}{\sin x} \qquad\qquad\qquad\qquad = \frac{2 - 2\sin^2 x}{2 \sin x \cos x}$$

$$\qquad\qquad\qquad\qquad\qquad = \frac{1 - \sin^2 x}{\sin x \cos x}$$

$$\qquad\qquad\qquad\qquad\qquad = \frac{\cos^2 x}{\sin x \cos x}$$

$$\qquad\qquad\qquad\qquad\qquad = \frac{\cos x}{\sin x}$$

Therefore $\dfrac{\sin 2x}{1 - \cos 2x} = 2 \csc 2x - \tan x$

EXERCISE 6.4

B *The following identities involve the reciprocal, quotient, and Pythagorean relationships. Prove each one.*

1. $\sin x \tan x = \sec x - \cos x$
2. $\cos^4 x - \sin^4 x = 1 - 2 \sin^2 x$
3. $\csc^2 x + \sec^2 x = \csc^2 x \sec^2 x$
4. $\cos^2 x \cos^2 y + \sin^2 x \sin^2 y + \sin^2 x \cos^2 y + \sin^2 y \cos^2 x = 1$
5. $\sec^2 x - \sec^2 y = \tan^2 x - \tan^2 y$
6. $\dfrac{\tan x + \tan y}{\cot x + \cot y} = (\tan x)(\tan y)$
7. $(\sec x - \cos x)(\csc x - \sin x) = \dfrac{\tan x}{1 + \tan^2 x}$
8. $\cos^6 x + \sin^6 x = 1 - 3 \sin^2 x + 3 \sin^4 x$
9. $\sec^6 x - \tan^6 x = 1 + 3 \tan^2 x \sec^2 x$

The following involve the addition and subtraction formulas.

10. $1 + \cot x \tan y = \dfrac{\sin(x + y)}{\sin x \cos y}$
11. $\cos(x + y)\cos y + \sin(x + y)\sin y = \cos x$
12. $\sin x - \tan y \cos x = \dfrac{\sin(x - y)}{\cos y}$
13. $\cos\left(\dfrac{3\pi}{4} + x\right) + \sin\left(\dfrac{3\pi}{4} - x\right) = 0$
14. $\dfrac{\tan\left(\dfrac{\pi}{4} + x\right) - \tan\left(\dfrac{\pi}{4} - x\right)}{\tan\left(\dfrac{\pi}{4} + x\right) + \tan\left(\dfrac{\pi}{4} - x\right)} = 2 \sin x \cos x$
15. $\sin(x + y)\sin(x - y) = \cos^2 y - \cos^2 x$
16. $\tan(x + y)\tan(x - y) = \dfrac{\sin^2 x - \sin^2 y}{\cos^2 x - \sin^2 y}$
17. $\dfrac{\tan(x - y) + \tan y}{1 - \tan(x - y)\tan y} = \tan x$
18. $\sin 5x = \sin x (\cos^2 2x - \sin^2 2x) + 2 \cos x \cos 2x \sin 2x$

The following involve related and co-related angles.

19. $\sin\left(\dfrac{\pi}{2} - x\right)\cot\left(\dfrac{\pi}{2} + x\right) = -\sin x$
20. $\cos(-x) + \cos(\pi - x) = \cos(\pi + x) + \cos x$

21. $\dfrac{\sin(\pi - x)}{\tan(\pi + x)} \dfrac{\cot\left(\dfrac{\pi}{2} - x\right)}{\tan\left(\dfrac{\pi}{2} + x\right)} \dfrac{\cos(2\pi - x)}{\sin(-x)} = \sin x$

22. $\dfrac{\sin(-x)}{\sin(\pi + x)} - \dfrac{\tan\left(\dfrac{\pi}{2} + x\right)}{\cot x} + \dfrac{\cos x}{\sin\left(\dfrac{\pi}{2} + x\right)} = 3$

23. $\dfrac{\csc(\pi - x)}{\sec(\pi + x)} \dfrac{\cos(-x)}{\cos\left(\dfrac{\pi}{2} + x\right)} = \cot^2 x$

24. $\dfrac{\cos\left(\dfrac{\pi}{2} + x\right)\sec(-x)\tan(\pi - x)}{\sec(2\pi + x)\sin(\pi + x)\cot\left(\dfrac{\pi}{2} - x\right)} = -1$

25. $\dfrac{\sin(\pi - x)\cos(\pi + x)\tan(2\pi - x)}{\sec\left(\dfrac{\pi}{2} + x\right)\csc\left(\dfrac{3\pi}{2} - x\right)\cot\left(\dfrac{3\pi}{2} + x\right)} = \sin^4 x - \sin^2 x$

The following involve the double angle formulas.

26. $\dfrac{\sin 2x}{1 + \cos 2x} = \tan x$

27. $\dfrac{1 + \cos x}{\sin x} = \cot \dfrac{x}{2}$

28. $2 \csc 2x = \sec x \csc x$

29. $2 \cot 2x = \cot x - \tan x$

30. $\dfrac{\cos 2x}{1 + \sin 2x} = \tan\left(\dfrac{\pi}{4} - x\right)$

31. $\dfrac{\cos x - \sin x}{\cos x + \sin x} = \sec 2x - \tan 2x$

32. $\dfrac{1 - \cos 2x + \sin 2x}{1 + \cos 2x + \sin 2x} = \tan x$

33. $\cos^6 x - \sin^6 x = \cos 2x\left(1 - \tfrac{1}{4} \sin^2 2x\right)$

34. $4(\cos^6 x + \sin^6 x) = 1 + 3 \cos^2 2x$

35. $\sec x - \tan x = \tan\left(\dfrac{\pi}{4} - \dfrac{x}{2}\right)$

36. $\dfrac{\sin 2x}{1 + \cos 2x} \dfrac{\cos x}{1 + \cos x} = \tan \dfrac{x}{2}$

The following involve a variety of formulas and identities.

37. $\sin^2 x + \cos^4 x = \cos^2 x + \sin^4 x$

38. $\tan x - \cot x = (\tan x - 1)(\cot x + 1)$

39. $\cos x = \sin x \tan^2 x \cot^3 x$

40. $(\sin x + \cos x)(\tan x + \cot x) = \sec x + \csc x$

41. $\sin^4 x + \cos^4 x = \sin^2 x(\csc^2 x - 2 \cos^2 x)$

42. $\sin^3 x + \cos^3 x = (1 - \sin x \cos x)(\sin x + \cos x)$

43. $\cos\left(\dfrac{\pi}{12} - x\right)\sec\dfrac{\pi}{12} - \sin\left(\dfrac{\pi}{12} - x\right)\csc\dfrac{\pi}{12} = 4 \sin x$

44. $\tan(x - y) + \tan(y - z) = \dfrac{\sec^2 y\,(\tan x - \tan z)}{(1 + \tan x \tan y)(1 + \tan y \tan z)}$

45. $\sin 8x = 8 \sin x \cos x \cos 2x \cos 4x$

46. $\sin x = 1 - 2 \sin^2\left(\dfrac{\pi}{4} - \dfrac{x}{2}\right)$

47. $\sin(x + y) + \sin(x - y) = 2 \sin x \cos y$

48. $\dfrac{\sin(x - y)}{\sin x \sin y} + \dfrac{\sin(y - z)}{\sin y \sin z} + \dfrac{\sin(z - x)}{\sin z \sin x} = 0$

49. $\tan x + \tan(\pi - x) + \cot\left(\dfrac{\pi}{2} + x\right) = \tan(2\pi - x)$

50. $\sin\left(\dfrac{\pi}{2} + x\right)\cos(\pi - x)\cot\left(\dfrac{3\pi}{2} + x\right)$

$= \sin\left(\dfrac{\pi}{2} - x\right)\sin\left(\dfrac{3\pi}{2} - x\right)\cot\left(\dfrac{\pi}{2} + x\right)$

51. $\tan\left(\dfrac{\pi}{2} - x\right) - \cot\left(\dfrac{3\pi}{2} - x\right) + \tan(2\pi - x) - \cot(\pi - x)$

$= \dfrac{4 - 2 \sec^2 x}{\tan x}$

52. $\tan(x + y + z) = \dfrac{\tan x + \tan y + \tan z - \tan x \tan y \tan z}{1 - \tan x \tan y - \tan x \tan z - \tan y \tan z}$

53. $\csc^2\left(\dfrac{\pi}{2} - x\right) = 1 + \sin^2 x \csc^2\left(\dfrac{\pi}{2} - x\right)$

54. $\tan\left(\dfrac{\pi}{4} + x\right) + \tan\left(\dfrac{\pi}{4} - x\right) = 2 \sec 2x$

55. $\dfrac{1 - \sin 2x}{\cos 2x} = \dfrac{\cos 2x}{1 + \sin 2x}$

56. $\dfrac{\sin 4x}{1 - \cos 4x} \times \dfrac{1 - \cos 2x}{\cos 2x} = \tan x$

6.5 SOLVING TRIGONOMETRIC EQUATIONS

Because of the periodic nature of the trigonometric functions, if no domain is specified, an infinite number of solutions to a trigonometric equation will exist, providing the equation has a solution. Knowledge of the range of the basic trigonometric functions and an ability to sketch their graphs may be very useful in this section. Refer to the Review and Preview at the beginning of this chapter if your memory needs jogging.

Example 1 If $\sin x = 1$, solve for x.

Solution Since no restrictions have been placed on x, an infinite number of solutions exist. We draw the graph of $y = \sin x$ and the horizontal line $y = 1$.

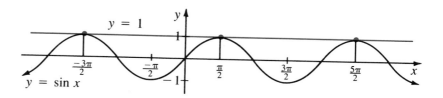

They intersect at $x = \ldots, -\frac{3}{2}\pi, \frac{1}{2}\pi, \frac{5}{2}\pi, \ldots$

or generally $x = \frac{\pi}{2} + 2k\pi, k \in I$

Example 2 If $\sin x = -1$, solve for x in the interval $[-2\pi, 2\pi]$.

Solution The given interval limits us to two solutions.

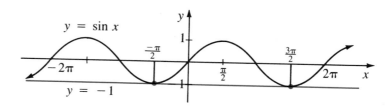

$x = -\frac{1}{2}\pi$ or $x = \frac{3}{2}\pi$

Example 3   If $\sin 3x = \frac{1}{2}$, solve for x in the interval $[-\pi, \pi]$.

Solution   The form of the restriction is changed to fit the argument $3x$. Since $-\pi \leqslant x \leqslant \pi$, we have $-3\pi \leqslant 3x \leqslant 3\pi$.

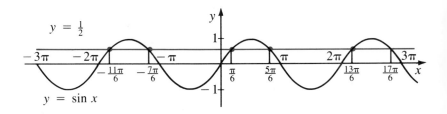

$y = \frac{1}{2}$

$y = \sin x$

In our domain $3x = -\frac{11}{6}\pi, -\frac{7}{6}\pi, \frac{1}{6}\pi, \frac{5}{6}\pi, \frac{13}{6}\pi,$ or $\frac{17}{6}\pi$

Therefore $x = -\frac{11}{18}\pi, -\frac{7}{18}\pi, \frac{1}{18}\pi, \frac{5}{18}\pi, \frac{13}{18}\pi,$ or $\frac{17}{18}\pi$

Although a variety of methods may be used to solve trigonometric equations, the following strategies are most frequently applied.
(1) *Make use of the established formulas and identities to express the equation in terms of a single trigonometric function*
(2) *Apply the double angle formulas to match the arguments*
(3) *Use algebraic methods to solve for the trigonometric function*
(4) *Finally, within the specified domain, solve for the variable*

Example 4   If $\sec 2x + \dfrac{1}{\cos x} = 0$, $0 \leqslant x \leqslant \pi$, solve for x.

Solution   Since $\sec 2x = \dfrac{1}{\cos 2x}$, we can express the equation in terms of the same function.

$$\frac{1}{\cos 2x} + \frac{1}{\cos x} = 0$$

$$\frac{\cos x + \cos 2x}{\cos 2x \cos x} = 0$$

Therefore $\cos x + \cos 2x = 0$ if $\cos 2x \cos x \neq 0$

We match the arguments using the formula $\cos 2x = 2 \cos^2 x - 1$.

$$\cos x + (2 \cos^2 x - 1) = 0$$
$$2 \cos^2 x + \cos x - 1 = 0$$
$$(2 \cos x - 1)(\cos x + 1) = 0$$

Solving for $\cos x$, $\cos x = \frac{1}{2}$ or $\cos x = -1$

Solving for x, $x \in [0, \pi]$, $x = \dfrac{\pi}{3}$ or $x = \pi$

We verify that $\cos 2x \cos x \neq 0$. If $x = \dfrac{\pi}{3}$,

$$\cos \frac{2\pi}{3} \cos \frac{\pi}{3} = \frac{-1}{2} \times \frac{1}{2} = \frac{-1}{4}$$

If $x = \pi$, $\cos 2\pi \cos \pi = 1(-1) = -1$

We examine three completely different solutions for the next example.

Example 5 If $1 + \sin x = \cos x$, solve for x in the interval $[-\pi, \pi]$.

Solution 1 We graph $y = 1 + \sin x$ and $y = \cos x$ on the same set of axes and read the value of x at the points of intersection.

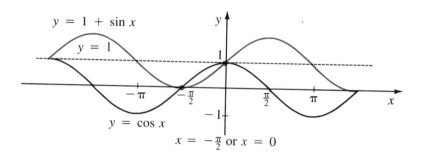

Solution 2 In order to express the equation in terms of a single trigonometric function, we square both sides to create a $\cos^2 x$ and replace it with $1 - \sin^2 x$.

$$1 + 2 \sin x + \sin^2 x = \cos^2 x$$
$$= 1 - \sin^2 x$$

Therefore $\quad\quad 2 \sin^2 x + 2 \sin x = 0$

$\quad\quad\quad\quad\quad\quad 2 \sin x(\sin x + 1) = 0$

Now $\quad\quad\quad\quad\quad \sin x = 0$ or $\sin x = -1$

and for $x \in [-\pi, \pi]$ $\quad\quad x = -\pi, -\dfrac{\pi}{2}, 0,$ or π

Since we squared both sides, we may have introduced roots that do not satisfy the original equation. We must verify each value of x.

If $x = -\pi$, $1 + \sin x = 1 + 0 = 1$ and $\cos x = -1$. Therefore $x = -\pi$ is inadmissible.

If $x = -\dfrac{\pi}{2}$, $1 + \sin x = 1 - 1 = 0$ and $\cos x = 0$. Therefore

$x = -\dfrac{\pi}{2}$ is a root.

Similarly it can be proved that $x = 0$ is a root, but $x = \pi$ is inadmissible.

Solution 3   The equation is not expressed in terms of a single trigonometric function. A Double Angle Formula enables us to eliminate the 1. Note that when the argument is changed the restriction on the variable must change accordingly.

$$1 + \sin x = \cos x$$

$$1 + 2 \sin \dfrac{x}{2} \cos \dfrac{x}{2} = 1 - 2 \sin^2 \dfrac{x}{2}$$

$$2 \sin^2 \dfrac{x}{2} + 2 \sin \dfrac{x}{2} \cos \dfrac{x}{2} = 0$$

$$2 \sin \dfrac{x}{2} \left(\sin \dfrac{x}{2} + \cos \dfrac{x}{2} \right) = 0$$

Therefore $\sin \dfrac{x}{2} = 0$ or $\sin \dfrac{x}{2} = -\cos \dfrac{x}{2}$

$\sin \dfrac{x}{2} = 0$ or $\tan \dfrac{x}{2} = -1$

Since $-\dfrac{\pi}{2} < \dfrac{x}{2} < \dfrac{\pi}{2}$, $\dfrac{x}{2} = 0$ or $\dfrac{x}{2} = -\dfrac{\pi}{4}$

and $x = 0$ or $x = -\dfrac{\pi}{2}$

If an equation contains algebraic as well as trigonometric functions it cannot be expressed in terms of a single function. In many cases the best we can do is approximate the root.

Example 6   Solve $\sin x = \dfrac{x}{2}$, $0 < x < 2.5$.

Solution   The equation $\sin x = \dfrac{x}{2}$ can be replaced by the equivalent system

$$\begin{cases} y = \sin x \\ y = \dfrac{x}{2} \end{cases}$$

An approximation can be obtained by graphing each on the same set of axes and estimating the value of x at the points of intersection.

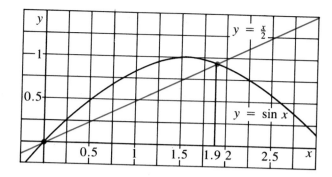

One solution occurs when $x = 0$. The other solution appears to be approximately 1.9. When $x = 1.9$, $\sin x \doteq 0.946\ 300$ and $\dfrac{x}{2} = .95$. Their difference is approximately .0037.

In Exercise 7.2 we will use Newton's method to solve this type of equation and our accuracy will be significantly improved. Our initial guess will be arrived at by approximating a solution using a graph as in Example 6.

EXERCISE 6.5

A **1.** Solve for x in the interval $[0, 2\pi]$.

(a) $\sin x = \dfrac{\sqrt{3}}{2}$ (b) $\cos x = \frac{1}{2}$ (c) $\tan x = -1$

(d) $\sec x = -2$ (e) $\sin x = -\frac{1}{2}$ (f) $\cos^2 x = \frac{1}{4}$

B **2.** Solve for x in the interval $[-\pi, 0]$.

(a) $\cos x = -\dfrac{1}{\sqrt{2}}$ (b) $\tan^2 x = \tan x$

(c) $\sin^2 x - \sin x = 2$ (d) $\sin^2 x = \frac{3}{4}$

(e) $4 \cos^2 x - 3 = 0$ (f) $(2 \csc x - 1)^2 = 9$

3. Solve for x in the given interval.

(a) $\sin x - \sin x \tan x = 0$, $[0, \pi]$

(b) $\sin x \tan 3x = 0$, $[-\pi, 0]$

(c) $6 \sin^2 x - 5 \cos x - 2 = 0$, $[0, 2\pi]$

(d) $\sqrt{2} \sin x + \tan x = 0$, $[-\pi, \pi]$

(e) $\cos^2 x - 3 \sin^2 x = 1$, $[-2\pi, 2\pi]$

(f) $2 \tan x = \sec x$, $[-2\pi, 0]$

4. Solve for x.

(a) $\cos 2x = \cos^2 x$, $-\pi \leqslant x \leqslant \pi$

(b) $\sin 2x = \cos x$, $-\pi \leqslant 2x \leqslant \pi$

(c) $\cos^2 x - 2 \sin x \cos x - \sin^2 x = 0$, $0 \leqslant 2x \leqslant \pi$

(d) $\tan 2x = 8 \cos^2 x - \cot x$, $0 \leqslant x \leqslant \dfrac{\pi}{2}$

(e) $\tan x + \sec 2x = 1$, $-\dfrac{\pi}{2} \leqslant x \leqslant \dfrac{\pi}{2}$

(f) $2(\sin^4 x + \cos^4 x) = 1$, $-\pi \leqslant x \leqslant \pi$

5. If $2 \tan x \cos^2 x + \sin x \tan x - 2 \tan x = 0$, $|x| < 2\pi$, solve for x.

6. If $\tan 2x = -\dfrac{24}{7}$, find the values of $\sin x$ and $\cos x$.

7. Find the values of x in the interval $\left[-\dfrac{1}{2}\pi, \dfrac{1}{2}\pi \right]$ that satisfy the equations. Approximating may be required.

(a) $\sin x = x$ (b) $\cos x = x$ (c) $\tan x = -x$

(d) $\cos x = -\dfrac{x}{3}$ (e) $\sin x = x \sin x$ (f) $\tan x = 2x$

C 8. If $x \sin A + y \cos A = p$ and $x \cos A - y \sin A = q$, find $x^2 + y^2$.

9. If $\sin A + \cos A = p$ and $\tan A + \cot A = q$, prove that $q(p^2 - 1) = 2$.

6.6 REVIEW EXERCISE

1. If x is in the interval $\left[0, \dfrac{\pi}{2} \right]$ and y is in the interval $\left[\dfrac{\pi}{2}, \pi \right]$ and $\tan x = \dfrac{4}{3}$ and $\csc y = \dfrac{13}{5}$, evaluate.

(a) $\sin(x + y)$ (b) $\tan(x - y)$ (c) $\cos 2(x + y)$

2. Evaluate.

(a) $\sin \dfrac{13\pi}{12}$ (b) $\cos\left(\dfrac{-11\pi}{12} \right)$ (c) $-\tan\left(-\dfrac{5\pi}{12} \right)$

(d) $\sin 15°$ (e) $\cos(-75°)$ (f) $-\tan 105°$

3. If $\tan x = -\dfrac{3}{4}$, $\dfrac{\pi}{2} \leqslant x \leqslant \pi$, evaluate.

(a) $\sin 2x$ (b) $\cos 2x$ (c) $\tan 2x$

4. If $\sin \dfrac{x}{2} = \dfrac{2}{3}$, $0 \leqslant x \leqslant \dfrac{\pi}{2}$, evaluate.

(a) $\cos x$ (b) $\tan x$ (c) $\sin \dfrac{x}{4}$

5. Find the value of

(a) $\sin 112\frac{1}{2}^{\circ}$ (b) $\cos \dfrac{\pi}{8}$ (c) $\tan \dfrac{3\pi}{16}$

6. Express each of the following as a function of its related acute angle and evaluate.

(a) $\sin 120^{\circ}$ (b) $\cos \dfrac{11\pi}{6}$ (c) $\tan\left(-\tfrac{7}{3}\pi\right)$

7. Express each of the following as a function of its co-related acute angle and evaluate.

(a) $\sin\left(-\dfrac{7\pi}{6}\right)$ (b) $\cos 495^{\circ}$ (c) $\tan \dfrac{39\pi}{4}$

8. Prove the following identities.

(a) $\tan x = \csc 2x - \cot 2x$ (b) $\dfrac{1 - \sin 2x}{\cos 2x} = \dfrac{1 - \tan x}{1 + \tan x}$

(c) $\cos x - \tan y \sin x = \sec y \cos(x + y)$

(d) $\sin(\pi + x) + \cos\left(\dfrac{\pi}{2} - x\right) + \tan\left(\dfrac{\pi}{2} + x\right) = -\cot x$

(e) $\dfrac{\sin 4x - \sin 2x}{\sin 2x} = \dfrac{\cos 3x}{\cos x}$

(f) $\cos x + \cos 2x + \cos 3x = \cos 2x\,(1 + 2\cos x)$

(g) $\sin(x + y) + \sin(x - y) = 2\sin x \cos y$

9. Solve.

(a) $2\sin x \cos x = 0,\ 0 \leqslant x \leqslant \pi$

(b) $\sin^2 x + \sin x = 0,\ -\pi \leqslant x \leqslant \pi$

(c) $\cos^2 x - \cos x = 0,\ 0 \leqslant x \leqslant 2\pi$

(d) $\sin^2 x - 2\sin x + 1 = 0,\ -2\pi \leqslant x \leqslant 2\pi$

(e) $\cos^2 2x + 2\cos 2x + 1 = 0,\ -\pi \leqslant x \leqslant \pi$

(f) $\sec^2 2x - 1 = 0,\ -2\pi \leqslant x \leqslant 2\pi$

(g) $\tan 4x - \tan 2x = 0,\ 0 < x < \pi$

(h) $\sqrt{3} \cos x + \sin x = 0,\ -2\pi \leqslant x \leqslant 0$

10. If $\tan x = 1$ and $\sin y = \tfrac{24}{25}$ with x and y in the interval $\left[0, \dfrac{\pi}{2}\right]$, evaluate.

(a) $\csc(x + y)$ (b) $\sec(x - y)$

11. Express $\cos 12a$ in terms of $\cos 3a$ and in terms of $\sin 3a$.

12. Use reflections to prove

(a) $\sin(b - \pi) = -\sin b,\ \pi < b < \dfrac{3\pi}{2}$.

(b) $\cos\left(b - \dfrac{3}{2}\pi\right) = -\sin b,\ \dfrac{\pi}{2} < b < \pi$.

13. Express $y = \sqrt{3} \sin x + \cos x$ as a sine function in the form $y = a \sin(x + b)$, $a > 0$. Use the result to graph the original function. (*Hint:* Use the Addition Formula for Sine and compare the coefficients of $\sin x$ and $\cos x$ in both equations.)

14. Express $y = \sqrt{3} \sin x - \cos x$ as a cosine function in the form $y = a \cos(x + b)$, $a > 0$.

15. If a, b, c, and d are the four smallest positive angles, in ascending order of magnitude, which have their sines equal to k, $k > 0$, prove that

$$4 \sin a + 3 \sin \frac{b}{2} + 2 \cos \frac{c}{2} + \sin \frac{d}{2} = 4k.$$

16. If $\theta = 18°$, prove that $\sin 2\theta = \cos 3\theta$. Find the exact value of (a) $\sin 18°$ and (b) $\cos 18°$.

17. If $x = 3 \sin \theta - \sin 3\theta$ and $y = \cos 3\theta + 3 \cos \theta$, prove that
$$x^{\frac{2}{3}} + y^{\frac{2}{3}} = 4^{\frac{2}{3}}.$$

18. If $\sin(x + y) = a \sin(x - y)$ and $\cos(x + y) = b \cos(x - y)$ where neither a nor b is ± 1, find an expression for $\cos 2x$ in terms of a and b.

6.7 CHAPTER 6 TEST

1. Find the exact value of each of the following.

   (a) $\cos\left(-\dfrac{\pi}{12}\right)$

   (b) $\sin\frac{3}{8}\pi$

   (c) $\dfrac{\tan 67° - \tan 22°}{1 + \tan 67° \tan 22°}$

   (d) $\left(\sin\dfrac{\pi}{8} + \cos\dfrac{\pi}{8}\right)^2$

   (e) $\sin\frac{13}{36}\pi \cos\frac{5}{36}\pi + \cos\frac{13}{36}\pi \sin\frac{5}{36}\pi$

2. If $\sin x = \frac{12}{13}$, x in the interval $\left[0, \dfrac{\pi}{2}\right]$ and $\cos y = \dfrac{4}{5}$, y in the

   interval $\left[-\dfrac{\pi}{2}, 0\right]$, find the value of $\sin[2(x - y)]$.

3. Find the value of $\tan 2x$, $\dfrac{\pi}{2} < x < \pi$, given $\sec x = -\dfrac{5}{4}$.

4. If $\sqrt{2}\cos x - 1 = \dfrac{1 + \sqrt{3}}{2}$ and $\sqrt{2}\cos x + 1 = \dfrac{1 - \sqrt{3}}{2}$, find

   the value of $\cos 4x$.

5. Prove.

   (a) $\dfrac{1 + \sin x + \cos x}{1 + \sin x - \cos x} = \cot\dfrac{x}{2}$

   (b) $-\sin^2 x - \sin^2 y + 1 = \cos(x + y)\cos(x - y)$

   (c) $\dfrac{\sin(x - \pi)}{\cos(\pi + x)} - \dfrac{\cos\left(\dfrac{\pi}{2} - x\right)}{\sin(-\pi - x)} = \dfrac{\sin x - \cos x}{\cos x}$

6. Solve for x in the given interval.

   (a) $\tan^2\left(2x - \dfrac{\pi}{12}\right) = 3, \left[-\dfrac{\pi}{2}, \dfrac{\pi}{2}\right]$

   (b) $\cos 2x - \cos^2 x - 2 \sin x + 3 = 0, [0, 2\pi]$

7. Develop a formula for $\tan(a + b - c)$ in terms of $\tan a$, $\tan b$, and $\tan c$.

FOUNDERS OF CALCULUS

In the seventeenth and eighteenth centuries the development of calculus and its applications was due in a large part to members of a single family, the Bernoullis. They, along with Euler, made Basel, Switzerland, famous as the birthplace of great mathematicians. In the course of a century, no less than eight members of this remarkable family distinguished themselves in mathematics.

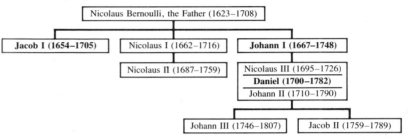

The most famous were the two brothers Jacob and Johann, staunch supporters and co-workers of Leibniz, and Johann's son Daniel, a close friend of Euler.

Johann I was more prolific than his brother Jacob, who had taught him mathematics. The two were often embroiled in controversy, especially in light of the fact that Johann had attempted to steal some of Jacob's ideas. Johann's competitive nature is evidenced by the fact that he threw his own son, Daniel, out of the house for having won a prize from the French Academy of Sciences that Johann himself coveted. He championed the cause of Leibniz over Newton, whom he detested, in their priority dispute over the invention of calculus.

It was a practice at that time for mathematicians to pose problems for each other. In 1696, Bernoulli posed the problem of the *brachistochrone*, the problem of finding the *curve of quickest descent* for "the shrewdest mathematicians of all the world," and fixed a six month limit for its solution. Leibniz solved the problem the day he received it and correctly predicted that only five solutions would be forthcoming, the solvers being Jacob and Johann Bernoulli, l'Hospital, Newton and himself.

Correspondence between scholars was the norm in these times, but Bernoulli was prodigious in his letter writing. He wrote more than 2500 letters to an estimated 110 scholars. He and Jacob picked up calculus where Newton and Leibniz left off. His contributions to integral calculus and the solution of differential equations were particularly significant. Johann developed *exponential calculus* when it was pointed out that Leibniz' published differential methods did not apply to the exponential function $y = a^x$.

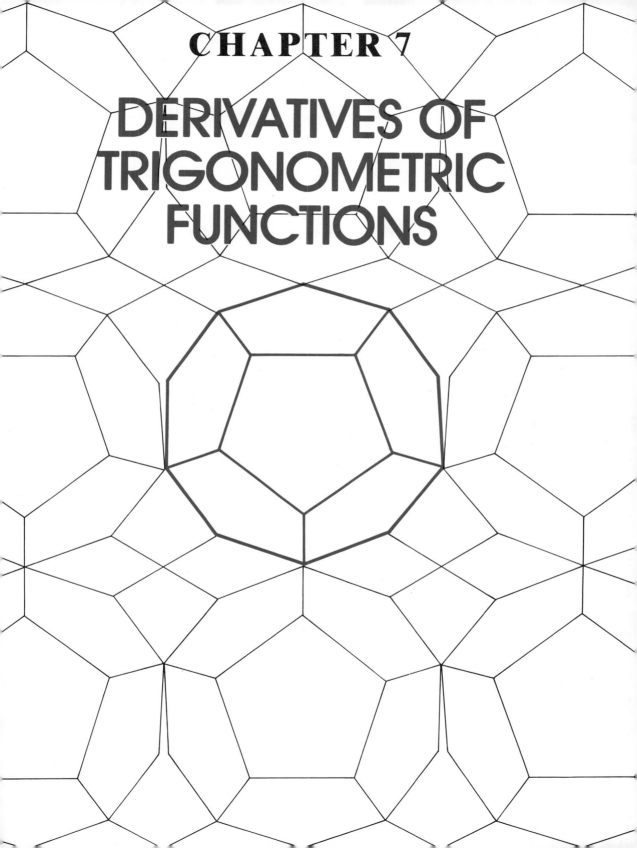

CHAPTER 7

DERIVATIVES OF TRIGONOMETRIC FUNCTIONS

REVIEW AND PREVIEW TO CHAPTER 7

Area of a Sector

The region of a circle cut off by two radii is called a **sector**. The angle contained by the radii at the centre of the circle is the **sector angle**. In this chapter, the formula for the area of a sector is required to develop a very important limit involving the sine function.

A simple proportion enables us to find the area of a sector given the sector angle in radians. Suppose we have a circle with radius r containing a sector with sector angle θ. We compare the area of the sector to the area of the circle.

$$\frac{\text{Area of sector}}{\text{Area of circle}} = \frac{\text{sector angle}}{1 \text{ revolution}} = \frac{\theta}{2\pi}$$

$$\frac{\text{Area of sector}}{\pi r^2} = \frac{\theta}{2\pi}$$

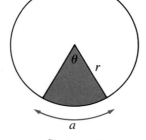

Sector area
$$= \tfrac{1}{2}r^2\theta$$
$$= \tfrac{1}{2}ar$$

Therefore

$$\boxed{\text{Sector area} = \tfrac{1}{2}r^2\theta, \ \theta \text{ in radians}}$$

Since $\theta = \dfrac{a}{r}$, we can express the sector area in terms of its arc length.

Similar to the formula
for the area of a triangle $\tfrac{1}{2}bh$

$$\boxed{\text{Sector area} = \tfrac{1}{2}ar}$$

Example 1   Calculate the area of the sector having sector angle 2 if the arc length is 3.5 cm.

Remember:
2 means 2 rad

Solution   The radius is required to calculate the area.

$$r = \frac{a}{\theta} = \frac{3.5}{2} = 1.75$$

$$\text{Sector area} = \tfrac{1}{2}ar = \tfrac{1}{2}(3.5)(1.75) = 3.0625$$

The area is 3.0625 cm².

EXERCISE 1

1. The radius of a circle is 10 cm. Calculate:
   (a) the arc length of the sector with sector angle 2.5.
   (b) the sector angle of the sector with arc length 12 cm.
   (c) the area of the sector with arc length 20 cm.
   (d) the area of the sector with sector angle $\frac{2}{3}\pi$.

2. A sector with area π cm² is contained in a circle with radius 6 cm. Find the arc length of the sector and the sector angle.

Inverse of a Function

A **function** f is a rule that assigns to each element a in a set A exactly one element, called $f(a)$, in a set B. The set A is called the **domain** of the function and the set of all possible values of $f(a)$ is called the **range**. In order to decide whether a graph is the graph of a function, we use the *Vertical Line Test*.

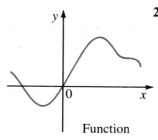

Function

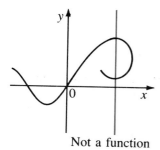

Not a function

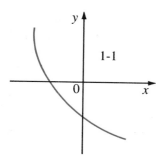

1-1

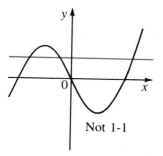

Not 1-1

Vertical Line Test

If each vertical line intersects a figure in at most one point, then the figure is the graph of a function. If there is at least one vertical line that intersects the graph in more than one point, then the figure is not the graph of a function.

Some functions are *one-to-one*.

A function f with domain A and range B is called a **one-to-one** (or 1–1) function if no two elements of A have the same image; that is, every element of B is the image of only one element of A. In symbols

$$f(a_1) \neq f(a_2) \text{ whenever } a_1 \neq a_2.$$

The *Horizontal Line Test* applied to the graph of a function determines if the function is 1–1.

Horizontal Line Test

If each horizontal line intersects the graph of a function f in at most one point, then f is 1–1. If there is at least one horizontal line that intersects the graph of f in more than one point then f is not 1–1.

In the following arrow diagram, notice that f is a 1–1 function. If we reverse the direction of the arrows, we get a new function g.

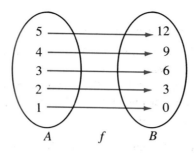 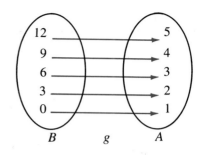

g is called the *inverse function* of f and is usually denoted by f^{-1}. (If f were not 1–1, then by reversing the arrows we would not get a function.)

Notice that

$$f(1) = 0 \quad \text{and} \quad f^{-1}(0) = 1$$
$$f(2) = 3 \quad \text{and} \quad f^{-1}(3) = 2$$
$$f(3) = 6 \quad \text{and} \quad f^{-1}(6) = 3$$

In general,

$$f(a) = b \quad \text{and} \quad f^{-1}(b) = a$$

If f maps a to b, then f^{-1} maps b back into a. In other words, the inverse function f^{-1} undoes what f does.

Notice also that

$$\text{domain of } f = A = \text{range of } f^{-1}$$
$$\text{range of } f = B = \text{domain of } f^{-1}$$

If f is a 1–1 function with domain A and range B then its **inverse function** f^{-1} has domain B and range A and is defined by

$$f^{-1}(b) = a \quad \text{if} \quad f(a) = b$$

for any $b \in B$.

The defining equation for f^{-1} is found by first solving the equation $y = f(x)$ for x and then interchanging x and y.

Example 1 Find the inverse of the function $y = \dfrac{1}{x - 1}$.

Solution Solve the equation for x.

$$y = \frac{1}{x - 1}$$
$$x - 1 = \frac{1}{y}$$
$$x = 1 + \frac{1}{y}$$

Now interchange x and y. The equation of the inverse is

$$y = 1 + \frac{1}{x}$$

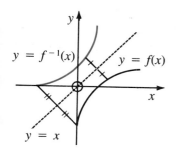

In Example 1, we performed the transformation $(x, y) \to (y, x)$. This is a reflection in the line $y = x$.

> The graph of f^{-1} is the reflection of the graph of f in the line $y = x$.

EXERCISE 2

1. Sketch the graph and determine if y is a function of x.
   - (a) $x = y^2$
   - (b) $x = y^2 - 2y$
   - (c) $y = x^2 + x$
   - (d) $x + 2y = 3$
   - (e) $2x + 5y < 1$
   - (f) $3y - x \geqslant 6$
   - (g) $x = \dfrac{2 - y}{7}$
   - (h) $x^2 + y^2 + 2x = 0$

2. Which of the following functions are 1–1?
   - (a) $f(x) = x + 1$
   - (b) $g(x) = |x|$
   - (c) $y = 3 - 2x$
   - (d) $h(x) = \dfrac{1}{x}$
   - (e) $F(x) = \dfrac{1}{x^2}$
   - (f) $y = 1 - x^2$
   - (g) $f(t) = -t^3$
   - (h) $f(t) = t^4$
   - (i) $y = \sqrt{x}$
   - (j) $f(x) = \dfrac{1}{x^2}, \ x < 0$

3. Find the inverse function.
   - (a) $y = \frac{1}{2}(x - 7)$
   - (b) $y = \frac{1}{5}(36 - x)$
   - (c) $y = 5x^3 - 6$
   - (d) $y = \sqrt{x}$
   - (e) $y = \sqrt{x - 3}$
   - (f) $y = 1 + \dfrac{1}{x}$
   - (g) $y = \dfrac{1}{1 + x}$
   - (h) $y = \dfrac{1 - x}{1 + x}$
   - (i) $y = \dfrac{4x - 1}{3x + 2}$
   - (j) $y = \dfrac{\pi - 3x}{x}$
   - (k) $y = x^4, \ x \geqslant 0$
   - (l) $y = 3(x - 1)^2, \ x \geqslant 1$
   - (m) $y = \sqrt{x^2 + 9}, \ x \geqslant 0$
   - (n) $y = \sqrt{25 - x^2}, \ x \leqslant 0$

4. Draw the graph of f^{-1} by reflecting the graph of f in the line $y = x$. Find an expression for $f^{-1}(x)$.
   - (a) $f(x) = 2x + 1$
   - (b) $f(x) = x^2 + 2, \ x \geqslant 0$
   - (c) $f(x) = x^3$
   - (d) $f(x) = -\dfrac{1}{x}$

INTRODUCTION

In this chapter we develop the derivatives of the trigonometric functions and the inverse trigonometric functions. These derivatives will be used to sketch curves and solve problems involving optimization or related rates.

7.1 LIMITS OF TRIGONOMETRIC FUNCTIONS

In order to find the derivatives of the trigonometric functions, we must first evaluate some special limits involving trigonometric functions. It is important to note that the arguments of the trigonometric functions in this section are expressed in radians.

Inspection of the graphs of $y = \sin \theta$ and $y = \cos \theta$ gives us our first two limits.

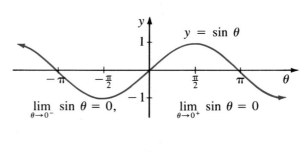

$$\lim_{\theta \to 0^-} \sin \theta = 0, \qquad \lim_{\theta \to 0^+} \sin \theta = 0$$

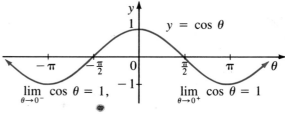

$$\lim_{\theta \to 0^-} \cos \theta = 1, \qquad \lim_{\theta \to 0^+} \cos \theta = 1$$

Therefore
$$\lim_{\theta \to 0} \sin \theta = 0 \qquad \qquad \lim_{\theta \to 0} \cos \theta = 1$$

The most important limit involving trigonometric functions is $\lim_{\theta \to 0} \dfrac{\sin \theta}{\theta}$. We examine the value of $\dfrac{\sin \theta}{\theta}$ for values of θ close to 0.

	Approaching 0 From the Right		Approaching 0 From the Left	
θ	$\dfrac{\sin \theta}{\theta}$		θ	$\dfrac{\sin \theta}{\theta}$
0.3	0.985 067		−0.3	0.985 067
0.2	0.993 347		−0.2	0.993 347
0.1	0.998 334		−0.1	0.998 334
0.05	0.999 583		−0.05	0.999 583
0.02	0.999 933		−0.02	0.999 933
0.01	0.999 983		−0.01	0.999 983

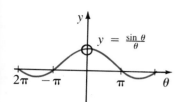

The trend of the values of $\dfrac{\sin \theta}{\theta}$ in the tables suggests that

$$\lim_{\theta \to 0} \frac{\sin \theta}{\theta} = 1. \text{ A proof follows.}$$

In the diagram, point A is on the unit circle $x^2 + y^2 = 1$. Point A determines angle θ, $0 < \theta < \dfrac{\pi}{2}$. The perpendicular drawn from point A meets the x-axis at B. The circle, radius OB, meets line segment OA at D.

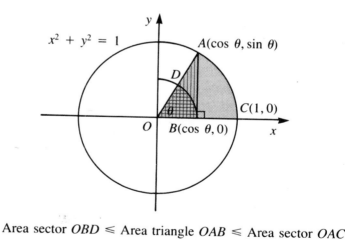

Sector area
$= \frac{1}{2}r^2\theta$

Area of Triangle
$= \frac{1}{2}bh$

Now   Area sector $OBD \leqslant$ Area triangle $OAB \leqslant$ Area sector OAC

Therefore $\frac{1}{2}(OB)^2 (\theta) \leqslant \frac{1}{2}(OB)(BA) \leqslant \frac{1}{2}(OC)^2(\theta)$

$\left(\frac{1}{2}\cos^2 \theta\right)(\theta) \leqslant \frac{1}{2}\cos \theta \sin \theta \leqslant \frac{1}{2}(1)^2(\theta)$

$\theta \cos^2 \theta \leqslant \cos \theta \sin \theta \leqslant \theta$

$\dfrac{\theta \cos^2 \theta}{\theta \cos \theta} \leqslant \dfrac{\cos \theta \sin \theta}{\theta \cos \theta} \leqslant \dfrac{\theta}{\theta \cos \theta}, \quad \theta \cos \theta > 0$

$\cos \theta \leqslant \dfrac{\sin \theta}{\theta} \leqslant \dfrac{1}{\cos \theta}$

Applying the squeeze or sandwich theorem.

and $\quad \displaystyle\lim_{\theta \to 0^+} \cos \theta \leq \lim_{\theta \to 0^+} \frac{\sin \theta}{\theta} \leq \lim_{\theta \to 0^+} \frac{1}{\cos \theta}$

Therefore $\quad 1 \leq \displaystyle\lim_{\theta \to 0^+} \frac{\sin \theta}{\theta} \leq 1$

and $\quad \displaystyle\lim_{\theta \to 0^+} \frac{\sin \theta}{\theta} = 1$

Since $f(\theta) = \dfrac{\sin \theta}{\theta}$ is an even function, $\displaystyle\lim_{\theta \to 0^-} \frac{\sin \theta}{\theta} = 1$.

Therefore $\quad \boxed{\displaystyle\lim_{\theta \to 0} \frac{\sin \theta}{\theta} = 1}$ ①

Most of the limit evaluations in this section will require us to produce this particular limit, since straight substitution will often produce $\frac{0}{0}$.

Example 1 Evaluate $\displaystyle\lim_{x \to 0} \frac{\sin x}{2x}$.

Solution We make use of the fact that $\displaystyle\lim_{x \to a} cf(x) = c \lim_{x \to a} f(x)$. (See Property 3 of limits in Section 1.2.) The technique is simple and is used in a variety of questions.

$$\lim_{x \to 0} \frac{\sin x}{2x} = \lim_{x \to 0} \frac{1}{2}\left(\frac{\sin x}{x}\right)$$
$$= \frac{1}{2}\left(\lim_{x \to 0} \frac{\sin x}{x}\right)$$
$$= \frac{1}{2}(1) \quad \text{(From ①)}$$
$$= \frac{1}{2}$$

Example 2 Evaluate $\displaystyle\lim_{x \to 0} \frac{\sin 2x}{x}$.

Solution In order to use ① the denominator must be identical to the argument of the sine function. Multiply the numerator and denominator by 2.

$$\lim_{x \to 0} \frac{\sin 2x}{x} = \lim_{x \to 0} 2\left(\frac{\sin 2x}{2x}\right)$$
$$= 2\left(\lim_{2x \to 0} \frac{\sin 2x}{2x}\right) \quad (\text{as } x \to 0, \, 2x \to 0)$$
$$= 2(1)$$
$$= 2$$

Example 3   Evaluate $\lim\limits_{x \to 0} \dfrac{\sin 7x}{\sin 4x}$.

Solution

$$\lim_{x \to 0} \frac{\sin 7x}{\sin 4x} = \lim_{x \to 0} \frac{7x\left(\dfrac{\sin 7x}{7x}\right)}{4x\left(\dfrac{\sin 4x}{4x}\right)}$$

$$= \frac{7}{4}\left(\frac{\lim\limits_{7x \to 0} \dfrac{\sin 7x}{7x}}{\lim\limits_{4x \to 0} \dfrac{\sin 4x}{4x}}\right)$$

$$= \left(\frac{7}{4}\right)\frac{(1)}{(1)}$$

$$= \frac{7}{4}$$

Calculator Approximation

x	$\dfrac{\sin 7x}{\sin 4x}$
0.1	1.654 308
0.01	1.749 038
0.001	1.749 990

Example 4   Evaluate $\lim\limits_{x \to 0} \dfrac{\cos x - 1}{x}$.

Solution 1   Multiply the numerator and denominator by $\cos x + 1$ and apply the identity $\sin^2 x + \cos^2 x = 1$ to get the expression in terms of $\sin x$.

$$\lim_{x \to 0} \frac{\cos x - 1}{x} = \lim_{x \to 0} \frac{(\cos x - 1)(\cos x + 1)}{x(\cos x + 1)}$$

$$= \lim_{x \to 0} \frac{\cos^2 x - 1}{x(\cos x + 1)}$$

$$= \lim_{x \to 0} \frac{-\sin^2 x}{x(\cos x + 1)}$$

$$= -\lim_{x \to 0} \frac{\sin x}{x} \lim_{x \to 0} \frac{\sin x}{1 + \cos x}$$

$$= -(1)\left(\frac{0}{1 + 1}\right)$$

$$= 0$$

Solution 2   We can also use the formula $\cos 2x = 1 - 2\sin^2 x$ to change from the cosine to the sine function.

$$\lim_{x \to 0} \frac{\cos x - 1}{x} = \lim_{x \to 0} \frac{1 - 2\sin^2 \dfrac{x}{2} - 1}{x}$$

$$= \lim_{x \to 0} \frac{-2\sin^2 \dfrac{x}{2}}{2\left(\dfrac{x}{2}\right)}$$

$$= -\lim_{\frac{x}{2} \to 0} \frac{\sin \frac{x}{2}}{\frac{x}{2}} \lim_{x \to 0} \sin \frac{x}{2}$$

$$= -(1)(0)$$
$$= 0$$

The limit in Example 4 is an important result. It will be used to develop the derivative of $y = \sin x$ in Section 7.2.

Example 5   Evaluate $\displaystyle\lim_{x \to \pi} \frac{\sin x}{\pi - x}$.

Solution   In order to use ① we need a variable to approach 0.

Now   as $x \to \pi$, $x - \pi \to 0$
Therefore $\pi - x \to 0$
Since $\sin x = \sin(\pi - x)$
we get $\displaystyle\lim_{x \to \pi} \frac{\sin x}{\pi - x} = \lim_{\pi - x \to 0} \frac{\sin(\pi - x)}{\pi - x} = 1$

EXERCISE 7.1

B   Use a calculator to estimate the value of each of the following limits.

1. $\displaystyle\lim_{x \to 0} \frac{\sin 3x}{x}$ **2.** $\displaystyle\lim_{x \to 0} \frac{\sin 2x}{\sin 3x}$ **3.** $\displaystyle\lim_{x \to 0} \frac{\sin^3 2x}{\sin^3 3x}$

4. $\displaystyle\lim_{x \to 0} \frac{1 - \cos^2 x}{x^2}$ **5.** $\displaystyle\lim_{x \to 0} \frac{1 - \cos x}{\tan x}$ **6.** $\displaystyle\lim_{x \to 0} \frac{\sin(\cos x)}{\sec x}$

Evaluate each of the following limits.

7. $\displaystyle\lim_{x \to 0} \frac{\sin 3x}{x}$ **8.** $\displaystyle\lim_{x \to 0} \frac{\sin ax}{\sin bx}$ **9.** $\displaystyle\lim_{x \to 0} \frac{\sin^3 2x}{\sin^3 3x}$

10. $\displaystyle\lim_{x \to 0} \frac{1 - \cos x}{x}$ **11.** $\displaystyle\lim_{x \to 0} (x^2 + \cos x)$ **12.** $\displaystyle\lim_{x \to \frac{\pi}{3}} (\sin x - \cos x)$

13. $\displaystyle\lim_{x \to \frac{\pi}{4}} \frac{\sin x}{3x}$ **14.** $\displaystyle\lim_{x \to -3\pi} x^3 \sin^4 x$ **15.** $\displaystyle\lim_{x \to 0} \frac{\sin 5x}{5}$

16. $\displaystyle\lim_{x \to \frac{\pi}{4}} \frac{\tan x}{4x}$ **17.** $\displaystyle\lim_{x \to 0} \frac{\tan 3x}{3 \tan 2x}$ **18.** $\displaystyle\lim_{x \to 0} \frac{\sin^2 3x}{x^2}$

19. $\displaystyle\lim_{x \to \frac{\pi}{6}} \sqrt{\sin x}$

20. $\displaystyle\lim_{x \to 0} \frac{\sin 6x}{\cos 4x}$

21. $\displaystyle\lim_{x \to 0} \frac{\cos x - 1}{\sin x}$

22. $\displaystyle\lim_{x \to 0} \frac{\tan x}{4x}$

23. $\displaystyle\lim_{x \to 0} \frac{x^3}{\tan^3 2x}$

24. $\displaystyle\lim_{x \to 0} \frac{1 - \cos x}{2x^2}$

25. $\displaystyle\lim_{x \to 0} \frac{x}{\sin \dfrac{x}{2}}$

26. $\displaystyle\lim_{x \to 0} \frac{2 \tan x}{x \sec x}$

27. $\displaystyle\lim_{x \to 0} \frac{1 - \cos^2 x}{x^2}$

28. $\displaystyle\lim_{x \to 0} \frac{1 - \cos 2x}{x^2}$

29. $\displaystyle\lim_{x \to \frac{\pi}{2}} \frac{\cot x}{\dfrac{\pi}{2} - x}$

30. $\displaystyle\lim_{x \to \pi} \frac{\sin x}{x - \pi}$

31. $\displaystyle\lim_{x \to 0} \frac{\sin^2 x \cos x}{1 - \cos x}$

32. $\displaystyle\lim_{x \to 0} \frac{\sin x}{\tan x}$

33. $\displaystyle\lim_{x \to 0} \frac{2 \sin x - \sin 2x}{x \cos x}$

34. $\displaystyle\lim_{x \to 0} \frac{\tan x - \sin x}{x \cos x}$

35. $\displaystyle\lim_{x \to 0} \frac{1 - \cos x}{\tan x}$

36. $\displaystyle\lim_{x \to 0} \frac{\csc x - \cot x}{\sin x}$

37. $\displaystyle\lim_{x \to 0} \frac{\sin 2x}{2x^2 + x}$

38. $\displaystyle\lim_{x \to 0} \frac{\sin(\cos x)}{\sec x}$

39. (a) Use a calculator to approximate the value of $\dfrac{\tan x - x}{x^3}$ for $x = 0.1, 0.01, 0.001,$ and 0.0001.

(b) Estimate the value of $\displaystyle\lim_{x \to 0} \dfrac{\tan x - x}{x^3}$ using the results from part (a).

(c) Use a calculator to approximate the value of $\dfrac{\tan x - x}{x^3}$ for $x = 0.00001, 0.000001,$ and 0.0000001 and examine your answer to part (b). Can you explain what went wrong?

C **40.** Does the $\displaystyle\lim_{x \to 0} \frac{\sin x}{|x|}$ exist? If so, what is it? If not, why not?

41. Evaluate $\displaystyle\lim_{x \to 0} \frac{\sin x}{x + \sin x}$.

42. Evaluate $\displaystyle\lim_{x \to 1^-} \frac{\sin(x - 1)}{|x - 1|}$.

43. Evaluate $\displaystyle\lim_{h \to 0} \frac{\sin(a + h) - \sin a}{h}$.

44. Evaluate $\displaystyle\lim_{h \to 0} \frac{\cos(a + h) - \cos a}{h}$.

7.2 DERIVATIVES OF THE SINE AND COSINE FUNCTIONS

If we apply the interpretation of $f'(x)$ as the slope of the tangent line at $(x, f(x))$ to the function $f(x) = \sin x$, it appears that $f'(x) = \cos x$. That is, the derivative of the sine function is the cosine function.

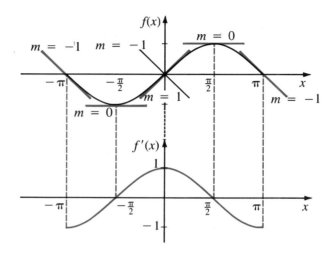

This conjecture is confirmed when we apply the definition of the derivative to calculate $f'(x)$ when $f(x) = \sin x$.

$$\frac{d}{dx} \sin x = \cos x$$

Proof

$$f(x) = \sin x$$

$$f'(x) = \lim_{h \to 0} \frac{f(x + h) - f(x)}{h}$$

$$= \lim_{h \to 0} \frac{\sin(x + h) - \sin x}{h}$$

$$= \lim_{h \to 0} \frac{\sin x \cos h + \cos x \sin h - \sin x}{h}$$

$$= \lim_{h \to 0} \frac{\sin x(\cos h - 1) + \cos x \sin h}{h}$$

$$= \sin x \lim_{h \to 0} \frac{\cos h - 1}{h} + \cos x \lim_{h \to 0} \frac{\sin h}{h}$$

$$= \sin x(0) + \cos x(1) \quad \text{(From Example 4, Section 7.1)}$$

$$= \cos x$$

The derivative of the cosine function can now be found. We use a co-related angle identity to obtain an equivalent sine function. The derivative is calculated and a co-related angle identity is used to create the desired form.

$$\frac{d}{dx}\cos x = -\sin x$$

Proof

$$f(x) = \cos x$$
$$= \sin\left(\frac{\pi}{2} - x\right)$$

Therefore, using the Chain Rule,

$$f'(x) = \cos\left(\frac{\pi}{2} - x\right)\frac{d}{dx}\left(\frac{\pi}{2} - x\right)$$
$$= (\sin x)(-1)$$
$$= -\sin x$$

Example 1   Differentiate.

(a) $y = \sin 3x$ (b) $y = \sin(x + 2)$ (c) $y = \sin(kx + d)$

Solution   We must always be aware of the use of the Chain Rule when we differentiate the trigonometric functions.

(a) $y = \sin 3x$

$$\frac{dy}{dx} = \cos 3x \frac{d}{dx} 3x$$
$$= 3 \cos 3x$$

(b) $y = \sin(x + 2)$

$$\frac{dy}{dx} = \cos(x + 2)\frac{d}{dx}(x + 2)$$
$$= \cos(x + 2)$$

(c) $y = \sin(kx + d)$

$$\frac{dy}{dx} = \cos(kx + d)\frac{d}{dx}(kx + d)$$
$$= k \cos(kx + d)$$

Example 2   Differentiate (a) $y = \sin(x^3)$, (b) $y = \sin^3 x$ and (c) $y = \sin^3(x^2 - 1)$.

Solution   Again we must be aware of the Chain Rule.

(a) $y = \sin(x^3)$

$$\frac{dy}{dx} = \cos(x^3)\frac{d}{dx}x^3$$
$$= 3x^2 \cos x^3$$

(b) $y = \sin^3 x$
$$y = (\sin x)^3$$
$$\frac{dy}{dx} = 3(\sin x)^2 \frac{d}{dx} \sin x$$
$$= 3 \sin^2 x \cos x$$

(c) We use the Chain Rule twice.

$$y = \sin^3(x^2 - 1)$$
$$y = [\sin(x^2 - 1)]^3$$
$$\frac{dy}{dx} = 3[\sin(x^2 - 1)]^2 \frac{d}{dx} \sin(x^2 - 1)$$
$$= 3 \sin^2(x^2 - 1)\cos(x^2 - 1) \frac{d}{dx}(x^2 - 1)$$
$$= 3 \sin^2(x^2 - 1)[\cos(x^2 - 1)](2x)$$
$$= 6x \sin^2(x^2 - 1)\cos(x^2 - 1)$$

Example 3   Differentiate $y = x^2 \cos x$.

Solution   We use the Product Rule.

$$y = x^2 \cos x$$
$$\frac{dy}{dx} = x^2 \frac{d}{dx} \cos x + \cos x \frac{d}{dx} x^2$$
$$= x^2(-\sin x) + (\cos x)(2x)$$
$$= -x^2 \sin x + 2x \cos x$$

Example 4   If $\sin x + \sin y = 1$ find the derivative of y with respect to x.

Solution   Differentiate implicitly.

$$\sin x + \sin y = 1$$
$$\cos x + \cos y \frac{dy}{dx} = 0$$
$$\cos y \frac{dy}{dx} = -\cos x$$
$$\frac{dy}{dx} = -\frac{\cos x}{\cos y}$$

Example 5   Find the equation of the tangent line to $y = \dfrac{\sin x}{\cos 2x}$ at the point where $x = \dfrac{\pi}{6}$.

Solution   To find the equation of a straight line, we need its slope and a point on the line.

When $x = \dfrac{\pi}{6}$, $y = \dfrac{\sin \dfrac{\pi}{6}}{\cos \dfrac{\pi}{3}} = \dfrac{\frac{1}{2}}{\frac{1}{2}} = 1$. The required point is $\left(\dfrac{\pi}{6}, 1\right)$.

Now $\qquad \dfrac{dy}{dx} = \dfrac{\cos 2x \dfrac{d}{dx} \sin x - \sin x \dfrac{d}{dx} \cos 2x}{(\cos 2x)^2}$

$$= \dfrac{\cos 2x \cos x - \sin x(-\sin 2x)\dfrac{d}{dx} 2x}{\cos^2 2x}$$

$$= \dfrac{\cos x \cos 2x + 2 \sin x \sin 2x}{\cos^2 2x}$$

Thus the slope of the tangent line at $x = \dfrac{\pi}{6}$ is

$$\left.\dfrac{dy}{dx}\right|_{x=\frac{\pi}{6}} = \dfrac{\dfrac{\sqrt{3}}{2}\left(\frac{1}{2}\right) + 2\left(\frac{1}{2}\right)\left(\dfrac{\sqrt{3}}{2}\right)}{\left(\frac{1}{2}\right)^2} = 3\sqrt{3}$$

The equation of the required tangent line is

$$y - 1 = 3\sqrt{3}\left(x - \dfrac{\pi}{6}\right)$$

$$y - 1 = 3\sqrt{3}x - \dfrac{\sqrt{3}\,\pi}{2}$$

$$6\sqrt{3}x - 2y = \pi\sqrt{3} - 2$$

Example 6   Use the procedure developed in Chapter 5 to sketch $f(x) = x - \cos x$, $-2\pi \le x \le 2\pi$.

Solution   A. **Domain.**   The restricted domain $-2\pi \le x \le 2\pi$ is given.

B. **Intercepts.**   The y-intercept is $f(0) = 0 - \cos 0 = -1$. The x-intercept occurs when $\cos x = x$. It cannot be given exactly, but a graph suggests that it is approximately 0.7. (Newton's Method gives the x-intercept $\doteq 0.739$. See Question 8 in Exercise 7.2.)

C. **Symmetry.**   Since $f(-x) = (-x) - \cos(-x)$

$$= -x - \cos x$$

$$\ne f(x) \quad \text{or} \quad -f(x)$$

The function is neither even nor odd. Therefore the curve is not symmetric about the y-axis or the origin.

D. **Asymptotes.**   None.

E. **Intervals of increase or decrease.**   The first derivative is

$$f'(x) = 1 + \sin x$$

Since $\quad -1 \le \sin x \le 1$

we have $\quad f'(x) \ge 0$

and the function is always increasing.

F. *Local Maximum and Minimum Values.* Since the curve is always increasing we examine the end points of the domain.
When $x = -2\pi$, the minimum value of y is

$$-2\pi - \cos(-2\pi) = -2\pi - 1$$

When $x = 2\pi$, the maximum value of y is

$$2\pi - \cos 2\pi = 2\pi - 1$$

G. *Concavity and Points of Inflection.* Find the points at which the second derivative is equal to zero and set up a chart to determine the concavity.

$$f''(x) = \cos x$$

Now $\cos x = 0$, $-2\pi \leqslant x \leqslant 2\pi$

when $x = -\frac{3}{2}\pi, -\frac{1}{2}\pi, \frac{1}{2}\pi,$ or $\frac{3}{2}\pi$

The chart summarizes our results.

Interval	$f''(x)$	$f(x)$
$-2\pi < x < -\frac{3}{2}\pi$	+	concave up on $\left(-2\pi, -\frac{3}{2}\pi\right)$
$-\frac{3}{2}\pi < x < -\frac{1}{2}\pi$	−	concave down on $\left(-\frac{3}{2}\pi, -\frac{1}{2}\pi\right)$
$-\frac{1}{2}\pi < x < \frac{1}{2}\pi$	+	concave up on $\left(-\frac{1}{2}\pi, \frac{1}{2}\pi\right)$
$\frac{1}{2}\pi < x < \frac{3}{2}\pi$	−	concave down on $\left(\frac{1}{2}\pi, \frac{3}{2}\pi\right)$
$\frac{3}{2}\pi < x < 2\pi$	+	concave up on $\left(\frac{3}{2}\pi, 2\pi\right)$

Values of x at which the concavity changes determine points of inflection.

$$f\left(-\frac{3}{2}\pi\right) = -\frac{3}{2}\pi \text{ gives point of inflection } \left(-\frac{3}{2}\pi, -\frac{3}{2}\pi\right)$$

$$f\left(-\frac{1}{2}\pi\right) = -\frac{1}{2}\pi \text{ gives point of inflection } \left(-\frac{1}{2}\pi, -\frac{1}{2}\pi\right)$$

$$f\left(\frac{1}{2}\pi\right) = \frac{1}{2}\pi \text{ gives point of inflection } \left(\frac{1}{2}\pi, \frac{1}{2}\pi\right)$$

$$f\left(\frac{3}{2}\pi\right) = \frac{3}{2}\pi \text{ gives point of inflection } \left(\frac{3}{2}\pi, \frac{3}{2}\pi\right)$$

G. *Sketch of the graph.*

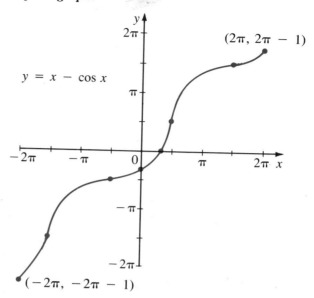

$y = x - \cos x$

$(2\pi, 2\pi - 1)$

$(-2\pi, -2\pi - 1)$

EXERCISE 7.2

B 1. Find the derivative of y with respect to x in each of the following.

(a) $y = \cos(-4x)$

(b) $y = \sin(3x + 2\pi)$

(c) $y = 4 \sin(-2x^2 - 3)$

(d) $y = -\frac{1}{2} \cos(4 + 2x)$

(e) $y = \sin x^2$

(f) $y = -\cos x^2$

(g) $y = \sin^{-2}(x^3)$

(h) $y = \cos(x^2 - 2)^2$

(i) $y = 3 \sin^4(2 - x)^{-1}$

(j) $y = x \cos x$

(k) $y = \dfrac{x}{\sin x}$

(l) $y = \dfrac{\sin x}{1 + \cos x}$

(m) $y = (1 + \cos^2 x)^6$

(n) $y = \sin \dfrac{1}{x}$

(o) $y = \sin(\cos x)$

(p) $y = \cos^3(\sin x)$

(q) $y = x \cos \dfrac{1}{x}$

(r) $y = \dfrac{\sin^2 x}{\cos x}$

(s) $y = \dfrac{1 + \sin x}{1 - \sin 2x}$

(t) $y = \sin^3 x + \cos^3 x$

(u) $y = \cos^2\left(\dfrac{1 - \sqrt{x}}{1 + \sqrt{x}}\right)$

2. Find $\dfrac{dy}{dx}$ in each of the following.

(a) $\sin y = \cos 2x$ (b) $x \cos y = \sin(x + y)$

(c) $\sin y + y = \cos x + x$ (d) $\sin(\cos x) = \cos(\sin y)$

(e) $\sin x \cos y + \cos x \sin y = 1$

(f) $\sin x + \cos 2x = 2xy$

3. Find an equation of the tangent line to the given curve at the given point.

(a) $y = 2 \sin x$ at $\left(\dfrac{\pi}{6}, 1\right)$ (b) $y = \dfrac{\sin x}{\cos x}$ at $\left(\dfrac{\pi}{4}, 1\right)$

(c) $y = \dfrac{1}{\cos x} - 2 \cos x$ at $\left(\dfrac{\pi}{3}, 1\right)$

(d) $y = \dfrac{\cos^2 x}{\sin^2 x}$ at $\left(\dfrac{\pi}{4}, 1\right)$

(e) $y = \sin x + \cos 2x$ at $\left(\dfrac{\pi}{6}, 1\right)$

(f) $y = \cos(\cos x)$ at $x = \dfrac{\pi}{2}$

4. Find the critical numbers, the intervals of increase and decrease, and any maximum or minimum values.

(a) $y = \sin^2 x$, $-\pi \leqslant x \leqslant \pi$

(b) $y = \cos x - \sin x$, $-\pi \leqslant x \leqslant \pi$

5. Determine the concavity and find the points of inflection.

(a) $y = 2 \cos x + \sin 2x$, $0 \leqslant x \leqslant 2\pi$

(b) $y = 4 \sin^2 x - 1$, $-\pi \leqslant x \leqslant \pi$

6. Use the procedure of Example 5 to sketch the graph of each of the following.

(a) $y = x + \sin x$, $0 \leqslant x \leqslant 2\pi$ (b) $y = x \cos x$, $0 \leqslant x \leqslant \pi$

7. If $f(x) = \sin x \cos 3x$, evaluate $f''\left(\dfrac{\pi}{3}\right)$.

8. Use Newton's method to find all roots of the given equation correct to 6 decimal places.

(a) $\cos x - x = 0$ (b) $2 \sin x = 2 - x$ (c) $\sin x = \dfrac{x}{2}$

C **9.** Use the results of this section to find the derivative of $y = \tan x$ and $y = \csc x$.

10. If $\sin y + \cos x = 1$ find $\dfrac{d^2y}{dx^2}$.

11. Find $\dfrac{dy}{dx}$ in each of the following.

(a) $y = \dfrac{1}{\sin(x - \sin x)}$

(b) $y = \sqrt{\sin\sqrt{x}}$

(c) $y = \sqrt[3]{x \cos x}$

(d) $y = \cos^3(\cos x) + \sin^2(\cos x)$

(e) $y = \sqrt{\cos(\sin^2 x)}$

12. Find an equation for the tangent line to the curve

$x \sin 2y = y \cos 2x$ at the point $\left(\dfrac{\pi}{4}, \dfrac{\pi}{2}\right)$

13. Find the derivative of y with respect to x if

$x + \tan(xy) = \sin y + \cos x$

PROBLEMS PLUS

If $f(x) = x \sin x$, find $f^{(100)}(0)$.

7.3 DERIVATIVES OF OTHER TRIGONOMETRIC FUNCTIONS

The trigonometric identities allow us to express the remaining trigonometric functions in terms of sine or cosine or both. We can then generate the derivatives of the remaining trigonometric functions using the Quotient and Chain Rules in conjunction with our differentiation formulas for sine and cosine.

$$\frac{d}{dx} \tan x = \sec^2 x$$

Proof

A basic identity transforms

$$y = \tan x$$

into

$$y = \frac{\sin x}{\cos x}$$

Applying the Quotient Rule, we get

$$\frac{dy}{dx} = \frac{\cos x \dfrac{d}{dx} \sin x - \sin x \dfrac{d}{dx} \cos x}{\cos^2 x}$$

$$= \frac{\cos x \cos x - \sin x(-\sin x)}{\cos^2 x}$$

$$= \frac{\cos^2 x + \sin^2 x}{\cos^2 x}$$

$$= \frac{1}{\cos^2 x}$$

$$= \sec^2 x$$

$$\boxed{\frac{d}{dx} \csc x = -\csc x \cot x}$$

Proof

A basic identity transforms

$$y = \csc x$$

into

$$y = \frac{1}{\sin x} = (\sin x)^{-1}$$

Therefore

$$\frac{dy}{dx} = -(\sin x)^{-2} \frac{d}{dx} \sin x$$

$$= -\frac{1}{\sin^2 x} \cos x$$

$$= \frac{-1}{\sin x} \frac{\cos x}{\sin x}$$

$$= -\csc x \cot x$$

The development of the formulas to differentiate the secant and cotangent functions is requested in Exercise 7.3. We collect the derivatives of the trigonometric functions in the table that follows.

Derivatives of the Trigonometric Functions	
$\dfrac{d}{dx} \sin x = \cos x$	$\dfrac{d}{dx} \csc x = -\csc x \cot x$
$\dfrac{d}{dx} \cos x = -\sin x$	$\dfrac{d}{dx} \sec x = \sec x \tan x$
$\dfrac{d}{dx} \tan x = \sec^2 x$	$\dfrac{d}{dx} \cot x = -\csc^2 x$

To help in the memorization of these formulas, note that there is a minus sign in the derivative of each of the "co" functions, that is, the cosine, cosecant, and cotangent functions.

Example 1   Differentiate $f(x) = \dfrac{1}{1 + \tan x}$

Solution
$$f(x) = \frac{1}{1 + \tan x}$$
$$= (1 + \tan x)^{-1}$$
$$f'(x) = -(1 + \tan x)^{-2} \frac{d}{dx}(1 + \tan x)$$
$$= -(1 + \tan x)^{-2}(\sec^2 x)$$
$$= \frac{-\sec^2 x}{(1 + \tan x)^2}$$

It is possible to use algebraic manipulation and trigonometric identities to change the form of the answer in Example 1 to

$$y = \frac{-1}{1 + \sin 2x}$$

If we need to find the second derivative it is easier to work with this form.

Example 2   Differentiate $y = 2\csc^3(3x^2)$

Solution   We rewrite in the form $y = 2[\csc(3x^2)]^3$. Note the repeated use of the Chain Rule.

$$\frac{dy}{dx} = 6[\csc(3x^2)]^2 \frac{d}{dx}\csc(3x^2)$$
$$= 6\csc^2(3x^2)[-\csc(3x^2)]\cot(3x^2)\frac{d}{dx}(3x^2)$$
$$= -6\csc^3(3x^2)[\cot(3x^2)](6x)$$
$$= -36x\csc^3(3x^2)\cot(3x^2)$$

Example 3   If $\tan y = x^2$ find the derivative of y with respect to x.

Solution   We differentiate implicitly.

$$\tan y = x^2$$
$$\sec^2 y \frac{dy}{dx} = 2x$$
$$\frac{dy}{dx} = \frac{2x}{\sec^2 y} = 2x\cos^2 y$$

Example 4 Find the slope of the tangent line to $y = \tan(\csc x)$ when $\sin x = \dfrac{1}{\pi}$, x in the interval $\left(0, \dfrac{\pi}{2}\right)$.

Solution Since the derivative is the slope of the tangent, first find the derivative.

$$\frac{dy}{dx} = \sec^2(\csc x)\, \frac{d}{dx}\, \csc x$$
$$= [\sec^2(\csc x)](-\csc x \cot x)$$

When $\sin x = \dfrac{1}{\pi}$, we have $\csc x = \pi$ and $\cot x = \sqrt{\pi^2 - 1}$.

The slope of the tangent is

$$\left.\frac{dy}{dx}\right|_{\sin x = \frac{1}{\pi}} = (\sec^2 \pi)(-\pi)(\sqrt{\pi^2 - 1})$$
$$= -\pi\sqrt{\pi^2 - 1}$$

Example 5 Prove that $y = \sec x + \tan x$ is concave up on $\left(-\dfrac{\pi}{2}, \dfrac{\pi}{2}\right)$.

Solution First we find the second derivative.

$$\frac{dy}{dx} = \sec x \tan x + \sec^2 x$$
$$\frac{d^2y}{dx^2} = \sec x \sec^2 x + \tan x \sec x \tan x + 2 \sec x \sec x \tan x$$
$$= \sec x(\sec^2 x + 2 \sec x \tan x + \tan^2 x)$$
$$= \sec x(\sec x + \tan x)^2$$

Now $\sec x > 0$ on $\left(-\dfrac{\pi}{2}, \dfrac{\pi}{2}\right)$. Thus, the second derivative is always positive and the curve is always concave up on $\left(-\dfrac{\pi}{2}, \dfrac{\pi}{2}\right)$.

Example 6 Find the vertical asymptotes of $y = \sec x + \tan x$ on $\left(-\dfrac{\pi}{2}, \dfrac{\pi}{2}\right)$.

Solution Since $\cos\left(-\dfrac{\pi}{2}\right) = \cos \dfrac{\pi}{2} = 0$, possible vertical asymptotes are

$$x = -\frac{\pi}{2} \text{ and } x = \frac{\pi}{2}.$$

$$\lim_{x \to -\frac{\pi}{2}^+} (\sec x + \tan x) = \lim_{x \to -\frac{\pi}{2}^+} \frac{1 + \sin x}{\cos x}$$

$$= \lim_{x \to -\frac{\pi}{2}^+} \frac{1 - \sin^2 x}{\cos x(1 - \sin x)}$$

$$= \lim_{x \to -\frac{\pi}{2}^+} \frac{\cos x}{1 - \sin x}$$

$$= \frac{0}{1 - (-1)}$$

$$= 0$$

$$\lim_{x \to \frac{\pi}{2}^-} (\sec x + \tan x) = \lim_{x \to \frac{\pi}{2}^-} \frac{1 + \sin x}{\cos x}$$

$$= \infty$$

Therefore $x = \dfrac{\pi}{2}$ is a vertical asymptote.

The function considered in Examples 5 and 6 is graphed in the following diagram.

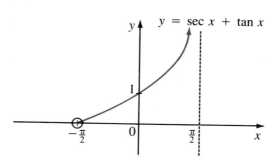

EXERCISE 7.3

B **1.** Find the derivative of each of the following.

(a) $y = 3 \tan 2x$

(b) $y = \frac{1}{3} \cot 9x$

(c) $y = 12 \sec \frac{1}{4}x$

(d) $y = -\frac{1}{4} \csc (-8x)$

(e) $y = \tan x^2$

(f) $y = \tan^2 x$

(g) $y = \sec \sqrt[3]{x}$

(h) $y = x^2 \csc x$

(i) $y = \cot^3(1 - 2x)^2$

(j) $y = \sec^2 x - \tan^2 x$

(k) $y = \dfrac{1}{\sqrt{(\sec 2x - 1)^3}}$

(l) $y = \dfrac{x^2 \tan x}{\sec x}$

(m) $y = 2x(\sqrt{x} - \cot x)$

(n) $y = \sin(\tan x)$

(o) $y = \tan^2(\cos x)$

(p) $y = [\tan(x^2 - x)^{-2}]^{-3}$

2. Find $\dfrac{dy}{dx}$.

(a) $\tan x + \sec y - y = 0$ (b) $\tan 2x = \cos 3y$

(c) $\cot(x + y) + \cot x + \cot y = 0$

(d) $y^2 - \csc(xy) = 0$

(e) $x^2 + \sec\left(\dfrac{x}{y}\right) = 0$

(f) $y^2 = \sin(\tan y) + x^2$

3. Find the equations of the tangent lines.

(a) $y = \cot^2 x$ when $x = \dfrac{\pi}{4}$ (b) $y = \sin x \tan \dfrac{x}{2}$ when $x = \dfrac{\pi}{3}$

(c) $y = \csc 2x$ when $x = -\dfrac{\pi}{8}$

(d) $y = \sec x + \csc x$ when $x = \dfrac{3\pi}{4}$

4. Prove that $y = \sec x + \tan x$ is always increasing on $\left(-\dfrac{\pi}{2}, \dfrac{\pi}{2}\right)$.

5. Find the vertical asymptotes.

(a) $y = \csc x - \cot x,\ 0 < x < \pi$

(b) $y = \sin x - \tan x,\ -\dfrac{\pi}{2} < x < \dfrac{3\pi}{2}$

6. Find the critical numbers, intervals of increase and decrease, and maximum and minimum values of $y = \csc x - \cot x$ on $(0, \pi)$.

7. Determine the concavity of $y = \sin x - \tan x$ on $\left(-\dfrac{\pi}{2}, \dfrac{3\pi}{2}\right)$.

8. Use the procedure described in Chapter 5 to sketch $y = x \tan x$ on $\left(-\dfrac{\pi}{2}, \dfrac{\pi}{2}\right)$.

9. Prove the following.

(a) $\dfrac{d}{dx} \sec x = \sec x \tan x$ (b) $\dfrac{d}{dx} \cot x = -\csc^2 x$

C **10.** If $f(x) = \cot 2x,\ 0 \leqslant x \leqslant 2\pi$ find all values of x for which $f(x) = f''(x)$.

11. If $x^2 + \tan^2 y = \sec^2 y - y$ find the values of x for which $\dfrac{dy}{dx} = \dfrac{dx}{dy}$.

12. If $f(x) = \sqrt{\sec^3(\sqrt[4]{x})}$ find $f'(x)$.

13. If $x = \cos 3t$ and $y = \sin^2 3t$ find $\dfrac{dy}{dx}$ and $\dfrac{d^2y}{dx^2}$.

7.4 APPLICATIONS

First we examine problems of optimization involving the trigonometric functions. In many problems trigonometric functions are inherent. Such is the case in Example 1.

Example 1   The position of a particle as it moves horizontally is described by the equation $s = 2 \sin t - \cos t$, $0 \le t \le 2\pi$ where s is the displacement in metres and t is the time in seconds. Find the maximum and minimum displacements.

Solution   Recall that local maximum or minimum displacement occurs when the velocity is zero and that velocity is the rate of change of displacement with respect to time.

$$v = \frac{ds}{dt} = 2 \cos t - (-\sin t) = 2 \cos t + \sin t$$

For critical numbers

$$2 \cos t + \sin t = 0$$
$$\sin t = -2 \cos t$$
$$\tan t = -2$$

It is not necessary to solve for t. Only the values of $\sin t$ and $\cos t$ are needed.

for $\dfrac{\pi}{2} < t < \pi$ for $\dfrac{3\pi}{2} < t < 2\pi$

$\sin t = \dfrac{2}{\sqrt{5}}$ and $\cos t = \dfrac{-1}{\sqrt{5}}$ $\sin t = \dfrac{-2}{\sqrt{5}}$ and $\cos t = \dfrac{1}{\sqrt{5}}$

$s = 2\left(\dfrac{2}{\sqrt{5}}\right) - \left(-\dfrac{1}{\sqrt{5}}\right)$ $s = 2\left(\dfrac{-2}{\sqrt{5}}\right) - \left(\dfrac{1}{\sqrt{5}}\right)$

$\quad = \dfrac{5}{\sqrt{5}}$ $\quad = -\dfrac{5}{\sqrt{5}}$

$\quad = \sqrt{5}$ $\quad = -\sqrt{5}$

Finally, we test the end points of the domain.
When $t = 0$, $s = 2 \sin 0 - \cos 0 = -1$
When $t = 2\pi$, $s = 2 \sin 2\pi - \cos \pi = 1$
Therefore, the absolute maximum displacement is $\sqrt{5}$ m and the absolute minimum displacement is $-\sqrt{5}$ m.

Although the statement of a problem may not contain reference to trigonometric functions, it is often advantageous to introduce an angle and apply a trigonometric solution. Two different solutions are given for Example 2. Compare them and decide which one you prefer.

Example 2   Find the maximum perimeter of a right triangle with hypotenuse 20 cm.

Solution 1   Let the base be x cm, $0 < x < 20$. Therefore the height is

$$\sqrt{400 - x^2}$$

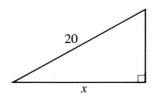

Let the perimeter be P cm. Therefore

$$P = x + (400 - x^2)^{\frac{1}{2}} + 20$$

$$\frac{dP}{dx} = 1 + \tfrac{1}{2}(400 - x^2)^{-\frac{1}{2}}(-2x) = 1 - x(400 - x^2)^{-\frac{1}{2}}$$

For critical numbers $1 - \dfrac{x}{\sqrt{400 - x^2}} = 0$

Squaring both sides $1 = \dfrac{x^2}{400 - x^2}$

Therefore $400 - x^2 = x^2$

$400 = 2x^2$

Since x is positive, $x = 10\sqrt{2}$

We test the second derivative:

$$\frac{d^2P}{dx^2} = 0 - \left[x\left(-\tfrac{1}{2}\right)(400 - x^2)^{-\frac{3}{2}}(-2x) + (400 - x^2)^{-\frac{1}{2}}(1) \right]$$

$$= \frac{-x^2}{\sqrt{(400 - x^2)^3}} + \frac{-1}{\sqrt{400 - x^2}}$$

< 0 for all values of x.

Therefore the maximum perimeter is

$$10\sqrt{2} + \sqrt{400 - 200} + 20 = 20 + 20\sqrt{2} \text{ cm.}$$

Solution 2   Let the base angle be θ, $0 < \theta < \dfrac{\pi}{2}$, as in the diagram. Let the perimeter be P cm.

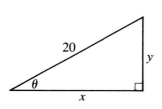

Now $\dfrac{x}{20} = \cos\theta$ and $\dfrac{y}{20} = \sin\theta$

So $x = 20\cos\theta$ and $y = 20\sin\theta$

and $P = 20 + 20\cos\theta + 20\sin\theta$

Therefore $\dfrac{dP}{d\theta} = -20\sin\theta + 20\cos\theta$

For critical numbers $-20 \sin \theta + 20 \cos \theta = 0$

so $\sin \theta = \cos \theta$

$$\tan \theta = 1$$

$$\theta = \frac{\pi}{4}$$

Test the second derivative:

$$\frac{d^2P}{d\theta^2} = -20 \cos \theta - 20 \sin \theta$$

$$< 0 \text{ for all values of } \theta$$

Therefore the maximum perimeter is

$$20 + \frac{20}{\sqrt{2}} + \frac{20}{\sqrt{2}} = 20 + \frac{40}{\sqrt{2}} = 20 + 20\sqrt{2} \text{ cm.}$$

The following examples are related rates problems involving trigonometric functions.

Example 3   Two sides of a triangle have lengths 15 m and 20 m. The angle between them is increasing at $\frac{\pi}{90}$ rad/s. How fast is the length of the third side changing when the angle between the sides is $\frac{\pi}{3}$?

Solution   Let the angle between the given sides be θ radians and the variable side be x m. Note that both are functions of time t measured in seconds.

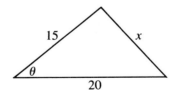

Applying the Law of Cosines,

$$x^2 = 15^2 + 20^2 - 2(15)(20) \cos \theta$$
$$x^2 = 625 - 600 \cos \theta$$

We differentiate both sides with respect to t:

$$2x \frac{dx}{dt} = -600\left(-\sin \theta \frac{d\theta}{dt}\right)$$

$$\frac{dx}{dt} = \frac{300 \sin \theta}{x} \frac{d\theta}{dt}$$

Law of Cosines

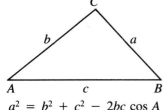

$$a^2 = b^2 + c^2 - 2bc \cos A$$

Now $\dfrac{d\theta}{dt}$ is the rate at which the angle is increasing, namely $\dfrac{\pi}{90}$ rad/s.

Therefore
$$\frac{dx}{dt} = \frac{300 \sin \theta}{x} \frac{\pi}{90}$$
$$= \frac{10\pi \sin \theta}{3x}$$

When $\theta = \dfrac{\pi}{3}$ $x^2 = 625 - 600 \cos \dfrac{\pi}{3} = 625 - 600\left(\tfrac{1}{2}\right) = 325$

and $x = \sqrt{325} = 5\sqrt{13}$

Therefore $\dfrac{dx}{dt} = \dfrac{10\pi \sin \dfrac{\pi}{3}}{15\sqrt{13}} = \dfrac{10\pi \dfrac{\sqrt{3}}{2}}{15\sqrt{13}} = \dfrac{5\sqrt{3}\pi}{15\sqrt{13}} = \dfrac{\pi}{\sqrt{39}} \doteq 0.50$

The third side is increasing at the rate of approximately 0.50 m/s. ⬡

Remember that you must develop a formula before you use the specific value that is given to solve the problem. For example, in Example 3 the value $\dfrac{\pi}{3}$ is substituted at the very end of the problem.

Example 4   A beacon, located a perpendicular distance of 315 m from point R on a straight shoreline, revolves at 1 rev/min. How fast does its beam sweep along the shoreline at point S on the shoreline 425 m from R?

Solution   Let the distance that the beam has swept from point R be x m. Let the angle between the perpendicular to point R and the beam be θ. The elapsed time t in seconds is measured from the moment the beam hits point R.

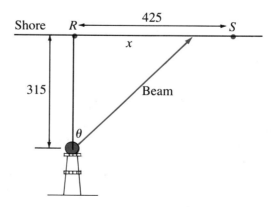

Now $\dfrac{x}{315} = \tan \theta$

Thus $x = 315 \tan \theta$

We differentiate implicitly with respect to t.

Therefore $\dfrac{dx}{dt} = 315 \sec^2 \theta \dfrac{d\theta}{dt}$

and so $\dfrac{dx}{dt} = 315 \sec^2 \theta \,(2\pi) = 630\pi \sec^2 \theta$

When $x = 425$ the distance from the beacon to point S is $\sqrt{315^2 + 425^2} \doteq 529$.

Now $\sec \theta \doteq \dfrac{529}{315}$

and $\dfrac{dx}{dt} \doteq 630\pi \left(\dfrac{529}{315}\right)^2 \doteq 5580$

Thus the beam is sweeping along the shore at approximately 5580 m/min.

EXERCISE 7.4

B **1.** Find the local maxima and/or minima of each of the following functions.

   (a) $f(x) = x - 2 \sin x$, $0 \leqslant x \leqslant 2\pi$
   (b) $f(x) = x + \cos x$, $0 \leqslant x \leqslant 2\pi$
   (c) $f(x) = \sin^4 x + \cos^4 x$, $0 \leqslant x \leqslant 2\pi$
   (d) $f(x) = x \sin x + \cos x$, $-\pi \leqslant x \leqslant \pi$

2. The position of a particle as it moves horizontally is described by the given equations. If s is the displacement in metres and t is the time in seconds find the absolute maximum and absolute minimum displacements.

   (a) $s = 2 \sin t + \sin 2t$, $-\pi \leqslant t \leqslant \pi$
   (b) $f(t) = \sin^2 t - 2 \cos^2 t$, $-\pi \leqslant t \leqslant \pi$

3. Triangle ABC is inscribed in a semicircle with diameter $BC = 10$ cm. Find the value of angle B that produces the triangle of maximum area.

4. Points A and B lie on a circle, centre O, radius 5 cm. Find the value of angle AOB that produces a maximum area for triangle AOB.

5. Triangle ABC has $AB = AC$. It is inscribed in a circle centre O, radius 10 cm. Find the value of angle BAC that produces a maximum area for triangle ABC.

6. Rectangle $ABCD$ has A and D on the equal sides of an isosceles triangle and B and C on its base. If $AB = 2$ cm and $BC = 6$ cm, find the value of the base angle that produces the triangle of minimum area.

7. A wall of height 8 m stands parallel to and 27 m from a tall building. A ladder with its foot on the ground is to pass over the wall and lean on the building. What angle will the shortest such ladder make with the ground?

8. The angle of elevation of the sun is decreasing at $\frac{1}{4}$ rad/h. How fast is the shadow cast by a building of height 50 m lengthening, when the angle of elevation of the sun is $\frac{\pi}{4}$?

9. A kite 40 m above the ground moves horizontally at the rate of 3 m/s. At what rate is the angle between the string and the horizontal decreasing when 80 m of string has been let out?

10. A revolving beacon is situated 925 m from a straight shore. It turns at 2 rev/min. How fast does the beam sweep along the shore at its nearest point? How fast does it sweep along the shore at a point 1275 m from the nearest point?

11. Two sides of a triangle are six and eight metres in length. If the angle between them decreases at the rate of 0.035 rad/s, find the rate at which the area is decreasing when the angle between the sides of fixed length is $\frac{\pi}{6}$.

12. A ladder 10 m long rests against a vertical wall. If the bottom of the ladder slides away from the wall at a speed of 2 m/s, how fast is the angle between the top of the ladder and the wall changing when the angle is $\frac{\pi}{4}$?

13. The base of an isosceles triangle is 20 cm and the altitude is increasing at the rate of 1 cm/min. At what rate is the base angle increasing when the area is 100 cm²?

14. A vehicle moves along a straight path with a speed of 4 m/s. A searchlight is located on the ground 20 m from the path and is kept focused on the vehicle. At what rate (in rad/s) is the searchlight rotating when the vehicle is 15 m from the point on the path closest to the searchlight?

C 15. Triangle *ABC* has *AB* = *AC*. It is circumscribed about a circle with a radius of 5 cm. What value of angle *BAC* produces the triangle of minimum area?

16. Rectangle *ABCD* has *AB* = 3 m and *BC* = 4 m. Find the maximum area of the rectangle that can be circumscribed about rectangle *ABCD*.

17. Prove that the maximum area of the quadrilateral that can be constructed with sides 2, 3, 4, and 5 m occurs when the opposite angles are supplementary.

18. Two corridors whose widths are 64 units and 27 units respectively meet at a right angle. Calculate the length of the longest rigid beam that can pass from one corridor to the other when it is slid along the floor. Assume that the width of the beam is negligible.

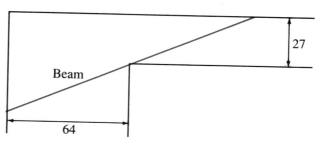

PROBLEMS PLUS

(a) Sketch the graph of the function $f(x) = |\cos x|$.
(b) At what values of x is f not differentiable?
(c) Give a formula for f' and sketch its graph.

**7.5 INVERSE TRIGONOMETRIC FUNCTIONS

At the outset we deal with the apparent contradiction in the title of this section. Examine the graph of $y = \sin x$ in the diagram.

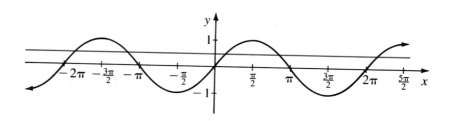

Different calculators use different notations. The most common for inverse sine are

(1) $\sin^{-1}$
(2) arcsin
(3) inv sin
(4) asn

The Horizontal Line Test indicates that it is not 1–1. Therefore the inverse of $y = \sin x$ is not a function. We create the **inverse sine function** or the **arcsine function** by restricting the domain of the sine function so that the resulting function is 1–1. The interval $\left[-\dfrac{\pi}{2}, \dfrac{\pi}{2}\right]$ is the domain that we choose. The notation we use for the inverse sine function is $\sin^{-1}$ or arcsin.

Example 1 Sketch the graph of $y = \sin x$, $-\dfrac{\pi}{2} \leqslant x \leqslant \dfrac{\pi}{2}$, and its inverse. State the domain and range of each.

Solution

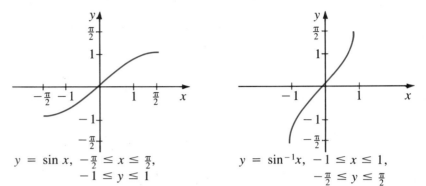

$y = \sin x$, $-\frac{\pi}{2} \leqslant x \leqslant \frac{\pi}{2}$,
$-1 \leqslant y \leqslant 1$

$y = \sin^{-1}x$, $-1 \leqslant x \leqslant 1$,
$-\frac{\pi}{2} \leqslant y \leqslant \frac{\pi}{2}$

Therefore, if $-1 \leqslant x \leqslant 1$, $\sin^{-1} x$ is the number y between $-\dfrac{\pi}{2}$ and $\dfrac{\pi}{2}$ having the value of its sine equal to x.

$$\sin^{-1} x = y \quad \Leftrightarrow \quad \sin y = x, \quad -\frac{\pi}{2} \leqslant y \leqslant \frac{\pi}{2}$$

Example 2 Find the exact value of

    (a) $\sin^{-1} \dfrac{\sqrt{3}}{2}$
                            (b) $\sin^{-1}\left(-\tfrac{1}{2}\right)$.

Solution   (a) Let $y = \sin^{-1} \dfrac{\sqrt{3}}{2}$
            (b) Let $y = \sin^{-1}\left(-\tfrac{1}{2}\right)$

$\sin y = \dfrac{\sqrt{3}}{2}, \quad -\dfrac{\pi}{2} \leqslant y \leqslant \dfrac{\pi}{2}$
      $\sin y = \left(-\tfrac{1}{2}\right), \quad -\dfrac{\pi}{2} \leqslant y \leqslant \dfrac{\pi}{2}$

$y = \dfrac{\pi}{3}$
                        $y = -\dfrac{\pi}{6}$

Example 3 Find the exact value of

    (a) $\sin^{-1}\left(\sin \dfrac{\pi}{4}\right)$
    (b) $\sin\left(\sin^{-1}\left(-\tfrac{1}{2}\right)\right)$
    (c) $\sin^{-1}\left(\sin \dfrac{7\pi}{6}\right)$

Solution   (a) Let $y = \sin^{-1}\left(\sin \dfrac{\pi}{4}\right)$

Therefore $\qquad y = \sin^{-1} \dfrac{1}{\sqrt{2}}$

$$\sin y = \dfrac{1}{\sqrt{2}}, \quad -\dfrac{\pi}{2} \leq y \leq \dfrac{\pi}{2}$$

$$y = \dfrac{\pi}{4}$$

The $\sin^{-1}$ undoes the sin and the result is $\dfrac{\pi}{4}$.

(b) Let $\qquad y = \sin^{-1}\left(-\tfrac{1}{2}\right)$

Therefore $\qquad \sin y = \left(-\tfrac{1}{2}\right), \quad -\dfrac{\pi}{2} \leq y \leq \dfrac{\pi}{2}$

$$y = -\dfrac{\pi}{6}$$

and $\qquad \sin\left(-\dfrac{\pi}{6}\right) = -\tfrac{1}{2}$

The sin undoes the $\sin^{-1}$ and the result is $-\tfrac{1}{2}$.

(c) Let $\qquad y = \sin^{-1}\left(\sin \dfrac{7\pi}{6}\right)$

Then $\qquad y = \sin^{-1}\left(-\tfrac{1}{2}\right)$

$$\sin y = -\tfrac{1}{2}, \quad -\dfrac{\pi}{2} \leq y \leq \dfrac{\pi}{2}$$

$$y = -\dfrac{\pi}{6}$$

In this case, the $\sin^{-1}$ does not undo the sin because $\dfrac{7\pi}{6}$ does not fall within the domain we chose to create the inverse sine function.

Examples 3(a) and 3(b) are particular cases of the general equations that are summarized below.

$$\sin^{-1}(\sin x) = x \quad \text{for} \quad -\dfrac{\pi}{2} \leq x \leq \dfrac{\pi}{2}$$

$$\sin(\sin^{-1} x) = x \quad \text{for} \quad -1 \leq x \leq 1$$

Example 4 Find the exact value of $\tan\left(\sin^{-1}\frac{3}{5}\right)$.

Solution We have done this type of question before. See Exercise 2, Question 4, in the Review and Preview to Chapter 6. We want the tangent of the angle whose sine has value $\frac{3}{5}$.

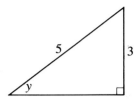

Let $\qquad y = \sin^{-1}\frac{3}{5}$

Then $\quad \sin y = \frac{3}{5}, 0 \leqslant y \leqslant \dfrac{\pi}{2}$

and from our basic definitions

$$\tan y = \frac{3}{4}$$

Thus $\quad \tan\left(\sin^{-1}\frac{3}{5}\right) = \frac{3}{4}$

We create the **inverse cosine function** or the **arccosine function** by restricting the domain of the cosine function so that the resulting function is $1-1$. The interval $[0, \pi]$ is the domain we choose. The notation for the inverse cosine function is $\cos^{-1}$ or arccos.

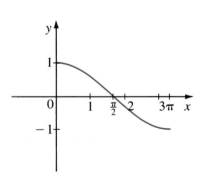

$y = \cos x, 0 \leqslant x \leqslant \pi,$
$\qquad\qquad -1 \leqslant y \leqslant 1$

$y = \cos^{-1} x, -1 \leqslant x \leqslant 1,$
$\qquad\qquad 0 \leqslant y \leqslant \pi$

$$\boxed{\cos^{-1} x = y \iff \cos y = x, 0 \leqslant y \leqslant \pi}$$

Example 5   Find the exact value of

(a) $\cos^{-1}\left(\cos\dfrac{5\pi}{6}\right)$

(b) $\cos\left(\cos^{-1}\left(-\dfrac{1}{\sqrt{2}}\right)\right)$

(c) $\cos^{-1}\left(\cos\dfrac{7\pi}{6}\right)$

Solution   (a) Let

$$y = \cos^{-1}\left(\cos\dfrac{5\pi}{6}\right)$$

Therefore

$$y = \cos^{-1}\left(-\dfrac{\sqrt{3}}{2}\right)$$

$$\cos y = -\dfrac{\sqrt{3}}{2}, \, 0 \leqslant y \leqslant \pi$$

$$y = \dfrac{5\pi}{6}$$

The $\cos^{-1}$ undoes the cos.

(b) Let

$$y = \cos^{-1}\left(-\dfrac{1}{\sqrt{2}}\right)$$

Therefore

$$\cos y = -\dfrac{1}{\sqrt{2}}, \, 0 \leqslant y \leqslant \pi$$

$$y = \dfrac{3\pi}{4}$$

and

$$\cos\left(\dfrac{3\pi}{4}\right) = -\dfrac{1}{\sqrt{2}}$$

The cos undoes the $\cos^{-1}$.

(c) Let

$$y = \cos^{-1}\left(\cos\dfrac{7\pi}{6}\right)$$

Then

$$y = \cos^{-1}\left(-\dfrac{\sqrt{3}}{2}\right)$$

Therefore $\cos y = -\dfrac{\sqrt{3}}{2}, \, 0 \leqslant y \leqslant \pi$

and

$$y = \tfrac{5}{6}\pi$$

In this case, the $\cos^{-1}$ does not undo the cos because $\dfrac{7\pi}{6}$ falls outside the domain of the inverse cosine function.

Examples 5(a) and 5(b) are particular cases of the general equations summarized below.

$$\cos^{-1}(\cos x) = x \quad \text{for } 0 \leqslant x \leqslant \pi$$
$$\cos(\cos^{-1} x) = x \quad \text{for } -1 \leqslant x \leqslant 1$$

We create the **inverse tangent function** by restricting the domain of the tangent function so that the resulting function is 1–1. The interval $\left(-\dfrac{\pi}{2}, \dfrac{\pi}{2}\right)$ is the domain we choose. The notation for the inverse tangent function is $\tan^{-1}$ or arctan.

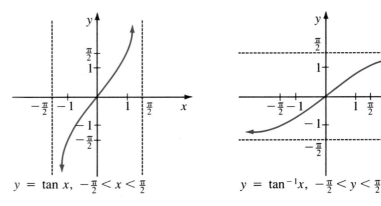

$$y = \tan x, \; -\tfrac{\pi}{2} < x < \tfrac{\pi}{2} \qquad\qquad y = \tan^{-1}x, \; -\tfrac{\pi}{2} < y < \tfrac{\pi}{2}$$

$$\tan^{-1} x = y \iff \tan y = x, \; -\frac{\pi}{2} < y < \frac{\pi}{2}$$

Notice that the inverse tangent function has two horizontal asymptotes. This fact is expressed by the following limits.

$$\lim_{x \to \infty} \tan^{-1} x = \frac{\pi}{2} \qquad\qquad \lim_{x \to -\infty} \tan^{-1} x = -\frac{\pi}{2}$$

The vertical asymptotes of the restricted tangent function have become the horizontal asymptotes of the inverse tangent function.

Example 6   Find the exact value of $\sin\left[2\ \tan^{-1}\left(-\frac{4}{3}\right)\right]$.

Solution   Let
$$y = \tan^{-1}\left(-\frac{4}{3}\right)$$

Therefore
$$\tan y = -\frac{4}{3}, \quad -\frac{\pi}{2} < y < \frac{\pi}{2}$$

Now
$$\sin\left[2\ \tan^{-1}\left(-\frac{4}{3}\right)\right] = \sin 2y$$
$$= 2\ \sin y \cos y$$
$$= 2\left(-\frac{4}{5}\right)\left(\frac{3}{5}\right)$$
$$= -\frac{24}{25}$$

Example 7   Find an equivalent algebraic expression for $\tan(\sin^{-1} x)$.

Solution   Let
$$\theta = \sin^{-1} x$$

Therefore $\sin \theta = x, \quad -\dfrac{\pi}{2} \leq \theta \leq \dfrac{\pi}{2}$

If $\theta > 0$, we can draw a right angle triangle with angle θ as in the diagram and use the Pythagorean Theorem to determine the length of the third side.

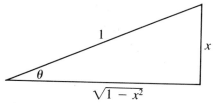

Now $\tan(\sin^{-1} x) = \tan \theta$
$$= \frac{x}{\sqrt{1 - x^2}}$$

Although the solution illustrates the case for $\theta > 0$, it is true for $\theta < 0$ as well.

Example 8   Evaluate $\displaystyle\lim_{x \to \infty} \tan^{-1}(1 - x)$

Solution   Let $t = 1 - x$
As $x \to \infty$, $1 - x \to -\infty$, so $t \to -\infty$
$$\lim_{x \to \infty} \tan^{-1}(1 - x) = \lim_{t \to -\infty} \tan^{-1} t$$
$$= -\frac{\pi}{2}$$

EXERCISE 7.5

B **1.** Evaluate.

(a) $\sin^{-1}\frac{1}{2}$ (b) $\cos^{-1}\left(-\frac{1}{2}\right)$ (c) $\tan^{-1}(-1)$

(d) $\sin^{-1}\left(-\frac{1}{\sqrt{2}}\right)$ (e) $\cos^{-1}\frac{1}{\sqrt{2}}$ (f) $\tan^{-1}\frac{\sqrt{3}}{3}$

2. Evaluate.

(a) $\sin\left(\tan^{-1}\frac{12}{13}\right)$ (b) $\cos\left(\sin^{-1}\frac{4}{5}\right)$ (c) $\tan\left(\cos^{-1}\left(-\frac{1}{3}\right)\right)$

(d) $\sin\left(\cos^{-1}\frac{7}{8}\right)$ (e) $\cos\left(\tan^{-1}\frac{7}{5}\right)$ (f) $\tan\left(\sin^{-1}\left(-\frac{2}{\sqrt{5}}\right)\right)$

3. Evaluate.

(a) $\sin\left(\sin^{-1}\frac{\sqrt{3}}{2}\right)$ (b) $\sin^{-1}\left(\sin\frac{3\pi}{7}\right)$ (c) $\sin^{-1}\left(\sin\frac{3\pi}{4}\right)$

(d) $\cos\left(\cos^{-1}\frac{\sqrt{2}}{2}\right)$ (e) $\cos^{-1}\left(\cos\frac{7\pi}{8}\right)$ (f) $\cos^{-1}\left(\cos\left(-\frac{\pi}{4}\right)\right)$

(g) $\tan(\tan^{-1}\sqrt{3})$ (h) $\tan^{-1}\left(\tan\frac{5\pi}{6}\right)$ (i) $\tan^{-1}\left(\tan\left(-\frac{\pi}{6}\right)\right)$

4. Express as an algebraic function in terms of x.

(a) $\cos(\sin^{-1}x)$ (b) $\sin(\cos^{-1}x)$ (c) $\tan(\sin^{-1}x)$
(d) $\tan(\cos^{-1}x)$ (e) $\sin(\tan^{-1}x)$ (f) $\cos(\tan^{-1}x)$
(g) $\cos(2\sin^{-1}x)$

5. Evaluate.

(a) $\sin\left(2\sin^{-1}\frac{3}{5}\right)$ (b) $\cos\left(2\sin^{-1}\frac{5}{13}\right)$

(c) $\sin\left(\sin^{-1}\frac{1}{3}+\sin^{-1}\frac{2}{3}\right)$ (d) $\cos\left(\sin^{-1}\frac{3}{4}+\cos^{-1}\frac{1}{4}\right)$

6. Find the domain.

(a) $y = \sin^{-1}(1-x)$ (b) $y = \sin^{-1}x^2$
(c) $y = \sin^{-1}(1-x^2)$ (d) $y = \cos^{-1}(-x^2)$
(e) $y = \cos^{-1}(x^2-4)$ (f) $y = \cos^{-1}\sqrt{x-1}$

7. Evaluate.

(a) $\lim_{x\to 2^-}\tan^{-1}\left(\frac{3}{x-2}\right)$ (b) $\lim_{x\to\infty}\tan^{-1}(x^2)$

(c) $\lim_{x\to\infty}\tan^{-1}(x-x^2)$ (d) $\lim_{x\to 3^+}\tan^{-1}\left(\frac{x}{3-x}\right)$

C **8.** Prove each of the following.

(a) $\tan^{-1}\frac{3}{5}+\sin^{-1}\frac{3}{5}=\tan^{-1}\frac{27}{11}$

(b) $\tan^{-1}\frac{1}{7}+\tan^{-1}\frac{1}{8}+\tan^{-1}\frac{1}{18}=\cot^{-1}3$

(c) $\sin(2\sin^{-1}x)=2x\sqrt{1-x^2}$

(d) $\tan^{-1}m + \tan^{-1}n = \cos^{-1}\frac{1-mn}{\sqrt{(1+m^2)(1+n^2)}}$

9. Prove that $\tan^{-1} a - \tan^{-1} c = \tan^{-1} \dfrac{a - b}{1 + ab} + \tan^{-1} \dfrac{b - c}{1 + bc}$.

10. If $\tan^{-1} x + \tan^{-1} y + \tan^{-1} z = \pi$, prove that $x + y + z = xyz$.

11. Sketch the graphs of the following functions.
    (a) $f(x) = \sin(\sin^{-1} x)$
    (b) $f(x) = \sin^{-1}(\sin x)$

PROBLEMS PLUS

Find $\angle A + \angle B + \angle C$ in the diagram.

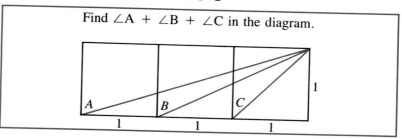

7.6 DERIVATIVES OF THE INVERSE TRIGONOMETRIC FUNCTIONS

In Section 7.5 we created the inverse sine function $y = \sin^{-1} x$, $-1 \leqslant x \leqslant 1$, $-\dfrac{\pi}{2} \leqslant y \leqslant \dfrac{\pi}{2}$ by restricting the domain of the function $y = \sin x$ to $-\dfrac{\pi}{2} \leqslant x \leqslant \dfrac{\pi}{2}$. We differentiate implicitly to find the derivative of $y = \sin^{-1} x$.

$$\frac{d}{dx} \sin^{-1} x = \frac{1}{\sqrt{1 - x^2}}$$

Proof

Recall that $y = \sin^{-1} x$ means that y is the angle having x as the value of its sine and can be written in form $x = \sin y$.

Now $\qquad \dfrac{d}{dx}(x) = \dfrac{d}{dx}(\sin y)$

$$1 = \cos y \frac{dy}{dx}$$

If $y \neq \pm\dfrac{\pi}{2}$, $\qquad \dfrac{dy}{dx} = \dfrac{1}{\cos y}$

We arrive at the desired form by noting that $\cos y$ is positive since $\dfrac{-\pi}{2} < y < \dfrac{\pi}{2}$ and isolating $\cos y$ in the identity $\sin^2 y + \cos^2 y = 1$ to produce $\cos y = +\sqrt{1 - \sin^2 y}$.

Thus $\qquad\qquad \dfrac{dy}{dx} = \dfrac{1}{\sqrt{1 - \sin^2 y}}$

Since $\sin y = x$, $\qquad \dfrac{dy}{dx} = \dfrac{1}{\sqrt{1 - x^2}}$

The derivatives of $y = \cos^{-1} x$ and $y = \tan^{-1} x$ are developed in a similar manner.

$$\boxed{\dfrac{d}{dx} \cos^{-1} x = -\dfrac{1}{\sqrt{1 - x^2}}}$$

Proof

$$y = \cos^{-1} x$$
$$x = \cos y, \; 0 \leqslant y \leqslant \pi$$
$$\dfrac{d}{dx}(x) = \dfrac{d}{dx}(\cos y)$$
$$1 = -\sin y \dfrac{dy}{dx}$$

If $y \neq 0$ or π, $\qquad \dfrac{dy}{dx} = -\dfrac{1}{\sin y}$

We arrive at the desired form by noting that $\sin y$ is positive since $0 < y < \pi$ and isolating $\sin y$ in the identity $\sin^2 y + \cos^2 y = 1$.

Therefore $\quad \dfrac{dy}{dx} = -\dfrac{1}{\sqrt{1 - \cos^2 y}} = -\dfrac{1}{\sqrt{1 - x^2}}$

$$\boxed{\dfrac{d}{dx} \tan^{-1} x = \dfrac{1}{1 + x^2}}$$

Proof

$$y = \tan^{-1} x$$

$$x = \tan y, \quad -\frac{\pi}{2} < y < \frac{\pi}{2}$$

$$\frac{d}{dx}(x) = \frac{d}{dx}(\tan y)$$

$$1 = \sec^2 y \frac{dy}{dx}$$

Since $\sec^2 y = 1 + \tan^2 y$, we have

$$\frac{dy}{dx} = \frac{1}{\sec^2 y} = \frac{1}{1 + \tan^2 y} = \frac{1}{1 + x^2}$$

The derivatives of the inverse trigonometric functions that we have developed are summarized in the table.

> **Derivatives of the**
> **Inverse Trigonometric Functions**
>
> $$\frac{d}{dx} \sin^{-1} x = \frac{1}{\sqrt{1 - x^2}}$$
>
> $$\frac{d}{dx} \cos^{-1} x = -\frac{1}{\sqrt{1 - x^2}}$$
>
> $$\frac{d}{dx} \tan^{-1} x = \frac{1}{1 + x^2}$$

Example 1   Differentiate $y = \sin^{-1}(1 - x^2)$.

Solution
$$\frac{dy}{dx} = \frac{1}{\sqrt{1 - (1 - x^2)^2}} \frac{d}{dx}(1 - x^2)$$

$$= \frac{-2x}{\sqrt{2x^2 - x^4}}$$

$$= \frac{-2x}{|x|\sqrt{2 - x^2}}$$

Since $|x| = x$ if $x \geq 0$ and $|x| = -x$ if $x < 0$, we could write the answer as

$$\frac{dy}{dx} = \begin{cases} \dfrac{2}{\sqrt{2 - x^2}} & \text{if } x < 0 \\[2mm] \dfrac{-2}{\sqrt{2 - x^2}} & \text{if } x > 0 \end{cases}$$

Example 2   Differentiate $y = x \tan^{-1} \sqrt{x}$.

Solution   We use the Product Rule.

$$\frac{dy}{dx} = x \frac{d}{dx}(\tan^{-1} \sqrt{x}) + \tan^{-1} \sqrt{x} \frac{d}{dx}(x)$$

$$= x \frac{1}{1 + (\sqrt{x})^2} \frac{d}{dx}(x^{\frac{1}{2}}) + \tan^{-1} \sqrt{x}(1)$$

$$= \frac{x}{1 + x}\left(\frac{1}{2}x^{-\frac{1}{2}}\right) + \tan^{-1} \sqrt{x}$$

$$= \frac{x^{\frac{1}{2}}}{2(1 + x)} + \tan^{-1} \sqrt{x}$$

$$= \frac{\sqrt{x}}{2(1 + x)} + \tan^{-1} \sqrt{x}$$

Example 3   Differentiate $y = \cos^{-1}(\sin x)$ and use the result to sketch the graph.

Solution $\dfrac{dy}{dx} = \dfrac{-1}{\sqrt{1 - \sin^2 x}} \dfrac{d}{dx} \sin x$

$$= \frac{-1}{\sqrt{\cos^2 x}} \cos x \qquad \text{(using the identity } \sin^2 x + \cos^2 x = 1)$$

$$= \frac{-\cos x}{|\cos x|}$$

$$= \begin{cases} 1 & \text{if } \cos x < 0 \\ -1 & \text{if } \cos x > 0 \end{cases}$$

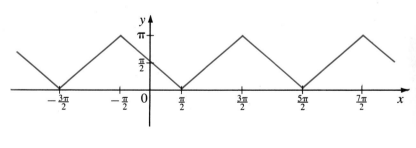

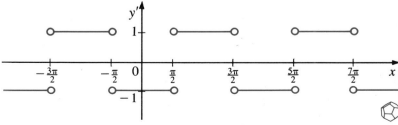

Example 4 If $y = \tan^{-1}\left(\dfrac{x}{y}\right)$ find $\dfrac{dy}{dx}$.

Solution

$$\frac{dy}{dx} = \frac{1}{1 + \left(\dfrac{x}{y}\right)^2} \frac{d}{dx}\left(\frac{x}{y}\right)$$

$$\frac{dy}{dx} = \frac{1}{1 + \dfrac{x^2}{y^2}} \frac{y\dfrac{d}{dx}(x) - x\dfrac{d}{dx}(y)}{y^2}$$

$$\frac{dy}{dx} = \frac{y^2}{x^2 + y^2} \frac{y(1) - x\dfrac{dy}{dx}}{y^2}$$

$$(x^2 + y^2)\frac{dy}{dx} = y - x\frac{dy}{dx}$$

$$(x^2 + y^2 + x)\frac{dy}{dx} = y$$

$$\frac{dy}{dx} = \frac{y}{x^2 + y^2 + x}$$

EXERCISE 7.6

B 1. Find $\dfrac{dy}{dx}$ in each of the following.

(a) $y = \sin^{-1}(x + 1)$ (b) $y = \cos^{-1}(x^2)$

(c) $y = \tan^{-1}(3x)$ (d) $y = (\sin^{-1} x)^2$

(e) $y = \cos^{-1}\left(\dfrac{x^3}{2}\right)$ (f) $y = (1 + x^2)\tan^{-1} x$

(g) $y = \cos^{-1}\sqrt{2x - 1}$ (h) $y = \tan^{-1}(\sin x)$

(i) $y = \sin^{-1}\left(\dfrac{\cos x}{1 + \sin x}\right)$ (j) $y = \dfrac{\sin^{-1} x}{\cos^{-1} x}$

(k) $y = (\tan^{-1} x)^{-1}$ (l) $y = (\cos^{-1} x^2)^{-2}$

(m) $y = \tan^{-1} x + \tan^{-1}\dfrac{1}{x}$ (n) $y = \dfrac{\sqrt{1 - x^2}}{x} + \sin^{-1} x$

(o) $y = \dfrac{x}{\sqrt{1 - x^2}} - \sin^{-1} x$

(p) $y = \sin^{-1} x + \cos^{-1}\sqrt{1 - x^2}$

(q) $y = \sin(\sin^{-1} x^2)$ (r) $y = \sin^{-1}(\tan^{-1} x)$

(s) $y = x^2 \cos^{-1}\left(\dfrac{2}{x}\right)$

2. Find the slope of the tangent line to $f(x) = x \tan^{-1} x$ at the point where $x = 1$.

3. Find the equation of the tangent line to
$$f(x) = x \sin^{-1}\left(\frac{x}{4}\right) + \sqrt{16 - x^2} \text{ at the point where } x = 2.$$

4. If $f(x) = (3 \tan^{-1} x)^4$, find $f'(\sqrt{3})$.

5. If $y^2 \sin x = \tan^{-1}x - y$ find y'.

6. If $f(x) = (x - 3)\sqrt{6x - x^2} + 9 \sin^{-1}\left(\frac{x - 3}{3}\right)$ find $f'(3)$.

7. Differentiate and use your result to sketch the graph of the given function.
   (a) $y = \sin^{-1}(\cos x)$ (b) $y = \cos^{-1}(\cos x)$
   (c) $y = \sin^{-1}(\sin x)$ (d) $y = \sin^{-1}(\cos 2x)$

7.7 REVIEW EXERCISE

1. Evaluate each of the following limits.

   (a) $\lim\limits_{x \to 0} \dfrac{\sin \frac{1}{2}x}{x}$
   (b) $\lim\limits_{x \to 0} \dfrac{\cos\left(\frac{\pi}{2} - x\right)}{x}$
   (c) $\lim\limits_{x \to 0} \dfrac{\sin 3x}{5x}$

   (d) $\lim\limits_{x \to 0} \dfrac{\sin^2 x}{x \cos x}$
   (e) $\lim\limits_{x \to 0} x \csc x$
   (f) $\lim\limits_{x \to 0} \dfrac{\sin x \cos x}{x}$

   (g) $\lim\limits_{x \to 0} \dfrac{1 - \cos 2x}{x}$
   (h) $\lim\limits_{x \to 0} \dfrac{2 \tan^2 x}{x^2}$
   (i) $\lim\limits_{x \to \frac{\pi}{2}} \dfrac{\frac{\pi}{2} - x}{\cos x}$

2. Differentiate y with respect to x.

   (a) $y = \tan^4 3x$
   (b) $y = \dfrac{\sin x}{1 - 2 \cos x}$
   (c) $y = \sec x^2$

   (d) $y = \dfrac{\cot^2 2x}{1 + x^2}$
   (e) $y = \csc(x^3 + 1)$
   (f) $y = 2 \sec \sqrt{x}$

   (g) $y = \sqrt[3]{x} \tan x$
   (h) $y = \cos^2(\tan x)$

   (i) $y = \dfrac{1}{\sin(x - \sin x)}$

3. Find $\dfrac{dy}{dx}$ by implicit differentiation.

   (a) $y = \cos(x - y)$ (b) $\sin(x + y) + \sin(x - y) = 1$
   (c) $y = \tan(x + y)$ (d) $\cos(x + y) = y \sin x$
   (e) $\cot xy + xy = 0$ (f) $\csc(x - y) + \sec(x + y) = x$

4. At what points on the curve $y = \sin x + \cos x$, $0 \le x \le 2\pi$, is the tangent line horizontal?

5. Find the equation of the tangent line to $y = \tan x$ when $x = \dfrac{\pi}{3}$.

6. Find the slope of the tangent line to $x \tan y = y - 1$ when $y = \dfrac{\pi}{4}$.

7. The length of the hypotenuse of a right triangle is 10 cm. One of the acute angles is decreasing at the rate of 5°/s. How fast is the area decreasing when this angle is 30°?

8. Triangle ABC has sides AB and AC increasing at rates of 2 cm/min and 3 cm/min respectively. The angle A between these sides is increasing at 1°/min. How fast is the area changing when $AB = 40$ cm, $AC = 75$ cm and $A = 30°$?

9. A radar antenna is located on a ship that is 4 km from a straight shore. It is rotating at 32 rev/min. How fast does the radar beam sweep along the shore when the angle between the beam and the shortest distance to the shore is $\frac{\pi}{4}$?

10. A triangle has adjacent sides of 4 cm and 6 cm. Prove that the triangle has maximum area when the angle enclosed by these sides is 90°.

11. A rain gutter is to be constructed from a metal sheet of width 30 cm by bending up one third of the sheet on each side through an angle θ. How should θ be chosen so that the gutter will carry the maximum amount of water?

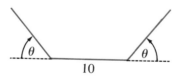

10

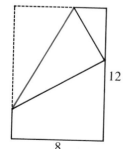

12

8

12. The upper left-hand corner of a piece of paper 8 cm wide by 12 cm long is folded over to the right hand edge. How would you fold it if you wish to minimize the length of the fold?

13. A rigid beam 25 m long is leaning against a vertical wall. If the bottom of the beam is pulled horizontally away from the wall at 3 m/s, how fast is the angle between the ladder and the ground changing when the bottom of the ladder is 15 m from the wall?

14. Use the procedure established in Chapter 5 to sketch the following.
    (a) $y = 2 \cos x + \cos^2 x$, $0 \leqslant x \leqslant 2\pi$
    (b) $y = x + \sin 2x$, $-\pi \leqslant x \leqslant \pi$

15. Find the point of intersection of the curve $y = \cos x$ with the line $y = -x$ to five decimal places.

16. Find the value of each of the following.

(a) $\cos^{-1}\dfrac{\sqrt{3}}{2}$ (b) $\sin^{-1}\dfrac{1}{\sqrt{2}}$ (c) $\tan^{-1}(-\sqrt{3})$

(d) $\sin\left(\cos^{-1}\dfrac{1}{2}\right)$ (e) $\cos\left(\tan^{-1}\dfrac{3}{4}\right)$ (f) $\tan\left(\sin^{-1}\dfrac{1}{\sqrt{5}}\right)$

(g) $\tan^{-1}\left(\cot\dfrac{\pi}{4}\right)$ (h) $\cos^{-1}\left(\sin\dfrac{\pi}{3}\right)$ (i) $\sin^{-1}\left(\dfrac{1}{2}\tan\dfrac{\pi}{4}\right)$

(j) $\sin^{-1}\left(\sin\dfrac{\pi}{3}\right)$ (k) $\sin^{-1}\left(\sin\dfrac{2\pi}{3}\right)$ (l) $\cos^{-1}\left(\cos\dfrac{4\pi}{3}\right)$

17. Find the derivative of y with respect to x.

(a) $y = \sin^{-1} x^2$ (b) $y = x^3 \sin^{-1}\left(\dfrac{x}{3}\right)$

(c) $y = \cos^{-1} \sqrt{x}$ (d) $y = x - \tan^{-1} x$

(e) $y = \sin^{-1}\dfrac{x - 1}{x + 1}$ (f) $y = \tan^{-1}(\sin^2 x)$

(g) $y = \cos^{-1}\left(\dfrac{1}{x}\right)$ (h) $y = \sin^{-1}(\sin^{-1} x)$

(i) $y = \tan^{-1}(\tan^{-1} x)$

18. Evaluate

(a) $\displaystyle\lim_{x \to 0^-} \tan^{-1}(x^{-1})$ (b) $\displaystyle\lim_{x \to 0^+} \tan^{-1}[(\sin x)^{-1}]$

19. Find $\dfrac{dy}{dx}$ in the following.

(a) $x \sin y + x^3 = \tan^{-1} y$ (b) $\sin^{-1}(xy) = \cos^{-1}(x + y)$

7.8 CHAPTER 7 TEST

1. Evaluate each of the following limits.

   (a) $\displaystyle\lim_{x\to 0}\frac{2\tan^2 x}{x^2}$

   (b) $\displaystyle\lim_{x\to 0}\frac{1-\cos x}{x\sin x}$

2. Find $\dfrac{dy}{dx}$ in each of the following.

   (a) $y = \sin^2(x^3 - 2)^{-4}$

   (b) $y = \tan(\cos^3 x)$

   (c) $y = \dfrac{\csc x}{1 + \cot x}$

   (d) $y = \dfrac{\cot^2 2x}{1 + x^2}$

   (e) $y = \tan^4 x - \sec^4 x$

   (f) $y = (\cos x \sin 2x)^{-2}$

3. If $x \cos y + y \cos x = xy$, find $\dfrac{dy}{dx}$.

4. Find the exact value of $\sin\left[2 \cos^{-1}\left(-\frac{3}{5}\right)\right]$.

5. Find the derivative of each of the following.

   (a) $y = \sin^{-1}\dfrac{x}{2}$

   (b) $y = \tan^{-1}\dfrac{x-1}{x+1}$

   (c) $y = \cos^{-1}(\sin x)$

6. For $y = 2 \sin x + \cos 2x, \ -\pi \leqslant x \leqslant \pi$,

   (a) find the critical numbers;

   (b) find the intervals of increase and decrease;

   (c) find the absolute maximum and minimum values.

7. An airplane flies west at 150 m/s at an altitude of 1000 m. A searchlight on the ground in the same vertical plane must be kept on the airplane. What is the rate of revolution of the searchlight when the airplane is 500 m due east of the searchlight?

8. The cross section of a trough is an inverted isosceles triangle. Prove that the trough has maximum capacity when the vertex angle is $\frac{\pi}{2}$ rad.

9. If $f(x) = \sin x + \cos x$, find the values of n for which $f^{(n)}(x) = f(x)$.

10. If $y = \cos^{-1}(\cos^{-1} x)$ prove that $\dfrac{dy}{dx} = \dfrac{1}{|\sin y|\sqrt{1 - x^2}}$.

CUMULATIVE REVIEW FOR CHAPTERS 4 TO 7

1. Find each limit.

   (a) $\displaystyle\lim_{x \to -3^+} \frac{x}{x + 3}$

   (b) $\displaystyle\lim_{x \to \infty} \frac{x}{x + 3}$

   (c) $\displaystyle\lim_{x \to 1} \frac{x + 2}{(x - 1)^4}$

   (d) $\displaystyle\lim_{x \to -\infty} (x^2 + x^3)$

   (e) $\displaystyle\lim_{x \to \infty} \frac{2x^2 + 1}{x^2 + 3x + 2}$

   (f) $\displaystyle\lim_{x \to -2^-} \frac{2x^2 + 1}{x^2 + 3x + 2}$

   (g) $\displaystyle\lim_{x \to 0^-} \cot x$

   (h) $\displaystyle\lim_{x \to 0} \frac{\sin 5x}{8x}$

   (i) $\displaystyle\lim_{x \to 0} \frac{\tan 6x}{2x}$

   (j) $\displaystyle\lim_{x \to 0} \frac{\cos 2x - 1}{2x^2}$

2. If $\sin x = \frac{3}{5}$, x in the interval $\left(0, \frac{\pi}{2}\right)$, and $\sin (x + y) = \frac{56}{65}$, y in the interval $\left(0, \frac{\pi}{2}\right)$, find the value of $\sin y$ if $\sin y + \cos y = \frac{17}{13}$.

3. Find the exact value of each of the following.

   (a) $\sin \dfrac{11\pi}{6} - \cos \dfrac{4\pi}{3}$

   (b) $\dfrac{\tan \frac{7}{18} \pi + \tan \frac{1}{9} \pi}{1 - \tan \frac{7}{18} \pi \tan \frac{1}{9} \pi}$

   (c) $\tan \dfrac{\pi}{12}$

   (d) $\cos^2 \dfrac{\pi}{16} - \sin^2 \dfrac{\pi}{16}$

   (e) $\sin \frac{5}{8} \pi \cos \frac{5}{8} \pi$

   (f) $\left(\sin \dfrac{\pi}{8} - \cos \dfrac{\pi}{8}\right)^2$

4. Prove.

   (a) $\sin (a + b) \sin (a - b) + \cos (a + b) \cos (a - b) = \cos 2b$

   (b) $\sin 3a \csc a - \cos 3a \sec a = 2$

   (c) $\tan 4a = \dfrac{4 \tan a (1 - \tan^2 a)}{1 - 6 \tan^2 a + \tan^4 a}$

   (d) $\dfrac{\sin (\pi - a) \cos \left(\frac{3\pi}{2} + a\right)}{(\tan \frac{\pi}{2} + a) \sin (-a)} = \tan a \sin a$

5. Solve for x.

   (a) $\sin x = \cos (2x - \pi)$, $-2\pi \le x \le 2\pi$

   (b) $2 \cos^2 x \sin^2 x - \cos x \sin x = 0$, $0 \le x \le 2\pi$

   (c) $\sin \dfrac{x}{2} + \cos \dfrac{x}{2} = \sqrt{2}$, $0 \le x \le 2\pi$

   (d) $\sin^2 \left(x + \dfrac{\pi}{6}\right) - \cos^2 \left(x + \dfrac{\pi}{6}\right) = \dfrac{\sqrt{2}}{2}$, $0 \le x \le \pi$

6. Evaluate.

(a) $\tan^{-1} \dfrac{1}{\sqrt{3}}$ (b) $\tan\left[\cos^{-1}\left(-\frac{1}{2}\right)\right]$ (c) $\sin^{-1}\left[\sin\left(-\frac{\pi}{6}\right)\right]$

7. Find the derivative of y with respect to x.

(a) $y = \dfrac{x}{\sin x + \cos x}$ (b) $y = \sqrt{\cos^2 x - \sin^2 x}$

(c) $y = \dfrac{\sin ax}{bx}$ (d) $y = \cos\left(\dfrac{2}{\sin x}\right)$

(e) $y = \dfrac{\tan 2x}{1 - \cot 2x}$ (f) $y = x^{-2} \csc x$

(g) $\sin (x - y) = y \cos x$ (h) $\tan^2 x = \sec^2 y$

(i) $y = \tan (\cos(\sin x))$ (j) $y = x^2 \sin^{-1} \dfrac{x}{2}$

(k) $y = \cos^{-1}\left(\dfrac{x}{x-1}\right)$ (l) $y = \tan^{-1} \sqrt{x}$

8. Find the local maximum and minimum values of f.
(a) $f(x) = 4x^3 - 9x^2 + 6x - 1$

(b) $f(x) = \dfrac{x^3}{x^2 - 1}$

(c) $f(x) = \sin x - \cos x, \dfrac{-\pi}{2} \le x \le \dfrac{\pi}{2}$

(d) $f(x) = 2 \sec x + \tan x, -\pi \le x \le 2\pi$

9. Find the absolute maximum and minimum values of each function.
(a) $f(x) = x^3 - 6x^2 + 9x + 2, \dfrac{1}{2} \le x \le \dfrac{9}{2}$

(b) $f(x) = \sin^2 x + 2 \sin x, 0 \le x \le \pi$

10. On what interval is the curve $y = \sin^2 x + 2 \cos x, 0 \le x \le 2\pi$, concave upward?

11. Discuss each curve under the headings A–H given in Section 5.5.

(a) $y = 2x^2 - x^4$ (b) $y = x\sqrt{x + 1}$ (c) $y = \dfrac{x^2}{x^2 - 1}$

(d) $y = \cos 2x - x$ in the interval $\left[-\frac{\pi}{2}, \frac{\pi}{2}\right]$

12. Sketch the graph of a function f that satisfies all the following conditions.
(a) $f(0) = 1, f(1) = 0$
(b) $f'(x) > 0$ for $|x| > 1, f'(x) < 0$ for $|x| < 1$
(c) $f''(x) > 0$ for $x > 0$ and $x < -2, f''(x) < 0$ for $-2 < x < 0$
(d) $\lim\limits_{x \to -\infty} f(x) = 0$

13. A ladder 5 m long rests against a vertical wall. The bottom of the ladder slides away from the wall at the rate of $\frac{1}{10}$ m/s. How fast is the angle between the ladder and the wall increasing when the bottom of the ladder is 3 m from the wall?

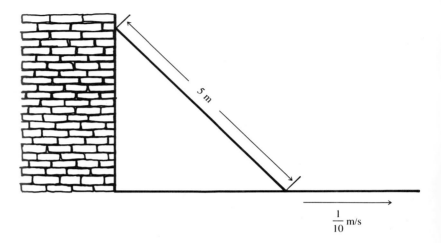

14. Find the points on the parabola $2x = y^2$ that are closest to the point $(3, 0)$.

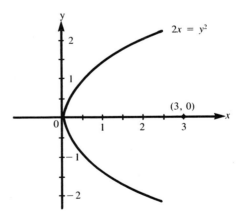

15. A sector of a circle is to have an area of 32. What value of the sector angle θ will give a sector with minimum perimeter?

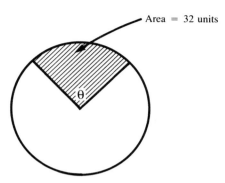

Area = 32 units

θ

16. A manufacturer of microwave ovens will, on the average, sell 800 units a month at $400 per unit. It has been determined that the company can sell an additional 100 ovens for each reduction of $20 in price.

(a) Find the demand function, assuming that it is linear.

(b) What price will maximize revenue?

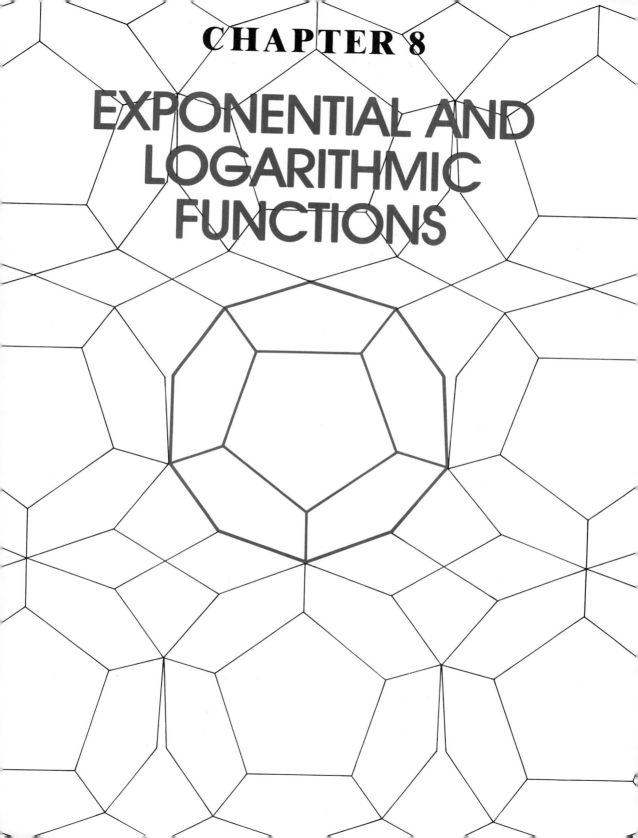

CHAPTER 8
EXPONENTIAL AND LOGARITHMIC FUNCTIONS

REVIEW AND PREVIEW TO
CHAPTER 8

Laws of Exponents

Rational powers are defined by

$$a^{\frac{m}{n}} = \sqrt[n]{a^m} = (\sqrt[n]{a})^m \quad (m, n \in I, n > 0)$$

If $a > 0$, $b > 0$, and $r, s \in Q$, then

$$a^r \times a^s = a^{r+s}$$
$$\frac{a^r}{a^s} = a^{r-s}$$
$$(a^r)^s = a^{rs}$$
$$(ab)^r = a^r b^r$$
$$\left(\frac{a}{b}\right)^r = \frac{a^r}{b^r}$$
$$a^0 = 1$$
$$a^{-r} = \frac{1}{a^r}$$

EXERCISE 1

1. Evaluate.
   (a) $(-3)^5$
   (b) 4^{-3}
   (c) $2^{-3} 5^4$
   (d) $3^{-2} - (1.7)^0$
   (e) $36^{\frac{1}{2}}$
   (f) $(-64)^{\frac{1}{3}}$
   (g) $125^{\frac{2}{3}}$
   (h) $9^{-\frac{7}{2}}$

2. Write each number as a power of 2.

    (a) 128

    (b) $2^6 \times 8^4$

    (c) $(2^9)^4$

    (d) $\frac{1}{4}$

    (e) $\dfrac{2^{3.1}}{2^{4.6}}$

    (f) $\sqrt{2}$

    (g) $4\sqrt{2}$

    (h) 1

3. Simplify and leave your answer with only positive exponents.

    (a) $(12x^2y^4)\left(\frac{1}{2}x^5y\right)$

    (b) $(2s^3t^{-1})\left(\frac{1}{4}s^6\right)(16t^4)$

    (c) $\dfrac{x^9(2x)^4}{x^3}$

    (d) $\dfrac{a^{-3}b^4}{a^{-5}b^5}$

    (e) $(rs)^3(2s)^{-2}(4r)^4$

    (f) $(2u^2v^3)^3(3u^3v)^{-2}$

    (g) $\dfrac{(x^2y^3)^4(xy^4)^{-3}}{x^2y}$

    (h) $\left(\dfrac{c^4d^3}{cd^2}\right)\left(\dfrac{d^2}{c^3}\right)^3$

    (i) $\dfrac{a^{-1}+b^{-1}}{(a+b)^{-1}}$

    (j) $\dfrac{(y^{10}z^{-5})^{\frac{1}{5}}}{(y^{-2}z^3)^{\frac{1}{3}}}$

    (k) $\dfrac{(9st)^{\frac{3}{2}}}{(27s^3t^{-4})^{\frac{2}{3}}}$

    (l) $\left(\dfrac{a^2b^{-3}}{x^{-1}y^2}\right)^3\left(\dfrac{x^{-2}b^{-1}}{a^{\frac{3}{2}}y^{\frac{1}{3}}}\right)$

Logarithms

The expression $\log_b x$ is read "the logarithm to the base b of x." It is defined as follows.

$$\boxed{\log_b x = y \quad \text{if and only if} \quad b^y = x}$$

    ①

In words, this says that

$$\boxed{\log_b x \text{ is the exponent to which the base } b \text{ must be raised to give } x}$$

In using ① to switch back and forth between the logarithmic form $\log_b x = y$ and the exponential form $b^y = x$, it is helpful to notice that in both cases the base is the same:

exponent   exponent

↓   ↓

$\log_b x = y \quad \Leftrightarrow \quad b^y = x$

↑   ↑

base   base

Example 1 Express in exponential form.

(a) $\log_2\left(\frac{1}{2}\right) = -1$ (b) $\log_{10} 100\ 000 = 5$ (c) $\log_3 z = t$

Solution (a) $\log_2\left(\frac{1}{2}\right) = -1$ (b) $\log_{10} 100\ 000 = 5$ (c) $\log_3 z = t$

$2^{-1} = \frac{1}{2}$ $10^5 = 100\ 000$ $3^t = z$

Example 2 Express in logarithmic form.

(a) $1000 = 10^3$ (b) $2^{-3} = \frac{1}{8}$ (c) $s = 5^r$

Solution (a) $10^3 = 1000$ (b) $2^{-3} = \frac{1}{8}$ (c) $5^r = s$

$\log_{10} 1000 = 3$ $\log_2\left(\frac{1}{8}\right) = -3$ $\log_5 s = r$

Example 3 Evaluate. (a) $\log_3 81$ (b) $\log_{16} 4$ (c) $\log_{10} 0.0001$

Solution (a) $\log_3 81 = 4$ because $3^4 = 81$

(b) $\log_{16} 4 = \frac{1}{2}$ because $16^{\frac{1}{2}} = 4$

(c) $\log_{10} 0.0001 = -4$ because $10^{-4} = 0.0001$

Example 4 Solve for x.

(a) $\log_2(25 - x) = 3$ (b) $3^{x+2} = 7$

Solution (a) $\log_2(25 - x) = 3$ (b) $3^{x+2} = 7$

$2^3 = 25 - x$ $\log_3 7 = x + 2$

$8 = 25 - x$ $x = \log_3 7 - 2$

$x = 17$

EXERCISE 2

1. Express each equation in exponential form.

(a) $\log_2 64 = 6$ (b) $\log_5 1 = 0$

(c) $\log_{10} 0.01 = -2$ (d) $\log_8 4 = \frac{2}{3}$

(e) $\log_8 512 = 3$ (f) $\log_2\left(\frac{1}{16}\right) = -4$

(g) $\log_a b = c$ (h) $\log_r v = w$

2. Express each equation in logarithmic form.

(a) $2^3 = 8$ (b) $10^5 = 100\ 000$

(c) $10^{-4} = 0.0001$ (d) $81^{\frac{1}{2}} = 9$

(e) $4^{-\frac{3}{2}} = 0.125$ (f) $6^{-1} = \frac{1}{6}$

(g) $r^s = t$ (h) $10^m = n$

3. Evaluate.
   (a) $\log_6 6^4$
   (b) $\log_2 32$
   (c) $\log_4 64$
   (d) $\log_8 8^{17}$
   (e) $\log_9 9$
   (f) $\log_6 1$
   (g) $\log_3\left(\frac{1}{27}\right)$
   (h) $\log_4 8$
   (i) $\log_8 0.25$
   (j) $\log_9 \sqrt{3}$

4. Solve each equation for x.
   (a) $\log_2 x = 10$
   (b) $\log_5 x = 4$
   (c) $\log_{10}(3x + 5) = 2$
   (d) $\log_3(2 - x) = 3$
   (e) $2^{1-x} = 3$
   (f) $3^{2x-1} = 5$
   (g) $\log_2(\log_3 x) = 4$
   (h) $10^{5^x} = 3$

Laws of Logarithms

Suppose that $x > 0$, $y > 0$, and r is any rational number. Then
1. $\log_b(xy) = \log_b x + \log_b y$
2. $\log_b\left(\dfrac{x}{y}\right) = \log_b x - \log_b y$
3. $\log_b(x^r) = r \log_b x$

Example 1 Use the Laws of Logarithms to rewrite the following.

(a) $\log_2(6x)$ (b) $\log_5 x^3 y^6$ (c) $\log_{10} \dfrac{ab}{\sqrt[3]{c}}$

Solution (a) $\log_2(6x) = \log_2 6 + \log_2 x$
(b) $\log_5(x^3 y^6) = \log_5 x^3 + \log_5 y^6 = 3 \log_5 x + 6 \log_5 y$
(c) $\log_{10} \dfrac{ab}{\sqrt[3]{c}} = \log_{10} ab - \log_{10} \sqrt[3]{c}$

$$= \log_{10} a + \log_{10} b - \log_{10} c^{\frac{1}{3}}$$

$$= \log_{10} a + \log_{10} b - \tfrac{1}{3} \log_{10} c$$

Example 2 Express $3 \log_2 s + \tfrac{1}{2} \log_2 t - 4 \log_2(t^2 + 1)$ as a single logarithm.

Solution $3 \log_2 s + \tfrac{1}{2} \log_2 t - 4 \log_2(t^2 + 1) = \log_2 s^3 + \log_2 t^{\frac{1}{2}} - \log_2(t^2 + 1)^4$

$$= \log_2(s^3 t^{\frac{1}{2}}) - \log_2(t^2 + 1)^4$$

$$= \log_2\left(\frac{s^3 \sqrt{t}}{(t^2 + 1)^4}\right)$$

EXERCISE 3

1. Use the Laws of Logarithms to rewrite each expression in a form with no logarithms of products, quotients, or powers.

    (a) $\log_2 x(x - 1)$

    (b) $\log_5\left(\dfrac{x}{2}\right)$

    (c) $\log_2(AB^2)$

    (d) $\log_6 \sqrt[4]{17}$

    (e) $\log_3(x\sqrt{y})$

    (f) $\log_2(xy)^{10}$

    (g) $\log_5 \sqrt[3]{x^2 + 1}$

    (h) $\log_b \dfrac{x^2}{yz^3}$

    (i) $\log_{10} \dfrac{x^3y^4}{z^6}$

    (j) $\log_{10} \dfrac{a^2}{b^4 \sqrt{c}}$

2. Evaluate.

    (a) $\log_5 \sqrt{125}$

    (b) $\log_2 112 - \log_2 7$

    (c) $\log_{10} 2 + \log_{10} 5$

    (d) $\log_{10} \sqrt{0.1}$

    (e) $\log_4 192 - \log_4 3$

    (f) $\log_{12} 9 + \log_{12} 16$

3. Rewrite each expression as a single logarithm.

    (a) $\log_{10} 12 + \frac{1}{2} \log_{10} 7 - \log_{10} 2$

    (b) $\log_2 A + \log_2 B - 2 \log_2 C$

    (c) $\log_5(x^2 - 1) - \log_5(x - 1)$

    (d) $4 \log_2 x - \frac{1}{3} \log_2(x^2 + 1) + \log_2(x - 1)$

    (e) $\frac{1}{2}[\log_5 x + 2 \log_5 y - 3 \log_5 z]$

    (f) $\log_a b + c \log_a d - r \log_a s$

INTRODUCTION

Some of the most important applications of calculus require the exponential function and its inverse function, the logarithmic function. In this chapter we learn how to differentiate these functions so that we can apply them to solve growth and decay problems.

8.1 EXPONENTIAL FUNCTIONS

An **exponential function** is a function of the form

$$f(x) = b^x$$

where the base b is a positive constant. We have defined b^x if x is a rational number, but what is meant by an irrational power such as $2^{\sqrt{3}}$? To help us answer this question we first look at the graph of the function $y = 2^x$, where x is rational. A representation of this graph is shown.

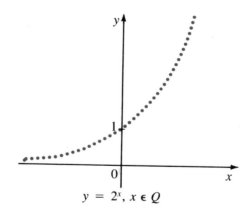

$$y = 2^x, \; x \in Q$$

We want to enlarge the domain of $y = 2^x$ to include both rational and irrational numbers. We want to fill in the holes in the graph by defining $f(x) = 2^x$, where $x \in R$, so that f is a continuous, increasing function.

In particular, since

$$1.7 < \sqrt{3} < 1.8$$

we must have

$$2^{1.7} < 2^{\sqrt{3}} < 2^{1.8}$$

Similarly, using better approximations for $\sqrt{3}$, we obtain better approximations for $2^{\sqrt{3}}$:

$$1.73 < \sqrt{3} < 1.74 \qquad \text{so} \qquad 2^{1.73} < 2^{\sqrt{3}} < 2^{1.74}$$
$$1.732 < \sqrt{3} < 1.733 \qquad \text{so} \qquad 2^{1.732} < 2^{\sqrt{3}} < 2^{1.733}$$
$$1.732\ 0 < \sqrt{3} < 1.732\ 1 \qquad \text{so} \qquad 2^{1.732\ 0} < 2^{\sqrt{3}} < 2^{1.732\ 1}$$
$$1.732\ 05 < \sqrt{3} < 1.732\ 06 \text{ so} \qquad 2^{1.732\ 05} < 2^{\sqrt{3}} < 2^{1.732\ 06}$$

It can be shown that there is exactly one number that is greater than all of the numbers

$$2^{1.7},\ 2^{1.73},\ 2^{1.732},\ 2^{1.732\ 0},\ 2^{1.732\ 05},\ \ldots$$

and less than all of the numbers

$$2^{1.8},\ 2^{1.74},\ 2^{1.733},\ 2^{1.732\ 1},\ 2^{1.732\ 06},\ \ldots$$

We define $2^{\sqrt{3}}$ to be this number. Using the above approximation process we can compute it correct to 6 decimal places:

$$2^{\sqrt{3}} \doteq 3.321\ 997$$

In general, if x is any irrational number we can define 2^x (or b^x, if $b > 0$) in a similar manner as a limit of approximations. It can be proved that the Laws of Exponents are still true when the exponents are real numbers.

The graph of $f(x) = 2^x$, where $x \in R$, is shown. It is a continuous, increasing function.

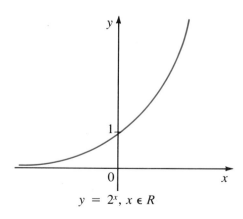

$$y = 2^x,\ x \in R$$

Example 1 Draw the graphs of the following functions.

(a) $f(x) = 3^x$

(b) $g(x) = \left(\frac{1}{3}\right)^x$

Solution We calculate values of $f(x)$ and $g(x)$, plot points, and join them to sketch the continuous graphs as shown.

x	$f(x) = 3^x$	$g(x) = \left(\frac{1}{3}\right)^x$
-3	$\frac{1}{27}$	27
-2	$\frac{1}{9}$	9
-1	$\frac{1}{3}$	3
0	1	1
1	3	$\frac{1}{3}$
2	9	$\frac{1}{9}$
3	27	$\frac{1}{27}$

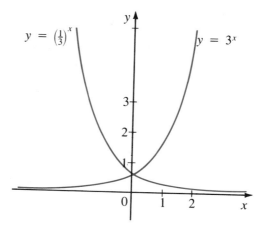

Notice that

$$g(x) = \left(\frac{1}{3}\right)^x = \frac{1}{3^x} = 3^{-x} = f(-x)$$

and so the graph of g could have been obtained from the graph of f by reflecting in the y-axis.

The graphs of the exponential functions $f(x) = b^x$ are shown for various values of the base b. Notice that all of these graphs pass through the same point $(0, 1)$ because $b^0 = 1$ for $b \neq 0$.

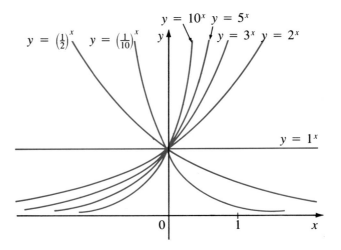

We see from these graphs that there are basically two kinds of exponential functions $y = b^x$, apart from the constant function $y = 1^x = 1$.

If $b > 1$, the function $y = b^x$ increases rapidly for x positive, and the larger the base the more rapid the increase. Notice that the graph approaches zero as x decreases through negative values, so the x-axis is a horizontal asymptote.

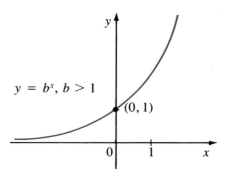

If $b > 1$, then $\lim_{x \to -\infty} b^x = 0$ and $\lim_{x \to \infty} b^x = \infty$.   ①

If $0 < b < 1$, the exponential function $y = b^x$ is decreasing and approaches zero as x becomes large. Again the x-axis is a horizontal asymptote.

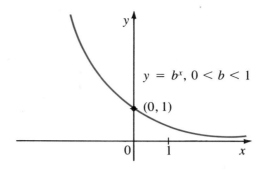

If $0 < b < 1$, then $\lim\limits_{x \to -\infty} b^x = \infty$ and $\lim\limits_{x \to \infty} b^x = 0$.

In both cases, the graph never touches the x-axis since $b^x > 0$ for all x. Thus, for $b \neq 1$, the exponential function $f(x) = b^x$ has domain R and range $(0, \infty)$.

In the next two examples we show how to graph certain functions, not by plotting points but by taking the basic graphs of the exponential functions and applying shifting and reflecting transformations.

Example 2   Use the graph of $y = 2^x$ to sketch the graphs of the following functions.
(a) $y = 3 + 2^x$ (b) $y = -2^x$

Solution   (a)   The graph of $y = 3 + 2^x$ is obtained by starting with the graph of $y = 2^x$ and shifting it three units upward.

We see from the graph that the line $y = 3$ is a horizontal asymptote. This can also be seen from the following limit.

$$\lim_{x \to -\infty} (3 + 2^x) = \lim_{x \to -\infty} 3 + \lim_{x \to -\infty} 2^x = 3 + 0 = 3$$

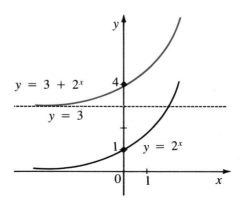

(b) Again we start with the graph of $y = 2^x$, but here we reflect in the x-axis to get the graph of $y = -2^x$. The horizontal asymptote is $y = 0$.

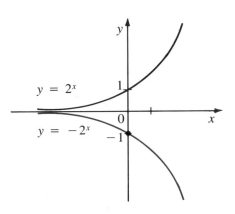

Example 3   (a)   Use the graph of $y = 10^x$ to sketch the graph of $y = 10^{x-1} - 2$.

(b)   State the asymptote, the domain, and the range of this function.

Solution   (a)   Recall that we get the graph of $y = f(x - c)$ from the graph of $y = f(x)$ by shifting c units to the right. Thus, we get the graph of $y = 10^{x-1} - 2$ by shifting the graph of $y = 10^x$ one unit to the right and two units downward as shown.

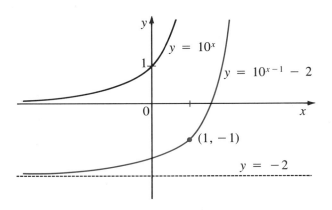

(b)   We see from the graph that the horizontal asymptote is $y = -2$. This also follows by computing the following limit.

$$\lim_{x \to -\infty} (10^{x-1} - 2) = \lim_{x \to -\infty} 10^{x-1} - \lim_{x \to -\infty} 2$$

$$= 0 - 2 \qquad (x - 1 \to -\infty \text{ as } x \to -\infty)$$

$$= -2$$

The domain is R and the range is $\{y \mid y > -2) = (-2, \infty)$

Example 4   Find $\lim_{x \to 3^-} 2^{\frac{1}{x-3}}$

Solution 1   When x is slightly less than 3, $x - 3$ is a small negative number and so $\dfrac{1}{x-3}$ is a large negative number. From ①, or the graph of $y = 2^x$, we see that $2^{\frac{1}{x-3}}$ is small number. Thus we have

$$\lim_{x \to 3^-} 2^{\frac{1}{x-3}} = 0$$

x	$2^{\frac{1}{x-3}}$
2.5	0.250 00
2.8	0.031 25
2.9	0.000 98

Solution 2   A more systematic method is to introduce a new variable t for the exponent and compute its limit first. Let

$$t = \frac{1}{x - 3}$$

As $x \to 3^-$, we have $x - 3 \to 0$ and $x - 3$ is negative, so $t \to -\infty$. Thus, by ①, we have

$$\lim_{x \to 3^-} 2^{\frac{1}{x-3}} = \lim_{t \to -\infty} 2^t = 0$$

EXERCISE 8.1

B **1.** Sketch the graph of each function by making a table of values, using a calculator if necessary.

(a) $f(x) = 6^x$

(b) $f(x) = \left(\frac{3}{2}\right)^x$

(c) $g(x) = \left(\frac{1}{4}\right)^x$

(d) $h(x) = (1.1)^x$

2. Use a table of values to graph the functions $y = 4^x$ and $y = 7^x$ using the same axes.

3. Use a table of values to graph the functions $y = \left(\frac{2}{3}\right)^x$ and $y = \left(\frac{4}{3}\right)^x$ using the same axes.

4. Graph the given function, not by plotting points but by starting from the graphs of $y = 2^x$, 10^x, $\left(\frac{1}{2}\right)^x$, and $\left(\frac{1}{10}\right)^x$ given in this section and using transformations. State the domain, range, and asymptote of each function.

(a) $f(x) = -10^x$

(b) $f(x) = 10^{-x}$

(c) $g(x) = 2^x - 5$

(d) $g(x) = 2^{x-5}$

(e) $y = 3 + \left(\frac{1}{2}\right)^x$

(f) $y = 4 - 2^x$

(g) $y = 10^{x+3}$

(h) $y = -\left(\frac{1}{10}\right)^x$

(i) $y = 2^{-2x}$

(j) $y = 1 + 2^{x+1}$

(k) $y = 5 - 2^{x-1}$

(l) $y = 1 + 3(1 - 10^{-x})$

5. Evaluate.

(a) $\displaystyle\lim_{x\to-\infty} 4^x$ (b) $\displaystyle\lim_{x\to\infty} (0.9)^x$

(c) $\displaystyle\lim_{x\to\infty} 10^{2x-1}$ (d) $\displaystyle\lim_{x\to\infty} 3^{-x}$

(e) $\displaystyle\lim_{x\to0^+} 5^{\frac{1}{x}}$ (f) $\displaystyle\lim_{x\to0^-} 5^{\frac{1}{x}}$

(g) $\displaystyle\lim_{x\to\infty} 10^{-x^2}$ (h) $\displaystyle\lim_{x\to\infty} 4^{\frac{1}{x}}$

(i) $\displaystyle\lim_{x\to-1^+} 8^{\frac{x}{x+1}}$ (j) $\displaystyle\lim_{t\to0^-} 2^{\csc t}$

6. (a) Compare the functions $f(x) = x^2$ and $g(x) = 2^x$ by evaluating each of them for $x = 0, 1, 2, 3, 4, 5, 6, 7, 8, 9, 10, 15$, and 20.

(b) Draw the graphs of f and g for $-4 \leqslant x \leqslant 6$ using the same set of axes.

7. If $f(x) = 10^x$, show that
$$\frac{f(x + h) - f(x)}{h} = 10^x\left(\frac{10^h - 1}{h}\right)$$

8. Sketch the graphs of the following functions.

(a) $y = 10^{|x|}$ (b) $y = 10^{-|x|}$

8.2 DERIVATIVES OF EXPONENTIAL FUNCTIONS

Let us try to compute the derivative of the exponential function $f(x) = b^x$ using the definition of a derivative:

$$f'(x) = \lim_{h\to0} \frac{f(x + h) - f(x)}{h}$$

$$= \lim_{h\to0} \frac{b^{x+h} - b^x}{h}$$

$$= \lim_{h\to0} \frac{b^x b^h - b^x}{h}$$

$$= \lim_{h\to0} \frac{b^x(b^h - 1)}{h}$$

$$f'(x) = b^x \lim_{h\to0} \frac{b^h - 1}{h} \qquad \text{①}$$

Notice that we were able to put the factor b^x in front of the limit because it does not depend on h.

The following table helps us to estimate the limit in ① for $b = 2$ and $b = 3$. (Values are given correct to four decimal places.)

h	$\dfrac{2^h - 1}{h}$	$\dfrac{3^h - 1}{h}$
0.1	0.7177	1.1612
0.01	0.6956	1.1047
0.001	0.6934	1.0992
0.0001	0.6932	1.0987

It appears that

$$\lim_{h \to 0} \frac{2^h - 1}{h} \doteq 0.69 \quad \text{and} \quad \lim_{h \to 0} \frac{3^h - 1}{h} \doteq 1.1$$

and so, from ①,

$$\frac{d}{dx}(2^x) \doteq (0.69)2^x \quad \text{and} \quad \frac{d}{dx}(3^x) \doteq (1.1)3^x$$

This suggests that, of all possible choices for the base b in ①, the simplest differentiation formula occurs when

$$\lim_{h \to 0} \frac{b^h - 1}{h} = 1$$

In view of the estimates of the limit for $b = 2$ and $b = 3$, it seems reasonable that there is a number b for which the limit is 1, and that it lies between 2 and 3. It is traditional to denote this value by the letter e. Thus

> e is the number such that
> $$\lim_{h \to 0} \frac{e^h - 1}{h} = 1$$

In Section 8.4 we will see that, correct to five decimal places,

$$e \doteq 2.718\ 28$$

If we put $b = e$ in Formula 1, we have the following simplified formula.

> If $f(x) = e^x$, then $f'(x) = e^x$.   ②

In Leibniz notation, we have

> $$\frac{d}{dx} e^x = e^x$$

Thus the exponential function $f(x) = e^x$ has the property that it is its own derivative. The geometrical significance of this fact is that the slope of a tangent line to the curve $y = e^x$ is equal to the y-coordinate of the point. In particular, if $f(x) = e^x$, then $f'(0) = e^0 = 1$. This means that of all the possible exponential functions $y = b^x$, $y = e^x$ is the one that crosses the y-axis with a slope of 1.

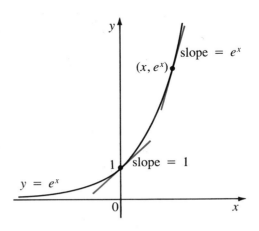

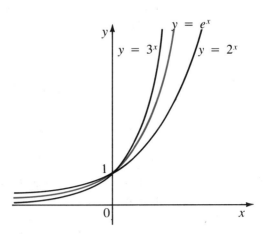

Example 1   Differentiate.   (a) $y = x^2e^x$ (b) $y = e^{\sin x}$

Solution   (a)   Using the Product Rule, we have

$$\frac{dy}{dx} = x^2 \frac{d}{dx} e^x + e^x \frac{d}{dx} x^2$$
$$= x^2e^x + e^x(2x)$$
$$= x(x + 2)e^x$$

(b) To use the Chain Rule, we let $u = \sin x$. Then we have $y = e^u$, so

$$\frac{dy}{dx} = \frac{dy}{du}\frac{du}{dx} = e^u \frac{du}{dx} = e^{\sin x} \cos x$$

In general if we combine Formula 2 with the Chain Rule, as in Example 1(b), we get

$$\frac{d}{dx} e^u = e^u \frac{du}{dx} \qquad \text{or} \qquad \frac{d}{dx} e^{g(x)} = e^{g(x)} g'(x)$$

Example 2   Find y' if $y = e^{-3x} \cos 2x$.

Solution $y' = e^{-3x} \dfrac{d}{dx} \cos 2x + \cos 2x \dfrac{d}{dx} e^{-3x}$

$= e^{-3x}(-\sin 2x)(2) + (\cos 2x)(e^{-3x})(-3)$

$= -e^{-3x}(2 \sin 2x + 3 \cos 2x)$

Example 3   Find the absolute maximum value of the function $f(x) = xe^{-x}$.

Solution   We differentiate to find any critical numbers.

$$f'(x) = xe^{-x}(-1) + e^{-x}(1) = e^{-x}(1 - x)$$

Since exponential functions are always positive, we see that $f'(x) > 0$ when $1 - x > 0$, that is, $x < 1$. Similarly, $f'(x) < 0$ when $x > 1$. By the First Derivative Test for Absolute Extreme Values, f has an absolute maximum value when $x = 1$ and the value is

$$f(1) = (1)e^{-1} = \frac{1}{e} \doteq 0.37$$

Example 4   Sketch the graph of $f(x) = e^{-x^2}$.

Solution   We use the headings of Section 5.5.

A. **Domain.**   The function is defined for all values of x, so the domain is R.

B. **Intercepts.**   Exponential functions are never 0, so there is no x-intercept. The y-intercept is $f(0) = 1$.

C. **Symmetry.** $f(-x) = e^{-x^2} = f(x)$, so f is even and the curve is symmetric about the y-axis.

D. **Asymptotes.**   As $x \to \infty$ or $x \to -\infty$, we have $-x^2 \to -\infty$, so

$$\lim_{x \to \pm\infty} e^{-x^2} = 0$$

Therefore $y = 0$ is a horizontal asymptote.

E. **Intervals of Increase or Decrease.**   The derivative of f is

$$f'(x) = -2xe^{-x^2}$$

Exponential functions are always positive, so $e^{-x^2} > 0$ for all x. Therefore $f'(x) > 0$ when $x < 0$, so f is increasing on $(-\infty, 0)$. Since $f'(x) < 0$ when $x > 0$, f is decreasing on $(0, \infty)$.

F. **Extreme Values.** The only critical number is 0. By the First Derivative Test, $f(0) = 1$ is a local (and absolute) maximum.

G. **Concavity.**
$$f''(x) = -2x(e^{-x^2})(-2x) + e^{-x^2}(-2)$$
$$= -2e^{-x^2}(1 - 2x^2)$$

Thus $f''(x) > 0$ when $1 - 2x^2 < 0$, so $x^2 > \frac{1}{2}$, or $|x| > \dfrac{1}{\sqrt{2}}$. Therefore f is concave upward on $\left(-\infty, -\dfrac{1}{\sqrt{2}}\right)$ and $\left(\dfrac{1}{\sqrt{2}}, \infty\right)$. Also $f''(x) < 0$ when $1 - 2x^2 > 0$ or $|x| < \dfrac{1}{\sqrt{2}}$. Thus f is concave downward on $\left(-\dfrac{1}{\sqrt{2}}, \dfrac{1}{\sqrt{2}}\right)$. The inflection points are $\left(\pm\dfrac{1}{\sqrt{2}}, \dfrac{1}{\sqrt{e}}\right)$.

H. **Sketch of the Curve.**

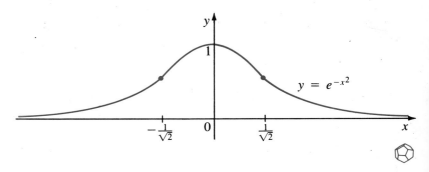

EXERCISE 8.2

A **1.** Simplify.

(a) $\dfrac{2}{e^{-x}}$ (b) $(e^x)^4$

(c) $e^{1-x}e^{3x}$ (d) $e^x e^{-x}$

(e) $e^{2x}(1 - 5e^{3x})$ (f) $\dfrac{6e^{8x}}{e^{3x}}$

B **2.** (a) Sketch the curve $y = 5^x$.

    (b) Use a calculator to evaluate the quantity
$$\frac{5^h - 1}{h}$$

for $h = 0.1, 0.01, 0.001,$ and 0.0001. What does the quantity represent?

(c) Estimate the value of the limit

$$\lim_{h \to 0} \frac{5^h - 1}{h}$$

correct to two decimal places.

(d) What does the limit in part (c) represent?

3. Use a calculator to estimate the values of the limits

(a) $\displaystyle\lim_{h \to 0} \frac{2.7^h - 1}{h}$

(b) $\displaystyle\lim_{h \to 0} \frac{2.8^h - 1}{h}$

to two decimal places.

4. Differentiate.

(a) $y = 2e^{-x}$

(b) $y = x^4 e^x$

(c) $y = e^{2x} \sin 3x$

(d) $y = e^{\sqrt{x}}$

(e) $y = e^{\tan x}$

(f) $y = \tan(e^x)$

(g) $y = \dfrac{e^x}{x}$

(h) $y = \dfrac{e^x}{1 - e^{2x}}$

(i) $y = e^{\sin(x^2)}$

(j) $y = xe^{\cot 4x}$

(k) $y = (1 + 5e^{-10x})^4$

(l) $y = \sqrt{x + e^{1 - x^2}}$

5. Find the equation of the tangent line to the curve $y = 1 + xe^{2x}$ at the point where $x = 0$.

6. Find y' if $e^{xy} = 2x + y$.

7. If $f(x) = e^{2x}$, find $f^{(6)}(0)$.

8. Find the intervals of increase and decrease for the function $f(x) = x^2 e^{-x}$.

9. Find the absolute minimum value of the function $f(x) = \dfrac{e^x}{x}$, $x > 0$.

10. For the function $f(x) = xe^x$, find

(a) the absolute minimum value,

(b) the intervals of concavity,

(c) the inflection point.

11. Evaluate.

(a) $\displaystyle\lim_{x \to \infty} e^{-x}$

(b) $\displaystyle\lim_{x \to -\infty} e^{-x}$

(c) $\displaystyle\lim_{t \to \frac{\pi}{2}^+} e^{\tan t}$

12. (a) Draw the graph of the exponential function $y = e^x$.

(b) Use the result of part (a) and transformations to graph the following functions.

(i) $y = e^{-x}$

(ii) $y = 1 - e^x$

13. Discuss each curve under the headings A–H of Section 5.5.

(a) $y = xe^{x^2}$

(b) $y = e^{\frac{1}{x^2}}$

14. (a) Sketch the graphs of the curves $y = e^x$ and $y = -x - 1$ (using the same axes) to show that there is exactly one solution of the equation $e^x = -x - 1$.

(b) Use Newton's method to find the root of the equation in part (a) correct to six decimal places.

C 15. Discuss the curve $y = e^{-\frac{1}{x}}$ under the headings of A–H of Section 5.5.

16. Find the millionth derivative of $f(x) = xe^{-x}$.

8.3 LOGARITHMIC FUNCTIONS

If $b > 0$, where $b \neq 1$, then the exponential function $f(x) = b^x$ is a one-to-one function by the Horizontal Line Test (see the diagram) and therefore has an inverse function.

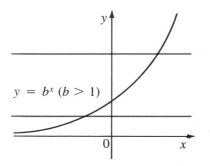

$y = b^x \ (b > 1)$

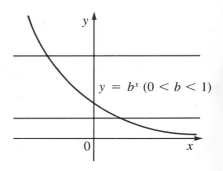

$y = b^x \ (0 < b < 1)$

The inverse function f^{-1} of the exponential function $f(x) = b^x$ is called the **logarithmic function with base b** and is denoted by $\log_b$. Recall that the inverse function f^{-1} is defined by

$$f^{-1}(x) = y \quad \text{if and only if} \quad f(y) = x$$

Thus, the definition of the logarithmic function as the inverse of the exponential function means the following.

$$\boxed{\log_b x = y \quad \text{if and only if} \quad b^y = x}$$ ①

It follows that

$$\log_b(b^x) = x \quad (x \in R)$$
$$b^{\log_b x} = x \quad (x > 0)$$

②

For instance, we have

$$\log_{10}(10^x) = x \quad \text{and} \quad 2^{\log_2 x} = x$$

Recall that if a one-to-one function f has domain A and range B, then its inverse function f^{-1} has domain B and range A. Since the exponential function $f(x) = b^x$, where $b \neq 1$, has domain R and range $(0, \infty)$, we conclude that its inverse function, $f^{-1}(x) = \log_b x$ has domain $(0, \infty)$ and range R.

The graph of $f^{-1}(x) = \log_b x$ is obtained by reflecting the graph of $f(x) = b^x$ in the line $y = x$. The diagram shows the case where $b > 1$. (The most important logarithmic functions have base $b > 1$.) The fact that $y = b^x$ ($b > 1$) is a very rapidly increasing function for $x > 0$ is reflected in the fact that $y = \log_b x$ is a very slowly increasing function for $x > 1$.

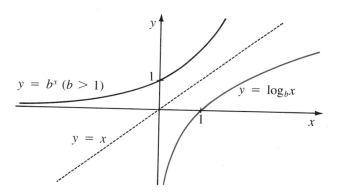

Notice that since $b^0 = 1$, we have

$$\log_b 1 = 0$$

and so the x-intercept of the function $y = \log_b x$ is 1. Notice also that since $y = b^x$ has the x-axis as a horizontal asymptote, the curve $y = \log_b x$ has the y-axis as a vertical asymptote. In fact, we have

$$\lim_{x \to 0^+} \log_b x = -\infty \quad \text{and} \quad \lim_{x \to \infty} \log_b x = \infty \text{ for } b > 1$$

③

The diagram shows the relationship among the graphs of the logarithmic functions with bases 2, 3, 5, and 10. These graphs were drawn by reflecting the graphs of $y = 2^x$, $y = 3^x$, $y = 5^x$, and $y = 10^x$ (see Section 8.1) in the line $y = x$.

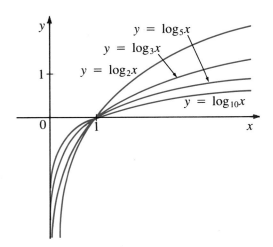

Example 1 Find the domain of the function $f(x) = \log_{10}(x - 3)$ and sketch its graph.

Solution The domain of $y = \log_b x$ is the interval $(0, \infty)$, so $\log_{10} x$ is defined only when $x > 0$. Therefore the domain of $f(x) = \log_{10}(x - 3)$ is

$$\{x \mid x - 3 > 0\} = \{x \mid x > 3\} = (3, \infty)$$

The graph of f is obtained from the graph of $y = \log_{10} x$ by shifting three units to the right. Notice that the line $x = 3$ is a vertical asymptote. This can also be seen from ③ by noting that $x - 3 \to 0^+$ as $x \to 3^+$ and so

$$\lim_{x \to 3^+} \log_{10}(x - 3) = -\infty$$

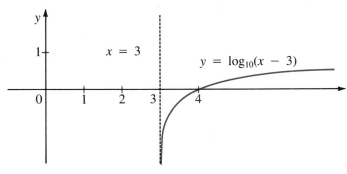

Natural Logarithms

In the next section we will see that, of all possible bases b for logarithms, the most convenient for the purposes of calculus is the number e, which was defined in Section 8.1. The logarithm with base e is called the **natural logarithm** and is given a special notation:

$$\log_e x = \ln x$$

(The abbreviation ln is short for *logarithmus naturalis.*)

Thus, the natural logarithmic function $y = \ln x$ is the inverse function of the exponential function $y = e^x$; they are both graphed in the following diagram.

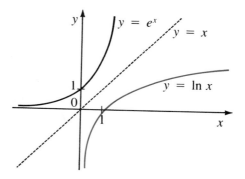

If we put $b = e$ and write ln for $\log_e$ in ① and ②, then the defining properties of the natural logarithm become

$$\ln x = y \iff e^y = x$$

④

and

$$\ln(e^x) = x \quad (x \in R)$$
$$e^{\ln x} = x \quad (x > 0)$$

⑤

In particular, it is worth noting that

$$\ln e = 1$$

and

$$\ln 1 = 0$$

Example 2 Solve for x: $\ln x = 8$.

Solution 1 From ④ we see that

$$\ln x = 8 \quad \text{means} \quad e^8 = x$$

Therefore $x = e^8$.

Solution 2   Start with the equation

$$\ln x = 8$$

and apply the natural exponential function to both sides of the equation:

$$e^{\ln x} = e^8$$

The second equation in ⑤ says that $e^{\ln x} = x$. Therefore $x = e^8$.

Example 3   Solve the equation $e^{3-2x} = 4$.

Solution   We take natural logarithms of both sides of the equation and use ⑤:

$$\ln(e^{3-2x}) = \ln 4$$
$$3 - 2x = \ln 4$$
$$2x = 3 - \ln 4$$
$$x = \tfrac{1}{2}(3 - \ln 4)$$

Since the natural logarithm is found on scientific calculators, we can give an approximation to the solution:

$$x \doteq 0.807$$

Example 4   Sketch the graphs of the following functions.
(a) $y = -\ln x$ (b) $y = \ln(-x)$

Solution   (a) We start with the graph of $y = \ln x$ and reflect in the x-axis to get the graph of $y = -\ln x$.
(b) To obtain the graph of $y = \ln(-x)$ we reflect the graph of $y = \ln x$ in the y-axis.

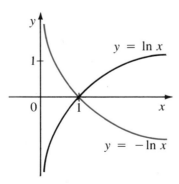

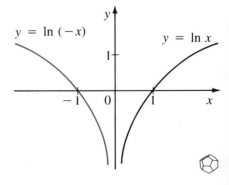

Example 5   Find the domain of the function $f(x) = \ln(4 - x^2)$.

Solution   As with any logarithmic function, $\ln x$ is defined when $x > 0$. Thus the domain of f is

$$\{x \mid 4 - x^2 > 0\} = \{x \mid x^2 < 4\} = \{x \mid |x| < 2\} = (-2, 2)$$

As a special case of ③ we have the following limits.

$$\lim_{x \to 0^+} \ln x = -\infty \qquad \lim_{x \to \infty} \ln x = \infty \qquad \text{⑥}$$

Example 6   Find $\lim\limits_{x \to 2^-} \ln(4 - x^2)$.

Solution   If we let $t = 4 - x^2$, then $t \to 0^+$ as $x \to 2^-$. So by ⑥ we have

$$\lim_{x \to 2^-} \ln(4 - x^2) = \lim_{t \to 0^+} \ln t = -\infty$$

Since $\ln$ is just a special logarithm, the laws of logarithms (see the Review and Preview to this chapter) also hold for the natural logarithm:

Suppose that $x > 0$, $y > 0$, and r is any real number. Then

1. $\ln(xy) = \ln x + \ln y$

2. $\ln\left(\dfrac{x}{y}\right) = \ln x - \ln y$

3. $\ln(x^r) = r \ln x$

Example 7   Express $\frac{1}{2} \ln x - 4 \ln y + \ln(x^2 + 1)$ as a single logarithm.

Solution $\frac{1}{2} \ln x - 4 \ln y + \ln(x^2 + 1) = \ln x^{\frac{1}{2}} - \ln y^4 + \ln(x^2 + 1)$

$$= \ln \frac{\sqrt{x}(x^2 + 1)}{y^4}$$

Change of Base

For some purposes it is useful to be able to change from logarithms in one base to logarithms in another base. Suppose that we are given $\log_b x$ and want to find $\log_a x$. Let

$$y = \log_a x$$

We write this in exponential form and take logarithms, with base b, of both sides.

$$a^y = x$$
$$\log_b(a^y) = \log_b x$$
$$y \log_b a = \log_b x$$
$$y = \frac{\log_b x}{\log_b a}$$

Thus we have proved the following formula.

Change of Base Formula

$$\log_a x = \frac{\log_b x}{\log_b a}$$

In particular, if we put $x = b$, then $\log_b b = 1$ and the change of base formula becomes

$$\log_a b = \frac{1}{\log_b a}$$

Example 8   Evaluate $\log_8 5$ correct to six decimal places.

Solution   There is no $\log_8$ key on a calculator, but we use the change of base formula with $a = 8$ and $b = e$ to convert to natural logarithms:

$$\log_8 5 = \frac{\ln 5}{\ln 8} \doteq 0.773\ 976$$

Logarithms with base 10 are called **common logarithms** and are often denoted by omitting the base:

$$\log x = \log_{10} x$$

Common logarithms are also found on scientific calculators, so an alternative solution to Example 8 is as follows:
Take $a = 8$ and $b = 10$ in the change of base formula. Then

$$\log_8 5 = \frac{\log_{10} 5}{\log_{10} 8} = \frac{\log 5}{\log 8} \doteq 0.773\ 976$$

EXERCISE 8.3

B **1.** Most scientific calculators have keys for both LN and LOG ($= \log_{10}$). Use such a calculator to draw the graphs of $y = \ln x$ and $y = \log_{10} x$, $0.1 \leqslant x \leqslant 10$, on the same axes.

2. Graph each function, not by plotting points, but by starting from the graphs of $y = \log_2 x$, $\log_{10} x$, and $\ln x$ given in this section and using transformations. State the domain, range, and asymptote of each function.

(a) $f(x) = \log_2(x - 4)$ (b) $f(x) = -\log_{10} x$
(c) $g(x) = \log(-x)$ (d) $g(x) = \ln(x + 2)$
(e) $y = 2 + \log_{10} x$ (f) $y = \log_2(x - 1) - 2$
(g) $y = 1 - \ln x$ (h) $y = 1 + \ln(-x)$
(i) $y = |\ln x|$ (j) $y = \ln|x|$

3. Evaluate without using a calculator.

(a) $e^{\ln 5}$ (b) $\ln e^2$
(c) $2 \ln e$ (d) $e^{5 \ln 2}$
(e) $\ln \sqrt{e}$ (f) $\ln 2 + 2 \ln 3 - \ln 18$

4. Solve for x.

(a) $e^x = 4$ (b) $\ln x = 6$
(c) $\ln(2x - 1) = 1$ (d) $e^{3x+5} = 10$
(e) $\ln(e^{3-x}) = 8$ (f) $\ln x = \ln 4 + \ln 7$
(g) $\ln(\ln x) = 2$ (h) $e^{e^x} = 5$

5. Find the solution of each equation correct to six decimal places.

(a) $\ln(x + 1) = 3$ (b) $e^{-x} = \frac{1}{2}$
(c) $e^{5x+3} = 10$ (d) $2^{x-5} = 3$

6. Express as a single logarithm.

(a) $\frac{1}{3} \ln x + 2 \ln(3x - 5)$

(b) $2 \ln x - \frac{1}{2} \ln(x^2 - 1) + 3 \ln(x^2 + 1)$

7. Find the domain of each function.

(a) $f(x) = \log_{10}(2 + 5x)$ (b) $f(x) = \log_2(10 - 3x)$
(c) $g(x) = \log_3(x^2 - 1)$ (d) $g(x) = \ln(x - x^2)$
(e) $h(x) = \ln x + \ln(2 - x)$
(f) $h(x) = \sqrt{x - 2} - \ln(10 - x)$

8. Compare the domains of the functions $f(x) = \ln x^2$ and $g(x) = 2 \ln x$.

9. Find each limit.

(a) $\lim\limits_{x \to -4^+} \ln(x + 4)$ (b) $\lim\limits_{x \to \infty} \ln(x + 4)$
(c) $\lim\limits_{x \to 1^+} \log_{10}(x^2 - x)$ (d) $\lim\limits_{t \to \pi^-} \ln(\sin t)$

10. Use the change of base formula and a calculator to evaluate the logarithm correct to six decimal places.
   (a) $\log_2 7$ (b) $\log_5 2$
   (c) $\log_3 11$ (d) $\log_6 92$

11. Use the change of base formula to show that $\log e = \dfrac{1}{\ln 10}$.

12. Simplify $(\log_2 5)(\log_5 7)$.

C 13. A **learning curve** is a graph of a function $P(t)$ that measures the performance of someone learning a skill as a function of the training time t. At first, the rate of learning is rapid. Then, as performance increases and approaches a maximal value M, the rate of learning decreases. It has been found that the function
$$P(t) = M - Ce^{-kt}$$
where k and C are positive constants and $C < M$, is a reasonable model for learning.
   (a) Sketch the graph of P.
   (b) Express the learning time t as a function of the performance level P.

14. Which is larger, $\log_4 17$ or $\log_5 24$?

15. (a) Find the domain of the function $f(x) = \log_2(\log_{10} x)$.
   (b) Find the inverse function of f.

16. (a) Find the domain of the function $f(x) = \ln(\ln(\ln x))$.
   (b) Find the inverse function of f.

17. Solve the equation $4^x - 2^{x+1} = 3$. (Hint: First write the equation as a quadratic equation in 2^x.)

18. Solve the equation $\log_2 x + \log_4 x + \log_8 x = 11$.

8.4 DERIVATIVES OF LOGARITHMIC FUNCTIONS

In this section we find the derivatives of the logarithmic functions $y = \log_b x$. First we differentiate the natural logarithmic function $y = \ln x$.

$$\boxed{\frac{d}{dx}(\ln x) = \frac{1}{x}}$$ ①

Proof

Let $\quad y = \ln x$

Then $\quad e^y = x$

Differentiating this equation implicitly with respect to x, we get

$$e^y \frac{dy}{dx} = 1$$

$$\frac{dy}{dx} = \frac{1}{e^y} = \frac{1}{x}$$

Example 1 Differentiate.   (a) $y = x \ln x$ (b) $y = \ln(x^2 + 2x - 5)$

Solution (a) Using the Product Rule, we have

$$\frac{dy}{dx} = x \frac{d}{dx}(\ln x) + \ln x \frac{d}{dx}(x)$$

$$= (x)\left(\frac{1}{x}\right) + (\ln x)(1)$$

$$= 1 + \ln x$$

(b) To use the Chain Rule we let $u = x^2 + 2x - 5$. Then $y = \ln u$, so

$$\frac{dy}{dx} = \frac{dy}{du}\frac{du}{dx} = \frac{1}{u}\frac{du}{dx} = \frac{1}{x^2 + 2x - 5}(2x + 2) = \frac{2(x + 1)}{x^2 + 2x - 5}$$

In general, if we combine Formula 1 with the Chain Rule, we get

$$\frac{d}{dx} \ln u = \frac{1}{u}\frac{du}{dx}$$

or

$$\frac{d}{dx} \ln[g(x)] = \frac{g'(x)}{g(x)}$$

Example 2 Find the derivative of $f(x) = \ln(\cos x)$.

Solution
$$f'(x) = \frac{d}{dx} \ln(\cos x)$$

$$= \frac{1}{\cos x}\frac{d}{dx} \cos x$$

$$= \frac{1}{\cos x}(-\sin x)$$

$$= -\tan x$$

Example 3 Differentiate $y = (\ln x)^4$.

Solution This time the logarithm is the inner function, so the Chain Rule gives

$$y' = 4(\ln x)^3 \frac{d}{dx}(\ln x) = \frac{4(\ln x)^3}{x}$$

Example 4   Find $\dfrac{d}{dx} \ln \dfrac{x}{\sqrt{x+1}}$.

Solution 1   We use the Chain Rule and then the Quotient Rule:

$$\frac{d}{dx} \ln \frac{x}{\sqrt{x+1}} = \frac{1}{\dfrac{x}{\sqrt{x+1}}} \, \frac{d}{dx} \frac{x}{\sqrt{x+1}}$$

$$= \frac{\sqrt{x+1}}{x} \left[\frac{\sqrt{x+1}(1) - (x)\dfrac{1}{2\sqrt{x+1}}}{x+1} \right]$$

$$= \frac{x+1-\frac{1}{2}x}{x(x+1)}$$

$$= \frac{x+2}{2x(x+1)}$$

Solution 2   If we first use the Laws of Logarithms to rewrite the function, then the differentiation becomes easier:

$$\frac{d}{dx} \ln \frac{x}{\sqrt{x+1}} = \frac{d}{dx} [\ln x - \tfrac{1}{2} \ln(x+1)]$$

$$= \frac{1}{x} - \frac{1}{2(x+1)}$$

(This answer can be left as it is, but if we were to use a common denominator we would see that it gives the same answer as in Solution 1.)   ⬡

Example 5   If $f(x) = \ln |x|$, find $f'(x)$.

Solution   If x is positive, then $|x| = x$, so

$$f'(x) = \frac{d}{dx} (\ln x) = \frac{1}{x}$$

If x is negative, then $|x| = -x$, so

$$f'(x) = \frac{d}{dx} \ln(-x) = \frac{1}{-x}(-1) = \frac{1}{x}$$

Therefore $f'(x) = \dfrac{1}{x}$ for all $x \neq 0$.   ⬡

The result of Example 5 is worth remembering:

$$\frac{d}{dx}\ln|x| = \frac{1}{x}$$

②

In Section 8.2 we showed that if $f(x) = b^x$ then

$$f'(x) = b^x \lim_{h \to 0} \frac{b^h - 1}{h}$$

Now we can show that the value of the limit is $\ln b$.

$$\frac{d}{dx}b^x = b^x \ln b$$

③

Proof

We use the fact that $e^{\ln b} = b$.

$$\frac{d}{dx}b^x = \frac{d}{dx}(e^{\ln b})^x$$

$$= \frac{d}{dx}e^{(\ln b)x}$$

$$= e^{(\ln b)x}\frac{d}{dx}(\ln b)x$$

$$= (e^{\ln b})^x(\ln b)$$

$$= b^x \ln b$$

Example 6 Find y' if $y = 2^{x^2}$.

Solution Combining Formula 3 with the Chain Rule, we get

$$y' = 2^{x^2}(\ln 2)\frac{d}{dx}x^2 = (2\ln 2)x2^{x^2}$$

Next we differentiate the general logarithmic function $y = \log_b x$.

$$\frac{d}{dx}\log_b x = \frac{1}{x\ln b}$$

④

Proof

Let $\quad y = \log_b x$

Then $\quad b^y = x$

Using Formula 3 we differentiate this equation implicitly with respect to x:

$$b^y (\ln b) \frac{dy}{dx} = 1$$

$$\frac{dy}{dx} = \frac{1}{b^y \ln b} = \frac{1}{x \ln b}$$

(Another proof of Formula 4 could be given using the Change of Base Formula. See Question 11 in Exercise 8.4.)

Example 7 Find $f'(x)$ if $f(x) = \log_{10}(3x + 1)^4$.

Solution First we rewrite f as

$$f(x) = 4 \log_{10}(3x + 1)$$

Then we combine Formula 4 with the Chain Rule.

$$f'(x) = (4) \frac{1}{(3x + 1)\ln 10} \frac{d}{dx}(3x + 1) = \frac{12}{(3x + 1)\ln 10}$$

From Formula 4 we see one of the main reasons that natural logarithms (logarithms with base e) are used in calculus: The differentiation formula is simplest when $b = e$ because $\ln e = 1$.

Example 8 Find the absolute maximum value of the function $f(x) = \dfrac{\ln x}{x}$.

Solution The Quotient Rule gives

$$f'(x) = \frac{x\left(\dfrac{1}{x}\right) - (\ln x)(1)}{x^2} = \frac{1 - \ln x}{x^2}$$

The critical numbers occur when $1 - \ln x = 0$, so $\ln x = 1$, or $x = e$.

Since $x^2 \geq 0$, we see that $f'(x) > 0$ when $1 - \ln x > 0$, so $\ln x < 1$, or $x < e$. Similarly $f'(x) < 0$ when $x > e$. Thus, by the First

Derivative Test for Absolute Extreme Values, the absolute maximum value occurs when $x = e$ and is

$$f(e) = \frac{\ln e}{e} = \frac{1}{e}$$

Example 9   Discuss the curve $y = f(x) = \ln(x^2 - 1)$ under the headings A–H of Section 5.5.

Solution   A. *Domain.*   The function is defined when $x^2 - 1 > 0$, so the domain is

$$\begin{aligned}\{x \mid x^2 > 1\} &= \{x \mid |x| > 1\} \\ &= \{x \mid x > 1 \text{ or } x < -1\} \\ &= (-\infty, -1) \cup (1, \infty)\end{aligned}$$

B. *Intercepts.*   The x-intercepts occur when $\ln(x^2 - 1) = 0$, so $x^2 - 1 = 1$, $x^2 = 2$, $x = \pm\sqrt{2}$. There is no y-intercept since $f(0)$ is undefined.

C. *Symmetry.* $f(-x) = f(x)$, so f is even and the curve is symmetric about the y-axis.

D. *Asymptotes.*   As $x \to 1^+$ or $x \to -1^-$, we have $x^2 - 1 \to 0^+$, so

$$\lim_{x \to 1^+} \ln(x^2 - 1) = -\infty \quad \text{and} \quad \lim_{x \to -1^-} \ln(x^2 - 1) = -\infty$$

Thus the lines $x = 1$ and $x = -1$ are vertical asymptotes. There is no horizontal asymptote since

$$\lim_{x \to \pm\infty} \ln(x^2 - 1) = \infty$$

E. *Intervals of Increase and Decrease.*

$$f'(x) = \frac{2x}{x^2 - 1}$$

Recall that $f(x)$ is defined only when $x > 1$ or $x < -1$. We have $f'(x) > 0$ for $x > 1$ and $f'(x) < 0$ for $x < -1$. Thus f is increasing on $(1, \infty)$ and decreasing on $(-\infty, -1)$.

F. *Extreme Values.*   There is no maximum or minimum value.

G. *Concavity.* $\quad f''(x) = \dfrac{(x^2 - 1)(2) - (2x)(2x)}{(x^2 - 1)^2} = \dfrac{-2x^2 - 2}{(x^2 - 1)^2}$

Thus $f''(x) < 0$, so f is concave downward on $(-\infty, -1)$ and $(1, \infty)$.

H. *Sketch of the Curve.*

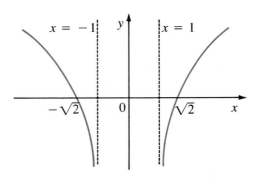

The Number *e* as a Limit

We have shown that if $f(x) = \ln x$, then $f'(x) = \dfrac{1}{x}$. Thus $f'(1) = 1$.

We now use this fact to express the number *e* as a limit.

From the definition of a derivative as a limit, we have

$$
\begin{aligned}
f'(1) &= \lim_{h \to 0} \frac{f(1 + h) - f(1)}{h} \\
&= \lim_{x \to 0} \frac{f(1 + x) - f(1)}{x} \\
&= \lim_{x \to 0} \frac{\ln(1 + x) - \ln 1}{x} \\
&= \lim_{x \to 0} \frac{1}{x} \ln(1 + x) && \text{(since } \ln 1 = 0\text{)} \\
&= \lim_{x \to 0} \ln(1 + x)^{\frac{1}{x}} && \text{(by Law 3 of logarithms)} \\
&= \ln\left[\lim_{x \to 0} (1 + x)^{\frac{1}{x}} \right] && \text{(since } \ln \text{ is continuous)}
\end{aligned}
$$

Since $f'(1) = 1$, we have

$$
\ln\left[\lim_{x \to 0} (1 + x)^{\frac{1}{x}} \right] = 1
$$

Therefore

$$
\boxed{\lim_{x \to 0} (1 + x)^{\frac{1}{x}} = e}
$$

⑤

Formula 5 is illustrated by the graph of the function $y = (1 + x)^{\frac{1}{x}}$ and a table of values for small values of *x*.

x	$(1 + x)^{\frac{1}{x}}$
0.1	2.593 742 46
0.01	2.704 813 83
0.001	2.716 923 93
0.000 1	2.718 145 93
0.000 01	2.718 268 24
0.000 001	2.718 280 47
0.000 000 1	2.718 281 69
0.000 000 01	2.718 281 82

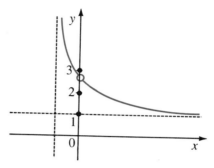

It appears that

$$e \doteq 2.718\ 282$$

In fact it can be shown that, correct to 15 decimal places,

$$e \doteq 2.718\ 281\ 828\ 459\ 045$$

See the biography of Euler at the end of this chapter.

The decimal expansion of e is nonrepeating because e is an irrational number. The notation e for this number was chosen by the Swiss mathematician Leonhard Euler in 1727 probably because it is the first letter of the word *exponential*.

If we put $n = \dfrac{1}{x}$ in Formula 5, then $n \to \infty$ as $x \to 0$ and an alternative expression for e is

$$e = \lim_{n \to \infty} \left(1 + \frac{1}{n}\right)^n$$

EXERCISE 8.4

B **1.** Differentiate.

(a) $f(x) = x^2 \ln x$

(b) $f(x) = \sqrt{\ln x}$

(c) $g(x) = \ln(x^3 + 1)$

(d) $g(x) = \ln(5x)$

(e) $y = \sin(\ln x)$

(f) $y = \ln(\sin x)$

(g) $y = \dfrac{\ln x}{x^3}$

(h) $y = (x + \ln x)^3$

(i) $y = \ln|2x + 1|$ 　　　　　　　(j) $y = \ln\left(\dfrac{x + 1}{x - 1}\right)$

(k) $y = \ln\sqrt{\dfrac{x}{2x + 3}}$ 　　　　　(l) $y = \ln\dfrac{x}{\sqrt{x^2 + 1}}$

(m) $y = \ln(\sec x + \tan x)$ 　　(n) $y = \tan[\ln(1 - 3x)]$

2. (a) If $f(x) = \ln(\ln x)$, find $f'(x)$.
    (b) Find the domains of f and f'.

3. Find the derivative of each function.
    (a) $f(x) = \log_2(x^2 + 1)$ 　　　　(b) $g(x) = x \log_{10} x$

    (c) $F(x) = \log_5(3x - 8)$ 　　　　(d) $G(x) = \dfrac{1 + \log_3 x}{x}$

4. Differentiate.
    (a) $y = x^3 + 3^x$ 　　　　　　(b) $y = 2^{x^4 - x}$
    (c) $y = x5^{\sqrt{x}}$ 　　　　　　(d) $y = 10^{\tan \pi x}$

5. Find the equation of the tangent line to each curve at the given point.
    (a) $y = \ln(x - 1)$, $(2, 0)$ 　　(b) $y = x^2 \ln x$, $(1, 0)$
    (c) $y = 10^x$, $(1, 10)$ 　　　　(d) $y = \log_{10} x$, $(100, 2)$

6. Find y' if $\ln(x + y) = y - 1$.

7. (a) Find the absolute minimum value of the function $f(x) = x \ln x$.
    (b) On what interval is it concave upward?

8. (a) Find the local maximum and minimum values of the function $f(x) = x(\ln x)^2$.
    (b) Find the inflection point of this function.

9. Discuss each curve under the headings A–H of Section 5.5.
    (a) $y = \ln(9 - x^2)$ 　　　　　(b) $y = x + \ln x$
    (c) $y = (\ln x)^2$ 　　　　　　(d) $y = \ln(\cos x)$

10. (a) Sketch the graphs of the curves $y = \ln x$ and $y = 2 - x$ (using the same axes) to show that there is exactly one solution of the equation $\ln x = 2 - x$.
    (b) Use Newton's method to find the root of the equation in part (a) correct to six decimal places.

11. Use Formula 1, together with the Change of Base Formula from Section 8.3, to prove Formula 4.

C 12. Evaluate $\lim\limits_{x \to 0} (1 + 3x)^{\frac{1}{x}}$. (Hint: Make the change of variable $t = 3x$ and use Formula 5.)

PROBLEMS PLUS

Prove that the number $\log_2 5$ is an irrational number.

8.5 EXPONENTIAL GROWTH AND DECAY

In many of the sciences, certain quantities grow or decay at a rate that is proportional to their size. In this section we see that such quantities occur in biology, chemistry, physics, and economics and are modelled by exponential functions.

If $y = f(t)$ is the value of a quantity y at time t and if the rate of change of y with respect to t is proportional to its size $f(t)$ at any time, then

$$f'(t) = kf(t) \qquad \text{or} \qquad \frac{dy}{dt} = ky \qquad \text{①}$$

where k is a constant. This equation is called the **Law of Natural Growth** (if $k > 0$) or the **Law of Natural Decay** (if $k < 0$).

To solve ①, all we have to do is think of a function whose derivative is a constant multiple of itself. Any exponential function has this property. In fact if $f(t) = Ce^{kt}$, where C is a constant, then

$$f'(t) = Ce^{kt}(k) = k(Ce^{kt}) = kf(t)$$

It can also be shown that *any* solution of ① must be of the form $f(t) = Ce^{kt}$.

Notice that

$$f(0) = Ce^{k(0)} = C$$

and so the value of the constant C is the size of the quantity at time $t = 0$. We call it the **initial value** of the function and we denote it by y_0.

The solution of the equation

$$\frac{dy}{dt} = ky$$

is given by

$$y = y_0 e^{kt}$$

$\qquad\qquad$ ②

where y_0 is the initial value of the function.

Exponential Growth

If $y = f(t)$ is the number of individuals in a population of animals or bacteria cells at time t, then it seems reasonable to expect that the rate of growth $f'(t)$ is proportional to the population $f(t)$:

$$f'(t) = kf(t)$$

(In a bacteria culture, for instance, the growth is a result of division of the bacteria and the more bacteria present at a given moment, the greater the opportunity for division.) This reasoning is valid under ideal conditions of adequate nutrition, freedom from disease, and unlimited environment. We make these assumptions throughout this chapter. Thus, from ②, the size of the population at time t is

$$y = y_0 e^{kt}$$

where y_0 is the initial size of the population.

Example 1   A bacteria culture starts with 2000 bacteria and after 3 h the estimated count is 10 000 bacteria.
(a)   Find the number of bacteria after t hours.
(b)   Find the number of bacteria after 2 h.
(c)   Find the rate of growth after 2 h.
(d)   When will the bacteria population reach 18 000?

Solution   (a)   Let $y = f(t)$ be the number of bacteria after t hours. We are given that the initial population size is $y_0 = f(0) = 2000$ and also $f(3) = 10\ 000$. From ② we have

$$f(t) = y_0 e^{kt} = 2000\ e^{kt}$$

and putting $t = 3$ we get

$$2000\ e^{3k} = 10\ 000$$
$$e^{3k} = 5$$
$$3k = \ln 5$$
$$k = \tfrac{1}{3} \ln 5$$

Putting this value of k back into the expression for $f(t)$, we get

$$y = f(t) = 2000\ e^{\left(\frac{1}{3} \ln 5\right)t}$$

Since $e^{\ln 5} = 5$, another way to write the answer is

$$y = (2000)(e^{\ln 5})^{\frac{t}{3}} = (2000)5^{\frac{t}{3}}$$

(b)   The number of bacteria after 2 h is

$$y = f(2) = (2000)5^{\frac{2}{3}} \doteq 5848$$

(c)   The rate of growth is

$$f'(t) = 2000\ e^{\left(\frac{1}{3} \ln 5\right)t} \left(\tfrac{1}{3} \ln 5\right)$$

After 2 h it is

$$f'(2) = 2000\ e^{\left(\frac{1}{3} \ln 5\right)(2)} \left(\tfrac{1}{3} \ln 5\right) \doteq 3137$$

The rate of growth after 2 h is about 3137 bacteria/h.

(d) We want to find the value of t such that $f(t) = 18\ 000$; that is,

$$2000\ e^{\left(\frac{1}{3}\ln 5\right)t} = 18\ 000$$

$$e^{\left(\frac{1}{3}\ln 5\right)t} = 9$$

We solve this equation for t by taking the natural logarithm of both sides.

$$\left(\tfrac{1}{3}\ln 5\right)t = \ln 9$$

$$t = \frac{3\ln 9}{\ln 5} \doteq 4.0$$

The population will reach 18 000 after about 4 h.

Radioactive Decay

Radioactive substances decompose by spontaneously emitting radiation. The rate of decay is proportional to the amount of the substance that has not yet disintegrated. Therefore if $y = f(t)$ is the mass of the substance that remains at time t, we have

$$\frac{dy}{dt} = ky$$

(Here k is a negative constant because f is a decreasing function.) From ② we then have

$$y = y_0 e^{kt}$$

where y_0 is the mass at time $t = 0$.

The **half-life** of a radioactive substance is the period of time during which any given amount decays until half of it remains.

Example 2 The half-life of Polonium-210 is 140 d and a sample of this element has a mass of 300 mg.
(a) Find the mass that remains after t days.
(b) Find the mass that remains after 50 d.
(c) Find the rate of decrease of the mass after 50 d.
(d) How long will the sample take to decay to a mass of 200 mg?

Solution (a) Let $y = f(t)$ be the mass of Polonium-210, in milligrams, that remains after t days. We are given that the initial mass is $y_0 = 300$ mg, so

$$f(t) = 300\ e^{kt}$$

To determine the value of k we use the fact that the half-life is 140 d and so $f(140) = 150$. Thus

$$300\,e^{140k} = 150$$

$$e^{140k} = \tfrac{1}{2}$$

$$140k = \ln\left(\tfrac{1}{2}\right) = -\ln 2$$

$$k = -\frac{\ln 2}{140}$$

Therefore the mass remaining after t days is

$$f(t) = 300e^{-\frac{\ln 2}{140}t}$$

Since $e^{\ln 2} = 2$, an alternative form of the answer is

$$f(t) = (300)2^{-\frac{t}{140}}$$

(b) The mass after 50 d is

$$f(50) = (300)2^{-\frac{50}{140}} \doteq 234 \text{ mg}$$

(c) The rate of change of the mass is

$$f'(t) = 300e^{-\frac{\ln 2}{140}t}\left(-\frac{\ln 2}{140}\right)$$

After 50 d it is

$$f'(50) = (300)2^{-\frac{50}{140}}\left(-\frac{\ln 2}{140}\right) \doteq -1.2$$

Thus the rate of decrease is about 1.2 mg/d.

(d) The mass will be 200 mg when

$$300\,e^{-\frac{\ln 2}{140}t} = 200$$

$$e^{-\frac{\ln 2}{140}t} = \tfrac{2}{3}$$

$$-\frac{\ln 2}{140}t = \ln \tfrac{2}{3}$$

$$t = -140\,\frac{\ln \tfrac{2}{3}}{\ln 2} \doteq 82$$

The time required is about 82 d.

Compound Interest

If an amount of money P, called the **principal**, is invested at an interest rate r, then the interest after one time period is Pr and the amount of money is

$$A = P + Pr = P(1 + r)$$

For instance, if $P = \$1000$ and the interest rate is 12% per annum, then $r = 0.12$ and the amount after one year is $\$1000(1.12) = \$1120$.

If the interest is reinvested, then the new principal is $P(1 + r)$ and the amount after another time period is

$$A = P(1 + r)(1 + r) = P(1 + r)^2$$

Similarly, after a third time period the amount is $P(1 + r)^3$, and in general after k periods it is

$$A = P(1 + r)^k$$

Notice that this is an exponential function with base $1 + r$.

If the interest rate is stated as 12% per annum compounded semi-annually, then the time period is six months and the interest rate per time period is

$$i = \frac{0.12}{2} = 0.06$$

If interest is compounded n times per annum, then in each time period the interest rate is

$$i = \frac{r}{n}$$

There are nt time periods in t years, so the amount after t years is

$$\boxed{A = P\left(1 + \frac{r}{n}\right)^{nt}}$$ ③

Example 3   A sum of $1000 is invested at an interest rate of 12% per annum. Find the amount in the account after three years if interest is compounded
(a) annually   (b) semiannually   (c) quarterly
(d) monthly   (e) daily

Solution   We use Formula 3 with $P = \$1000$, $r = 0.12$, and $t = 3$.
(a) With annual compounding, $n = 1$:

$$A = 1000(1.12)^3 = \$1404.93$$

(b) With semiannual compounding, $n = 2$:

$$A = 1000\left(1 + \frac{0.12}{2}\right)^{2(3)} = 1000(1.06)^6 = \$1418.52$$

(c) With quarterly compounding, $n = 4$:

$$A = 1000\left(1 + \frac{0.12}{4}\right)^{4(3)} = 1000(1.03)^{12} = \$1425.76$$

(d) With monthly compounding, $n = 12$:

$$A = 1000\left(1 + \frac{0.12}{12}\right)^{12(3)} = 1000(1.01)^{36} = \$1430.77$$

(e) With daily compounding, $n = 365$:

$$A = 1000\left(1 + \frac{0.12}{365}\right)^{365(3)} = \$1433.24$$

We see from Example 3 that the interest paid increases as the number of compounding periods (n) increases. In general, let us see what happens as n increases indefinitely. If we let $m = \dfrac{n}{r}$, then

$$A = P\left(1 + \frac{r}{n}\right)^{nt} = P\left[\left(1 + \frac{r}{n}\right)^{\frac{n}{r}}\right]^{rt} = P\left[\left(1 + \frac{1}{m}\right)^{m}\right]^{rt}$$

Recall that as m becomes large, the quantity $\left(1 + \dfrac{1}{m}\right)^{m}$ approaches the number e. Thus the amount approaches

$$\boxed{A = Pe^{rt}} \qquad ④$$

When interest is paid according to Formula 4, we say that interest is **compounded continuously**.

Example 4   Find the amount after three years if $1000 is invested at an interest rate of 12% per annum compounded continuously.

Solution   Using Formula 4 with $P = \$1000$, $r = 0.12$, and $t = 3$, we have

$$A = 1000\, e^{(0.12)3} = 1000\, e^{0.36} = \$1433.33$$

EXERCISE 8.5

B **1.** A bacteria culture starts with 1000 bacteria. After 2 h the estimated count is 10 000 bacteria.
(a) Find the number of bacteria after t hours.
(b) Find the number of bacteria after 5 h.
(c) Find the rate of growth after 5 h.
(d) When will the bacteria population reach 15 000?

2. The initial size of a bacteria culture is 400. After an hour there are 1200 bacteria.
(a) Find the number of bacteria after t hours.
(b) In what period of time does the population double?

3. A cell of the bacterium Escherichia coli in a nutrient broth medium divides into two cells every 20 min. Suppose that there are initially 500 cells. Find
   (a) the number of cells after t hours
   (b) the number of cells after 8 h
   (c) the time required for the size to reach 6000 cells

4. The count in a bacteria culture was 5000 after 15 min and 40 000 after 1 h.
   (a) What was the initial size of the culture?
   (b) Find the population after t hours.
   (c) Find the rate of growth after 15 min.
   (d) When will the size of the population be 150 000?

5. The population of a certain city grows at a rate of 4% per year. The population in 1980 was 275 000.
   (a) What was the population in 1985?
   (b) Predict the population in the year 2000, assuming the growth rate remains constant.

6. The population of the world is doubling about every 35 a. In 1987 the total population reached 5 billion.
   (a) Find the projected world population
       (i) for the year 2001   (ii) for the year 2100
   (b) When will the world population reach 50 billion?

7. Uranium-238 has a half-life of 4.5×10^9 a.
   (a) Find the mass that remains from a 100 mg sample after t years.
   (b) Find the mass that remains from this sample after 10 000 a.
   (c) Find the rate of decrease of the mass after 10 000 a.

8. An isotope of sodium, ^{24}Na, has a half-life of 15 h. A sample of this isotope has a mass of 2 g.
   (a) Find the mass that remains after t hours.
   (b) Find the mass that remains after 5 h.
   (c) Find the rate of decrease of the mass after 5 h.
   (d) How long will the sample take to decay to a mass of 0.4 g?

9. Uranium-234 has a half-life of 2.5×10^5 a.
   (a) Find the amount remaining from a 10 mg sample after a thousand years.
   (b) How long would it take this sample to decompose until its mass is 7 mg?

10. A sample of Bismuth-210 decayed to 33% of its original mass after eight days.
    (a) Find the half-life of this element.
    (b) Find the mass remaining after twelve days.

11. $1000 is borrowed at a rate of 16% interest per annum. Find the amount due at the end of two years if the interest is compounded

(a) annually   (b) quarterly   (c) monthly

(d) weekly   (e) daily   (f) continuously

12. $10 000 is invested at an interest rate of 10% per annum. Find the amount of the investment at the end of four years if the interest is compounded

(a) annually   (b) semiannually   (c) monthly

(d) daily   (e) hourly   (f) continuously

13. Which of the following would be the better investment?

(a) An account paying $9\frac{1}{4}$% per annum compounded semiannually, or

(b) an account paying 9% per annum compounded continuously.

14. How long would it take for an investment to double in value if the interest rate is 8.5% per annum compounded continuously?

15. If the chemical reaction
$$2N_2O_5 \rightarrow 4\,NO_2 + O_2$$
takes place at 45°C, the rate of reaction of dinitrogen pentoxide is proportional to its concentration:
$$-\frac{d[N_2O_5]}{dt} = 0.0005[N_2O_5]$$
(See Section 3.3.)

(a) If the initial concentration is C, find the concentration $[N_2O_5]$ after t seconds.

(b) After what period of time will the concentration be reduced to half its original value?

16. Scientists can determine the age of ancient objects by a method called **radiocarbon dating**. The bombardment of the upper atmosphere by cosmic rays converts nitrogen to a radioactive isotope of carbon, ^{14}C, with a half-life of about 5570 a. Vegetation absorbs carbon dioxide through the atmosphere and animal life assimilates ^{14}C through food chains. When a plant or animal dies it stops replacing its carbon and the amount of ^{14}C begins to decrease through radioactive decay. Therefore the level of radioactivity must also decay exponentially.

A parchment fragment was discovered that had about 77% as much ^{14}C radioactivity as does plant material on earth today. Estimate the age of the parchment.

PROBLEMS PLUS

Show that if $x > 0$ and $x \neq 1$, then

$$\frac{1}{\log_2 x} + \frac{1}{\log_3 x} + \frac{1}{\log_5 x} + \frac{1}{\log_7 x} = \frac{1}{\log_{210} x}$$

8.6   LOGARITHMIC DIFFERENTIATION

The calculation of derivatives of complicated functions involving products, quotients, and powers can often be simplified by taking logarithms. The method used in the following example is called **logarithmic differentiation**.

Example 1   Differentiate $y = \dfrac{e^x \sqrt{x^2 + 1}}{(x^2 + 2)^3}$.

Solution   It is possible to differentiate this function using the Quotient and Product Rules, but it is easier to take natural logarithms of both sides.

$$\ln y = \ln\left[\frac{e^x(x^2 + 1)^{\frac{1}{2}}}{(x^2 + 2)^3}\right]$$
$$= \ln(e^x) + \ln(x^2 + 1)^{\frac{1}{2}} - \ln(x^2 + 2)^3$$
$$= x + \tfrac{1}{2}\ln(x^2 + 1) - 3\ln(x^2 + 2)$$

If we now differentiate implicitly with respect to x, we get

$$\frac{1}{y}\frac{dy}{dx} = 1 + \left(\tfrac{1}{2}\right)\frac{2x}{x^2 + 1} - (3)\frac{2x}{x^2 + 2}$$

Solving for the derivative, we have

$$\frac{dy}{dx} = y\left[1 + \frac{x}{x^2 + 1} - \frac{6x}{x^2 + 2}\right]$$
$$= \frac{e^x \sqrt{x^2 + 1}}{(x^2 + 2)^3}\left[1 + \frac{x}{x^2 + 1} - \frac{6x}{x^2 + 2}\right]$$

Steps in Logarithmic Differentiation

1. Take logarithms of both sides of an equation $y = f(x)$.
2. Differentiate implicitly with respect to x.
3. Solve the resulting equation for y'.

Notice that, in Example 1, y was positive and so there was no problem using logarithms. If it happens that $f(x) < 0$ for some values of x, then $\ln y$ is not defined. However we can always write $|y| = |f(x)|$ and use Formula 2 from Section 8.4:

$$\frac{d}{dx} \ln |x| = \frac{1}{x}$$

This procedure is illustrated in the following example.

Example 2   Find y' if $y = \sqrt[3]{\dfrac{x \cos x}{x^2 - 1}}$.

Solution   Since y can be negative, we write

$$|y| = \left| \sqrt[3]{\frac{x \cos x}{x^2 - 1}} \right| = \left[\frac{|x||\cos x|}{|x^2 - 1|} \right]^{\frac{1}{3}}$$

Then $\ln |y| = \frac{1}{3}[\ln |x| + \ln |\cos x| - \ln |x^2 - 1 |]$

Differentiating with respect to x, we have

$$\frac{1}{y} y' = \frac{1}{3} \left[\frac{1}{x} + \frac{-\sin x}{\cos x} - \frac{2x}{x^2 - 1} \right]$$

$$y' = \frac{1}{3} \sqrt[3]{\frac{x \cos x}{x^2 - 1}} \left[\frac{1}{x} - \tan x - \frac{2x}{x^2 - 1} \right]$$

The technique of logarithmic differentiation can be used to prove the General Power Rule as stated in Section 2.2:

If n is any real number, then $\dfrac{d}{dx}(x^n) = nx^{n-1}$.

Proof

Let $y = x^n$

Then $|y| = |x^n|$

          $= |x|^n$

$\ln |y| = \ln(|x|^n)$

          $= n \ln |x|$

$\dfrac{y'}{y} = n\left(\dfrac{1}{x}\right)$

$y' = n\left(\dfrac{y}{x}\right) = n\,\dfrac{x^n}{x} = nx^{n-1}$

We should note carefully the difference between the Power Rule

$$\frac{d}{dx} x^n = nx^{n-1} \quad \text{(variable base, constant exponent)}$$

and the rule for differentiating exponential functions

$$\frac{d}{dx} b^x = b^x \ln b \quad \text{(constant base, variable exponent)}$$

But what do we do when faced with a function such as

$$y = x^{\sin x}$$

where both the base and exponent are variable? There is no differentiation rule for such a function, but we can use logarithmic differentiation.

Example 3   Differentiate $y = x^{\sin x}$, $x > 0$.

Solution   Using logarithmic differentiation, we have

$$\ln y = \ln(x^{\sin x})$$
$$= \sin x \ln x$$
$$\frac{y'}{y} = (\sin x) \frac{1}{x} + \cos x \ln x$$
$$y' = y \left[\frac{\sin x}{x} + \cos x \ln x \right]$$
$$y' = x^{\sin x} \left[\frac{\sin x}{x} + \cos x \ln x \right]$$

EXERCISE 8.6

B **1.**   Use logarithmic differentiation to find the derivative of each function.

(a) $y = (x^2 + 1)^2(x^2 + x + 1)^3$

(b) $y = (x - 1)^4(2x + 3)^5(x^2 - 2x + 3)^3$

(c) $y = e^{x^2}x^3(x^2 + 8)^4$

(d) $y = \dfrac{(x + 1)^3}{(x + 2)^5(x + 3)^7}$

(e) $y = \dfrac{x\sqrt{x + 1}}{(x + 2)(x^3 + 1)}$

(f) $y = \sqrt{\dfrac{x^2 + 1}{x^2 + 4}}$

2.   Differentiate.

(a) $y = x^{x^2}$

(b) $y = x^{\sqrt{x}}$

(c) $y = x^{\cos x}$

(d) $y = (\cos x)^x$

(e) $y = (\ln x)^x$

(f) $y = (\cos x)^{\sin x}$

3. Find the equation of the tangent line to the curve $y = x^x$ at the point $(2, 4)$.

C 4. Let $f(x) = x^{-\ln x}$.
   (a) Compute $\lim\limits_{x \to 0^+} x^{-\ln x}$ and $\lim\limits_{x \to \infty} x^{-\ln x}$ by writing
   $$x^{-\ln x} = (e^{\ln x})^{-\ln x} = e^{-(\ln x)^2}$$
   (b) Use logarithmic differentiation to find $f'(x)$.
   (c) Find the interval on which f is increasing or decreasing.
   (d) Find the absolute maximum value of f.
   (e) Find the intervals of concavity and inflection points.
   (f) Sketch the graph of f.

PROBLEMS PLUS

Solve the inequality

$$\log_2\left(1 + \frac{1}{x}\right) + \log_{\frac{1}{2}}(1 + x) \geq 1$$

8.7 REVIEW EXERCISE

1. Graph each function starting from the graphs of the basic exponential and logarithmic functions.
   (a) $y = 1 + 2^x$
   (b) $y = \log_{10}(x - 1)$
   (c) $y = \ln(-x)$
   (d) $y = e^{-x}$
   (e) $y = 1 - 10^x$
   (f) $y = -\log_2 x$

2. Evaluate.
   (a) $\lim\limits_{x \to -\infty} (1 + 2^x)$
   (b) $\lim\limits_{x \to 1^+} \log_{10}(x - 1)$
   (c) $\lim\limits_{x \to \infty} \ln(x^2 + x + 1)$
   (d) $\lim\limits_{x \to -1^-} e^{\frac{2}{x+1}}$
   (e) $\lim\limits_{x \to \frac{\pi}{2}^-} e^{\tan x}$
   (f) $\lim\limits_{x \to 10^-} \ln(10 - x)$

3. Find the domain, range, and asymptote of the following functions.
   (a) $y = 1 + \ln(x + 2)$
   (b) $y = 1 + 3e^{2x}$
   (c) $y = 10 - e^{-x}$
   (d) $y = \ln(1 - 2x)$

4. Evaluate.
   (a) $\ln 1$
   (b) $e^{\ln 10}$
   (b) $e^{3 \ln 2}$
   (d) $\ln\left(\frac{1}{e}\right)$

5. Solve each equation. State your answer exactly and also correct to six decimal places.
   (a) $\ln x = \frac{1}{2}$
   (b) $e^x = 7$
   (c) $e^{5 - 3x} = 2$
   (d) $\ln(4x + 7) = 4$

6. Express as a single logarithm.
   (a) $2 \ln x + 3 \ln(1 + x) - 4 \ln(2 + x)$
   (b) $\frac{1}{2} \ln x - 2 \ln(x^2 + x + 1)$

7. Differentiate.
   (a) $f(x) = \ln(x^2 + 1)$
   (b) $f(x) = e^{x^3}$
   (c) $f(x) = \sqrt{x}\, e^x$
   (d) $f(x) = \dfrac{\ln x}{x^2}$
   (e) $y = x^4 - 4^x$
   (f) $y = \ln \sqrt{\dfrac{2x + 3}{4x - 5}}$
   (g) $y = \sin(e^{2x})$
   (h) $y = e^{2 \sin x}$
   (i) $y = \log_{10}(1 - x + x^3)$
   (j) $y = e^x \ln x$
   (k) $y = \dfrac{e^{x^2}}{x^2}$
   (l) $y = \sqrt{1 + (\ln x)^4}$

8. Find the equation of the tangent line to each curve at the given point.
   (a) $y = 2^x$, $(0, 1)$
   (b) $y = \dfrac{\ln x}{x}$, $(1, 0)$

9. If $f(x) = e^{-x} \cos 2x$, find $f''(0)$.

10. Use logarithmic differentiation to find the derivative of each function.
   (a) $y = x^5 e^x \sqrt{x^2 - x + 1}$
   (b) $y = \sqrt{x}^x$

11. On what intervals is the function $f(x) = 2x^2 - \ln x$ increasing or decreasing?

12. Find the absolute minimum value of the function $g(x) = e^x - x$.

13. Discuss each curve under the headings A–H of Section 5.5.
   (a) $y = e^x + e^{-2x}$
   (b) $y = \ln(1 + x^2)$

14. (a) Use the change of base formula and a calculator to evaluate $\log_2 93.5$ correct to six decimal places.
   (b) Use the change of base formula to show that
   $$\ln b = \frac{1}{\log_b e}$$
   Deduce that the formula for differentiating a logarithmic function can be written as
   $$\frac{d}{dx} \log_b x = \frac{1}{x} \log_b e$$

15. The initial size of a bacteria culture is 800. After 4 h there are 7200 bacteria.
   (a) Find the number of bacteria after t hours.
   (b) Find the number of bacteria after 6 h.
   (c) Find the rate of growth after 6 h.
   (d) When will the bacteria population reach 20 000?

16. Yeast in a sugar solution is growing at such a rate that 1 g becomes 1.2 g after 10 h.
   (a) Find the mass of the yeast after t hours.
   (b) Find the mass of the yeast after 24 h.
   (c) In what period of time does the mass double?

17. An isotope of lead, ^{214}Pb, has a half-life of 26.8 min. A sample of this isotope has a mass of 15 g.
   (a) Find the mass that remains after t minutes.
   (b) Find the mass that remains after an hour.
   (c) Find the rate of decrease after an hour.
   (d) How long would it take this sample to decay until its mass is 1 g?

18. (a) A sum of $5000 is invested at an interest rate of 8% per year. Find the amount due at the end of three years if the interest is compounded
   (i) annually   (ii) semiannually
   (iii) daily   (iv) continuously
   (b) How long would it take for the value of the investment to reach $8000 if the interest is compounded continuously?

PROBLEMS PLUS

Let $f(x) = \log_2(\log_3(\log_4 x))$.
(a) Find the domain of f.   (b) Find $f'(x)$.

8.8 CHAPTER 8 TEST

1. Draw the graphs of the functions $f(x) = e^x$ and $g(x) = \ln x$ using the same axes.

2. By applying transformations to your graph in Question 1, draw the graph of the function $y = 6 - e^{-x}$. Find the domain, range, and asymptote of this function.

3. Evaluate the following limits.

    (a) $\displaystyle\lim_{x \to 8^+} \ln(x - 8)$ (b) $\displaystyle\lim_{x \to \infty} e^{-x^2}$

4. Evaluate $e^{-2 \ln 3}$.

5. Find the exact solution of the equation $e^{1-2x} = 5$.

6. Differentiate.

    (a) $y = x^2 \ln(x^3 + 2x - 1)$ (b) $y = \dfrac{e^{4x}}{x^2 + 1}$

    (c) $y = e^{\tan \sqrt{x}}$ (d) $y = 2^{-\frac{1}{x}}$

    (e) $y = x^{x^3}$

7. A bacteria culture starts with 1000 bacteria and grows to a population of 7000 after an hour.

    (a) Find the size of the population after t hours.

    (b) Find the size of the population after 3 h.

    (c) Find the rate of growth of the population after 3 h.

    (d) When will the population reach 10 000?

8. How long does it take for an investment to double in value if the interest rate is 9% compounded continuously?

9. Discuss the curve $y = \ln(9 - x^2)$ under the following headings.

    (a) Domain

    (b) Intercepts

    (c) Symmetry

    (d) Asymptotes

    (e) Intervals of increase or decrease

    (f) Local maximum and minimum values

    (g) Concavity

    (h) Sketch of the curve

FOUNDERS OF CALCULUS

Leonhard Euler (1707–1783) was born in Basel, Switzerland, and studied there under Johann Bernoulli. He left Basel for the last time when he was twenty to assume a research position in St. Petersburg in Russia. Euler contributed new ideas in calculus, algebra, geometry, number theory, and probability. He also worked in many areas of applied mathematics, including acoustics, optics, astronomy, ship design, navigation, mechanics, statistics, and finance. He is the most prolific scientist ever; his *Collected Works* fill three or four rows of shelves in a university library. Much of his work was done after he became blind in one eye in 1735, and totally blind in 1766.

Mathematical notation owes much to Euler. For example, e, i, π and Σ, the summation symbol, were either invented or popularized by him through his many textbooks. These texts were written in Latin, German, or French but translated into all European languages. The three numbers just named are related by his famous formula:

$$e^{i\pi} + 1 = 0$$

which is a special case of

$$e^{ix} = \cos x + i \sin x$$

Euler competed with the Bernoullis in the solving of many problems. A problem that he solved, which they could not, was to evaluate the sum of the reciprocals of the squares of the natural numbers. By a very ingenious method, he proved

$$\sum_{n=1}^{\infty} \frac{1}{n^2} = \frac{\pi^2}{6}$$

We say that two natural numbers are *relatively prime* if they have no common divisor greater than one. Euler invented the function $\phi(n)$, called to this day *Euler's phi function*, which counts the number of natural numbers less than n and relatively prime to it. He proved

$$\lim_{n \to \infty} \frac{\phi(n)}{n} = \frac{6}{\pi^2}$$

We can restate this in probabilistic terms: the probability that two numbers chosen at random are relatively prime is

$$\frac{6}{\pi^2}$$

Euler was the first to show the deep interconnection between calculus (analysis) and number theory. His ideas still have an impact on these areas of mathematics.

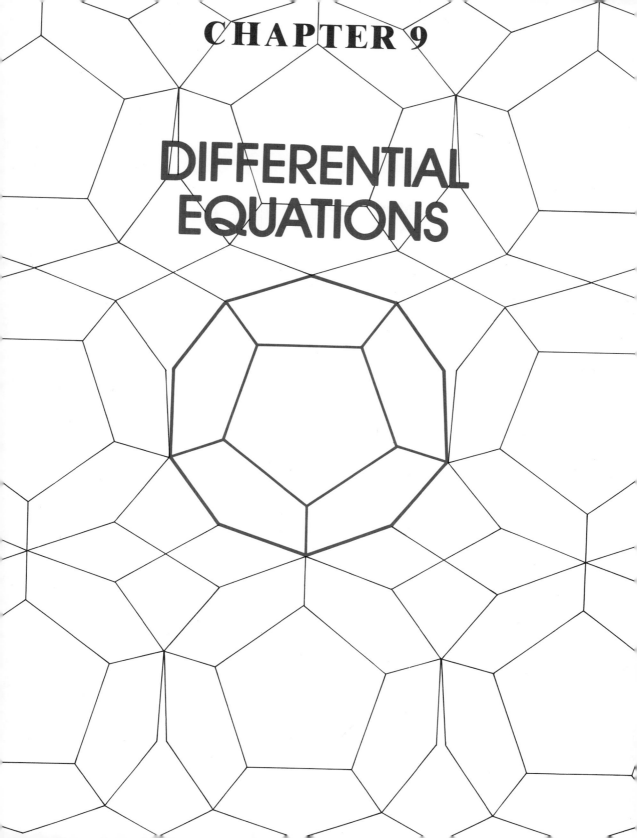

CHAPTER 9

DIFFERENTIAL EQUATIONS

REVIEW AND PREVIEW TO CHAPTER 9

Differentiation

EXERCISE 1

1. Find F'.
   (a) $F(x) = 1.6x^{10} - 1.8x^5 + 1.5x^2 + \pi$
   (b) $F(x) = 2.6x^{1.5} - 3.7x^{1.9} - 1$
   (c) $F(x) = -3 \ln x - \dfrac{5}{x} + 6$
   (d) $F(x) = \ln(2x + 7) + \sqrt{x - 3} + 11$
   (e) $F(x) = \dfrac{6}{x^2} - \dfrac{5}{x} + 3 \ln 4x^2 - 2$
   (f) $F(x) = -\frac{1}{2} \cos 2x + 2 \sin x + 8$
   (g) $F(x) = 7 \sin 3x - 11 \cos 7x + 13$
   (h) $F(x) = -4 \sin(x + 2) + 5 \cos(3x - 7) + 6$
   (i) $F(x) = \frac{1}{2}e^{2x} - \frac{1}{3}e^{-3x} + \frac{1}{4}e^{4x}$
   (j) $F(x) = -5e^{8x} + 2e^{-6x} - 37.1$
   (k) $F(x) = \sqrt{x} + \sqrt{1 - x}$
   (l) $F(x) = \ln(x - x^2)$
   (m) $F(x) = \ln\left(\dfrac{x^4}{(1 - x)^5}\right)$
   (n) $F(x) = 2e^{x^2} - 3e^{2x^2}$
   (o) $F(x) = \sin x \cos x$
   (p) $F(x) = \sqrt{x^2 + 1}$
   (q) $F(x) = \ln(x^3 + 6x + 7)$
   (r) $F(x) = \ln \cos x$

2. Find y''.
   (a) $y = 3 \cos 4x - 5 \sin 4x$ (b) $y = 2 \cos x + 7 \sin x$
   (c) $y = \cos \sqrt{2}x + 3 \sin \sqrt{2}x$ (d) $y = a \cos \sqrt{k}x + b \sin \sqrt{k}x$

INTRODUCTION

Many of the general laws of nature find their most useful form in equations that involve rates of change. These equations are called **differential equations** because they contain functions and their differential quotients. Some examples of differential equations are:

$$\frac{dy}{dx} = 2x \qquad \qquad ①$$

$$\frac{dv}{dt} = -9.8 \qquad \qquad ②$$

$$P' = 3P \qquad \qquad ③$$

In these equations we have to solve

Equation 1	Equation 2	Equation 3
for y in terms of x,	for v in terms of t,	for P in terms of t.

In the first three sections we deal with differential equations of the form $y' = f(x)$; solutions to these equations are called **antiderivatives** of $f(x)$. So we talk of finding antiderivatives as well as, or instead of, solving differential equations of the form $y' = f(x)$.

In the later sections we discuss differential equations that involve both the function and its derivative; Equation 3 is an example of this type and was seen previously in Section 8.5. The equations in these sections are used to solve cooling/warming problems, mixing problems, population processes, and cyclical (periodic) phenomena.

9.1 ANTIDERIVATIVES

A function F is an **antiderivative** of f on an interval if $F'(x) = f(x)$ for all x in that interval.

We consider the problem of finding all the antiderivatives of $f(x) = 2x$. Certainly $F(x) = x^2$ is an antiderivative of $2x$ since $\frac{dx^2}{dx} = 2x$, by the Power Rule. But $G(x) = x^2 + 1$, and $H(x) = x^2 - 4$ are also antiderivatives of $2x$. Indeed, for any constant C, $F(x) = x^2 + C$ is an antiderivative of $f(x) = 2x$.

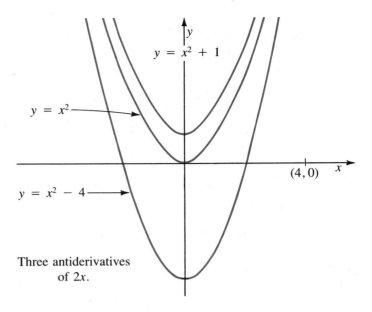

$y = x^2 + 1$

$y = x^2$

$(4, 0)$

$y = x^2 - 4$

Three antiderivatives
of $2x$.

In fact, every antiderivative of $2x$ is of the form $F(x) = x^2 + C$, for some constant C. For if $F'(x) = 2x$ then

$$y = F(x) - x^2$$

satisfies

$$y' = F'(x) - 2x$$
$$= 2x - 2x.$$

So $\quad y' = 0$

on an interval. It can be shown that in these circumstances

$$y = C$$

Hence, we have shown that

$$F(x) - x^2 = C$$
$$F(x) = x^2 + C$$

This shows that any two antiderivatives of $2x$ differ by a constant. This result is true in general.

If F is an antiderivative of f on an interval, then the most general antiderivative of f on that interval is

$$F(x) + C$$

where C is an arbitrary constant.

Example 1   Find the (most general) antiderivative of $f(x) = 4x^3 - 6x^2 + 11$ on the interval $(-\infty, \infty)$.

Solution   The result above tells us we need only find a single antiderivative of $4x^3 - 6x^2 + 11$; we can find all by adding an arbitrary constant.

Because the derivative of a sum is the sum of the derivatives, we look at each term in $4x^3 - 6x^2 + 11$ in order to find an antiderivative.

Now the derivative of x^4 is $4x^3$, the derivative of x^3 is $3x^2$, and the derivative of x is 1. So

$$x^4 \text{ is an antiderivative of } 4x^3$$
$$-2x^3 \text{ is an antiderivative of } -6x^2$$
$$11x \text{ is an antiderivative of } 11$$

Thus

$$F(x) = x^4 - 2x^3 + 11x + C$$

is the most general antiderivative of $f(x) = 4x^3 - 6x^2 + 11$ on the interval $(-\infty, \infty)$.

We see from this example that to find antiderivatives we use our knowledge of derivatives. In effect, we use differentiation tables backwards. Here is a table of commonly encountered antiderivatives.

Function	Particular antiderivative
0	1
1	x
$x^n \; (n \neq -1)$	$\dfrac{1}{n+1}x^{n+1}$
$\dfrac{1}{x}$	$\ln\lvert x \rvert$
$e^{kx} \; (k \neq 0)$	$\dfrac{1}{k}e^{kx}$
$\cos kx \; (k \neq 0)$	$\dfrac{1}{k}\sin kx$
$\sin kx \; (k \neq 0)$	$-\dfrac{1}{k}\cos kx$

Example 2   Find the antiderivative of f.
(a) $f(x) = 2x^2 - x + 7$ (b) $f(x) = \cos x - \sin x$
(c) $f(x) = -3e^{-x} + 6e^{2x}$

Solution   We use the table above.

(a)
$$F(x) = 2\left(\tfrac{1}{3}x^3\right) - \left(\tfrac{1}{2}x^2\right) + 7(x) + C$$
$$= \tfrac{2}{3}x^3 - \tfrac{1}{2}x^2 + 7x + C$$

(b) $F(x) = \sin x - (-\cos x) + C$
$$= \sin x + \cos x + C$$

(c) $F(x) = -3\left(\dfrac{1}{-1}e^{-x}\right) + 6\left(\dfrac{1}{2}e^{2x}\right) + C$
$$= 3e^{-x} + 3e^{2x} + C$$

Example 3   Find the antiderivative of f on the interval $(0, \infty)$.

(a) $f(x) = \dfrac{2}{x^2} - \dfrac{5}{x} + x$ (b) $f(x) = \sin x + \dfrac{1}{x^3}$

Solution   (a) We rewrite f in a form suitable for using the table.

$$f(x) = 2x^{-2} - 5\left(\dfrac{1}{x}\right) + x$$

So $F(x) = 2\left(\dfrac{1}{-2+1}x^{-2+1}\right) - 5\ln|x| + \tfrac{1}{2}x^2 + C$

$$= -2x^{-1} - 5\ln|x| + \tfrac{1}{2}x^2 + C$$

Since we are considering the problem on the interval $(0, \infty)$, we have $|x| = x$, so

$$F(x) = -\dfrac{2}{x} - 5\ln x + \tfrac{1}{2}x^2 + C$$

is the most general antiderivative of f on $(0, \infty)$.

(b) Since $f(x) = \sin x + \dfrac{1}{x^3}$ we can write $f(x) = \sin x + x^{-3}$. So the antiderivative of f is

$$F(x) = -\cos x + \dfrac{1}{-3+1}x^{-3+1} + C$$

$$= -\cos x - \dfrac{1}{2x^2} + C$$

We end this section by considering an example where the antiderivative occurs in many equivalent forms.

Example 4   Find the most general antiderivative of $f(x) = \sin x \cos x$.

Solution 1   Since $\cos x = \dfrac{d}{dx}\sin x$ we see that

$$f(x) = \sin x \dfrac{d}{dx}\sin x$$

Hence,

$$F(x) = \tfrac{1}{2}\sin^2 x + C_1$$

as is easily verified. Here C_1 is an arbitrary constant.

Solution 2   Since $\sin x = -\dfrac{d}{dx}\cos x$ we see that

$$f(x) = -\cos x \dfrac{d}{dx}\cos x$$

Hence,

$$F(x) = -\tfrac{1}{2}\cos^2 x + C_2$$

is the most general antiderivative on $(-\infty, \infty)$.

Solution 3   Since $\sin x \cos x = \tfrac{1}{2}\sin 2x$, we have from the table that

$$F(x) = \tfrac{1}{2}\left(-\tfrac{1}{2}\cos 2x\right) + C_3$$

is the most general antiderivative of f.

Let us look more closely at these seemingly different answers. First we sketch the antiderivatives corresponding to $C_1 = C_2 = 0$ in Solutions 1 and 2.

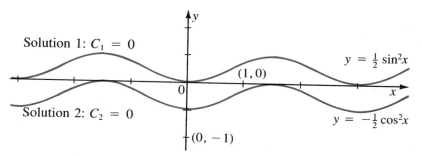

We see that the graphs are a constant vertical distance apart. So the curves have parallel tangent lines, and thus have identical slopes at points whose x-coordinates are the same.

Algebraically, we see that

$$\tfrac{1}{2}\sin^2 x + C_1 = \tfrac{1}{2}(1 - \cos^2 x) + C_1$$
$$= -\tfrac{1}{2}\cos^2 x + \tfrac{1}{2} + C_1$$

So the arbitrary constants in Solutions 1 and 2 are related by

$$\tfrac{1}{2} + C_1 = C_2$$

Similarly, the constants in Solutions 2 and 3 are related by

$$-\tfrac{1}{4} + C_2 = C_3$$

(A proof of this is requested in the Exercise.)

EXERCISE 9.1

B 1. Find the most general antiderivative of the given function on the interval $(-\infty, \infty)$.

(a) $f(x) = 2x + 1$ (b) $f(x) = 4x^3 - 11$
(c) $f(x) = 16x^9 - 9x^4 + 3x$ (d) $f(x) = x^7 + x^5 + x^3 + x$

2. Find the antiderivative of f on $(0, \infty)$.

(a) $f(x) = \dfrac{2}{x^7} + \dfrac{x^5}{2}$ (b) $f(x) = \sqrt{x} + \sqrt[3]{x}$

(c) $f(x) = \dfrac{-3}{x} + \dfrac{5}{x^2}$ (d) $f(x) = \dfrac{1}{x^7} + \dfrac{1}{x^5} + \dfrac{1}{x^3} + \dfrac{1}{x}$

3. Find the antiderivative of f on $(-\infty, 0)$.

(a) $f(x) = \dfrac{1}{x}$ (b) $f(x) = \dfrac{2}{x^3} - \dfrac{3}{x^2}$

(c) $f(x) = \sqrt{-x}$ (d) $f(x) = \dfrac{1}{x^4} + x^3 + \dfrac{1}{x^2}$

4. Find the antiderivative of f on $(-\infty, \infty)$.

(a) $f(x) = \sin 2x + 2 \cos x$ (b) $f(x) = -3 \cos 5x + 8 \sin x$
(c) $f(x) = 7 \cos x - 11 \sin 11x$ (d) $f(x) = -4 \cos(x + 2)$

5. Find the most general antiderivative of f on $(-\infty, \infty)$.

(a) $f(x) = e^x + e^{-x}$ (b) $f(x) = e^x - e^{-x}$
(c) $f(x) = 4e^{2x} - 6e^{-3x}$ (d) $f(x) = e^x - e^{-2x} + e^{3x}$

6. Find the antiderivative of f on $(0, 1)$.

(a) $f(x) = \sqrt{x} - \sqrt{1 - x}$ (b) $f(x) = \dfrac{1}{x} - \dfrac{1}{1 - x}$

(c) $f(x) = \dfrac{1}{\sqrt{1 - x}} + \dfrac{1}{\sqrt{x}}$ (d) $f(x) = \dfrac{4}{x} + \dfrac{5}{1 - x}$

7. Find the antiderivative of f on $(-\infty, \infty)$.

(a) $f(x) = xe^{x^2}$ (b) $f(x) = \sin^2 x \cos x$

(c) $f(x) = \dfrac{2x}{x^2 + 1}$ (d) $f(x) = \dfrac{x}{\sqrt{x^2 + 1}}$

C 8. Find the most general antiderivative of f on the indicated interval.

(a) $f(x) = \dfrac{1}{x^2 + 1}$ on $(-\infty, \infty)$

(b) $f(x) = -\tan x$ on $\left(-\dfrac{\pi}{2}, \dfrac{\pi}{2}\right)$

(c) $f(x) = \sec x \tan x$ on $\left(-\dfrac{\pi}{2}, \dfrac{\pi}{2}\right)$

(d) $f(x) = e^{\ln x}$ on $(0, \infty)$

9. Prove that the constants C_2 of Solution 2 and C_3 of Solution 3 in Example 4 are related by $C_3 = C_2 - \frac{1}{4}$.

10. Let $F(x) = \begin{cases} \ln|x| + 3 & \text{if } x > 0 \\ \ln|x| - 7 & \text{if } x < 0 \end{cases}$

(a) Show that $F'(x) = \dfrac{1}{x}$ for all $x \neq 0$.

(b) Show that there is no constant C such that $F(x) = \ln|x| + C$ for all $x \neq 0$.

(c) Deduce that it is not true that the most general antiderivative of $F'(x) = f(x)$ is of the form $F(x) + C$ for an arbitrary constant.

(d) Show that part (c) does not contradict our statement about the most general antiderivative being of the form $F(x) + C$.

9.2 DIFFERENTIAL EQUATIONS WITH INITIAL CONDITIONS

In the applications of differential equations in this chapter, we often deal with time-dependent processes where information is available at specific instants, usually the initial instant, $t = 0$.

Example 1 Solve $\dfrac{ds}{dt} = 2t$, with the initial condition: $s = 3$ when $t = 0$.

Solution We see that $s = t^2 + C$ is the most general antiderivative of $2t$, using the results of Section 9.1. We want the particular solution that has the value 3 when $t = 0$. So we set

$$3 = 0^2 + C$$

Thus, $C = 3$ and

$$s = t^2 + 3$$

is the desired solution.

This example is typical in that the initial condition specifies a particular value of the arbitrary constant in the most general antiderivative.

Sometimes conditions on differential equations are specified geometrically.

Example 2 Find the curve $y = F(x)$ that passes through $(-1, 0)$ and satisfies $\dfrac{dy}{dx} = 6x^2 + 6x$.

Solution Since $\dfrac{dy}{dx} = F'(x)$, we see that

$$F'(x) = 6x^2 + 6x,$$

and the most general antiderivative is

$$F(x) = 2x^3 + 3x^2 + C$$

Now $F(-1) = 0$ since $(-1, 0)$ is on $y = F(x)$, so

$$0 = 2(-1)^3 + 3(-1)^2 + C$$

Thus $C = -1$ and $y = 2x^3 + 3x^2 - 1$

is the desired curve.

The diagram shows three curves satisfying $\dfrac{dy}{dx} = 6x^2 + 6x$ with the particular curve that passes through $(-1, 0)$ shown in red.

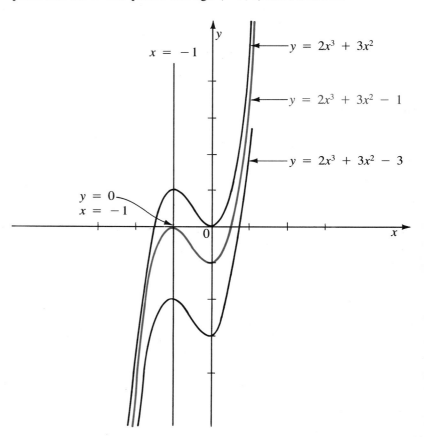

We say that the graphs $y = F(x)$ and $y = G(x)$ are **parallel** if there is a constant vertical distance between points with the same x-coordinate: in symbols

$$F(x) - G(x) = C$$

for all x.

If graphs are parallel, their tangent lines are parallel because they have the same slope.

Example 3 Suppose for the graph G that at every point

$$\frac{dy}{dx} = e^{-x}$$

Find the equation of a graph parallel to G that passes through the origin.

Solution From $\dfrac{dy}{dx} = e^{-x}$, we deduce that

$$y = -e^{-x} + C$$

is the most general antiderivative. So every graph parallel to G has an equation of the form $y = -e^{-x} + C$ for a suitable constant C. The graph we seek passes through $(0, 0)$, so substituting $x = 0$, $y = 0$ we obtain

$$0 = -e^0 + C$$

Since $e^0 = 1$, we have $C = 1$ and the desired graph has the equation $y = 1 - e^{-x}$.

EXERCISE 9.2

B **1.** Solve the differential equation $\dfrac{dy}{dx} = 4x - 3$ with the initial condition
 (a) $y = 0$ when $x = 0$ (b) $y = -1$ when $x = 0$
 (c) $y = 2$ when $x = -1$ (d) $y = 0$ when $x = 3$

2. Solve the differential equation with the initial condition $s = 0$ when $t = 0$.
 (a) $\dfrac{ds}{dt} = 9.8t$ (b) $\dfrac{ds}{dt} = t^3 - t$

 (c) $\dfrac{ds}{dt} = \sin t$ (d) $\dfrac{ds}{dt} = e^{0.1t}$

3. Find the function F given that the point $(2, 3)$ is on the graph $y = F(x)$.
 (a) $F'(x) = 3x^2 - 2x + 6$ (b) $F'(x) = 3\sqrt{2x}$
 (c) $F'(x) = 2e^{\frac{x}{2}}$ (d) $F'(x) = \sqrt{x} - \sqrt{4 - x}$

4. The slope of the tangent to the graph G is given at each point. Find the equation of a graph parallel to G that passes through the origin.
 (a) $\dfrac{dy}{dx} = \cos x + \sin x$ (b) $\dfrac{dy}{dx} = e^x + e^{-x}$

 (c) $\dfrac{dy}{dx} = \dfrac{1}{\sqrt{x + 1}}$ (d) $\dfrac{dy}{dx} = x(x^2 + 1)$

5. The line $x + y = 0$ is tangent to the graph of $y = F(x)$. Find $F(x)$ if

   (a) $F'(x) = x$ (b) $F'(x) = x^3$

   (c) $F'(x) = -x^5$ (d) $F'(x) = -1$

6. Find an equation for a graph parallel to $y = e^x$ that has $y = 4$ as a horizontal asymptote.

C 7. The lines $x + y = 0$ and $x + y = \frac{4}{3}$ are tangent to the graph of $y = F(x)$ where F is an antiderivative of $-x^2$. Find F.

8. Using double angle formulas solve:

   (a) $\dfrac{ds}{dt} = \cos^2 t - \sin^2 t$; $s = 1$ when $t = \dfrac{\pi}{4}$

   (b) $\dfrac{ds}{dt} = \sin^2 t$; $s = 0$ when $t = \dfrac{\pi}{2}$

9.3 PROBLEMS INVOLVING MOTION

In this section we study the problem of determining the motion of a particle along a straight line path under the action of predetermined forces.

We use the variables t for time, s for displacement, and v for velocity, as we did in Chapter 3.

Example 1   If a body moves so that its velocity is proportional to the time elapsed, then $v = at$ where a is constant. Show that $v^2 = 2as$.

Solution   Since $v = \dfrac{ds}{dt}$, and $v = at$ we have the differential equation

$$\frac{ds}{dt} = at$$

Thus, s is an antiderivative of at and so

$$s = \tfrac{1}{2}at^2 + C$$

for some constant C.

Since $s = 0$ when $t = 0$, by the way s, t are defined, we have

$$0 = \tfrac{1}{2}a(0)^2 + C$$

Hence $C = 0$, and we deduce that

$$s = \tfrac{1}{2}at^2$$

Multiplying this equation by $2a$ we obtain the desired form:

$$2as = 2a\left(\tfrac{1}{2}at^2\right)$$
$$2as = (at)^2$$
$$2as = v^2$$

Example 2   A particle is accelerated in a line so that its velocity in metres per second is equal to the square root of the time elapsed, measured in seconds. How far does the particle travel in the first hour?

Solution   We are told that

$$v = \sqrt{t}$$

So $$\frac{ds}{dt} = \sqrt{t} = t^{\frac{1}{2}}$$

and $$s = \tfrac{2}{3}t^{\frac{3}{2}} + C$$

When $t = 0$ we have $s = 0$, so substituting, we obtain

$$0 = \tfrac{2}{3}(0) + C$$

Thus $C = 0$ and it follows that

$$s = \tfrac{2}{3}t^{\frac{3}{2}}$$

Since $\dfrac{ds}{dt} > 0$,

distance
= displacement

We are asked to find s when $t = 1$ h $= 3600$ s, so we substitute

$$s = \tfrac{2}{3}(3600)^{\frac{3}{2}} = \tfrac{2}{3}60^3 = 144\ 000$$

The particle travels 144 000 m, that is, 144 km, in the first hour.

Next we consider a problem where we do not choose the standard variables s, t.

Example 3   A stone is tossed upward with a velocity of 8 m/s from the edge of a cliff 63 m high. How long will it take the stone to hit the ground at the foot of the cliff?

Solution   We let h denote the height, in metres, of the stone above the ground at time t, and we let $v = \dfrac{dh}{dt}$ denote its velocity.

Since gravity is the force acting on the stone we have

$$\frac{dv}{dt} = -9.8$$

where 9.8 m/s² is the gravitational constant near the surface of the earth. We see that v is an antiderivative of -9.8 so

$$v = -9.8t + C_1$$

for some constant C_1. Since we are told that the stone is tossed upward at the initial instant with a velocity of 8 m/s, we can substitute $v = 8$, $t = 0$ to deduce

$$8 = -9.8(0) + C_1$$

This shows that $C_1 = 8$, and consequently

$$v = -9.8t + 8$$

We rewrite this expression for v as a differential equation for h:

$$\frac{dh}{dt} = -9.8t + 8$$

From this we deduce that h is an antiderivative of $-9.8t + 8$, so

$$h = -4.9t^2 + 8t + C_2$$

for a suitable constant C_2. Since $h = 63$ when $t = 0$,

$$63 = -4.9(0^2) + 8(0) + C_2$$

Thus $C_2 = 63$ and so

$$h = -4.9t^2 + 8t + 63$$

We can now answer the question. The stone hits the ground when t is such that $h = 0$. So we solve the quadratic equation

$$-4.9t^2 + 8t + 63 = 0$$

From the quadratic formula we obtain the roots

$$t = \frac{-8 + \sqrt{8^2 - 4(-4.9)(63)}}{-9.8} \doteq -2.86$$

and $\qquad t = \dfrac{-8 - \sqrt{1298.8}}{-9.8} \doteq 4.49$

Because the negative root has no physical significance in this problem, we see that about 4.5 s after being tossed up the stone hits the ground.

EXERCISE 9.3

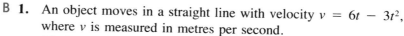

B **1.** An object moves in a straight line with velocity $v = 6t - 3t^2$, where v is measured in metres per second.
   (a) How far does the object move in the first second?
   (b) How far does the object move in the first two seconds?
   (c) The object is back where it started when $t = 3$. How far did it travel to get there?

2. A canister is dropped from a helicopter hovering 500 m above the ground. Unfortunately its parachute does not open. It has been designed to withstand an impact velocity of 100 m/s. Will it burst or not?

3. A stone is tossed down, with a speed of 8 m/s, from the edge of a cliff 63 m high. How long will it take the stone to hit the ground at the foot of the cliff?

4. A pebble is tossed upward at 5 m/s from the roof of a building 80 m high. When will it hit the ground?

5. Margaret has found that by a proper choice of gears she can steadily increase her speed on her bicycle. One day she sets out and, ten minutes later, she achieves her cruising speed of 30 km/h by increasing her speed steadily. How far did she travel in that ten minutes?

6. Since raindrops grow as they fall, their surface area increases and therefore the resistance to their falling increases. A raindrop has an initial downward speed of 10 m/s and its downward acceleration a is given by
$$a = \begin{cases} 9 - 0.9t & 0 \leqslant t \leqslant 10 \\ 0 & t > 10 \end{cases}$$
   (a) How far does the raindrop fall in the first 10 seconds?
   (b) What is the velocity of the raindrop after 1 s?
   (c) If the raindrop is initially 600 m above the ground, how long does it take to fall?

C **7.** A cliff is h_0 m high. A stone is tossed off the cliff with a velocity of v_0 m/s. Thus if the stone is tossed up, v_0 is positive. How long does it take the stone to reach the ground?

9.4 THE LAW OF NATURAL GROWTH

We saw in Section 8.5 that the differential equation

$$\frac{dy}{dx} = ky$$

corresponds to exponential growth if k is positive, and exponential decay if k is negative. We also saw that the solutions to the differential equation are easily described.

> The most general solution of
>
> $$\frac{dy}{dx} = ky$$
>
> is given by
>
> $$y = Ce^{kx}$$
>
> where C is an arbitrary constant.

Example 1   The population of bacteria grown in a culture follows the law of natural growth, with a growth rate of 15% per hour. If there are 10 000 bacteria present initially, how many will there be after four hours?

Solution   Let P denote the number of bacteria at time t. Then

$$\frac{dP}{dt} = kP$$

since we are assuming the law of natural growth. Now $k = \dfrac{1}{P}\dfrac{dP}{dt}$ is the per capita growth rate, and we are told that $k = 15\% = 0.15$, so

$$\frac{dP}{dt} = 0.15P$$

The general solution of this differential equation is

$$P = Ce^{0.15t}$$

for a suitable constant C.

Initially, when $t = 0$, $P = 10\ 000$, so

$$10\ 000 = Ce^{0}$$

Hence $C = 10\ 000$ and we see that

$$P = 10\ 000e^{0.15t}$$

We can now answer the question as to how many bacteria there are after four hours by substituting $t = 4$ in the expresson for P:

$$P = 10\ 000e^{0.15(4)} \doteq 18\ 000$$

There will be approximately 18 000 bacteria present after four hours.

The law of natural growth occurs in many contexts; here is one.

Newton's Law of Cooling

The rate at which a hot body cools to the temperature of its surroundings is proportional to the temperature difference between the body and its surroundings.

This law says, for example, that a cup of tea at 60° above its surroundings cools degree by degree twice as rapidly as when it is 30° above its surroundings.

Example 2   Suppose a hot body is initially at temperature T_0, while the surroundings are at temperature A. Using Newton's Law of Cooling, find a formula for the temperature T, at an arbitrary instant, in terms of the time t and the constants T_0 and A.

Solution   Newton's Law of Cooling can be stated as a differential equation:

$$\frac{dT}{dt} = k(T - A)$$

This is almost the law of natural growth, except that we have T related to $T - A$. But A is constant, so $\dfrac{dA}{dt} = 0$.

Hence
$$\frac{d(T - A)}{dt} = \frac{dT}{dt} - \frac{dA}{dt}$$
$$= \frac{dT}{dt} - 0$$
$$\frac{d(T - A)}{dt} = k(T - A)$$

Thus, the variable $T - A$ obeys the law of natural growth. Consequently, there is a constant C such that

$$T - A = Ce^{kt}$$

In order to evaluate C, we use the fact that $T = T_0$ when $t = 0$:

$$T_0 - A = Ce^0$$

Hence $C = T_0 - A$ and

$$T - A = (T_0 - A)e^{kt}$$

So the formula is

$$\boxed{T = A + (T_0 - A)e^{kt}}$$

We observe that in the formula just given there are *three* constants:

A is the temperature of the surroundings
T_0 is the initial temperature of the body
k is a characteristic of the material of the body

We consider a numerical example to show how A, T_0, and k are determined from the given information.

Example 3   In a steel mill, rod steel at 900°C is cooled by forced air at a temperature of 20°C. The temperature of the steel after one second is 400°C. When will the steel reach a temperature of 40°C?

Solution   Let T denote the temperature in °C of the steel t seconds after encountering the forced air. Then

$$T = A + (T_0 - A)e^{kt}$$

by Newton's Law of Cooling. Since A is the temperature of the surroundings, in this case the forced air, we have $A = 20$. Since T_0 is the initial temperature of the steel, we have $T_0 = 900$. Hence,

$$T = 20 + (900 - 20)e^{kt}$$
$$T = 20 + 880e^{kt}$$

We only need to determine k: this is done by using the fact that $T = 400$ when $t = 1$. Substituting we have

$$400 = 20 + 880e^{k(1)}$$
$$380 = 880e^{k}$$
$$e^{k} = \frac{380}{880}$$

Taking natural logarithms we have

$$k = \ln\left(\frac{380}{880}\right) \doteq -0.84.$$

Hence

$$T \doteq 20 + 880e^{-0.84t}$$

We can now answer the question: find t when $T = 40$. Now we have

$$40 \doteq 20 + 880e^{-0.84t}$$

so

$$e^{-0.84t} \doteq \frac{40 - 20}{880}$$

Taking natural logarithms we obtain

$$-0.84t \doteq \ln\left(\frac{20}{880}\right)$$
$$-0.84t \doteq -3.78$$
$$t \doteq 4.5$$

Thus, in 4.5 s the temperature of the steel is about 40°C.

In our last example we see how to use three temperatures of the body, at distinct times, to find the temperature of the surroundings.

Example 4   On a hot day a thermometer is taken outside from an air-conditioned room where the temperature is 20°C. After one minute it reads 26°C and after two minutes it reads 29°C. What is the outdoor temperature?

Solution   Let T denote the reading on the thermometer t minutes after it has been taken outdoors. Then, by Newton's Law of Cooling (in this case *Warming*)

$$T = A + (T_0 - A)e^{kt}$$

We know that the initial reading T_0 is 20, so

$$T = A + (20 - A)e^{kt}$$

Next we use our knowledge of T when $t = 1$ and $t = 2$:

$$26 = A + (20 - A)e^{k(1)}$$
$$29 = A + (20 - A)e^{k(2)}$$

Therefore

$$26 - A = (20 - A)e^k \qquad \qquad ①$$
$$29 - A = (20 - A)e^{2k} \qquad \qquad ②$$

Keeping in mind that we want to determine A, we eliminate k from these equations by squaring Equation 1 to obtain the term e^{2k} that occurs in Equation 2. Thus

$$(26 - A)^2 = (20 - A)^2 e^{2k} \qquad \qquad ③$$

Now dividing Equation 3 by Equation 2 gives

$$\frac{(26 - A)^2}{29 - A} = \frac{(20 - A)^2 e^{2k}}{(20 - A)e^{2k}}$$

$$\frac{(26 - A)^2}{29 - A} = 20 - A$$

$$(26 - A)^2 = (29 - A)(20 - A)$$

$$26^2 - 52A + A^2 = 29(20) - 49A + A^2$$

$$-3A = 580 - 676$$

$$A = 32$$

Hence the outdoor temperature is 32°C.

EXERCISE 9.4

B **1.**   Annette buys an investment certificate for $1000 that yields 6.25% (continuously compounded) per year. For how much will she redeem this certificate five years from now?

2.   The population of a town is following the law of natural growth, with a growth rate of 1.6% per annum. A new sewage treatment plant must be in place before the population doubles. How long does the town have to build the plant?

3.   In a certain forest there are two species of moth, grey and black. Presently there are twice as many grey as black, but the intrinsic growth rate of the black moth is 4% per month, while that of the grey is only 3% per month. In how many months will there be twice as many black as grey?

4.   A metal ball is heated to a temperature of 100°C and then immersed in water that is maintained at 10°C. After one second the temperature of the ball is 25°C.
   (a)   How long after immersion did the ball have a temperature of 50°C?
   (b)   When will the ball's temperature be 12°C?

5.   A thermometer reading −7°C is brought into a room kept at 23°C. Half a minute later the thermometer reads 8°C. What is the temperature reading of the thermometer after three minutes?

6.   A pie is removed from a 175°C oven. The room temperature is 24°C. How long will it take the pie to cool to 37°C (body temperature) if it cooled 60° in the first four minutes?

7.   On a hot day (35°C) a thermometer is taken from a cool room. After one minute outdoors it reads 29°C and after a further minute it reads 32°C. What is the temperature of the room?

C **8.** (The learning curve.) Psychologists have found that people initially learn a new subject rapidly and then slow down. A possible model for this can be formulated as follows. Suppose that M is the total amount of new knowledge that a person can learn and A is the amount learned up to time t. Then the rate of change of A is proportional to the amount still left to learn.

(a) State a differential equation that expresses the relationship stated.

(b) Solve this differential equation with the initial condition that $A = 0$ when $t = 0$.

(c) Suppose Jim can memorize 40 syllables in a row in an hour but he cannot learn 41 syllables in a row even if given a whole day. Suppose further that Jim learns 13 syllables in the first five minutes. How long does it take him to learn 36 syllables?

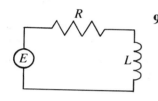

9. The varying current I in a circuit containing only a constant resistance R and an inductance L (also constant) in series with a constant voltage E is governed by $L\dfrac{dI}{dt} + RI = E$. Solve this differential equation if $I = 0$ when $t = 0$.

9.5 MIXING PROBLEMS

In this section we see how to formulate a differential equation for a **mixing process**.

Example 1   A tank contains 100 L of salt water, at a salt concentration of 15 g/L. Water containing 23 g/L of salt is pumped in at a rate of 3 L/min and the mixture, being steadily stirred, is pumped out of the tank at the same rate.

(a) Write a differential equation relating the amount of salt in the tank to the time.

(b) Find the general solution of this differential equation.

(c) Find a formula for the amount of salt in the tank at time t.

(d) Determine how much salt is in the tank after one hour.

Solution   (a) We introduce variables to describe the process. Let A denote the amount (in grams) of salt present t minutes after the process began. We want to express A as a function of t.

In order to write a differential equation, we need to make a statement about what is happening *instantaneously*. So we see what changes occur over a short time interval, then take the limit.

Let ΔA denote the change in the amount of salt in the tank during the brief time interval Δt. Now

$$\Delta A = [\text{salt in}] - [\text{salt out}]$$

so to estimate ΔA we need to estimate the quantities [salt in] and [salt out].

First,

$$\begin{aligned} \text{[salt in]} &= \text{[volume of water in]} \times \text{[concentration of salt]} \\ &= \text{[rate of water in]} \times \Delta t \times \text{[concentration of salt]} \\ &= 3 \times \Delta t \times 23 \end{aligned}$$

Before going on, we check units:

$$\text{g} = \frac{\text{L}}{\text{min}} \times \text{min} \times \frac{\text{g}}{\text{L}}$$

Next,

$$\begin{aligned} \text{[salt out]} &= \text{[volume of water out]} \times \text{[concentration of salt]} \\ &= \text{[rate of water out]} \times \Delta t \times \text{[concentration of salt]} \\ &= 3 \times \Delta t \times \text{[concentration of salt going out]} \end{aligned}$$

Now, we do not know the concentration of the salt leaving the tank because it depends on the amount of salt in the tank; and that is what we are trying to determine. However, we can say that the amount of salt present during the brief time interval Δt does not change much from the amount A present at the beginning of the interval. Thus,

$$\text{[concentration of salt going out]} \doteq \frac{A}{100}$$

where 100 L is the volume of the tank.

We have shown that

$$\text{[salt out]} \doteq 3 \times \Delta t \times \frac{A}{100}$$

Once again we check units:

$$\text{g} = \frac{\text{L}}{\text{min}} \times \text{min} \times \frac{\text{g}}{\text{L}}$$

Returning to ΔA we have

$$\Delta A \doteq 3 \times \Delta t \times 23 - 3 \times \Delta t \times \frac{A}{100}$$

$$\frac{\Delta A}{\Delta t} \doteq 69 - \frac{3}{100}A$$

In the limit as Δt tends to 0 we get

$$\lim_{\Delta t \to 0} \frac{\Delta A}{\Delta t} = \frac{dA}{dt}$$

and

$$\lim_{\Delta t \to 0} \left(69 - \frac{3A}{100}\right) = 69 - \frac{3A}{100}$$

Thus we arrive at the differential equation

$$\frac{dA}{dt} = 69 - \frac{3A}{100} \tag{1}$$

(b)   In order to solve this differential equation we write it in a more easily solved form, motivated by our approach to the equation arising in Newton's Law of Cooling in Section 9.4.

From
$$\frac{dA}{dt} = \frac{-3}{100}(A - 2300)$$

we deduce that
$$\frac{d(A - 2300)}{dt} = \frac{-3}{100}(A - 2300)$$

Hence, there is a constant C such that

$$A - 2300 = Ce^{-\frac{3t}{100}} \qquad ②$$

is the general solution of Equation 1.

(c)   To find a formula for A we determine the constant C. At time $t = 0$ the tank contains

$$100 \text{ L} \times 15 \frac{\text{g}}{\text{L}} = 1500 \text{ g}$$

of salt. Substituting these values in Equation 2 we have

$$1500 - 2300 = Ce^0$$

so $C = -800$. Thus the formula is

$$A - 2300 = -800e^{-0.03t}$$
$$A = 2300 - 800e^{-0.03t} \qquad ③$$

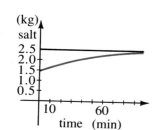

(kg) salt

(d)   To find out how much salt is in the tank after one hour we substitute $t = 60$ in Equation 3:

$$A = 2300 - 800e^{-0.03(60)}$$
$$\doteq 2300 - 800(0.165)$$
$$\doteq 2170$$

There are approximately 2170 g of salt in the tank after one hour.

Next we look at a different type of situation that still fits a "mixing" treatment.

Example 2   George has a savings account with a balance of $4500. This account earns 6% interest a year, compounded daily. He plans to withdraw $30 each week for the three years he attends college. What will his bank balance be when he graduates?

Solution   The processes here are not continuous: the interest is added daily and the withdrawals are weekly. However, we can get a very good approximation by assuming continuity.

Let B denote the balance (in $) of George's account at time t (in years). Then $\frac{dB}{dt} =$ [rate money in] $-$ [rate money out]. Now the rate at which money comes in depends on the balance B. Since we can approximate daily interest by continuously compounded interest, we have

$$[\text{rate money in}] \doteq 0.06B$$

Next,

$$[\text{rate money out}] = 52 \times 30 = 1560$$

Thus we have shown that

$$\frac{dB}{dt} = 0.06B - 1560 \qquad \text{①}$$

is a reasonable differential equation for this process.

In order to solve this equation we rewrite it as

$$\frac{dB}{dt} = 0.06(B - 26\ 000)$$

$$\frac{d(B - 26\ 000)}{dt} = 0.06(B - 26\ 000)$$

$$B - 26\ 000 = Ce^{0.06t}$$

$$B = 26\ 000 + Ce^{0.06t} \qquad \text{②}$$

Now $B = 4500$ when $t = 0$, so we can determine C:

$$4500 = 26\ 000 + Ce^0$$

Hence $C = -21\ 500$, and we deduce that

$$B = 26\ 000 - 21\ 500e^{0.06t} \qquad \text{③}$$

When George graduates $t = 3$, and his bank balance is found by substituting $t = 3$ in Equation 3.

$$\begin{aligned} B &= 26\ 000 - 21\ 500e^{0.06(3)} \\ &\doteq 26\ 000 - 21\ 500(1.197) \\ &\doteq 260 \end{aligned}$$

When he graduates, George will have about \$260 in his bank account.

EXERCISE 9.5

B 1. Twenty kilograms of salt is dissolved in a tank holding 1000 L of water. A brine solution is pumped into the tank at a rate of eight litres per minute and the well-stirred solution flows out at the same rate. If the brine entering the tank has a concentration of 100 g/L determine
   (a) the amount of salt present after one hour, and
   (b) the time needed for there to be 80 kg of salt in the tank.

2. Suppose that in Question 1 the flow rate is 20 L/min. Answer (a) and (b).

3. Suppose that in Question 1 the initial amount of salt is 5 kg instead of 20 kg. Answer (a) and (b).

4. Suppose that in Question 1 the volume of the tank is 500 L instead of 1000 L. Answer (a).

5. When a quantity of sugar is placed in a container of water the sugar dissolves at a rate proportional to the amount of undissolved sugar. Suppose that 30 g of sugar is placed in 1 L of water and that 5 min later the concentration of sugar dissolved in the water is 25 g/L.
   (a) Let A denote the amount in grams of sugar dissolved at time t. Find a formula relating A and t.
   (b) When was half the sugar dissolved?
   (c) How long will it take for 29 g to be dissolved?

6. A man, initially having a mass of 95 kg, decides to lose weight through a scientific program of diet and exercise. He controls his intake to 2600 calories each day, of which 1320 go to basal metabolism. So he knows that his daily intake contributing to weight gain is actually 1280 ($= 2600 - 1320$) calories.
   He exercises daily so that he expends 16 calories for each kilogram of his body mass. Assume that the storage of fat is 100% efficient and that one kilogram of fat contains ten thousand calories.
   (a) Find how his mass varies with time.
   (b) What mass is he aiming for with this program?
   (c) When will he be halfway to his goal?

C **7.** The rate of growth of the mass m of a falling raindrop is km for some positive constant k. Newton's Law of Motion, applied to the raindrop, is $\dfrac{d(mv)}{dt} = gm$, where $g = 9.8$ m/s^2 is the acceleration due to gravity and v is the velocity of the raindrop, directed down.

Show that $\lim\limits_{t \to \infty} v$ exists and determine it. This limit is the *terminal velocity* of the raindrop.

8. There are V litres of water with A_0 kilograms of dissolved salt in a tank into which brine, with a concentration of c kilograms per litre, is entering at a rate of r litres per minute. The well-stirred solution leaves the tank by an overflow mechanism at the same rate of r litres per minute.

Let A denote the amount, in kilograms, of salt present at time t. Find A as a function of t.

9.6 THE LOGISTIC EQUATION

The law of natural growth

$$\frac{1}{P}\frac{dP}{dt} = k$$

is used to model population growth when populations are small relative to the capacity of the environment to support them.

A more realistic model for population growth is obtained by recognizing that a given environment can carry only a limited number K of individuals, and that as the population approaches this number, the unit rate of growth decreases toward zero.

A differential equation that has these more realistic properties is the **logistic differential equation**.

$$\boxed{\frac{1}{P}\frac{dP}{dt} = k\left(1 - \frac{P}{K}\right)}$$

where k and K are positive constants.

We can solve the logistic differential equation by considering a new variable Q defined by

$$Q = \frac{P}{K - P}$$

and showing that

$$\frac{1}{Q}\frac{dQ}{dt} = k \qquad \qquad \text{①}$$

as follows:

$$\frac{d(K - P)}{dt} = -\frac{dP}{dt}$$

since K is a constant

$$\frac{1}{Q}\frac{dQ}{dt} = \frac{1}{Q}\frac{(K - P)\dfrac{dP}{dt} - P\dfrac{d(K - P)}{dt}}{(K - P)^2}$$

$$= \frac{1}{Q(K - P)^2}\left[(K - P)\frac{dP}{dt} + P\frac{dP}{dt}\right]$$

$$= \frac{1}{Q}\frac{K}{(K - P)^2}\frac{dP}{dt}$$

$$= \frac{K - P}{P} \times \frac{K}{(K - P)^2} \times \frac{dP}{dt}$$

$$= \frac{K}{K - P} \times \frac{1}{P}\frac{dP}{dt}$$

$$= \frac{K}{K - P}k\left(1 - \frac{P}{K}\right)$$

$$= k\left(\frac{K}{K - P}\right)\left(\frac{K - P}{K}\right)$$

$$= k$$

From Equation 1 we deduce that there is a constant c such that

$$Q = ce^{kt}$$

Now $Q = \dfrac{P}{K - P}$ gives $P = \dfrac{KQ}{Q + 1} = \dfrac{K}{1 + Q^{-1}}$ so

$$P = \frac{K}{1 + c^{-1}e^{-kt}}$$

since $Q^{-1} = c^{-1}e^{-kt}$

Letting $C = c^{-1}$, we have proved:

**General Solution
of Logistic Equation**

If $\dfrac{1}{P}\dfrac{dP}{dt} = k\left(1 - \dfrac{P}{K}\right)$

then $P = \dfrac{K}{1 + Ce^{-kt}}$

for an arbitrary constant C.

The function $P = \dfrac{K}{1 + Ce^{-kt}}$ is called a **logistic growth function**.

The diagram shows the graph of a typical logistic growth function: it has a characteristic S shape and for this reason is called an *S-curve* or a *sigmoid curve*.

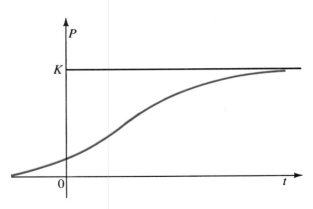

Example 1 Fish biologists put 200 fish into a lake whose carrying capacity for that species is estimated to be 10 000. The number of fish quadruples in the first year.

(a) Obtain a formula relating P, the number of fish in the lake, with t, the number of years since the fish were introduced.

(b) How many years will it take for there to be 5000 fish in the lake?

(c) When there are 5000 fish in the lake fishermen are allowed to catch 20% of them. How long will it take for the population to increase to 5000 again?

(d) When there are 7000 fish in the lake a 20% catch is allowed again. How long will it take for the population to return to 7000 fish?

Solution (a) Since we are dealing with a population in a limited environment, we assume that the logistic differential equation adequately describes what is happening. So, we see that P and t are related by

$$P = \frac{K}{1 + Ce^{-kt}}$$

for suitable constants K, C, and k.

We have identified K as the carrying capacity, so $K = 10\ 000$, and thus

$$P = \frac{10\ 000}{1 + Ce^{-kt}}$$

To determine C we use the initial condition that $P = 200$ when $t = 0$:

$$200 = \frac{10\ 000}{1 + Ce^0}$$

Thus $1 + C = \dfrac{10\ 000}{200}$, so $C = 49$. Now we have

$$P = \frac{10\ 000}{1 + 49e^{-kt}}$$

To determine k we use the fact that the population quadrupled in the first year; that is, $P = 800$ when $t = 1$.

$$800 = \frac{10\ 000}{1 + 49e^{-k(1)}}$$

$$1 + 49e^{-k} = \frac{10\ 000}{800}$$

$$49e^{-k} = 11.5$$

$$e^{-k} = \frac{11.5}{49}$$

Taking natural logarithms we obtain

$$-k = \ln\left(\frac{11.5}{49}\right) \doteq -1.45$$

so $k \doteq 1.45$. Therefore, a formula relating P and t is

$$P = \frac{10\ 000}{1 + 49e^{-1.45t}}$$

This is the formula we use to answer the remaining questions. All our answers are approximate, since the carrying capacity is estimated, and surely the quadrupling of the numbers in the first year is only a close figure.

(b) We find t such that $P = 5000$.

If
$$5000 = \frac{10\ 000}{1 + 49e^{-1.45t}}$$

then $\quad 1 + 49e^{-1.45t} = 2$

so $\quad\quad\quad\quad e^{1.45t} = 49$

and $\quad\quad\quad\quad 1.45t = \ln 49.$

Hence $t \doteq 2.7$. Therefore in about 32 months (2.7 a) the population will number 5000.

(c) We need to find how long the population takes to increase from 4000 ($= 5000$ less 20%) to 5000. So we find t when $P = 4000$.

$$4000 = \frac{10\ 000}{1 + 49e^{-1.45t}}$$

$$1 + 49e^{-1.45t} = 2.5$$

$$e^{1.45t} = \frac{49}{1.5}$$

$$1.45t = \ln\left(\frac{49}{1.5}\right)$$

Thus $t \doteq 2.4$, and the length of time needed to increase from 4000 to 5000 is $2.7 - 2.4 = 0.3$ a, which is about 4 months.

(d) We need to find how long the population takes to increase from 5600 ($= 7000$ less 20%) to 7000. So we find the respective values of t from the formula and take their difference. We solve for t algebraically.

$$P = \frac{10\ 000}{1 + 49e^{-kt}}$$

$$1 + 49e^{-kt} = \frac{10\ 000}{P}$$

$$49e^{-kt} = \frac{10\ 000}{P} - 1$$

$$e^{kt} = \frac{49}{\dfrac{10\ 000}{P} - 1}$$

Thus

$$t = \frac{1}{k} \ln\left(\frac{49}{\dfrac{10\ 000}{P} - 1} \right)$$

$$t = \frac{1}{1.45} \ln\left(\frac{49}{\dfrac{10\ 000}{P} - 1} \right)$$

So when $P = 5600$, $t \doteq \dfrac{1}{1.45} \ln(62.36) \doteq 2.85$

and when $P = 7000$, $t \doteq \dfrac{1}{1.45} \ln(114) \doteq 3.27$

The length of time needed to increase from 5600 to 7000 is $3.27 - 2.85 = 0.42$ a, which is about 5 months.

We see from this example that the larger population takes longer to recover from a 20% harvest than the smaller does. This type of analysis, using logistic growth, helps in deciding when to harvest certain species, such as salmon. For this purpose, accurate population levels must be determined.

Example 2 (Spread of an epidemic.) One law suggested for explaining the spread of an epidemic is that the rate of spread is jointly proportional to the fraction that is infected and the fraction that is uninfected.

In a small town of 5000, 160 people have a disease at the beginning of the week and 1200 have it at the end of the week.

(a) Find a formula relating the fraction F of infected people in the town and the number t of weeks since the disease was noticed.

(b) Show that in 11 days over half the town is infected.

(c) How long does it take for 4000 people to be infected?

Solution   (a) The differential equation expressing the law is

$$\frac{dF}{dt} = kF(1 - F)$$

We see that this is the logistic differential equation with $K = 1$, as no more than 100% of the town can be infected. From our result on the general solution to the logistic differential equation, we deduce that

$$F = \frac{1}{1 + Ce^{-kt}}$$

We have to determine C and k. Initially, at $t = 0$, $F = \frac{160}{5000} = 0.032$, so

$$0.032 = \frac{1}{1 + Ce^0}$$

Hence $C = 30.25$, and therefore

$$F = \frac{1}{1 + 30.25e^{-kt}}$$

To determine k we use the fact that when $t = 1$, $F = \frac{1200}{5000} = 0.24$. So

$$0.24 = \frac{1}{1 + 30.25e^{-k(1)}}$$
$$1 + 30.25e^{-k} = \frac{1}{0.24}$$
$$e^k \doteq 9.55$$

Therefore $k \doteq \ln(9.55) \doteq 2.26$, and hence

$$F = \frac{1}{1 + 30.25e^{-2.26t}}$$

This is the desired formula relating F and t. We use it to answer the remaining questions.

(b) In 11 d, $t = \frac{11}{7}$ weeks, so

$$F = \frac{1}{1 + 30.25e^{-2.26\left(\frac{11}{7}\right)}} \doteq 0.54$$

Hence about 54% of the population is infected after 11 d.

(c) We find t such that

$$0.8 = \frac{1}{1 + 30.25e^{-2.26t}}$$

$$30.25e^{-2.26t} = 0.25$$

$$e^{2.26t} = \frac{30.25}{0.25}$$

Thus $t = \dfrac{1}{2.26} \ln\left(\dfrac{30.25}{0.25}\right) \doteq 2.12.$

We conclude that in about 15 d 80% of the population will be infected.

EXERCISE 9.6

B **1.** Three hundred fish are put into a lake whose carrying capacity is six thousand. The number of fish doubles in the first year.
(a) Obtain a formula relating P, the number of fish in the lake, to the number t of years since the fish were introduced.
(b) How many fish are in the lake after four years?
(c) How long does it take for there to be 4800 fish in the lake?

2. Yeast is grown in a laboratory under conditions that ensure a limiting population of 700 cells. If the initial number of cells is 10 and after nine hours there are 500, when were 350 cells present?

3. In an isolated town of 2000 people, the disease Rottenich creates an epidemic. The initial number of infected is 12 but by the end of the first week 100 people have caught the disease.
(a) How long does it take for half the town to be infected?
(b) How many new cases appear in the week following the time when half were infected?

4. (a) Use a logistic growth model to predict the carrying capacity of Canada given the census figures following.

Year	Population (in millions)
1950	14.0
1960	18.2
1970	21.6

(b) Use your resulting formula to predict the population of Canada in 1980. (The actual population was 24.04 million.)
(c) From your model, predict when the population will pass 25 million. (Our population actually passed that mark in 1984.)

5. Cigarette consumption in Canada increased from 50 per capita in 1900 to 3900 per capita in 1960. Assume that the growth in cigarette consumption is governed by the logistic equation with limiting consumption being 4000 per capita. Estimate consumption of cigarettes in the years 1910, 1920, 1930, 1940, 1950, and 1970.

(Per capita consumption of cigarettes began to decrease in the 1970s due, in part, to the publicity given to health hazards, so the logistic equation no longer applies.)

6. Graph $y = \dfrac{10}{1 + e^{-x}}$.

C **7.** Suppose that P is positive and less than K and that there is a positive constant k, such that $\dfrac{dP}{dt} = kP - \dfrac{k}{K}P^2$ for all t. Set $Q = \dfrac{dP}{dt}$ and show that Q reaches a maximum when $P = \dfrac{K}{2}$ by evaluating $\dfrac{dQ}{dt} = \dfrac{dQ}{dP}\dfrac{dP}{dt}$. This shows that a population growing according to the logistic equation has maximum rate of growth when it reaches half the carrying capacity. So a sustainable resource is best harvested then.

*9.7 A SECOND ORDER DIFFERENTIAL EQUATION

The differential equation we consider in this section is

$$y'' + ky = 0$$

$$y'' = \frac{d^2y}{dx^2}$$

where k is a positive constant. This equation arises where the acceleration (or trend) is opposite to the state. These situations occur in many periodic phenomena. The swinging pendulum and the oscillating spring are examples from mechanics. However, this process is also recognized implicitly in the principle that prices are lowest when supplies are highest. We observe, too, that people on a roller-coaster scream after the falling is over. Finally, we recall the saying: it is always darkest before the dawn.

Example 1 Show that $y'' + 25y = 0$ if $y = -2\cos 5x + 7\sin 5x$.

Solution

$$y' = -2(-5)\sin 5x + 7(5)\cos 5x$$

So,
$$y' = 10\sin 5x + 35\cos 5x$$

Hence
$$y'' = 10(5)\cos 5x + 35(-5)\sin 5x$$
$$= 50\cos 5x - 175\sin 5x$$
$$y'' + 25y = 50\cos 5x - 175\sin 5x - 50\cos 5x + 175\sin 5x$$
$$= 0$$

We see that the periodic functions $\cos 5x$ and $\sin 5x$ are indeed involved in the solution of $y'' + 25y = 0$. In fact, this sort of result generally holds.

Theorem

If $y'' + ky = 0$, where k is a positive constant, then there are constants A, B such that

$$y = A \cos(\sqrt{k}x) + B \sin(\sqrt{k}x)$$

We note that the equation $y'' + ky = 0$ involves the *second* derivative of y and that the solution depends on *two* arbitrary constants (denoted A, B above).

Example 2   Solve $\dfrac{d^2s}{dt^2} + 4s = 0$ with $s = 0$ and $\dfrac{ds}{dt} = 1$ when $t = 0$.

Solution   From the theorem we deduce that there are constants A, B such that

$$s = A \cos(\sqrt{4}t) + B \sin(\sqrt{4}t)$$
$$s = A \cos 2t + B \sin 2t$$

Now $s = 0$ when $t = 0$ so

$$0 = A \cos 0 + B \sin 0$$

Hence $A = 0$ and thus

$$s = B \sin 2t$$

Next, we differentiate to obtain

$$\frac{ds}{dt} = 2B \cos 2t$$

Substituting $t = 0$, $\dfrac{ds}{dt} = 1$ we obtain

$$1 = 2B \cos 0$$

Hence $B = \frac{1}{2}$, and thus we have shown that $s = \frac{1}{2} \sin 2t$ is the solution.

We end this introduction to periodic motion by considering the motion of a mass on the end of a spring.

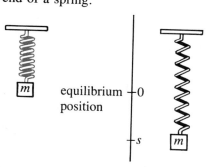

There are two laws to be aware of here. First, Hooke's Law, which states that the force $F(s)$ required to stretch a spring s units beyond its natural length is proportional to s.

$$F(s) = ks, \; k > 0.$$

Second, Newton's Law of Motion, which states

$$F = ma$$

where m is the mass of the object in motion and a is its acceleration. In the situation of a mass on a spring, the acceleration, $a = \dfrac{d^2s}{dt^2}$, is a *restoring force* so it acts opposite to the direction of the displacement. Hence

$$ks = -m\frac{d^2s}{dt^2}$$

and so s satisfies the differential equation

$$\frac{d^2s}{dt^2} + \frac{k}{m}s = 0$$

where $\dfrac{k}{m}$ is a positive constant depending on the system.

Example 3   A spring with mass 1.3 kg has natural length 0.60 m. A force of 20.8 N is required to stretch it to a length of 1.00 m. If the spring is stretched to a length of 0.86 m then released from rest, find the displacement s of the mass at time t.

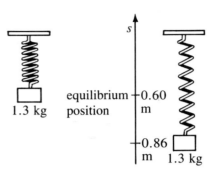

Solution   We first determine k, the positive constant of proportionality, in Hooke's Law. The force required to stretch the spring $1.00 - 0.60 = 0.4$ m is 20.8 N. Thus

$$20.8 = k(0.40)$$

and therefore $k = 52$.

Since $m = 1.3$ the equation for s is

$$\frac{d^2s}{dt^2} + \frac{52}{1.3}s = 0$$

or $$\frac{d^2s}{dt^2} + 40s = 0$$

From the theorem we deduce that

$$s = A \cos(\sqrt{40}t) + B \sin(\sqrt{40}t)$$

We know that when $t = 0$, $s = 0.60 - 0.86 = -0.26$. Substituting, we get

$$-0.26 = A \cos 0 + B \sin 0$$

So $A = -0.26$. After differentiating, we have

$$\frac{ds}{dt} = A(-\sqrt{40})\sin(\sqrt{40}t) + B \sqrt{40} \cos(\sqrt{40}t)$$

Because the mass is at rest when $t = 0$, $\dfrac{ds}{dt} = 0$. So

$$0 = A(-\sqrt{40})\sin 0 + B \sqrt{40} \cos 0$$

Hence $B = 0$. We can now state that

$$s = -0.26 \cos(\sqrt{40}t)$$

is a formula for the displacement.

Since $\cos(\sqrt{40}t)$ varies regularly between 1 and -1, we see that s in Example 3 varies regularly between -0.26 m and 0.26 m. Of course a real spring only behaves like this for a short time. Eventually, *damping* takes over, and the motion slows down. There is a differential equation that describes this very well, but that story must wait.

EXERCISE 9.7

B **1.** Solve the differential equation $\dfrac{d^2s}{dt^2} + 4s = 0$ with the indicated initial conditions.

(a) When $t = 0$, $s = 0$ and $\dfrac{ds}{dt} = 0$.

(b) When $t = 0$, $s = 1$ and $\dfrac{ds}{dt} = 0$.

(c) When $t = 0$, $s = -1$ and $\dfrac{ds}{dt} = 2$.

(d) When $t = 0$, $s = 3$ and $\dfrac{ds}{dt} = -5$.

2. Solve.
(a) $y'' + y = 0$ (b) $y'' + 9y = 0$
(c) $4y'' + 9y = 0$ (d) $y'' + 2y = 0$

3. Find $f(x)$ given that the point $(0, 1)$ is on the graph $y = f(x)$, and that the line $2x + y = 1$ is tangent to $y = f(x)$ at the point $(0, 1)$. Moreover f satisfies the differential equation.
(a) $f'' + f = 0$ (b) $f'' + 4f = 0$
(c) $4f'' + 9f = 0$ (d) $f'' + 2f = 0$

4. A spring with mass 1.3 kg has natural length 0.60 m. A force of 20.8 N is required to stretch it to a length of 1.00 m. If the spring is stretched or compressed to the length given then released from rest, find the displacement s at time t.
(a) 0.70 m   (b) 0.42 m
(c) 1.00 m   (d) 0.21 m

5. A spring with mass 1.3 kg has natural length 0.60 m. A force of 20.8 N is required to stretch it to a length of 1.00 m. If the spring is stretched to a length of 0.86 m then released with the given velocity, find the displacement s at time t.
(a) 1 m/s   (b) -2 m/s
(c) 3.7 m/s   (d) -4.1 m/s

6. Find the maximum value of $f(x)$.
   (a) $f(x) = \cos x + \sin x$
   (b) $f(x) = \cos x + \sqrt{3} \sin x$
   (c) $f(x) = 3 \cos x - 4 \sin x$
   (d) $f(x) = -2 \cos 3x + \sin 3x$

C **7.** A spring with mass 1.0 kg has a natural length of 0.53 m. A force of 4.25 N is required to stretch it to a length of 0.70 m. If the spring is stretched to a length of 0.66 m then released with a downward speed of 2.1 m/s, find the maximum displacement of the mass.

9.8 REVIEW EXERCISE

1. Find the antiderivative of f on $(-\infty, \infty)$.
   (a) $f(x) = 3x - \pi$
   (b) $f(x) = e \sin x + \sqrt{2} \cos x$
   (c) $f(x) = 4e^{\sqrt{2}x} - \frac{1}{7}e^{-\pi x}$
   (d) $f(x) = \dfrac{4x^3}{x^4 + 1}$

2. Find the antiderivative of f on $(0, \infty)$.
   (a) $f(x) = \dfrac{1}{10x} + \dfrac{\sqrt{2}}{x^2}$
   (b) $f(x) = 4x^{1.5} - 3x^{2.7}$
   (c) $f(x) = \sqrt{x} + \sqrt{2x} + \sqrt{3x}$
   (d) $f(x) = -\dfrac{1}{x^2}e^{\frac{1}{x}}$

3. Find the function F given that the point $(-1, 4)$ is on the graph of $y = F(x)$ and that
   (a) $F'(x) = 2x^2 - 3x$
   (b) $F'(x) = e^x - e^{-2x}$
   (c) $F'(x) = \sin x - \cos x$
   (d) $F'(x) = \sqrt{3 + 2x}$

4. A pebble is tossed upward at 30 m/s from the edge of a bridge 210 m above the river below. How many seconds elapse between toss and splash?

5. A raindrop has an initial downward speed of 13 m/s and its acceleration a downward is given by
$$a = \begin{cases} 8.4 - 0.7t & 0 \leqslant t \leqslant 12 \\ 0 & t > 12 \end{cases}$$
   (a) How far does the raindrop fall in the first 12 s?
   (b) What is the velocity of the raindrop after 12 s?
   (c) If the raindrop is initially 1 km above the ground, how long does it take to fall?

6. A metal ball is heated to 105°C and then immersed in water that is maintained at 17°C. After one second the temperature of the ball is 37°C. What will the ball's temperature be after one more second?

7. Ten kilograms of salt is dissolved in 800 L of water in a large tank. A brine solution, having a salt concentration of 75 g/L, enters the tank at 24 L/min and the well-stirred solution overflows at the same rate.
   (a) Find the amount of salt present after one hour.
   (b) When will there be 35 kg of salt in the tank?

8. The species of protozoa called *Paramecium caudatum* has been used to verify that the logistic growth model is applicable in some situations. Suppose 20 Paramecia are placed in a small test tube containing enough nutrient that the carrying capacity is 420 individuals. Suppose that by the end of the first day the number of individuals present increases to 160.
   (a) Find a formula relating P, the number of Paramecia present, to t, the number of days since the experiment began.
   (b) Use this formula to find how many Paramecia were present after three days.
   (c) How long does it take for the population to reach 220?

9. Solve $y'' + 25y = 0$ with the initial conditions:
   (a) When $x = 0$, $y = 0$, $y' = -3$.
   (b) When $x = 0$, $y = 2$, $y' = 1$.
   (c) When $x = \pi$, $y = -1$, $y' = 0$.
   (d) When $x = 2\pi$, $y = 3$, $y' = 3$.

10. A particle moves in a straight line path in such a way that $\dfrac{d^2s}{dt^2} = -3s$, where s is the displacement. Suppose that $s = 0$ when $t = 0$, and $\dfrac{ds}{dt} = 4$ when $t = 0$.
    (a) Find s as a function of t.
    (b) What is the maximum value of s?

9.9 CHAPTER 9 TEST

1. (a) Define the expression "F is an antiderivative of f" where f is a given function, continuous on an interval.
   (b) Find the most general antiderivative of
   $$f(x) = x^2 + 3e^{-x} + 4 \sin x$$

2. Suppose $F'(x) = \sqrt{2x} + 6$ and the point $(2, 5)$ is on $y = F(x)$. Find F.

3. A pebble is tossed upward at 25 m/s from the edge of a bridge 46 m above the lake below. How many seconds elapse between toss and splash?

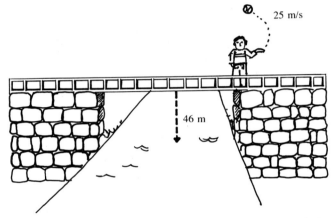

4. A cup of coffee is at 80°C when first brought into the classroom where the temperature is 22°C. After one minute the temperature of the coffee is 60°C. How much longer does it take for the coffee to reach 33°C?

5. Fresh water enters a tank, containing 100 L brine, at a rate of 15 L/min. If the mixture is stirred and leaves the tank at 15 L/min, how long will it take for the solution to be half as salty, given that the initial concentration is 10 g/L?

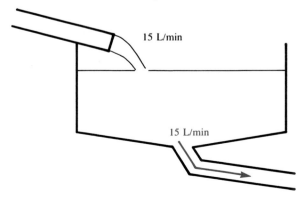

6. A good model for the spread of rumours by word of mouth in a town is that the rate of spread of the rumour is jointly proportional to the number of people who have heard the rumour and the number of those who have not yet heard it.

    (a) Write down a differential equation expressing this model.

    (b) Solve this differential equation using the extra information that the town has 1500 rumour-prone inhabitants, 6 people knew the rumour initially, and after three days half the people had heard the rumour.

7. Solve $9y'' + 4y = 0$ where $y = 2$, $y' = -3$ at $x = 0$.

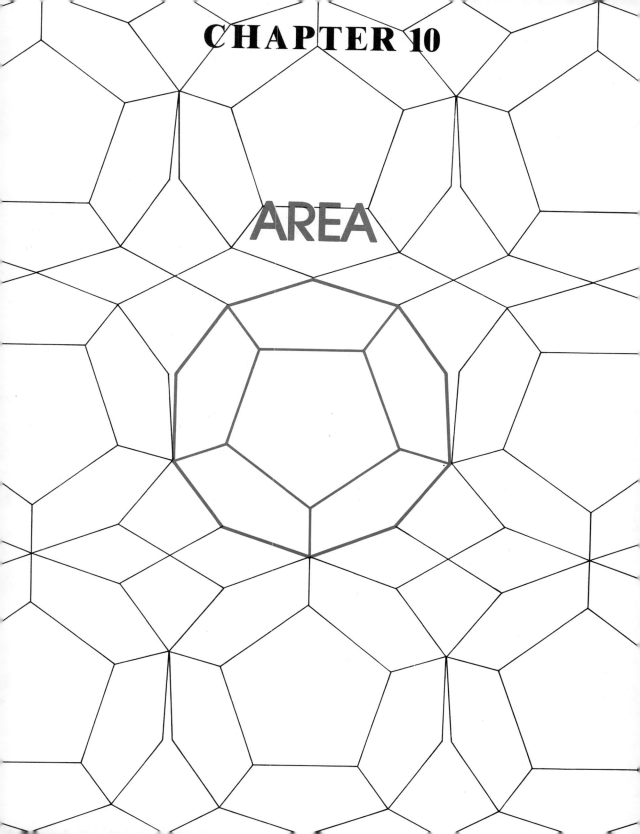

CHAPTER 10

AREA

REVIEW AND PREVIEW TO
CHAPTER 10

Area of a Trapezoid

A **trapezoid** is a quadrilateral with one pair of opposite sides parallel. The trapezoid in the diagram has parallel sides of lengths a and b. The perpendicular distance between these parallel sides is the height, h, of the trapezoid.

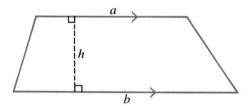

We calculate the area of the trapezoid by drawing a diagonal and summing the areas of the two triangles. Let the area of the trapezoid be A.

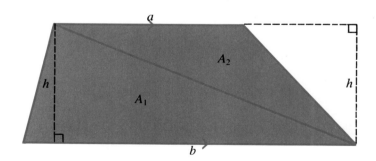

$$A = A_1 + A_2$$
$$= \tfrac{1}{2}bh + \tfrac{1}{2}ah$$
$$= \tfrac{1}{2}h(a + b)$$

Area of a Trapezoid
$A = \tfrac{1}{2}h(a + b)$

Example 1 Find the area of the shaded region in the diagram.

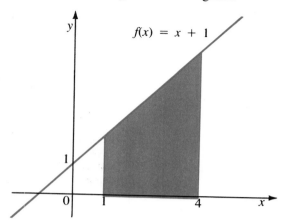

$f(x) = x + 1$

Solution The shaded region is a trapezoid with parallel sides of length $f(1) = 2$ and $f(4) = 5$. The distance between the parallel sides is $h = 4 - 1 = 3$. Therefore

$$A = \tfrac{1}{2}(3)(2 + 5)$$
$$= 10.5$$

EXERCISE 1

1. Calculate the area of the shaded region.

(a)

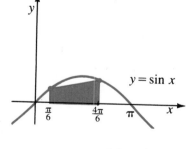

$y = \sin x$

(b)

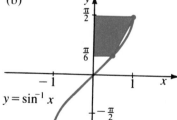

$y = \sin^{-1} x$

(c)

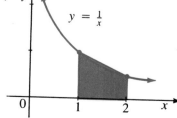

$y = \dfrac{1}{x}$

Sigma Notation

A series is the sum of a sequence. We can write a series using sigma notation.

$$\sum_{i=1}^{n} t_i = t_1 + t_2 + t_3 + \ldots + t_n$$

Example 1   Express the series $1 + 3 + 5 + 7 + 9$ in sigma notation.

Solution   We need the general term to express the series in sigma notation. Since we are dealing with consecutive odd numbers, each term is of the form $2i - 1$, $i \in N$.

Therefore $1 + 3 + 5 + 7 + 9 = \sum_{i=1}^{5}(2i - 1)$

The properties of Sigma Notation that we use in this section are summarized in the chart.

Basic Properties of Sigma Notation

(1) $\sum_{i=1}^{n} c = c + c + c + \ldots + c = nc$, c is a constant.

(2) $\sum_{i=1}^{n} ct_i = c \sum_{i=1}^{n} t_i$, c is a constant.

(3) $\sum_{i=1}^{n} (t_i + s_i) = \sum_{i=1}^{n} t_i + \sum_{i=1}^{n} s_i$

Example 1   Use the basic properties of sigma notation to express $\sum_{i=1}^{n} (3i - 2)^2$ in terms of monomial summations.

Solution $\sum_{i=1}^{n} (3i - 2)^2 = \sum_{i=1}^{n} (9i^2 - 12i + 4)$

$$= \sum_{i=1}^{n} 9i^2 + \sum_{i=1}^{n} (-12i) + \sum_{i=1}^{n} 4 \quad \text{(by Property 3)}$$

$$= 9 \sum_{i=1}^{n} i^2 - 12 \sum_{i=1}^{n} i + 4n \quad \text{(by Properties 2 and 1)}$$

EXERCISE 2

1. Write each series in expanded form.

   (a) $\displaystyle\sum_{i=1}^{5}(i^2 + 1)$ (b) $\displaystyle\sum_{i=1}^{4}\frac{i}{4}f(i)$ (c) $\displaystyle\sum_{i=1}^{n}\frac{3}{n}f\left(1 + \frac{3}{4}i\right)$

2. Write each series in sigma notation.

   (a) $1 + 4 + 7 + 10 + 13 + 16$

   (b) $1 - 1 + 1 - 1 + 1 - 1 + 1$

   (c) $x + x^2 + x^3 + \ldots + x^n$

   (d) $\frac{1}{6}f\left(\frac{1}{6}\right) + \frac{2}{6}f\left(\frac{2}{6}\right) + \frac{3}{6}f\left(\frac{3}{6}\right) + \frac{4}{6}f\left(\frac{4}{6}\right) + \frac{5}{6}f\left(\frac{5}{6}\right) + f(1)$

   (e) $\frac{1}{n}f\left(\frac{2(1) - 2}{n}\right) + \frac{2}{n}f\left(\frac{2(2) - 2}{n}\right) + \frac{3}{n}f\left(\frac{2(3) - 2}{n}\right) + \ldots$
   $+ \frac{n}{n}f\left(\frac{2(n) - 2}{n}\right)$

3. Express in terms of monomial summations.

   (a) $\displaystyle\sum_{i=1}^{n}(2 + i)^2$ (b) $\displaystyle\sum_{i=1}^{20}(3i^2 - 12i)$

   (c) $\displaystyle\sum_{i=1}^{n}(2i^3 - 3i^2 + 5i - 12)$

Sum of a Series

In this chapter we need the sums of the special series that are listed below. Refer to Chapter 11 in Algebra and Geometry or Chapter 4 in Finite Mathematics for more detail.

1. Sum of an arithmetic series:

$$a + (a + d) + (a + 2d) + \ldots + [a + (n - 1)d]$$
$$= \frac{n}{2}(2a + (n - 1)d)$$

2. Sum of a geometric series:

$$a + ar + ar^2 + \ldots + ar^{n-1} = \frac{a(r^n - 1)}{r - 1}$$

3. Sum of the natural numbers:

$$\sum_{i=1}^{n} i = \frac{n(n + 1)}{2}$$

4. Sum of the squares of the natural numbers:

$$\sum_{i=1}^{n} i^2 = \frac{n(n+1)(2n+1)}{6}$$

5. Sum of the cubes of the natural numbers:

$$\sum_{i=1}^{n} i^3 = \frac{n^2(n+1)^2}{4}$$

Example 1   Evaluate $\sum_{i=1}^{n} (3i^2 - 2i)$.

Solution

$$\sum_{i=1}^{n} (3i^2 - 2i) = 3\sum_{i=1}^{n} i^2 - 2\sum_{i=1}^{n} i$$

$$= 3\frac{n(n+1)(2n+1)}{6} - 2\frac{n(n+1)}{2}$$

$$= \frac{3n(n+1)(2n+1) - 6n(n+1)}{6}$$

$$= \frac{3n(n+1)[(2n+1) - 2]}{6}$$

$$= \frac{n(n+1)(2n-1)}{2}$$

EXERCISE 3

1. Evaluate.
    (a) $3 + 7 + 11 + \ldots + (4n - 1)$
    (b) $1 + 3 + 9 + 27 + \ldots + 3^{n-1}$
    (c) $\sum_{i=1}^{n} (3i^2 - i)$ (d) $\sum_{i=1}^{n} (2i^3 + 3i - 2)$
    (e) $\sum_{i=1}^{20} (i + 3)$ (f) $\sum_{i=41}^{100} (i^3 - 2i)$

INTRODUCTION

Finite regions with straight sides pose few problems when we have to calculate their areas.

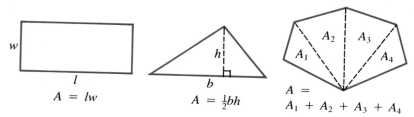

$$A = lw \qquad A = \tfrac{1}{2}bh \qquad A = A_1 + A_2 + A_3 + A_4$$

In this chapter we tackle the problem of calculating the area of a region with curved sides. It is interesting to note that, historically, the area problem preceded the tangent problem that we have already discussed in Section 1.1, and that there is a definite connection between the two concepts. Newton's teacher at Cambridge, Isaac Barrow (1630–1677), discovered that these two problems are closely related. Newton and Leibniz exploited the relationship and used it to develop calculus into a systematic mathematical method.

10.1 AREA UNDER A CURVE

If $y = f(x)$ is a positive function, the **area of the region under $y = f(x)$ from a to b** is the area of the region below $y = f(x)$ and above the x-axis ($y = 0$), to the right of the vertical line $x = a$ and left of $x = b$. Region R in the following diagram fulfills these requirements. The **area problem** involves finding the area of such a region.

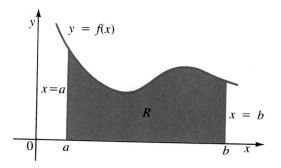

To find the area of such a region we need to create an area function. If a is a fixed value, then the distance x that we move to the right of a determines the area of the region. Thus the area is a function of x.

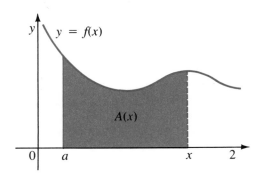

$A(x)$ is the area of the region under $y = f(x)$ from a to x. It is important to note that $A(a) = 0$.

Example 1 Sketch the region under $y = 2x + 1$ from 1 to x and
(a) find the area function,
(b) compare the derivative of the area function with the equation of the straight line.

Solution

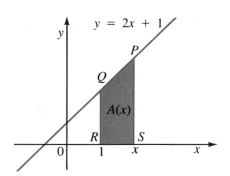

(a) The required area $A(x)$ is the area of trapezoid $PQRS$. The lengths of the parallel sides are $RQ = f(1) = 3$ and $SP = f(x) = 2x + 1$. The height is $RS = x - 1$.

Therefore
$$A(x) = \tfrac{1}{2}(x - 1)(3 + 2x + 1)$$
$$= \tfrac{1}{2}(x - 1)(2x + 4)$$
$$= \tfrac{1}{2}(2x^2 + 2x + 4)$$
$$= x^2 + x + 2$$

(b)
$$A'(x) = 2x + 1$$
$$= f(x)$$

In Example 1 the derivative of the area function turned out to be the function that defined the straight line. The area problem can be solved if we can establish that the relationship $A'(x) = f(x)$ is generally true.

Let $A(x)$ be the area under the function $y = f(x)$ from a to x, where $y = f(x)$ is continuous and positive.

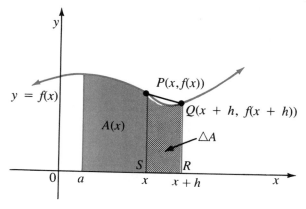

The area is uniquely determined by the position of point $P(x, f(x))$ on the curve. Select a point $Q(x+h, f(x+h))$ very close to P. The area of the curved region $PQRS$ is the change in area (ΔA) as x changes to $x + h$.

$$A'(x) = \lim_{h \to 0} \frac{\Delta A}{h}$$

$$= \lim_{h \to 0} \frac{A(x + h) - A(x)}{h}$$

Now $A(x + h) - A(x)$, the area of the curved region $PQRS$, can be approximated by the area of trapezoid $PQRS$. The smaller h gets, the better the approximation becomes, with equality in the limit.

Thus $A(x + h) - A(x) \doteq \frac{1}{2}h[f(x) + f(x + h)]$

and
$$A'(x) = \lim_{h \to 0} \frac{\frac{1}{2}h[f(x) + f(x + h)]}{h}$$

$$= \lim_{h \to 0} \frac{f(x) + f(x + h)}{2}$$

$$= \frac{f(x) + f(x)}{2}$$

$$\boxed{A'(x) = f(x)}$$

In the next example we find the area of a region by solving the differential equation $A'(x) = f(x)$ subject to a particular initial condition.

Example 2   Find the area under $y = x^2 + 2$ from $x = 2$ to $x = 4$.

Solution   The required area $A(4)$ is shown in the diagram.

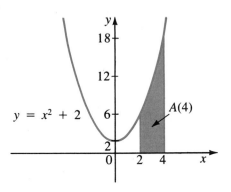

Since $A'(x) = x^2 + 2$

we have $A(x) = \frac{1}{3}x^3 + 2x + C$

The initial condition is $A(2) = 0$

Therefore $0 = \frac{8}{3} + 4 + C$

                                    $C = -\frac{20}{3}$

and $A(x) = \frac{1}{3}x^3 + 2x - \frac{20}{3}$

The required area $A(4) = \frac{64}{3} + 8 - \frac{20}{3} = \frac{68}{3}$.

Now we are ready to tackle the area problem. We want to find the area under $y = f(x)$ from a to b.

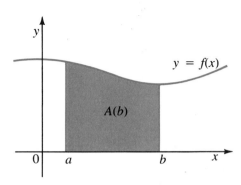

The required area $A(b)$ is shown in the above diagram.

Now $A'(x) = f(x)$

Therefore $\qquad A(x) = F(x) + C$, where $F(x)$ is any antiderivative of $f(x)$

The initial condition

$$A(a) = 0$$

gives us $\qquad\qquad 0 = F(a) + C$
and $\qquad\qquad\quad C = -F(a)$
Therefore $\qquad\quad A(x) = F(x) - F(a)$
and $\qquad\qquad A(b) = F(b) - F(a)$

If F is any antiderivative of the positive function f, the area under $y = f(x)$ from a to b is $A(b) = F(b) - F(a)$.

In practice, we choose the antiderivative with constant 0. If $f(x) = e^{2x}$ we would select $F(x) = \frac{1}{2}e^{2x}$ not $F(x) = \frac{1}{2}e^{2x} + C$.

Example 3 Find the area between $y = \sin x$ and the x-axis from $x = \dfrac{\pi}{6}$ to $x = \dfrac{\pi}{2}$.

Solution We sketch the curve and locate the required area $A\left(\dfrac{\pi}{2}\right)$.

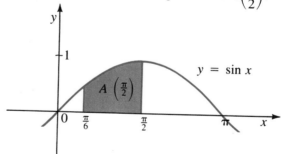

We choose the antiderivative

$$F(x) = -\cos x$$

The required area is

$$A\left(\frac{\pi}{2}\right) = F\left(\frac{\pi}{2}\right) - F\left(\frac{\pi}{6}\right)$$

$$= -\cos\frac{\pi}{2} - \left(-\cos\frac{\pi}{6}\right)$$

$$= 0 + \frac{\sqrt{3}}{2}$$

$$= \frac{\sqrt{3}}{2}$$

Example 4 Find the area of the region below $y = 4 - x^2$ and above the x-axis.

Solution First we set $4 - x^2 = 0$ and solve for the x-intercepts ± 2. This helps us sketch the curve and locate the required area $A(2)$.

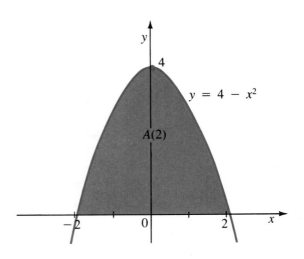

We choose the antiderivative

$$F(x) = 4x - \frac{x^3}{3}$$

The required area is
$$A(2) = F(2) - F(-2)$$
$$= 8 - \tfrac{8}{3} - \left(-8 + \tfrac{8}{3}\right)$$
$$= 8 - \tfrac{8}{3} + 8 - \tfrac{8}{3}$$
$$= \tfrac{32}{3}$$

EXERCISE 10.1

B 1. Find the area under the given curve from a to b.

(a) $y = x^2 + 1$ from 0 to 4

(b) $y = -x^2 + 1$ from $-\frac{1}{2}$ to $\frac{1}{4}$

(c) $y = x^2 - 1$ from -4 to -2

(d) $y = \dfrac{1}{x}$ from e to e^2

(e) $y = 2\cos x$ from $-\dfrac{\pi}{2}$ to 0

(f) $y = \sqrt{x}$ from 0 to 4

    (g) $y = -\sin x$ from $-\pi$ to 0

    (h) $y = \sec^2 x$ from $-\dfrac{\pi}{4}$ to $\dfrac{\pi}{3}$

    (i) $y = e^{-x}$ from -2 to 4

    (j) $y = x^3$ from 1 to 3

    (k) $y = x^2 - x + 2$ from -2 to 1

    (l) $y = 2e^{-2x}$ from 0 to 1

    (m) $y = \sin\left(\dfrac{x}{2}\right)$ from 0 to $\dfrac{3\pi}{4}$

    (n) $y = 3\cos(2x)$ from $-\dfrac{\pi}{4}$ to $\dfrac{\pi}{8}$

    (o) $y = \dfrac{1}{(x + 1)^2}$ from 0 to 10

    (p) $y = x(x^2 + 1)^4$ from 1 to 2

2. Find the area below the given curve and above the x-axis.

    (a) $y = 4x - x^2$ (b) $y = 9 - x^2$

    (c) $y = x^2 - x^3$ from -2 to 1 (d) $y = x^2 - x^4$

    (e) $y = -\cos x$ from $-\pi$ to π (f) $y = 10 - 11x - 6x^2$

    (g) $y = x^3 - 3x^2 - 9x + 27$ (h) $y = 4 + 3x - x^2$

3. Calculate the area between $y = \dfrac{1}{x}$ and the x-axis from $x = 1$ to the given line.

    (a) $x = 2$ (b) $x = 3$ (c) $x = e$ (d) $x = n$

4. Calculate the area between $y = \dfrac{1}{x}$ and the x-axis from the given line to $x = 1$.

    (a) $x = \frac{1}{2}$ (b) $x = \frac{1}{3}$ (c) $x = \frac{1}{e}$ (d) $x = \frac{1}{10}$

C 5. Find the area between $y = x^3 - 1$ and the x-axis from $x = -1$ to $x = 1$.

6. Find the area between $y = x^2 - 4$ and the x-axis from -1 to 3.

7. Find the area between $y = \sin x \cos x$ and the x-axis from $-\dfrac{\pi}{2}$ to $\dfrac{3\pi}{4}$.

10.2 AREA BETWEEN CURVES

In this section we examine a more general area problem, that of finding the area between two curves in a particular interval. Region R in the diagram is between $y = f_1(x)$ and $y = f_2(x)$ from a to x. If a is fixed, the area of region R is a function of x and is denoted by $A(x)$.

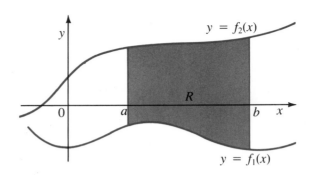

In the interval $[a, x]$, $f_2(x) > f_1(x)$ and an argument similar to that in Section 10.1 establishes the result

$$A'(x) = f_2(x) - f_1(x), \quad f_2(x) - f_1(x) \geq 0$$

or $\quad A'(x) = f(x)$, where $f(x) = f_2(x) - f_1(x)$

Thus, the problem of finding the area between two curves has been reduced to our original problem of finding the area under a curve. Generally, if f and g are continuous functions in $[a, b]$ and $f \geq g$ in $[a, b]$, the area between f and g from a to b is the area under $f - g$ from a to b.

Example 1 Find the area between $y = x^2 + 1$ and $y = x$ from $x = 1$ to $x = 3$.

Solution 1 We sketch both curves, identify the required region R, and note that $y = x^2 + 1$ is always above $y = x$.

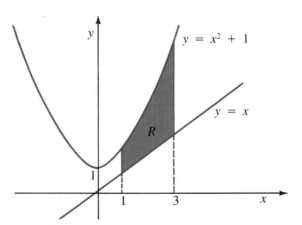

Since

$$A'(x) = x^2 + 1 - x$$

we choose the antiderivative

$$F(x) = \frac{x^3}{3} + x - \frac{x^2}{2}$$

The area of R is

$$A(3) = F(3) - F(1)$$
$$= 9 + 3 - \frac{9}{2} - \left(\frac{1}{3} + 1 - \frac{1}{2}\right)$$
$$= \frac{20}{3}$$

Solution 2 $A(3)$ can be calculated using the areas $A_1(3)$ and $A_2(3)$ in the diagrams.

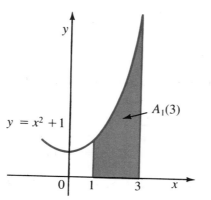
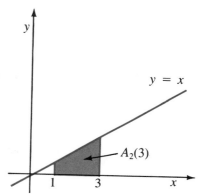

Now $\quad A_1'(x) = x^2 + 1$

$\qquad\qquad\qquad\qquad\qquad\qquad A_2'(x) = x$

We choose the antiderivatives

$$F_1(x) = \tfrac{1}{3}x^3 + x$$

$\qquad\qquad\qquad\qquad\qquad\qquad F_2(x) = \tfrac{1}{2}x^2$

and $\quad A_1(3) = F_1(3) - F_1(1)$

$\qquad\qquad\qquad\qquad\qquad\qquad A_2(3) = F_2(3) - F_2(1)$

$$= 9 + 3 - \tfrac{1}{3} - 1$$

$\qquad\qquad\qquad\qquad\qquad\qquad = \tfrac{9}{2} - \tfrac{1}{2}$

$$= \tfrac{32}{3}$$

$\qquad\qquad\qquad\qquad\qquad\qquad = 4$

Therefore, $\quad A(3) = A_1(3) - A_2(3)$

$$= \tfrac{32}{3} - 4$$

$$= \tfrac{20}{3}$$

Example 2 Find the area of the region bounded by the parabolas $y = x^2$ and $y = 2x - x^2$.

Solution First we find the points of intersection of the two curves to determine the required interval. They also help us to sketch the curves and identify the region R whose area we wish to calculate.

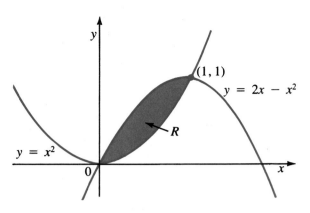

To find the points of intersection set

$$x^2 = 2x - x^2$$

Therefore, $\quad 2x^2 - 2x = 0$

$$2x(x - 1) = 0$$

and $\qquad\qquad x = 0 \quad \text{or} \quad x = 1$

The points of intersection are $(0, 0)$ and $(1, 1)$.

Since $y = 2x - x^2$ is above $y = x^2$, for $0 < x < 1$,

$$A'(x) = 2x - x^2 - x^2$$
$$= 2x - 2x^2$$

We choose the antiderivative

$$F(x) = x^2 - \tfrac{2}{3}x^3$$

The area of R is $\qquad A(1) = F(1) - F(0)$

$$= 1 - \tfrac{2}{3} - 0$$

$$= \tfrac{1}{3}$$

Example 3 Find the area of the region between the curves $y = \sin x$ and $y = \cos x$ from 0 to $\dfrac{\pi}{2}$.

Solution Two separate regions, R_1 and R_2, fall within the required boundaries. Their areas must be evaluated separately and the results added.

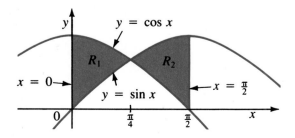

To find the points of intersection set

$$\sin x = \cos x$$

Therefore $\tan x = 1, 0 \leqslant x \leqslant \dfrac{\pi}{2}$

and $x = \dfrac{\pi}{4}$

The point of intersection is $\left(\dfrac{\pi}{4}, \dfrac{1}{\sqrt{2}}\right)$.

Since region R_1 has $y = \cos x$ above $y = \sin x$,

$$A_1'(x) = \cos x - \sin x$$

We choose the antiderivative

$$F_1(x) = \sin x + \cos x$$

Therefore the area of region R_1 is

$$A_1\left(\frac{\pi}{4}\right) = F_1\left(\frac{\pi}{4}\right) - F_1(0)$$

$$= \sin\frac{\pi}{4} + \cos\frac{\pi}{4} - \sin 0 - \cos 0$$

$$= \frac{1}{\sqrt{2}} + \frac{1}{\sqrt{2}} - 0 - 1$$

$$= \frac{2}{\sqrt{2}} - 1$$

$$= \sqrt{2} - 1$$

Since region R_2 has $y = \sin x$ above $y = \cos x$,

$$A_2'(x) = \sin x - \cos x$$

We choose the antiderivative

$$F_2(x) = -\cos x - \sin x$$

Therefore, the area of region R_2 is

$$A_2\left(\frac{\pi}{2}\right) = F_2\left(\frac{\pi}{2}\right) - F_2\left(\frac{\pi}{4}\right)$$

$$= -\cos\frac{\pi}{2} - \sin\frac{\pi}{2} + \cos\frac{\pi}{4} + \sin\frac{\pi}{4}$$

$$= 0 - 1 + \frac{1}{\sqrt{2}} + \frac{1}{\sqrt{2}}$$

$$= \frac{2}{\sqrt{2}} - 1$$

$$= \sqrt{2} - 1$$

The required area is $\sqrt{2} - 1 + \sqrt{2} - 1 = 2\sqrt{2} - 2$

If at the outset we had noticed that R_2 is the reflection of R_1 in the line $x = \frac{\pi}{4}$, then the required area is $2A_1\left(\frac{\pi}{4}\right)$ and our calculations would have been considerably reduced.

Example 4   Find the area between $y = -\sin x$ and the x-axis from $\frac{\pi}{6}$ to $\frac{\pi}{2}$.

Solution   First we sketch the curve and identify the required region R. We treat this as the area between two curves with one of the curves being the x-axis ($y = 0$).

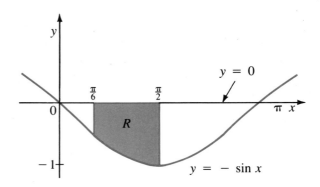

Since region R has $y = 0$ above $y = -\sin x$,
$$A'(x) = 0 - (-\sin x) = \sin x$$
We choose the antiderivative
$$F(x) = -\cos x$$
The area of R is

$$A\left(\frac{\pi}{2}\right) = F\left(\frac{\pi}{2}\right) - F\left(\frac{\pi}{6}\right)$$

$$= -\cos\frac{\pi}{2} - \left(-\cos\frac{\pi}{6}\right)$$

$$= 0 + \frac{\sqrt{3}}{2}$$

$$= \frac{\sqrt{3}}{2}$$

An alternative solution would be to reflect the region in the x-axis. This would not change its area. The image of $y = -\sin x$ is $y = \sin x$ and we would find the area under $y = \sin x$ from $\frac{\pi}{6}$ to $\frac{\pi}{2}$. See Example 3 in Section 10.1.

EXERCISE 10.2

B **1.** Find the area of the region between the given curves. Include a sketch of the region.

    (a) $y = x^2 + 3$ and $y = x + 1$ from 2 to 4

    (b) $y = 2 - x^2$ and $y = -2x + 3$ from -1 to 1

    (c) $y = x^2$ and $y = 2x$

    (d) $y = 4 - x^2$ and $2x - y + 1 = 0$

    (e) $y = 4 - x^2$ and $y = 2x^2 - 8$

    (f) $y = x^2$ and $y = 8\sqrt{x}$

    (g) $y = 2x - x^2$ and $y = -x$

    (h) $y = x^2$ and $y = x^3$

    (i) $y = x^3 + 8$ and $y = 4x + 8$

    (j) $y = \dfrac{4}{x^2}$ and $y = 5 - x^2$

    (k) $y^2 = 4x$ and $x^2 = 4y$

    (l) $y = x^3 - x$ and $y = 0$

    (m) $y = x$ and $y = -\dfrac{x}{2}$ and $y = 5x - 44$

    (n) $x + y = 1$ and $x + y = 5$ and $y = 2x + 1$ and $y = 2x + 6$

    (o) $y = \sin x$ and $y = \cos x$ from $-\pi$ to π

    (p) $y = \sec^2 x$ and $y = x - 1$ from 0 to $\dfrac{\pi}{4}$

    (q) $y = e^{-x}$ and $y = -x$ from $-\ln 3$ to $\ln 3$

    (r) $y = \dfrac{1}{x}$ and $x + y = 2$ from $\frac{1}{2}$ to 3

    (s) $y = \sin x$ and $y = \cos 2x$ from $\dfrac{\pi}{6}$ to $\dfrac{5\pi}{6}$

    (t) $y = 3 \sin x$ and $y = \sin 3x$ from 0 to π

C **2.** Sketch the area bounded by the given curves and find the area of the region.

    (a) $y = |x - 1| + |x + 1|$ and $y = 3 - x^2$

    (b) $y = |x| - x$ and $y = -x^2 - x + 2$

    (c) $xy - 3y + 1 = 0$ and $x^2y + y = 1$

 3. Sketch the region bounded by the given curves and find the area of the region.

    (a) $y = \dfrac{1}{x}$, $x = 0$, $y = 1$, and $y = 2$

    (b) $x = y^2$ and $x = -2y^2 + 1$

    (c) $y = x - 1$ and $y^2 = 2x + 6$

10.3 THE NATURAL LOGARITHM AS AN AREA

In Chapter 8 we defined $y = \ln x$ as the inverse of the function $y = e^x$ and found its derivative, namely $\frac{d}{dx} \ln x = \frac{1}{x}$. The function $y = \frac{1}{x}$ is continuous and positive in the interval $(0, \infty)$. We find the area under $y = \frac{1}{x}$ from 1 to x.

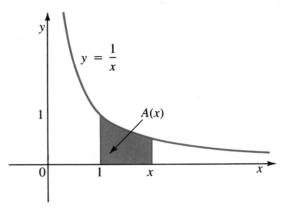

The required area $A(x)$ is shown in the diagram above.

Since
$$A'(x) = \frac{1}{x}$$

we choose the antiderivative

$$F(x) = \ln x$$

Therefore
$$A(x) = F(x) - F(1)$$
$$= \ln x - \ln 1$$
$$= \ln x$$

> If $x > 1$, the natural logarithm $\ln x$ is the area under the curve $y = \frac{1}{x}$ from 1 to x.

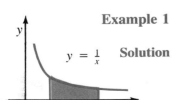

Example 1 Find the area under $y = \frac{1}{x}$ from $x = 1$ to $x = e$.

Solution The required area is $\ln e = 1$.

Example 2   Find the area under $y = \dfrac{1}{x}$ from x to 1, $0 < x < 1$.

Solution   The required area $A(1)$ is shown in the following diagram.

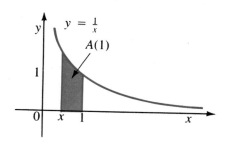

Since $A'(x) = \dfrac{1}{x}$

we choose the antiderivative
$$F(x) = \ln x$$
Therefore $A(1) = F(1) - F(x)$
$$= \ln 1 - \ln x$$
$$= -\ln x$$

Since $\ln x = -A(1)$ in Example 2, we draw the following conclusion:

The natural logarithm $\ln x$ is the negative of the area under the curve $y = \dfrac{1}{x}$ from x to 1 for $0 < x < 1$.

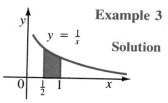

Example 3   Find the area under $y = \dfrac{1}{x}$ from $x = 0.5$ to $x = 1$.

Solution   Since $0 < 0.5 < 1$, the required area is $-\ln 0.5 \doteq 0.693\ 147$.

Example 4   (a) Prove that the area of region
$$R = \{(x, y) \mid 4 \le x \le 9,\ 0 \le xy \le 1\} \text{ is } 2 \ln 1.5.$$
(b) Use an area to prove that $\ln 1.5 < \dfrac{65}{144}$.

Solution   (a) R is the region under $y = \dfrac{1}{x}$ from 4 to 9.

The area under $y = \dfrac{1}{x}$ from 1 to 9 is ln 9.

The area under $y = \dfrac{1}{x}$ from 1 to 4 is ln 4.

Therefore the area of R is

$$\ln 9 - \ln 4 = \ln\left(\tfrac{9}{4}\right)$$
$$= \ln 2.25$$
$$= \ln(1.5)^2$$
$$= 2 \ln 1.5$$

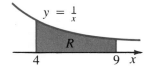

(b) The area of R is less than the area of the trapezoid. The area A of the trapezoid is

$$A = \tfrac{1}{2}(9 - 4)\left(\tfrac{1}{4} + \tfrac{1}{9}\right)$$
$$= \tfrac{1}{2}(5)\left(\tfrac{13}{36}\right)$$
$$= \tfrac{65}{72}$$

Therefore $2 \ln 1.5 < \tfrac{65}{72}$

and $\ln 1.5 < \tfrac{65}{144}$

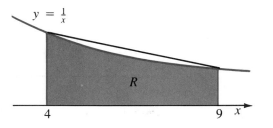

Example 5   Prove that $A = A_1 + A_2$ if A, A_1, and A_2 are the areas in the diagrams.

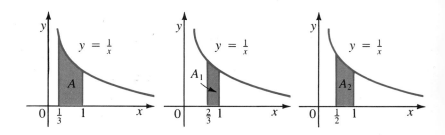

Solution   Since the three areas are under the curve $y = \dfrac{1}{x}$ and have $x = 1$ as the right-hand boundary, each can be expressed as a natural logarithm.

Now
$$A = -\ln \tfrac{1}{3}$$
$$= -\ln\left(\tfrac{2}{3} \times \tfrac{1}{2}\right)$$
$$= -\left(\ln \tfrac{2}{3} + \ln \tfrac{1}{2}\right)$$
$$= -\ln \tfrac{2}{3} - \ln \tfrac{1}{2}$$
$$= A_1 + A_2$$

EXERCISE 10.3

B **1.** State the area of the shaded region.

(a)

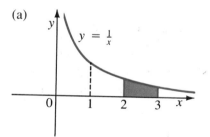

(b)

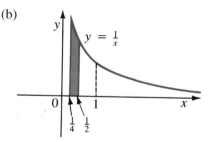

(c)

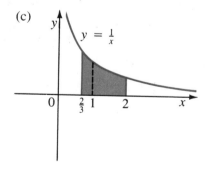

(d)

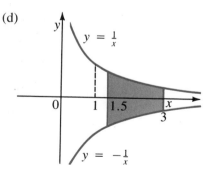

2. Sketch an area represented by each of the following:

(a) $\ln 4$ (b) $-\ln \tfrac{1}{4}$ (c) $\ln 2 + \ln 4$

(d) $\ln 6 - \ln 3$ (e) $2 \ln 2$ (f) $-\ln 0.75$

(g) $-\ln 0.5 - \ln 0.25$ (h) $-\tfrac{1}{2} \ln \tfrac{1}{9}$

(i) $-\ln \tfrac{1}{3} + \ln 3$

3. Prove that $A = A_1 - A_2$ if A, A_1, and A_2 are the areas in the diagrams.

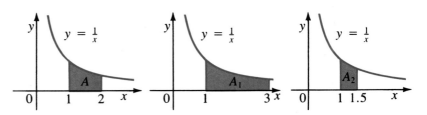

4. Prove that $A_1 = A_2$ if A_1 and A_2 are the areas in the diagrams.

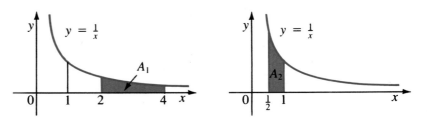

5. Refer to Example 4 of this section and

    (a) find the equation of the tangent to $y = \dfrac{1}{x}$ that is parallel to the slanted side of the trapezoid;

    (b) use an area to prove that $\ln 1.5 > \frac{55}{144}$.

6. (a) Prove that the area of the region
        $R = \{(x, y) \mid 3 \leqslant x \leqslant 6, 0 \leqslant xy \leqslant 1\}$ is $\ln 2$.
    (b) Use an area to establish an upper bound for the value of $\ln 2$.

7. Repeat Problem 6 for the region
    $R = \{(x, y) \mid 18 \leqslant x \leqslant 36, 0 \leqslant xy \leqslant 1\}$.

8. By comparing areas show that

    (a) $\frac{1}{2} + \frac{1}{3} + \frac{1}{4} + \ldots + \dfrac{1}{n} < \ln n < 1 + \frac{1}{2} + \frac{1}{3} + \frac{1}{4} + \ldots + \dfrac{1}{n-1}$

    (b) $\ln 2 < 1 < \ln 3$

10.4 AREAS AS LIMITS

In this section we examine a different method of calculating area. The region whose area we wish to calculate is divided into narrow strips and a rectangle is used to approximate the area of each strip. The sum of the areas of these rectangles approximates the area of the region.

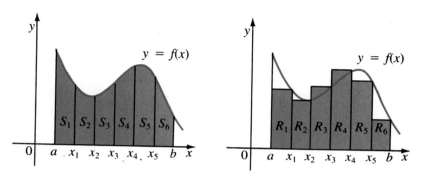

The region under $y = f(x)$ from a to b has been divided into six strips, $S_1, S_2, \ldots, S_6$. Rectangles, $R_1, R_2, \ldots, R_6$, have been constructed to approximate the area of each strip. In this case, the base of the rectangle is the width of the strip and the height of the rectangle is the value of the function at the right-hand endpoint of each strip. Rectangle R_3 has width $x_3 - x_2$ and height $f(x_3)$.

The left-hand endpoint or any point in between, such as the mid-point of the base, could have been chosen to determine the height of a rectangle but we will be using the right-hand endpoint exclusively.

Example 1 (a) Calculate the area under $y = x$, from 0 to 1.
(b) Approximate the same area by subdividing the region into six strips of equal width and finding the sum of the areas of the rectangles determined by the right-hand endpoint of each interval.
(c) Repeat part (b) using twelve strips of equal width.

Solution (a)

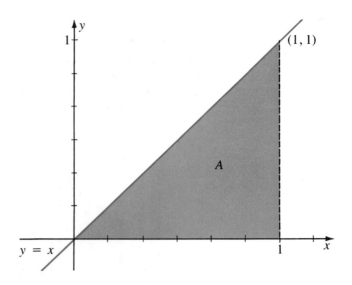

The required area is a right triangle with base 1 and height 1. Since the formula for the area of a triangle is $\frac{1}{2}bh$, the required area is $\frac{1}{2}(1)(1) = \frac{1}{2} = 0.5$.

(b)

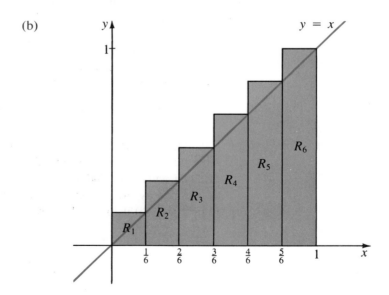

The required area is approximately the sum of the areas of the rectangles R_1, R_2, R_3, R_4, R_5, and R_6.

Now the width of each rectangle is $\frac{1}{6}$.

So, Area $\doteq \frac{1}{6}f\left(\frac{1}{6}\right) + \frac{1}{6}f\left(\frac{2}{6}\right) + \frac{1}{6}f\left(\frac{3}{6}\right) + \frac{1}{6}f\left(\frac{4}{6}\right) + \frac{1}{6}f\left(\frac{5}{6}\right) + \frac{1}{6}f\left(\frac{6}{6}\right)$

$= \frac{1}{6}\left(\frac{1}{6} + \frac{2}{6} + \frac{3}{6} + \frac{4}{6} + \frac{5}{6} + \frac{6}{6}\right)$

$= \frac{1}{36}(1 + 2 + 3 + 4 + 5 + 6)$

$= \frac{21}{36}$

$\doteq 0.583$

(c)

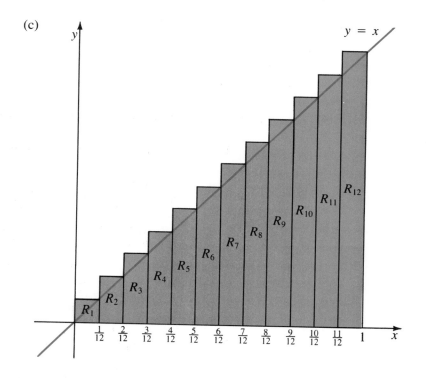

The required area is approximately the sum of the areas of the rectangles $R_1, R_2, R_3, \ldots, R_{12}$.

Now the width of each rectangle is $\frac{1}{12}$.

So, Area $\doteq \frac{1}{12}\left[f\left(\frac{1}{12}\right) + f\left(\frac{2}{12}\right) + f\left(\frac{3}{12}\right) + \ldots + f\left(\frac{12}{12}\right)\right]$

$= \frac{1}{12}\left(\frac{1}{12} + \frac{2}{12} + \frac{3}{12} + \ldots + \frac{12}{12}\right)$

$= \frac{1}{144}(1 + 2 + 3 + \ldots + 12)$

$= \frac{1}{144}\left(\frac{12 \times 13}{2}\right)$

$= \frac{78}{144}$

$\doteq 0.542$

Intuitively, the more rectangles that are constructed the better the approximation becomes. Suppose we constructed 100 rectangles of equal width $\frac{1}{100}$.

$$\text{Area} \doteq \frac{1}{100}\left[f\left(\tfrac{1}{100}\right) + f\left(\tfrac{2}{100}\right) + f\left(\tfrac{3}{100}\right) + \dots + f\left(\tfrac{100}{100}\right)\right]$$

$$\doteq \frac{1}{100}\left(\tfrac{1}{100} + \tfrac{2}{100} + \tfrac{3}{100} + \dots + \tfrac{100}{100}\right)$$

$$= \frac{1}{100^2}(1 + 2 + 3 + \dots + 100)$$

$$= \frac{1}{100^2}\left(\tfrac{100 \times 101}{2}\right)$$

$$= \frac{101}{200}$$

$$= 0.505$$

This is much closer to the actual area of 0.5 calculated in Example 1(a).

If we subdivide the region into n strips of equal width $\frac{1}{n}$ we could construct n rectangles and

$$\text{Area} \doteq \frac{1}{n}\left[f\left(\frac{1}{n}\right) + f\left(\frac{2}{n}\right) + f\left(\frac{3}{n}\right) + \dots + f\left(\frac{n}{n}\right)\right]$$

$$= \frac{1}{n}\left(\frac{1}{n} + \frac{2}{n} + \frac{3}{n} + \dots + \frac{n}{n}\right)$$

$$= \frac{1}{n^2}(1 + 2 + 3 + \dots + n)$$

$$= \frac{1}{n^2}\left[\frac{n(n + 1)}{2}\right]$$

$$= \frac{n^2 + n}{2n^2}$$

Now as $n \to \infty$ the number of rectangles increases and their width $\frac{1}{n}$ approaches 0 and the limit of the sum of the rectangles as $n \to \infty$ produces the actual area.

$$\text{Area} = \lim_{n \to \infty} \frac{n^2 + n}{2n^2} = \lim_{n \to \infty} \frac{1 + \dfrac{1}{n}}{2} = \tfrac{1}{2} = 0.5$$

We use sigma notation to write the series in the rest of the examples.

Example 2   Find the area under $y = x^2$ from $x = 0$ to $x = 2$.

Solution   Subdivide the region into n strips of equal width, $\frac{2}{n}$. Consider a general rectangle, which we call the ith rectangle, having width $\Delta x = \frac{2}{n}$ and height $f\left(\frac{2i}{n}\right)$ determined by the right-hand endpoint.

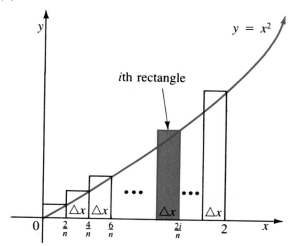

Using sigma notation, the sum of the areas of the n rectangles is

$$\sum_{i=1}^{n} \frac{2}{n} f\left(\frac{2i}{n}\right) = \sum_{i=1}^{n} \left(\frac{2}{n}\right)\left(\frac{4i^2}{n^2}\right)$$

$$= \frac{8}{n^3} \sum_{i=1}^{n} i^2$$

$$= \frac{8}{n^3} \left[\frac{n(n + 1)(2n + 1)}{6}\right]$$

$$= \frac{4(2n^2 + 3n + 1)}{3n^2}$$

Therefore, $\text{Area} = \dfrac{4}{3} \lim_{n \to \infty} \dfrac{2n^2 + 3n + 1}{n^2}$

$$= \frac{4}{3} \lim_{n \to \infty} \left(2 + \frac{3}{n} + \frac{1}{n^2}\right)$$

$$= \tfrac{4}{3}(2 + 0 + 0)$$

$$= \frac{8}{3}$$

Example 3   Find the area under $y = x^3 + x$ from $x = 1$ to $x = 4$.

Solution   Subdivide the region into n strips of equal width

$$\Delta x = \frac{4 - 1}{n} = \frac{3}{n}$$

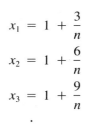

$$x_1 = 1 + \frac{3}{n}$$

$$x_2 = 1 + \frac{6}{n}$$

$$x_3 = 1 + \frac{9}{n}$$

.
.
.

The ith rectangle has right-hand endpoint

$$x_i = 1 + \frac{3i}{n}$$

and height $f\!\left(1 + \frac{3i}{n}\right)$

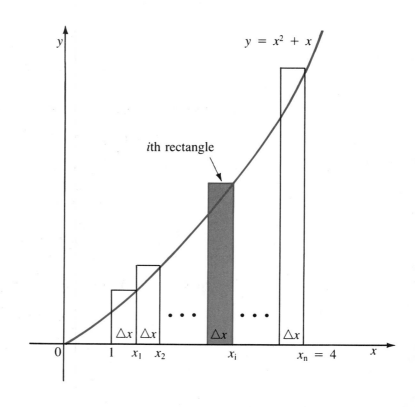

$$\text{Area} = \lim_{n \to \infty} \sum_{i=1}^{n} \frac{3}{n} f\left(1 + \frac{3i}{n}\right)$$

$$= \lim_{n \to \infty} \sum_{i=1}^{n} \frac{3}{n}\left[\left(1 + \frac{3i}{n}\right)^3 + \left(1 + \frac{3i}{n}\right)\right]$$

$$= \lim_{n \to \infty} \sum_{i=1}^{n} \left(\frac{3}{n} + \frac{27i}{n^2} + \frac{81i^2}{n^3} + \frac{81i^3}{n^4} + \frac{3}{n} + \frac{9i}{n^2}\right)$$

$$= \lim_{n \to \infty} \left(\frac{81}{n^4}\sum_{i=1}^{n} i^3 + \frac{81}{n^3}\sum_{i=1}^{n} i^2 + \frac{36}{n^2}\sum_{i=1}^{n} i + \frac{6}{n}\sum_{i=1}^{n} 1\right)$$

$$= \lim_{n \to \infty} \left[\frac{81n^2(n+1)^2}{4n^4} + \frac{81n(n+1)(2n+1)}{6n^3} + \frac{36n(n+1)}{2n^2} + \frac{6n}{n}\right]$$

$$= \lim_{n \to \infty} \left[\frac{81}{4}\left(1 + \frac{1}{n}\right)^2 + \frac{81}{6}\left(1 + \frac{1}{n}\right)\left(2 + \frac{1}{n}\right) + 18\left(1 + \frac{1}{n}\right) + 6\right]$$

$$= \frac{81}{4} + \frac{81}{3} + 18 + 6$$

$$= \frac{285}{4}$$

We develop a formula to find the area under $y = f(x)$ from a to b for f continuous and positive. We subdivide the region into n strips of equal width

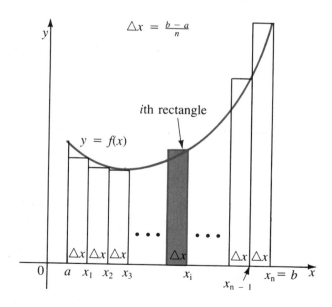

From the diagram we see that the right-hand endpoints of the intervals are

$$x_1 = a + \Delta x$$
$$x_2 = a + 2\Delta x$$
$$x_3 = a + 3\Delta x$$

.

.

.

The right-hand endpoint of the ith interval is

$$x_i = a + i\Delta x$$

The height of the ith rectangle is $f(x_i)$, so its area is

$$\text{height} \times \text{width} = f(x_i)\Delta x$$

To find the required area, we take the limit of the sums of the areas of the rectangles.

$$\text{Area} = \lim_{n \to \infty} \sum_{i=1}^{n} f(x_i)\Delta x$$

$$\text{where } \Delta x = \frac{b - a}{n} \text{ and } x_i = a + i\Delta x$$

EXERCISE 10.4

B **1.** *R* is the region under $y = x + 1$ from 0 to 6.
   (a) Calculate the area of *R* using the formula for the area of a trapezoid.
   (b) Approximate the area of *R* by dividing it into six subintervals of equal width and summing the areas of rectangles.

  2. *R* is the region under $y = x^2 + 1$ from 1 to 3.
   (a) Calculate the area of *R* using the differential equation $A'(x) = f(x)$.
   (b) Approximate the area of *R* by dividing it into ten subintervals of equal width and summing the areas of rectangles.

  3. Use methods of this section to calculate the area of the given region.
   (a) under $y = x^3$ from 0 to 4
   (b) under $y = 2 + x^2$ from 0 to 3
   (c) under $y = x + 2x^3$ from 0 to 2
   (d) under $y = 3x^3 + 2x^2 + x$ from 0 to 1

4. Use methods of this section to calculate the area of the given region.
   (a) $y = -x^2 + 16$ from 1 to 3
   (b) $y = x^2 + 3x - 2$ from 1 to 4
   (c) $y = \frac{1}{2}x^3$ from 2 to 4
   (d) $y = x^2 + x + 1$ from -1 to 3

5. Approximate the area under $y = \sin x$ from 0 to π by summing the areas of six rectangles of equal width.

C 6. Find the area between the given curves by summing the areas of n rectangles of equal width.
   (a) $y = x^2 + 4$ and $y = x + 2$ from $x = 0$ to $x = 2$
   (b) $y = x^3 - 4x$ and $y = 5x$

PROBLEMS PLUS

(a) Show that
$$2 \sin \tfrac{1}{2}x \cos ix = \sin\left(i + \tfrac{1}{2}\right)x - \sin\left(i - \tfrac{1}{2}\right)x$$

(b) Use the identity in part (a) to show that
$$\sum_{i=1}^{n} \cos ix = \frac{\sin\left(n + \tfrac{1}{2}\right)x - \sin \tfrac{1}{2}x}{2 \sin \tfrac{1}{2}x}$$

(c) Deduce from part (b) that
$$\sum_{i=1}^{n} \cos ix = \frac{\sin \tfrac{1}{2}nx \cos \tfrac{1}{2}(n + 1)x}{\sin \tfrac{1}{2}x}$$

(d) Use part (c) to find the area under the curve $y = \cos x$ from 0 to b, $0 \le b \le \dfrac{\pi}{2}$, as a limit of sums.

10.5 NUMERICAL METHODS

We can accurately evaluate an area under $y = f(x)$ if we can find an antiderivative of f. Sometimes it is difficult or even impossible to find such an antiderivative. In such cases we can only approximate the area under the curve. In Section 10.4, we approximated the area of a region by subdividing it into narrow strips and approximating the area of each strip with a rectangle. The sum of the areas of the rectangles approximated the area of the region. As the widths of the strips became narrower, the number of rectangles increased and the approximation became better.

In this section we examine other methods of approximating the area of a curved region. In particular, we are looking for better approximations using fewer subintervals.

Example 1   Find the area under $f(x) = x^2$ from $x = 1$ to $x = 3$ by dividing the interval into four subintervals of equal width and approximating the area using

(a) rectangles with height determined by the left-hand endpoint;
(b) rectangles with height determined by the right-hand endpoint;
(c) trapezoids;
(d) rectangles with height determined by the midpoint.

Solution   (a)

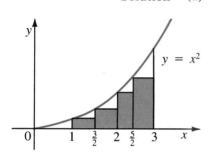

$$\text{Area} \doteq \tfrac{1}{2}f(1) + \tfrac{1}{2}f\left(\tfrac{3}{2}\right) + \tfrac{1}{2}f(2) + \tfrac{1}{2}f\left(\tfrac{5}{2}\right)$$
$$= \tfrac{1}{2}\left(1 + \tfrac{9}{4} + 4 + \tfrac{25}{4}\right)$$
$$= \tfrac{1}{2}\left(\tfrac{54}{4}\right)$$
$$= 6.75$$

(b)

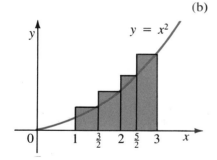

$$\text{Area} \doteq \tfrac{1}{2}f\left(\tfrac{3}{2}\right) + \tfrac{1}{2}f(2) + \tfrac{1}{2}f\left(\tfrac{5}{2}\right) + \tfrac{1}{2}f(3)$$
$$= \tfrac{1}{2}\left(\tfrac{9}{4} + 4 + \tfrac{25}{4} + 9\right)$$
$$= \tfrac{1}{2}\left(\tfrac{86}{4}\right)$$
$$= 10.75$$

(c)

$$A \doteq \tfrac{1}{2}\left(\tfrac{1}{2}\right)\left[f(1) + f\left(\tfrac{3}{2}\right)\right] + \tfrac{1}{2}\left(\tfrac{1}{2}\right)\left[f\left(\tfrac{3}{2}\right) + f(2)\right] + \tfrac{1}{2}\left(\tfrac{1}{2}\right)\left[f(2) + f\left(\tfrac{5}{2}\right)\right]$$
$$+ \tfrac{1}{2}\left(\tfrac{1}{2}\right)\left[f\left(\tfrac{5}{2}\right) + f(3)\right]$$
$$= \tfrac{1}{4}\left[f(1) + 2f\left(\tfrac{3}{2}\right) + 2f(2) + 2f\left(\tfrac{5}{2}\right) + f(3)\right]$$
$$= \tfrac{1}{4}\left(1 + \tfrac{9}{2} + 8 + \tfrac{25}{2} + 9\right)$$
$$= \tfrac{1}{4}\left(\tfrac{70}{2}\right)$$
$$= 8.75$$

(d)

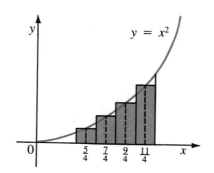

$$A \doteq \frac{1}{2}f\left(\frac{1+\frac{3}{2}}{2}\right) + \frac{1}{2}f\left(\frac{\frac{3}{2}+2}{2}\right) + \frac{1}{2}f\left(\frac{2+\frac{5}{2}}{2}\right) + \frac{1}{2}f\left(\frac{\frac{5}{2}+3}{2}\right)$$

$$= \frac{1}{2}\left(\left(\frac{5}{4}\right)^2 + \left(\frac{7}{4}\right)^2 + \left(\frac{9}{4}\right)^2 + \left(\frac{11}{4}\right)^2\right)$$

$$= \frac{1}{32}(25 + 49 + 81 + 121)$$

$$= \frac{276}{32}$$

$$= 8.625$$

We can find the area in Example 1 by solving the differential equation

$$A'(x) = x^2$$

We choose the antiderivative

$$F(x) = \frac{x^3}{3}$$

The required area is

$$A(3) = F(3) - F(1)$$

$$= 9 - \frac{1}{3}$$

$$= 8\frac{2}{3}$$

$$\doteq 8.667$$

Neither of the first two sets of rectangles produces a good approximation, but the average of the two results, $\frac{10.75 + 6.75}{2} = 8.75$, is a good approximation. In fact, we get the approximation determined by the trapezoids. This is not surprising. The diagram illustrates that the area of the trapezoid is the average of the areas of the upper and lower rectangles.

A_1 = area of *lower rectangle*

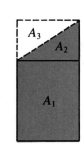

$A_1 + A_2 + A_3$ = area of the *upper rectangle*

$A_2 = A_3$

$$\frac{A_1 + (A_1 + A_2 + A_3)}{2}$$

$$= \frac{2A_1 + A_2 + A_2}{2}$$

$$= A_1 + A_2$$

$$= \text{area of } trapezoid$$

The trapezoids and the rectangles with height determined by the midpoint of the interval produced very good approximations with a small number of subintervals. We shall concentrate on these two methods in this section. Note the similarity in the following approximations.

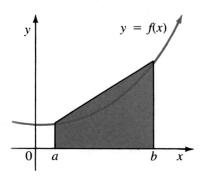

$$\text{Area} \doteq (b - a)\frac{(f(a) + f(b))}{2}$$

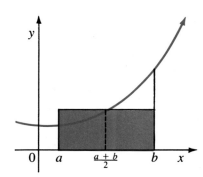

$$\text{Area} \doteq (b - a) f\left(\frac{a + b}{2}\right)$$

Example 2   (a)   Approximate the area of the region under $y = e^{x^2}$ from 0 to 1 using 2 rectangles of equal width with height determined by the midpoint of the base.

          (b)   Repeat part (a) using 4 rectangles.

Solution   (a)   The width of each rectangle is $\dfrac{1 - 0}{2} = \dfrac{1}{2}$.

The midpoint of the first interval is $\dfrac{0 + \frac{1}{2}}{2} = \dfrac{1}{4}$.

The midpoint of the second interval is $\dfrac{\frac{1}{2} + 1}{2} = \dfrac{3}{4}$.

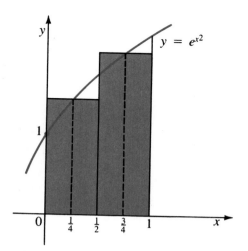

$$\text{Area} \doteq \frac{1}{2}f\left(\frac{1}{4}\right) + \frac{1}{2}f\left(\frac{3}{4}\right)$$

$$= \frac{1}{2}\left(e^{\frac{1}{16}} + e^{\frac{9}{16}}\right)$$

$$\doteq 1.409\ 775$$

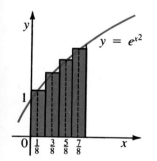

(b) The width of each interval is $\dfrac{1 - 0}{4} = \dfrac{1}{4}$.

The successive midpoints are $\dfrac{1}{8}, \dfrac{3}{8}, \dfrac{5}{8},$ and $\dfrac{7}{8}$.

$$\text{Area} \doteq \frac{1}{4}\left[f\left(\frac{1}{8}\right) + f\left(\frac{3}{8}\right) + f\left(\frac{5}{8}\right) + f\left(\frac{7}{8}\right)\right]$$

$$= 0.25\left(e^{\frac{1}{64}} + e^{\frac{9}{64}} + e^{\frac{25}{64}} + e^{\frac{49}{64}}\right)$$

$$\doteq 1.448\ 745$$

Example 3 (a) Approximate the area of the region under $y = \dfrac{\sin x}{x}$ from $\dfrac{\pi}{4}$ to $\dfrac{3\pi}{4}$ using two trapezoids of equal height.

(b) Repeat part (a) using 4 trapezoids.

Solution (a) The width of each interval, hence the height of each trapezoid, is

$$\frac{\dfrac{3\pi}{4} - \dfrac{\pi}{4}}{2} = \frac{\pi}{4}$$

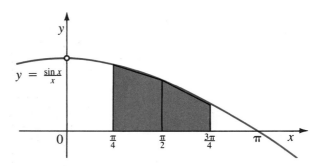

The first trapezoid has parallel sides with lengths $f\left(\dfrac{\pi}{4}\right)$ and $f\left(\dfrac{\pi}{2}\right)$.

The second trapezoid has parallel sides of length $f\left(\dfrac{\pi}{2}\right)$ and $f\left(\dfrac{3\pi}{4}\right)$.

$$
\begin{aligned}
\text{Area} &\doteq \frac{1}{2}\left(\frac{\pi}{4}\right)\left[f\left(\frac{\pi}{4}\right) + f\left(\frac{\pi}{2}\right)\right] + \frac{1}{2}\left(\frac{\pi}{4}\right)\left[f\left(\frac{\pi}{2}\right) + f\left(\frac{3\pi}{4}\right)\right] \\
&= \frac{\pi}{8}\left[f\left(\frac{\pi}{4}\right) + 2f\left(\frac{\pi}{2}\right) + f\left(\frac{3\pi}{4}\right)\right] \\
&= \frac{\pi}{8}\left(\frac{\sin\frac{\pi}{4}}{\frac{\pi}{4}} + 2\,\frac{\sin\frac{\pi}{2}}{\frac{\pi}{2}} + \frac{\sin\frac{3\pi}{4}}{\frac{3\pi}{4}}\right) \\
&\doteq 0.971\ 405
\end{aligned}
$$

(b) The width of each interval, hence the height of each trapezoid, is

$$\frac{\dfrac{3\pi}{4} - \dfrac{\pi}{4}}{4} = \frac{\pi}{8}$$

The lengths of the parallel sides of the first trapezoid are $f\left(\dfrac{\pi}{4}\right)$ and $f\left(\dfrac{3\pi}{8}\right)$.

The lengths of the parallel sides of the second trapezoid are $f\left(\dfrac{3\pi}{8}\right)$ and $f\left(\dfrac{\pi}{2}\right)$.

The lengths of the parallel sides of the third trapezoid are $f\left(\dfrac{\pi}{2}\right)$ and $f\left(\dfrac{5\pi}{8}\right)$.

The lengths of the parallel sides of the fourth trapezoid are $f\left(\dfrac{5\pi}{8}\right)$ and $f\left(\dfrac{3\pi}{4}\right)$.

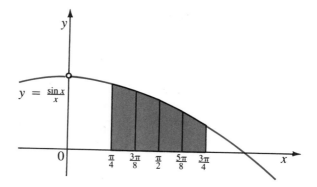

$$\text{Area} \doteq \frac{1}{2}\left(\frac{\pi}{8}\right)\left[f\left(\frac{\pi}{4}\right) + 2f\left(\frac{3\pi}{8}\right) + 2f\left(\frac{\pi}{2}\right) + 2f\left(\frac{5\pi}{8}\right) + f\left(\frac{3\pi}{4}\right)\right]$$

$$= \frac{\pi}{16}\left(\frac{\sin\frac{\pi}{4}}{\frac{\pi}{4}} + 2\frac{\sin\frac{3\pi}{8}}{\frac{3\pi}{8}} + 2\frac{\sin\frac{\pi}{2}}{\frac{\pi}{2}} + 2\frac{\sin\frac{5\pi}{8}}{\frac{5\pi}{8}} + \frac{\sin\frac{3\pi}{4}}{\frac{3\pi}{4}}\right)$$

$$\doteq 0.978\ 438$$

In general, increasing the number of intervals, and hence the number of trapezoids or rectangles, increases the accuracy of the approximation. This is true up to a point. If many arithmetic operations are required, the accumulated round-off error may start to reduce the accuracy of the approximation.

If we divide the region under $y = f(x)$ from a to b into n subintervals of equal width, $\frac{b-a}{n}$, and approximate the area of each subinterval by the area of a trapezoid, then we can approximate the area of the region using the formula below.

Trapezoidal Rule

$$A \doteq \frac{1}{2}\left(\frac{b-a}{n}\right)[f(a) + 2f(x_1) + 2f(x_2) + \ldots + 2f(x_{n-2})$$
$$+ 2f(x_{n-1}) + f(b)]$$

where $x_i = a + \frac{b-a}{n}i$

Example 2 Use the Trapezoidal Rule with ten subintervals to approximate the value of ln 2.

Solution Recall that ln 2 is the area under $f(x) = \dfrac{1}{x}$ from $x = 1$ to $x = 2$. We set $n = 10$, $a = 1$, and $b = 2$ in the Trapezoidal Rule.

$$\ln 2 \doteq \frac{1}{2}\left(\frac{2-1}{10}\right)[f(1) + 2f(1.1) + 2f(1.2) + \ldots + 2f(1.9) + f(2)]$$

$$= \frac{1}{20}\left(1 + \frac{2}{1.1} + \frac{2}{1.2} + \ldots + \frac{2}{1.9} + \frac{1}{2}\right)$$

$$\doteq 0.693\ 771$$

EXERCISE 10.5

B *Round off all approximations to six decimal places.*

1. (a) Estimate the area of the region under $y = e^x$ from 0 to 2,
    (i) using 4 trapezoids, and (ii) using 4 rectangles with height determined by the midpoint of the base.
   (b) Compare the approximations in part (a) with the actual area.

2. Repeat Question 1 for the region $y = \sin x$ from $\dfrac{\pi}{4}$ to π.

3. Use six trapezoids to estimate the area of the region under $y = xe^x$ from 1 to 3.

4. Use three rectangles with height determined by the midpoint of the base to approximate the area of the region under $y = \tan x$ from 0 to $\dfrac{\pi}{4}$.

5. Sum the areas of four trapezoids to approximate the value of ln 3.

6. Use the trapezoidal rule with $n = 12$ to approximate the area under $y = \dfrac{x}{e^x}$ from 1 to 2.

COMPUTER APPLICATION

The following pseudocode and BASIC program illustrate the use of the Trapezoidal Rule in finding the area under $y = e^{x^2}$ from 0 to 3

Pseudocode

```
input the number of trapezoids, N
calculate the width of each trapezoid
set the x-coordinates to the corners of
  the base of the first trapezoid

loop N times to calculate the areas of the N
trapezoids,
  calculate the area of the trapezoid:
    (the lengths of the parallel sides are the y-
    coordinates of the points on the function whose
    x-coordinates are the corners of the base of the
    trapezoid)
  sum the areas
  reset the variables for next trapezoid,
endloop

output the SUM,
```

A BASIC Version

```
DEF function(x)=exp(x^2)
LET a=0
LET b=3

PRINT ``Enter the number of parts in which to divide
the region'';
INPUT n
LET width=(b-a)/n
LET xleft=a
LET xright=a+width

FOR x=1 to n
     LET area=1/2*width*(function(xleft)
        +function(xright))
     LET sum=sum+area
     LET xleft=xright
     LET xright=xright+width
NEXT x

PRINT USING ``the area is #############'':N sum
END
```

Output

Number of Parts N	Area
3	4 109.358 398 437 500
30	1 484.775 634 765 625
300	1 444.932 128 906 250
3000	1 444.368 652 343 750

10.6 REVIEW EXERCISE

B   *Round all approximations to six decimal places.*

1. Find the area of the region under:

    (a) $y = \dfrac{1}{x^3}$ from 1 to 3

    (b) $y = 1 - 4x^2$ from $-\dfrac{1}{2}$ to $\dfrac{1}{4}$

    (c) $y = 1 + \sin x$ from $\dfrac{\pi}{6}$ to $\dfrac{5\pi}{6}$

    (d) $y = x^2 + \cos\left(\tfrac{1}{2}x\right)$ from $-\dfrac{\pi}{2}$ to $\dfrac{\pi}{2}$

    (e) $y = 3e^x - x$ from 0 to 2   (f) $y = \dfrac{1}{x} - 1$ from $\dfrac{1}{2}$ to 1

2. Find the area bounded by the given curve and the x-axis.

    (a) $y = 4 - x^2$ (b) $y = x^3 - x^4$

    (c) $y = x^2 - x - 12$

3. Find the area between the curve and the x-axis in the given interval.

    (a) $y = x^2 - 4$ from -1 to 3   (b) $y = 2 \sin x$ from $-\dfrac{\pi}{2}$ to π

    (c) $y = (x - 1)^3$ from -1 to 2   (d) $y = -\cos 2x$ from $-\pi$ to $\dfrac{\pi}{2}$

4. Find the area between the given curves.

    (a) $y = x^2 - 6x, \; y = 12x - 2x^2$

    (b) $y = \dfrac{4}{x^2}, \; y = 5 - x^2$

    (c) $y = \sin x, \; y = \cos 2x, \; -\dfrac{\pi}{2} \leqslant x \leqslant \dfrac{5\pi}{6}$

    (d) $y = \dfrac{1}{x} - 1, \; y = 1 - \dfrac{1}{x}, \; x = 4$

5. Sketch the area determined by each of the following.

    (a) $-\ln \tfrac{3}{4}$ (b) $\ln 12 - \ln 4$

6. (a) Calculate the area of the region

    $$R = \{(x, y) \mid 4 \leqslant x \leqslant 12, \, 0 \leqslant xy \leqslant 1\}.$$

    (b) Use an area to establish an upper bound for the value of $\ln 3$.

7. Prove that $A = A_1 + A_2$ if A, A_1, and A_2 are the areas in the diagrams.

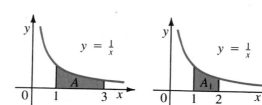
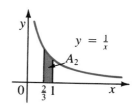

8. Calculate the required area by finding the limit of the sum of an infinite number of rectangles.
   (a) The area under $y = x^2 - 2x$ from 0 to 2.
   (b) The area under $y = x^3 - 1$ from 1 to 3.
   (c) The area between $y = x^3 + x^2 + 1$ from 2 to 6.

9. (a) Use six trapezoids to estimate the area under $y = \dfrac{1}{x^2}$ from 1 to 4.

   (b) Use three trapezoids to estimate the area under $y = \dfrac{x}{\sin x}$ from $\dfrac{\pi}{4}$ to $\dfrac{3\pi}{4}$.

10. Use four rectangles with heights determined by the midpoint of the base to approximate the area under $y = \dfrac{e^x}{x}$ from 1 to 5.

11. Approximate the value of ln 10 by summing the areas of four rectangles.

12. (a) Find the value of $\displaystyle\lim_{n \to \infty} \dfrac{1^5 + 2^5 + 3^5 + \ldots + n^5}{n^6}$ by showing that the limit is the area under $y = x^5$ from $x = 0$ to $x = 1$ and calculating the area.

    (b) Find the value of $\displaystyle\lim_{n \to \infty} \dfrac{1}{n^4}(1^3 + 2^3 + 3^3 + \ldots + n^3)$

13. (a) Find the area bounded by $y = x^2$ and $y = 4$.
    (b) The line $y = c$ cuts the region in part (a) into two equal parts. Find the value of c.

10.7 CHAPTER 10 TEST

1. Find the area under $y = (x - 1)^3 + 1$ from 1 to 3.
2. Find the area between $y = x^2 - 6x$ and $y = 2x - x^2$.
3. Find the area enclosed by $y = x^3 - 4x$ and the x-axis.
4. Find the area between $y = x^4 - 2x^2$ and $y = 2x^2$.
5. Find the area between $y = 2 \sin x$ and $y = 1$ from $x = -\dfrac{\pi}{4}$ to $x = \pi$.
6. (a) Find the area of the region

    $$R = \{(x, y) \mid 2 \leqslant x \leqslant 5, 0 \leqslant xy \leqslant 1\}$$

    (b) Use an area to prove that $\ln 2.5 < 1.05$.
7. Find the exact area under $y = x^2 + 2x$ from 0 to 3 by taking the limit of the sum of areas of rectangles.
8. Use four trapezoids to approximate the area under $y = x \cos x$ from 0 to $\dfrac{\pi}{2}$. Give your answer to six decimal places.
9. Approximate the area under $y = \dfrac{e^x}{x}$ from 2 to 6 using three rectangles with height determined by the midpoint of the base. Give your answer to six decimal places.
10. Find the area between $y = |x^2 - 1|$ and $y = -|x|$ from $x = -2$ to $x = 3$.

CUMULATIVE REVIEW FOR CHAPTERS 8 TO 10

1. (a) Graph $y = 1 - e^x$ starting from the graph of $y = e^x$.
   (b) State the domain, range, and asymptote of the function in part (a).

2. (a) Graph $y = \ln(x + 6)$ starting from the graph of $y = \ln x$.
   (b) State the domain, range, and asymptote of the function in part (a).

3. Evaluate.
   (a) $\displaystyle\lim_{x \to \infty} \left(1 + e^{-x^2}\right)$
   (b) $\displaystyle\lim_{x \to 0^+} \ln(\sin x)$

4. Evaluate.
   (a) $\ln(e^2)$
   (b) $e^{2 \ln 3}$

5. Solve each equation. State your answer exactly and also correct to six decimal places.
   (a) $e^{2x+1} = 20$
   (b) $\ln(1 - x) = -2$

6. Differentiate.

   (a) $y = (x + 1)e^{3-4x}$
   (b) $y = \dfrac{\ln(x^2 + 1)}{x}$

   (c) $y = \ln(1 + e^{x^2})$
   (d) $y = 10^{-\sqrt{x}}$

   (e) $y = \ln\sqrt{\dfrac{x}{1 - x^3}}$
   (f) $y = x^{\tan x}$

7. If f is a differentiable function, find the derivatives of the following functions.
   (a) $g(x) = e^{f(x)}$
   (b) $h(x) = f(e^x)$

8. Find the equation of the tangent line to the curve $y = e^x$ that is parallel to the line $3x - y = 6$.

9. For the function $f(x) = xe^x$, determine
   (a) the intervals of increase and decrease,
   (b) the maximum and minimum values,
   (c) the intervals of concavity and inflection points.

10. Find the general antiderivative of f on $(-\infty, \infty)$.
   (a) $f(x) = 12x^3 - 9x^2 + 8x + 31$
   (b) $f(x) = 4 \sin 2x + 5 \cos(3x + 1)$
   (c) $f(x) = -2e^{3x} + \tfrac{1}{3}e^{-4x}$

11. Find the general antiderivative of f on $(0, \infty)$.
   (a) $f(x) = \dfrac{\sqrt{2}}{x + 1} - \dfrac{\sqrt{3}}{x}$
   (b) $f(x) = \sqrt{2x} + \sqrt{5x} + \sqrt{8x}$

12. Find the function F given that the point $(2, 3)$ is on the graph $y = F(x)$, where
   (a) $F'(x) = 3x^2 + 2x$
   (b) $F'(x) = \dfrac{1}{\sqrt{x}} - x$
   (c) $F'(x) = 3e^{4x}$

13. A stone is hurled straight down at 20 m/s from the edge of a bridge 155 m above the bay below. How many seconds later does the splash occur?

14. A bacteria culture starts with 1200 bacteria. After an hour the estimated count is 4000.
    (a) Find the number of bacteria after t hours.
    (b) Find the number of bacteria after 3 h.
    (c) Find the rate of growth after 3 h.
    (d) When will the bacteria population reach 10 000?

15. An isotope of bismuth, ^{214}Bi, has a half-life of 19.7 min. A sample of ^{214}Bi has a mass of 50 g.
    (a) Find the mass that remains after t minutes.
    (b) Find the mass that remains after 2 h.
    (c) Find the rate of decay after 2 h.
    (d) How long does it take the sample to decay until its mass is 1 g?

16. Bread is removed from a 150°C oven and placed in a cooling rack maintained at 30°C. The bread cools 50° in the first 3 min. How many more minutes will it take to reach a temperature of 40°C?

17. Three kilograms of salt are dissolved in 450 L of water. A brine solution having a salt concentration of 17 g/L is pumped into the tank at a rate of 6 L/min. The water is well stirred and the tank has an overflow mechanism so that there is always 450 L of salt water in the tank. Find the amount of salt in the tank after half an hour.

18. Two hundred fish are put into a lake whose carrying capacity is 6000. The number of fish triples in the first year. When will there be 3000 fish in the lake?

19. Solve the differential equation

$$\frac{d^2s}{dt^2} + 1.44s = 0$$

with $s = 1.7$ and $\dfrac{ds}{dt} = 1.8$ when $t = 0$.

20. A spring with mass 1.2 kg has natural length 0.50 m. A force of 9 N is required to stretch it to a length of 0.80 m. The spring is compressed to a length of 0.35m and then released from rest.
    (a) How long does it take to return to that position?
    (b) Find its speed when its displacement is zero.

21. Find the area of the given region.
    (a) Under $y = -x^2 + 16$ from -1 to 3
    (b) Under $xy = 1$ from 3 to 5
    (c) Under $y = e^{-x}$ from 0 to 7

22. Find the area of the given region.
   (a) Between $y = x^4$ and $y = 2x - x^2$
   (b) Between $y = x^2 - 4x + 3$ and $x - y - 1 = 0$
   (c) Between $y = \sin x$ and $y = -\cos x$ from $-\pi$ to π
   (d) Between $y = -\cos x$ and the x-axis from 0 to π
   (e) Between $y = x^3 - 2x^2 - 5x + 6$ and the x-axis from -1 to 2

23. Find the area of the given region by taking the limit of the sum of areas of rectangles.
   (a) Under $y = mx$ from 0 to a
   (b) Under $y = -x^2 + 2x$ from 0 to 2

24. Approximate the area under $y = xe^x$ from 2 to 4 using four trapezoids. Give your answer to 6 decimal places.

25. Estimate the area under $y = \dfrac{\sin x}{x}$ from 0 to π using four rectangles with height determined by the mid-point of the base. Give your answer to six decimal places.

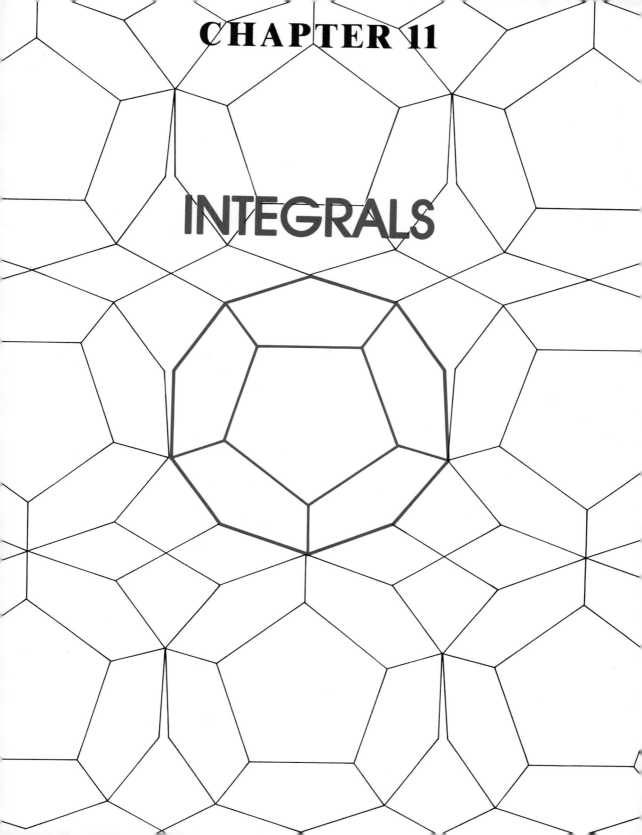

CHAPTER 11

INTEGRALS

REVIEW AND PREVIEW TO
CHAPTER 11

Volume of a Cylinder

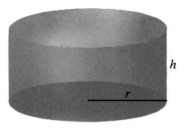

$$V = \pi r^2 h$$
where r = radius of base
h = height

EXERCISE 1

1. Find the volume of each solid.

(a)

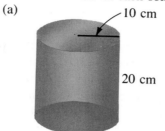

10 cm

20 cm

(b)

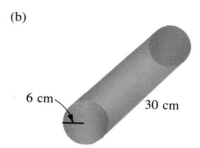

6 cm

30 cm

(c)

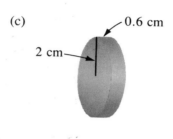

0.6 cm

2 cm

(d)

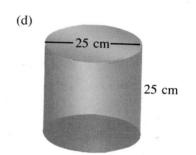

25 cm

25 cm

(e)

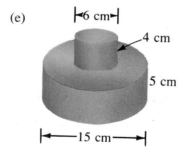

6 cm

4 cm

5 cm

15 cm

(f)

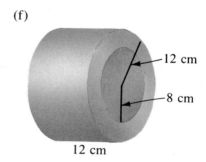

12 cm

8 cm

12 cm

INTRODUCTION

There are two main branches of calculus, differential calculus and integral calculus. The first nine chapters of this book were concerned with differential calculus, whose central idea is that of a derivative and which arose from the solution to the tangent problem.

The main concept in integral calculus is the definite integral, and we will see in this chapter that it arises from the solution of the area problem. We discover how the Fundamental Theorem of Calculus links the two branches of calculus and enables us to compute integrals in terms of antiderivatives. Then we study a number of techniques for calculating integrals and use them to find volumes.

Chapters 10 and 11 of this book constitute an introduction to integral calculus and we apply it to find areas between curves and volumes of solids of revolution. In further courses you will see that integrals can also be used to compute lengths of curves and areas of surfaces in geometry; work, forces, and centres of mass in physics; and other quantities in probability, chemistry, biology, and economics.

11.1 THE DEFINITE INTEGRAL

In Section 10.4 we saw that a limit of the form

$$\lim_{n \to \infty} \sum_{i=1}^{n} f(x_i)\, \Delta x \qquad \text{①}$$

where $\Delta x = \dfrac{b - a}{n}$ and $x_i = a + i\Delta x$

arises in finding the area under the curve $y = f(x)$ from a to b.

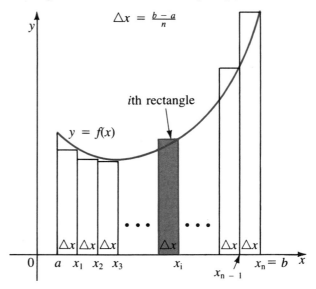

In Section 11.7 we will see that similar limits occur in calculating volumes. In fact, it turns out that limits of the form ① also arise in computing lengths of curves, areas of surfaces, and physical quantities such as work and force. Since this type of limit occurs so frequently, we give it a special name and notation.

Let f be a continuous function defined on an interval $[a, b]$. The **definite integral of f from a to b** is

$$\int_a^b f(x)dx = \lim_{n \to \infty} \sum_{i=1}^{n} f(x_i)\,\Delta x$$

where $\quad \Delta x = \dfrac{b - a}{n} \quad$ and $\quad x_i = a + i\Delta x$

The symbol $\int$ was introduced by Leibniz and is called an **integral sign**. It is an elongated S and he chose it because an integral is a limit of sums. In the notation $\int_a^b f(x)dx$, $f(x)$ is called the **integrand** and a and b are called the **limits of integration**; a is the **lower limit** and b is the **upper limit**. You should regard $\int_a^b f(x)dx$ as a single symbol; the significance of dx will be explained in Section 11.3. The procedure of calculating an integral is called **integration**.

If the integrand is a positive function, then the integral represents an area. In fact, from Section 10.4 we know the following.

For the special case where $f(x) \geq 0$,

$$\int_a^b f(x)dx = \text{the area under the graph of } f \text{ from } a \text{ to } b$$

In general, however, *an integral need not represent an area*. This is the case in the following example.

Example 1   Evaluate $\displaystyle\int_0^5 (3x - x^2)dx$.

Solution   We apply the definition of a definite integral with integrand $f(x) = 3x - x^2$, lower limit $a = 0$, and upper limit $b = 5$. Thus

$$\Delta x = \frac{b - a}{n} = \frac{5 - 0}{n} = \frac{5}{n}$$

and $\qquad x_i = a + i\Delta x = 0 + i\left(\frac{5}{n}\right) = \frac{5i}{n}$

Therefore we have

$$\int_0^5 (3x - x^2)dx = \lim_{n \to \infty} \sum_{i=1}^{n} f(x_i)\,\Delta x$$

$$= \lim_{n \to \infty} \sum_{i=1}^{n} f\left(\frac{5i}{n}\right)\frac{5}{n}$$

$$= \lim_{n \to \infty} \sum_{i=1}^{n} \left[3\left(\frac{5i}{n}\right) - \left(\frac{5i}{n}\right)^2\right]\frac{5}{n}$$

$$= \lim_{n \to \infty} \sum_{i=1}^{n} \left(\frac{75i}{n^2} - \frac{125i^2}{n^3}\right)$$

$$= \lim_{n \to \infty} \left(\frac{75}{n^2}\sum_{i=1}^{n} i - \frac{125}{n^3}\sum_{i=1}^{n} i^2\right)$$

$$= \lim_{n \to \infty} \left[\left(\frac{75}{n^2}\right)\frac{n(n+1)}{2} - \left(\frac{125}{n^3}\right)\frac{n(n+1)(2n+1)}{6}\right]$$

$$= \lim_{n \to \infty} \left[\frac{75}{2}\left(1 + \frac{1}{n}\right) - \frac{125}{6}\left(1 + \frac{1}{n}\right)\left(2 + \frac{1}{n}\right)\right]$$

$$= \frac{75}{2}(1) - \frac{125}{6}(1)(2)$$

$$= -\frac{25}{6}$$

Notice that the value of the integral in Example 1 is a negative number. This is not surprising because the function $f(x) = 3x - x^2$ takes on both positive and negative values for $0 \le x \le 5$, and so the integral does not represent an area. In the following example we compute the value of the approximating sum for $n = 10$ and show that it is negative. This will enable us to see what the integral does represent.

Example 2   If $f(x) = 3x - x^2$, $a = 0$, and $b = 5$, find the value of the sum

$$\sum_{i=1}^{10} f(x_i)\,\Delta x$$

Solution   With $n = 10$ we have

$$\Delta x = \frac{b - a}{n} = \frac{5 - 0}{10} = \frac{1}{2}$$

Therefore

$$\sum_{i=1}^{10} f(x_i)\Delta x = \tfrac{1}{2}\sum_{i=1}^{10} f(x_i)$$

$$= \tfrac{1}{2}[f(0.5) + f(1) + f(1.5) + f(2) + f(2.5) + f(3)$$
$$+ f(3.5) + f(4) + f(4.5) + f(5)]$$
$$= \tfrac{1}{2}[1.25 + 2 + 2.25 + 2 + 1.25 + 0 - 1.75$$
$$- 4 - 6.75 - 10]$$
$$= -6.875$$

The following diagram illustrates Example 2. Notice that the function $f(x) = 3x - x^2$ is positive for $0 < x < 3$ and negative for $3 < x \leqslant 5$. As in Section 10.4, the areas of the grey rectangles represent the first five terms in the sum. The areas of the red rectangles are the negatives of the last four terms in the sum. Thus the total sum represents the areas of the rectangles that lie above the x-axis minus the areas of the rectangles below the x-axis.

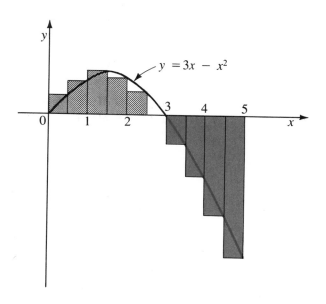

When we take the limit of such sums we get the value of the integral in Example 1. This suggests that the integral can be interpreted as the area of the grey region minus the area of the red region in the following diagram.

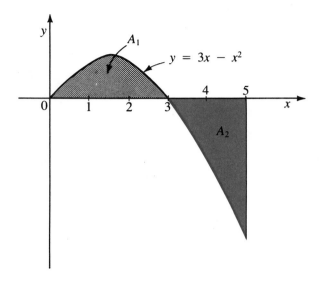

$$\int_0^5 (3x - x^2)\,dx = A_1 - A_2$$

In general, if a function f takes on both positive and negative values, then we can interpret $\int_a^b f(x)\,dx$ as a difference of areas:

$$\int_a^b f(x)\,dx = A_1 - A_2$$

where A_1 = area of region above the x-axis and below the graph of f
A_2 = area of the region below the x-axis and above the graph of f

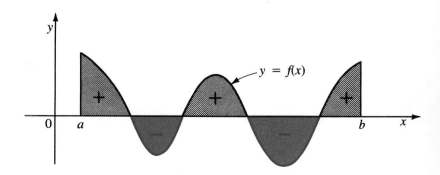

Example 3   Evaluate $\int_{-1}^{2} x^3 \, dx$ and interpret the value as a difference of areas.

Solution   We have $a = -1$, $b = 2$, and $f(x) = x^3$, so

$$\Delta x = \frac{b - a}{n} = \frac{2 - (-1)}{n} = \frac{3}{n}$$

$$x_i = a + i\Delta x = -1 + \frac{3i}{n}$$

and

$$\int_{-1}^{2} x^3 dx = \lim_{n \to \infty} \sum_{i=1}^{n} f(x_i) \Delta x$$

$$= \lim_{n \to \infty} \sum_{i=1}^{n} f\left(-1 + \frac{3i}{n}\right)\frac{3}{n}$$

$$= \lim_{n \to \infty} \sum_{i=1}^{n} \left(-1 + \frac{3i}{n}\right)^3 \frac{3}{n}$$

$$= \lim_{n \to \infty} \sum_{i=1}^{n} \left(-1 + \frac{9i}{n} - \frac{27i^2}{n^2} + \frac{27i^3}{n^3}\right)\frac{3}{n}$$

$$= \lim_{n \to \infty} \sum_{i=1}^{n} \left(-\frac{3}{n} + \frac{27i}{n^2} - \frac{81i^2}{n^3} + \frac{81i^3}{n^4}\right)$$

$$= \lim_{n \to \infty} \left(-\frac{3}{n} \sum_{i=1}^{n} 1 + \frac{27}{n^2} \sum_{i=1}^{n} i - \frac{81}{n^3} \sum_{i=1}^{n} i^2 + \frac{81}{n^4} \sum_{i=1}^{n} i^3\right)$$

$$= \lim_{n \to \infty} \left[-\frac{3}{n} n + \frac{27}{n^2}\frac{n(n+1)}{2} - \frac{81}{n^3}\frac{n(n+1)(2n+1)}{6} + \frac{81}{n^4}\frac{n^2(n+1)^2}{4}\right]$$

$$= \lim_{n \to \infty} \left[-3 + \frac{27}{2}\left(1 + \frac{1}{n}\right) - \frac{81}{6}\left(1 + \frac{1}{n}\right)\left(2 + \frac{1}{n}\right) + \frac{81}{4}\left(1 + \frac{1}{n}\right)^2\right]$$

$$= -3 + \frac{27}{2}(1) - \frac{81}{6}(1)(2) + \frac{81}{4}(1)$$

$$= 3.75$$

Since $x^3 \geq 0$ for $0 \leq x \leq 2$ and $x^3 \leq 0$ for $-1 \leq x \leq 0$, the integral can be interpreted as $A_1 - A_2$, where A_1 and A_2 are the areas shown in the diagram.

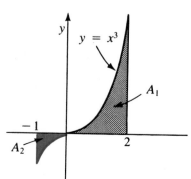

EXERCISE 11.1

B 1. (a) Evaluate the integral $\int_0^4 (x^2 - 2x)dx$.

(b) Find the value of the approximating sum
$$\sum_{i=1}^{8} f(x_i)\Delta x$$
where $f(x) = x^2 - 2x$, $a = 0$, and $b = 4$.

(c) Draw a diagram showing the approximating rectangles (like the diagram following Example 2).

(d) Interpret the integral in part (a) as a difference of areas and illustrate with a diagram.

2. Evaluate each integral.

    (a) $\int_{-2}^{3} (1 - 4x)dx$ (b) $\int_0^1 (1 + 4x - 6x^2)dx$

    (c) $\int_0^1 x^3\, dx$ (d) $\int_1^4 (x^2 - 6)dx$

3. Evaluate each integral and interpret the value as a difference of areas.

    (a) $\int_0^3 (1 - x^2)dx$ (b) $\int_3^5 (2x - 7)dx$

4. Evaluate $\int_a^b x^2\, dx$.

5. (a) Use the methods of Chapter 5 to sketch the curve $y = x^3 - 4x$.

(b) Evaluate the integral $\int_{-2}^{2} (x^3 - 4x)dx$.

(c) Give a geometric explanation for the value of the integral in part (b).

11.2 THE FUNDAMENTAL THEOREM OF CALCULUS

In Section 11.1 we used the definition of an integral to calculate integrals as limits of sums. This procedure is sometimes long and difficult and so we now give a much easier method, based on the Fundamental Theorem of Calculus.

For the special case where $f(x) \geq 0$, we know that the definite integral $\int_a^b f(x)dx$ represents the area under the curve $y = f(x)$ from a to b. From Section 10.1 we know that this area is equal to $F(b) - F(a)$, where F is any antiderivative of f. Therefore, in this case, we have

$$\int_a^b f(x)dx = F(b) - F(a) \qquad \text{where } F' = f$$

It turns out that this equation is true even when f is not a positive function.

Fundamental Theorem of Calculus

If f is continuous on the interval $[a, b]$, then

$$\int_a^b f(x)dx = F(b) - F(a)$$

where F is any antiderivative of f.

Example 1   Evaluate $\int_{-1}^2 x^3\, dx$.

Solution   The function $f(x) = x^3$ is a polynomial, so it is continuous on the interval $[-1, 2]$. An antiderivative of f is $F(x) = \frac{1}{4}x^4$, so the Fundamental Theorem of Calculus gives

$$\int_{-1}^2 x^3\, dx = F(2) - F(-1)$$

$$= \tfrac{1}{4}(2)^4 - \tfrac{1}{4}(-1)^4$$

$$= \tfrac{15}{4}$$

If you compare this solution with Example 3 in Section 11.1, you will see that the Fundamental Theorem of Calculus gives a much simpler solution.

We often use the notation

$$F(b) - F(a) = F(x)\Big]_a^b \quad \text{or} \quad F(x)\Big|_a^b$$

and so the conclusion of the Fundamental Theorem of Calculus can be written as

$$\int_a^b f(x)dx = F(x)\Big]_a^b \quad \text{where } F' = f$$

Thus the solution of Example 1 could be streamlined as follows:

$$\int_{-1}^2 x^3\, dx = \frac{x^4}{4}\Big]_{-1}^2 = \frac{2^4 - (-1)^4}{4} = \frac{15}{4}$$

Example 2   Find $\displaystyle\int_{\pi}^{2\pi} \sin x\, dx$.

Solution   An antiderivative of $\sin x$ is $-\cos x$, so

$$\int_{\pi}^{2\pi} \sin x\, dx = -\cos x \Big]_{\pi}^{2\pi}$$
$$= (-\cos 2\pi) - (-\cos \pi)$$
$$= -1 - 1$$
$$= -2$$

In order to make effective use of the Fundamental Theorem of Calculus, we must have a supply of antiderivatives of functions and we list a number of them in the following table. We use the traditional notation $\int f(x)dx$ for an antiderivative of f. (This notation is used because of the relation between integrals and antiderivatives given by the Fundamental Theorem.) The antiderivative $\int f(x)dx$ is often called an **indefinite integral of** f.

Table of Indefinite Integrals (Antiderivatives)

$$\int x^n\, dx = \frac{x^{n+1}}{n+1} + C \ (n \neq -1) \qquad \int \frac{1}{x}\, dx = \ln|x| + C$$

$$\int \sin x\, dx = -\cos x + C \qquad \int \cos x\, dx = \sin x + C$$

$$\int \sec^2 x\, dx = \tan x + C \qquad \int \csc^2 x\, dx = -\cot x + C$$

$$\int \sec x \tan x\, dx = \sec x + C \qquad \int \csc x \cot x\, dx = -\csc x + C$$

$$\int e^x\, dx = e^x + C \qquad \int a^x\, dx = \frac{a^x}{\ln a} + C \ (a \neq 1)$$

$$\int \frac{1}{x^2 + 1}\, dx = \tan^{-1} x + C \qquad \int \frac{1}{\sqrt{1 - x^2}}\, dx = \sin^{-1} x + C$$

Any formula in this table can be verified by differentiating the function on the right side. For instance,

$$\int \sec^2 x\, dx = \tan x \quad \text{because} \quad \frac{d}{dx} \tan x = \sec^2 x$$

We should distinguish carefully between definite and indefinite integrals. A definite integral $\int_a^b f(x)dx$ is a number, whereas an indefinite integral $\int f(x)dx$ is a function. The Fundamental Theorem of Calculus gives the connection between them:

$$\int_a^b f(x)dx = \int f(x)dx \Big]_a^b$$

In finding antiderivatives of more complicated functions, we use the following rules:

Properties of Integrals

$$\int cf(x)dx = c \int f(x)dx \quad (c \text{ a constant})$$

$$\int [f(x) + g(x)]dx = \int f(x)dx + \int g(x)dx$$

These can be verified by differentiating both sides of each equation.

In view of the Fundamental Theorem of Calculus, it follows that the definite integral has similar properties:

$$\int_a^b cf(x)dx = c \int_a^b f(x)dx \quad (c \text{ a constant})$$

$$\int_a^b [f(x) + g(x)]dx = \int_a^b f(x)dx + \int_a^b g(x)dx$$

Example 3 Find the general indefinite integral $\int (6x^2 + \csc^2 x)dx$.

Solution From the table, we have

$$\int (6x^2 + \csc^2 x)dx = 6 \int x^2 \, dx + \int \csc^2 x \, dx$$

$$= 6 \left(\frac{x^3}{3}\right) + (-\cot x) + C$$

$$= 2x^3 - \cot x + C$$

Example 4 Find $\int_2^5 (2x^3 - 3x^2 + 7x + 2)dx$.

Solution $\int_2^5 (2x^3 - 3x^2 + 7x + 2)dx = 2\left(\dfrac{x^4}{4}\right) - 3\left(\dfrac{x^3}{3}\right) + 7\left(\dfrac{x^2}{2}\right) + 2x\Bigg]_2^5$

$$= \tfrac{1}{2}x^4 - x^3 + \tfrac{7}{2}x^2 + 2x\Bigg]_2^5$$

$$= \left[\tfrac{1}{2}(5)^4 - 5^3 + \tfrac{7}{2}(5)^2 + 2(5)\right]$$

$$- \left[\tfrac{1}{2}(2)^4 - 2^3 + \tfrac{7}{2}(2)^2 + 2(2)\right]$$

$$= 267$$

Example 5   Evaluate $\int_1^8 \dfrac{1}{\sqrt[3]{x^2}}\,dx$.

Solution $\displaystyle\int_1^8 \dfrac{1}{\sqrt[3]{x^2}}\,dx = \int_1^8 x^{-\frac{2}{3}}\,dx$

$$= \left.\dfrac{x^{-\frac{2}{3}+1}}{-\frac{2}{3}+1}\right|_1^8$$

$$= \left.3x^{\frac{1}{3}}\right|_1^8$$

$$= 3(2) - 3(1)$$

$$= 3$$

Example 6   Find $\int_1^4 \dfrac{t^2 + \sqrt{t} - 2}{t}\,dt$.

Solution $\displaystyle\int_1^4 \dfrac{t^2 + \sqrt{t} - 2}{t}\,dt = \int_1^4 \left(t + \dfrac{1}{\sqrt{t}} - \dfrac{2}{t}\right)dt$

$\ln |t| = \ln t$
since $t > 0$

$$= \int_1^4 \left(t + t^{-\frac{1}{2}} - \dfrac{2}{t}\right)dt$$

$$= \left.\dfrac{t^2}{2} + 2t^{\frac{1}{2}} - 2\ln t\right]_1^4$$

$$= (8 + 4 - 2\ln 4) - \left(\tfrac{1}{2} + 2 - 2\ln 1\right)$$

$$= 9.5 - 2\ln 4$$

Example 7   Find $\int_0^1 \dfrac{1}{x^2 + 1}\,dx$.

Solution $\displaystyle\int_0^1 \dfrac{1}{x^2 + 1}\,dx = \left.\tan^{-1} x\right|_0^1$

$$= \tan^{-1} 1 - \tan^{-1} 0$$

$$= \dfrac{\pi}{4} - 0$$

$$= \dfrac{\pi}{4}$$

The Fundamental Theorem of Calculus says that if f is continuous, then

$$\int_a^b f(x)dx = F(b) - F(a) \quad \text{where } F' = f$$

Thus, putting $f = F'$ in the left side, we can rewrite the equation as

$$\int_a^b F'(x)dx = F(b) - F(a)$$

This version says that if we take a function F, differentiate it, and then integrate the result, we arrive at an expression that involves the original function F. Thus the Fundamental Theorem says that differentiation and integration are inverse processes. This inverse relationship, first noticed by Isaac Barrow, was used by Newton and Leibniz to make calculus a powerful method for solving problems in mathematics and science.

EXERCISE 11.2

1. Evaluate the following definite integrals.

    (a) $\int_{-6}^{7} 2\, dx$

    (b) $\int_{-1}^{5} (6x - 7)dx$

    (c) $\int_{1}^{2} (5 + 4x - 6x^2)dx$

    (d) $\int_{0}^{1} (t^2 + 6t - 1)dt$

    (e) $\int_{-1}^{2} (x^3 - x^2 + 4x)dx$

    (f) $\int_{0}^{1} (x^{99} + 1)dx$

    (g) $\int_{2}^{3} \frac{1}{t^2}\, dt$

    (h) $\int_{1}^{4} (x - \sqrt{x})dx$

    (i) $\int_{0}^{1} \sqrt[4]{x^5}\, dx$

    (j) $\int_{1}^{8} \frac{2}{\sqrt[3]{x}}\, dx$

    (k) $\int_{1}^{2} \frac{x^3 + x^2 + 1}{x^3}\, dx$

    (l) $\int_{1}^{4} \left(\frac{\sqrt{x} + 1}{x}\right)dx$

    (m) $\int_{0}^{64} \sqrt{y}(1 + \sqrt[3]{y})dy$

    (n) $\int_{0}^{\frac{\pi}{2}} (8x + \cos x)dx$

    (o) $\int_{0}^{\frac{\pi}{6}} (\sec x \tan x)dx$

    (p) $\int_{\frac{\pi}{4}}^{\frac{\pi}{3}} (3 \sin \theta - \sec^2 \theta)d\theta$

2. Find the following general indefinite integrals.

    (a) $\int (x^5 - 2x^3 + 4)dx$

    (b) $\int x^2\sqrt{x}\, dx$

    (c) $\int \left(t + \frac{2}{t}\right)dt$

    (d) $\int (1 + \sqrt{x})^2 dx$

    (e) $\int \frac{x - 5}{\sqrt[4]{x}}\, dx$

    (f) $\int (\cos \theta + \sin \theta)d\theta$

    (g) $\int (5x^4 - 2 \csc x \cot x)dx$

    (h) $\int (2 \csc^2 x + 1)dx$

3. Evaluate each integral.

(a) $\int_0^1 e^x \, dx$

(b) $\int_{-1}^1 2^x \, dx$

(c) $\int_0^{\frac{1}{2}} \frac{1}{\sqrt{1-x^2}} \, dx$

(d) $\int_1^{\sqrt{3}} \frac{12}{1+x^2} \, dx$

(e) $\int_{-1}^1 \left(x + 1 + \frac{3}{x^2 + 1} \right) dx$

(f) $\int_{-\pi}^0 (2e^x + \sin x) dx$

4. What is wrong with the following calculation?

$$\int_{-2}^1 \frac{1}{x^4} \, dx = \frac{x^{-3}}{-3} \Big]_{-2}^1 = -\frac{1}{3x^3} \Big]_{-2}^1 = -\frac{1}{3} - \frac{1}{24} = -\frac{9}{24}$$

PROBLEMS PLUS

Given that the area above the x-axis is equal to the area below the x-axis, find the equation of the parabola.

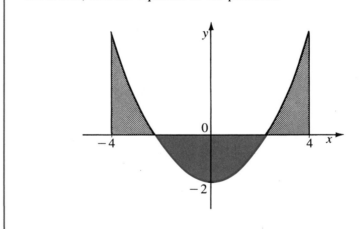

11.3   THE SUBSTITUTION RULE

If we use the Chain Rule to differentiate $y = \sqrt{x^2 + 1}$, we get

$$\frac{d}{dx} \sqrt{x^2 + 1} = \frac{1}{2}(x^2 + 1)^{-\frac{1}{2}}(2x) = \frac{x}{\sqrt{x^2 + 1}}$$

Therefore in terms of indefinite integrals, we have

$$\int \frac{x}{\sqrt{x^2 + 1}} \, dx = \sqrt{x^2 + 1} + C$$

Many other integrals can also be evaluated by reversing the Chain Rule, so first let us recall the general version of the Chain Rule:

$$\frac{d}{dx}[F(g(x))] = F'(g(x))\, g'(x)$$

Turning this around and stating it in terms of integrals, we get

$$\int F'(g(x))g'(x)dx = F(g(x)) + C$$

Let us change from the variable x to the variable $u = g(x)$. Then we have

$$\int F'(g(x))g'(x)dx = F(g(x)) + C = F(u) + C = \int F'(u)du$$

If we now write $F' = f$, we get

$$\int f(g(x))g'(x)dx = \int f(u)du$$

Thus we have the following rule for evaluating an indefinite integral when we make a *substitution* or *change of variable* $u = g(x)$.

Substitution Rule for Indefinite Integrals

If $u = g(x)$, then

$$\int f(g(x))g'(x)dx = \int f(u)du$$

Example 1 Find $\int (x^2 - 5)^8\, 2x\, dx$.

Solution 1 We let

$$u = g(x) = x^2 - 5 \quad \text{and} \quad f(u) = u^8$$
$$\text{Then} \quad g'(x) = 2x \quad \text{and} \quad f(g(x)) = (x^2 - 5)^8$$

so we have

$$\int (x^2 - 5)^8\, 2x\, dx = \int f(g(x))g'(x)dx$$
$$= \int f(u)du \qquad \text{(Substitution Rule)}$$
$$= \int u^8\, du$$
$$= \frac{u^9}{9} + C$$
$$= \frac{(x^2 - 5)^9}{9} + C$$

The Substitution Rule can be remembered most easily through the idea of a *differential*. If $u = g(x)$ is a differentiable function, we define the **differential** dx to be an independent variable; that is, dx can be given the value of any real number. Then the **differential** du is defined in terms of dx by the equation

$$du = g'(x)dx$$

For example, if $u = 8x^4$, then $du = 32x^3\ dx$.

If we now regard the dx and the du after integral signs as differentials, we have

$$\int f(g(x))g'(x)dx = \int f(u)du$$

which is the Substitution Rule. This means that in using the Substitution Rule, all we have to do is treat dx and du after integral signs as differentials. For instance, we could solve Example 1 as follows:

Solution 2   Let $u = x^2 - 5$. Then $du = 2x\ dx$, so

$$\int (x^2 - 5)^8\ 2x\ dx = \int u^8\ du = \frac{u^9}{9} + C = \frac{(x^2 - 5)^9}{9} + C$$

Example 2   Evaluate $\displaystyle\int \frac{x^2}{\sqrt{1 - x^3}}\ dx$.

Solution   Let $u = 1 - x^3$. Then $du = -3x^2\ dx$. We notice that $x^2\ dx$ occurs in the integrand, so we solve for it: $x^2\ dx = -\frac{1}{3}\ du$. Thus

$$\int \frac{x^2}{\sqrt{1 - x^3}}\ dx = \int \frac{-\frac{1}{3}\ du}{\sqrt{u}}$$

$$= -\frac{1}{3}\int u^{-\frac{1}{2}}\ du$$

$$= \left(-\frac{1}{3}\right)2u^{\frac{1}{2}} + C$$

$$= -\frac{2}{3}(1 - x^3)^{\frac{1}{2}} + C$$

In using the Substitution Rule, the idea is to replace a complicated integral by a simpler integral by changing to a new variable u. For instance, in Example 1 we started with the integral $\int (x^2 - 5)^8\ 2x\ dx$ and obtained the simpler integral $\int u^8\ du$.

In thinking of an appropriate substitution, *we try to choose u to be some function in the integrand whose differential also occurs (except perhaps for a constant factor).* In Example 1, we chose $u = x^2 - 5$ because $du = 2x\ dx$ occurs. In Example 2, we chose $u = 1 - x^3$ because $du = -3x^2\ dx$ is a constant multiple of $x^2\ dx$.

Example 3   Find $\displaystyle\int \frac{\ln x}{x}\ dx$.

Solution   We let $u = \ln x$ because its differential is $du = \dfrac{1}{x}\, dx$. Thus

$$\int \frac{\ln x}{x}\, dx = \int u\, du$$

$$= \tfrac{1}{2}u^2 + C$$

$$= \tfrac{1}{2}(\ln x)^2 + C$$

Example 4   Find $\int \sin 4x\, dx$.

Solution   Here we let $u = 4x$. Then $du = 4\, dx$, so $dx = \tfrac{1}{4}\, du$. Therefore,

$$\int \sin 4x\, dx = \int (\sin u)(\tfrac{1}{4}\, du)$$

$$= \tfrac{1}{4} \int \sin u\, du$$

$$= \tfrac{1}{4}(-\cos u) + C$$

$$= -\tfrac{1}{4} \cos 4x + C$$

Example 5   Find $\int (2 + \sin x)^{10} \cos x\, dx$.

Solution   Observe that if we let $u = 2 + \sin x$, then $du = \cos x\, dx$. So,

$$\int (2 + \sin x)^{10} \cos x\, dx = \int u^{10}\, du$$

$$= \frac{u^{11}}{11} + C$$

$$= \tfrac{1}{11}(2 + \sin x)^{11} + C$$

When performing a definite integration using substitution, we have to change the limits of integration so that they are the appropriate values of u.

Substitution Rule for Definite Integrals

If $u = g(x)$, then

$$\int_a^b f(g(x))g'(x)\, dx = \int_{g(a)}^{g(b)} f(u)\, du$$

Example 6   Evaluate $\displaystyle\int_1^9 \frac{e^{\sqrt{x}}}{\sqrt{x}}\, dx$.

Solution   Let $u = \sqrt{x}$. Then

$$du = \tfrac{1}{2}x^{-\frac{1}{2}}\, dx = \frac{1}{2\sqrt{x}}\, dx$$

So $\quad \dfrac{1}{\sqrt{x}}\, dx = 2\, du$

Now we find the new limits of integration as follows.

When $x = 1$, $u = \sqrt{1} = 1$.
When $x = 9$, $u = \sqrt{9} = 3$.

Thus, $\quad \displaystyle\int_1^9 \dfrac{e^{\sqrt{x}}}{\sqrt{x}}\, dx = \int_1^3 e^u(2\, du)$

$$= 2\int_1^3 e^u\, du$$

$$= 2e^u\Big]_1^3$$

$$= 2(e^3 - e)$$

Example 7   Find the area under the curve $y = \dfrac{1}{2x + 1}$ from 0 to 1.

Solution   Since the given function is positive for $0 \leqslant x \leqslant 1$, the area under its graph is equal to the integral:

$$A = \int_0^1 \dfrac{1}{2x + 1}\, dx$$

Let $u = 2x + 1$. Then $du = 2\, dx$, so $dx = \tfrac{1}{2}\, du$. We find the new limits of integration.

When $x = 0$, $u = 2(0) + 1 = 1$.
When $x = 1$, $u = 2(1) + 1 = 3$.

Therefore $\quad A = \displaystyle\int_0^1 \dfrac{1}{2x + 1}\, dx$

$$= \int_1^3 \dfrac{\tfrac{1}{2}\, du}{u}$$

$$= \tfrac{1}{2}\int_1^3 \dfrac{1}{u}\, du$$

$$= \tfrac{1}{2}\ln|u|\Big]_1^3$$

$$= \tfrac{1}{2}(\ln 3 - \ln 1)$$

$$= \tfrac{1}{2}\ln 3$$

EXERCISE 11.3

A 1. Suggest an appropriate substitution for each integral.

(a) $\displaystyle\int \sin(x^2)\, 2x\, dx$

(b) $\displaystyle\int \frac{(\ln x)^2}{x}\, dx$

(c) $\displaystyle\int \cos 5x\, dx$

(d) $\displaystyle\int \sqrt{\sin x}\, \cos x\, dx$

B 2. Evaluate each integral by making the given substitution.

(a) $\displaystyle\int x(1 - x^2)^{10}\, dx,\ u = 1 - x^2$

(b) $\displaystyle\int e^{5x}\, dx,\ u = 5x$

(c) $\displaystyle\int \sqrt{x - 1}\, dx,\ u = x - 1$

(d) $\displaystyle\int \frac{x + 1}{x^2 + 2x - 6}\, dx,\ u = x^2 + 2x - 6$

3. Evaluate the following indefinite integrals.

(a) $\displaystyle\int x(x^2 + 4)^8\, dx$

(b) $\displaystyle\int x^2\sqrt{x^3 + 2}\, dx$

(c) $\displaystyle\int (x + 6)^{10}\, dx$

(d) $\displaystyle\int \frac{1}{(3x - 1)^2}\, dx$

(e) $\displaystyle\int \sec^2 3x\, dx$

(f) $\displaystyle\int (1 + 2x^4)x^3\, dx$

(g) $\displaystyle\int \sin^2 x \cos x\, dx$

(h) $\displaystyle\int \frac{\sqrt{\ln x}}{x}\, dx$

(i) $\displaystyle\int t^2 e^{t^3}\, dt$

(j) $\displaystyle\int \frac{1}{1 - x}\, dx$

(k) $\displaystyle\int \frac{3x^2 - 2}{(x^3 - 2x + 1)^3}\, dx$

(l) $\displaystyle\int \frac{\sin \sqrt{x}}{\sqrt{x}}\, dx$

(m) $\displaystyle\int e^{3-x}\, dx$

(n) $\displaystyle\int e^{\cos x} \sin x\, dx$

(o) $\displaystyle\int \sqrt{1 + \tan x}\, \sec^2 x\, dx$

(p) $\displaystyle\int x \sin(x^2)\, dx$

(q) $\displaystyle\int \sin x \sin(\cos x)\, dx$

(r) $\displaystyle\int \frac{\tan^{-1} x}{1 + x^2}\, dx$

4. Evaluate the following definite integrals.

(a) $\displaystyle\int_0^1 e^{2x+1}\, dx$

(b) $\displaystyle\int_0^2 \frac{1}{(1 + 5x)^4}\, dx$

(c) $\displaystyle\int_0^2 x\sqrt{4 - x^2}\, dx$

(d) $\displaystyle\int_0^1 \sin \pi t\, dt$

(e) $\displaystyle\int_{\frac{\pi}{6}}^{\frac{\pi}{2}} \frac{\cos \theta}{\sin^3 \theta}\, d\theta$

(f) $\displaystyle\int_0^1 x^4(x^5 + 1)^5\, dx$

(g) $\displaystyle\int_{\frac{1}{2}}^{1} \frac{\left(1 + \dfrac{1}{x}\right)^5}{x^2}\, dx$

(h) $\displaystyle\int_1^2 (x + 1)e^{3x^2 + 6x - 4}\, dx$

5. Find (a) $\int \tan x \, dx$ (b) $\int \cot x \, dx$

6. Find the area under the curve $y = \sqrt{4x + 1}$ from 0 to 10.

7. Find the area under the curve $y = \cos\left(\dfrac{x}{2}\right)$, $0 \leqslant x \leqslant \pi$.

8. Find the area bounded by the curves $y = e^{-x}$, $y = e^{2x}$, and $x = 1$.

C **9.** Evaluate

(a) $\displaystyle\int \frac{1}{x + \sqrt{x}} \, dx$ (b) $\displaystyle\int \frac{x + 1}{x + 2} \, dx$

11.4 INTEGRATION BY PARTS

For every differentiation rule there is a corresponding integration rule. Just as we reversed the Chain Rule to get the Substitution Rule, we can reverse the Product Rule to get the rule for integration by parts.

The Product Rule states that if f and g are differentiable functions, then

$$\frac{d}{dx}[f(x)g(x)] = f(x)g'(x) + f'(x)g(x)$$

In terms of integrals, this becomes

$$\int [f(x)g'(x) + f'(x)g(x)]dx = f(x)g(x)$$

or $$\int f(x)g'(x)dx + \int f'(x)g(x)dx = f(x)g(x)$$

We can rewrite this equation as follows.

Integration by Parts
$$\int f(x)g'(x)dx = f(x)g(x) - \int f'(x)g(x)dx \qquad \textcircled{1}$$

Example 1   Find $\int xe^x \, dx$.

Solution   Suppose we choose

$$f(x) = x \quad \text{and} \quad g'(x) = e^x$$
$$\text{Then} \quad f'(x) = 1 \qquad\qquad g(x) = e^x$$

(For g we can choose *any* antiderivative of g'.) Then Formula 1 gives

$$\int xe^x \, dx = f(x)g(x) - \int f'(x)g(x)dx$$
$$= xe^x - \int e^x \, dx$$
$$= xe^x - e^x + C$$

In integration by parts the aim is to get a simpler integral than the one we started with. Thus, in Example 1 we started with $\int xe^x \, dx$ and expressed it in terms of the simpler integral $\int e^x \, dx$. If we had chosen $f(x) = e^x$ and $g'(x) = x$, then $f'(x) = e^x$ and $g(x) = \frac{1}{2}x^2$, so integration by parts gives

$$\int xe^x \, dx = e^x\left(\tfrac{1}{2}x^2\right) - \tfrac{1}{2}\int x^2 e^x \, dx$$

But $\int x^2 e^x \, dx$ is a more difficult integral than the one we started with. In general, *we try to choose f to be a function that becomes simpler when differentiated, as long as g'(x) can be readily integrated to give g(x).*

Formula 1 is often stated in differential notation. Let $u = f(x)$ and $v = g(x)$. Then $du = f'(x)dx$ and $dv = g'(x)dx$. By the Substitution Rule, Formula 1 can be written as follows.

Integration by Parts in Differential Notation

$$\int u \, dv = uv - \int v \, du \qquad \textcircled{2}$$

Using Formula 2, we could rewrite the solution to Example 1 as follows:

Pattern

$u = \blacksquare \searrow dv = \blacksquare$

$du = \blacksquare \longleftarrow v = \blacksquare$

Let $u = x$ $dv = e^x \, dx$

Then $du = dx$ $v = e^x$

So, $\underbrace{\int}\ \underbrace{xe^x}_{u}\ \underbrace{dx}_{dv} = \underbrace{xe^x}_{uv} - \underbrace{\int}\ \underbrace{e^x}_{v}\ \underbrace{dx}_{du} = xe^x - e^x + C$

Example 2   Find $\int x \cos 3x \, dx$.

Solution   Let

$$u = x \qquad\qquad dv = \cos 3x \, dx$$
Then $du = dx$ $v = \tfrac{1}{3} \sin 3x$

Thus, $\int x \cos 3x \, dx = x\left(\tfrac{1}{3}\sin 3x\right) - \tfrac{1}{3}\int \sin 3x \, dx$

$$= \tfrac{1}{3} x \sin 3x + \tfrac{1}{9} \cos 3x + C$$

Example 3   Evaluate $\int x^2 \sin 3x \, dx$.

Solution   Let

$$u = x^2 \qquad\qquad dv = \sin 3x \, dx$$
Then $du = 2x \, dx$ $v = -\tfrac{1}{3} \cos 3x$

So, $\int x^2 \sin 3x \, dx = x^2\left(-\tfrac{1}{3}\cos 3x\right) - \int\left(-\tfrac{1}{3}\cos 3x\right)(2x)dx$

$$= -\tfrac{1}{3} x^2 \cos 3x + \tfrac{2}{3}\int x \cos 3x \, dx$$

The integral we have obtained, $\int x \cos 3x \, dx$, was evaluated in Example 2. Using the result of that example, we get

$$\int x^2 \sin 3x \, dx = -\tfrac{1}{3} x^2 \cos 3x + \tfrac{2}{3} \int x \cos 3x \, dx$$

$$= -\tfrac{1}{3} x^2 \cos 3x + \tfrac{2}{3} \left(\tfrac{1}{3} x \sin 3x + \tfrac{1}{9} \cos 3x + C \right)$$

$$= -\tfrac{1}{3} x^2 \cos 3x + \tfrac{2}{9} x \sin 3x + \tfrac{2}{27} \cos 3x + \tfrac{2}{3} C$$

But $\tfrac{2}{3} C$ is a constant; let us call it K. Then

$$\int x^2 \sin 3x \, dx = -\tfrac{1}{3} x^2 \cos 3x + \tfrac{2}{9} x \sin 3x + \tfrac{2}{27} \cos 3x + K$$

Example 4   Find $\int x^2 \ln x \, dx$.

Solution   In this example it is not appropriate to let $u = x^2$ because we don't have a formula for the integral of $\ln x$. So we let

$$u = \ln x \qquad\qquad dv = x^2 \, dx$$
$$du = \frac{1}{x} \, dx \qquad\qquad v = \tfrac{1}{3} x^3$$

Then, $\int x^2 \ln x \, dx = (\ln x)(\tfrac{1}{3} x^3) - \int (\tfrac{1}{3} x^3) \dfrac{1}{x} \, dx$

$$= \tfrac{1}{3} x^3 \ln x - \tfrac{1}{3} \int x^2 \, dx$$

$$= \tfrac{1}{3} x^3 \ln x - \tfrac{1}{9} x^3 + C$$

When using integration by parts to find a definite integral, we evaluate both sides of the equation between the appropriate limits. For instance, Formula 1 becomes the following.

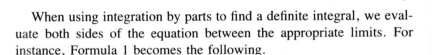

Definite Integration by Parts

$$\int_a^b f(x)g'(x)dx = f(x)g(x) \Big]_a^b - \int_a^b f'(x)g(x)dx$$

Example 5   Evaluate $\displaystyle\int_1^e \ln x \, dx$.

Solution   Here there is not much choice:

$$u = \ln x \qquad\qquad dv = dx$$
$$du = \frac{1}{x} \, dx \qquad\qquad v = x$$

$$\int_1^e \ln x \, dx = x \ln x \Big]_1^e - \int_1^e (x)\frac{1}{x} \, dx$$

$$= e \ln e - 1 \ln 1 - \int_1^e 1 \, dx$$

$$= e(1) - 1(0) - x\Big]_1^e$$

$$= e - (e - 1)$$

$$= 1$$

EXERCISE 11.4

B **1.** Evaluate the following indefinite integrals.

(a) $\displaystyle\int x \cos x \, dx$

(b) $\displaystyle\int xe^{2x} \, dx$

(c) $\displaystyle\int x \ln x \, dx$

(d) $\displaystyle\int t \sec^2 t \, dt$

(e) $\displaystyle\int x^2 e^x \, dx$

(f) $\displaystyle\int (3x - 5)e^{-4x} \, dx$

(g) $\displaystyle\int \tan^{-1} x \, dx$

(h) $\displaystyle\int \frac{xe^x}{(x + 1)^2} \, dx$

2. Evaluate the following definite integrals.

(a) $\displaystyle\int_0^\pi x \sin x \, dx$

(b) $\displaystyle\int_0^1 xe^{-x} \, dx$

(c) $\displaystyle\int_1^2 x^4 \ln x \, dx$

(d) $\displaystyle\int_0^{2\pi} x^2 \cos x \, dx$

3. (a) Show that if $n \geqslant 1$, then

$$\int_0^1 x^n e^x \, dx = e - n\int_0^1 x^{n-1} e^x \, dx$$

(b) Use the formula in part (a) repeatedly to evaluate the integral $\displaystyle\int_0^1 x^3 e^x \, dx$.

4. Evaluate the integral $\displaystyle\int e^{\sqrt{x}} \, dx$ by first making the substitution $t = \sqrt{x}$ and then integrating by parts.

5. Find the area under the curve $y = xe^{-3x}$ from 0 to 2.

6. Find the area of the region bounded by the curves $y = \ln x$, $y = 0$, and $x = 5$.

C **7.** Evaluate $\int e^x \sin x \, dx$. [*Hint:* Integrate by parts twice.]

11.5   TRIGONOMETRIC SUBSTITUTION

In this section we learn how to integrate certain combinations of trigonometric functions. Then we apply this knowledge to integrate functions containing radicals such as $\sqrt{1 - x^2}$. This will enable us to find the area enclosed by an ellipse.

Example 1   Evaluate $\int_0^{\frac{\pi}{2}} \cos^3 x \sin^4 x \, dx$.

Solution   We write

$$\cos^3 x = (\cos^2 x)(\cos x) = (1 - \sin^2 x)\cos x$$

Now the integrand is expressed in terms of $\sin x$, except for the extra factor of $\cos x$:

$$\cos^3 x \sin^4 x = (1 - \sin^2 x)\cos x \sin^4 x$$
$$= (\sin^4 x - \sin^6 x)\cos x$$

This is useful because if we make the substitution $u = \sin x$, then $du = \cos x \, dx$. We change the limits of integration as follows:

When $x = 0$, $u = \sin 0 = 0$.

When $x = \dfrac{\pi}{2}$, $u = \sin \dfrac{\pi}{2} = 1$.

Thus, $\displaystyle\int_0^{\frac{\pi}{2}} \cos^3 x \sin^4 x \, dx = \int_0^{\frac{\pi}{2}} (\sin^4 x - \sin^6 x)\cos x \, dx$

$$= \int_0^1 (u^4 - u^6)du$$

$$= \frac{u^5}{5} - \frac{u^7}{7}\bigg]_0^1$$

$$= \tfrac{1}{5} - \tfrac{1}{7}$$

$$= \tfrac{2}{35}$$

In general, we can integrate a product of the form $\sin^m x \cos^n x$ if either m or n is an odd positive integer. For instance, if m is odd, we change all but one sine into cosines (using $\sin^2 \theta = 1 - \cos^2 \theta$) and make the substitution $u = \cos \theta$.

m or n odd

An example where both m and n are even follows.

Example 2   Find $\int \sin^2 x \, dx$.

Solution   Recall that $\sin^2 x$ occurs in one of the double angle formulas for cosine:

$$\cos 2x = 1 - 2 \sin^2 x$$

Solving for $\sin^2 x$, we have

$$\sin^2 x = \tfrac{1}{2}(1 - \cos 2x)$$

Thus, $\displaystyle\int \sin^2 x \, dx = \int \tfrac{1}{2}(1 - \cos 2x)dx$

$$= \tfrac{1}{2}\int (1 - \cos 2x)dx$$

$$= \tfrac{1}{2}\!\left(x - \tfrac{1}{2}\sin 2x\right) + C$$

$$= \tfrac{1}{2}x - \tfrac{1}{4}\sin 2x + C$$

In general, we can integrate $\sin^m x \cos^n x$, where both m and n are even, by using the formulas

m and n even

$$\sin^2 x = \tfrac{1}{2}(1 - \cos 2x) \qquad \cos^2 x = \tfrac{1}{2}(1 + \cos 2x)$$

Functions that involve an expression of the form $\sqrt{a^2 - x^2}$ can be integrated by making the *trigonometric substitution* $x = a \sin\theta$, where $-\dfrac{\pi}{2} \le \theta \le \dfrac{\pi}{2}$. Use of the identity $1 - \sin^2\theta = \cos^2\theta$ will convert such an integral into an integral involving $\sin\theta$ and $\cos\theta$.

Example 3   Evaluate $\displaystyle\int \frac{1}{x^2\sqrt{1 - x^2}}\, dx$.

Solution   Let $x = \sin\theta$, $-\dfrac{\pi}{2} \le \theta \le \dfrac{\pi}{2}$. Then $dx = \cos\theta \, d\theta$ and

$$\sqrt{1 - x^2} = \sqrt{1 - \sin^2\theta} = \sqrt{\cos^2\theta}$$

But $\cos\theta \ge 0$ for $-\dfrac{\pi}{2} \le \theta \le \dfrac{\pi}{2}$, and so

$$\sqrt{1 - x^2} = \cos\theta$$

Thus, the Substitution Rule gives

$$\int \frac{1}{x^2\sqrt{1 - x^2}}\, dx = \int \frac{\cos\theta}{\sin^2\theta \cos\theta}\, d\theta$$

$$= \int \frac{1}{\sin^2\theta}\, d\theta$$

$$= \int \csc^2\theta \, d\theta$$

$$= -\cot\theta + C$$

Since this is an indefinite integral, we must return to the original variable x. This can be done by looking at the diagram. Since $\sin\theta = x$, we label the sides as shown and see that

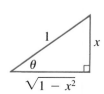

$$\cot\theta = \frac{\sqrt{1 - x^2}}{x}$$

Thus $\displaystyle\int \frac{1}{x^2\sqrt{1-x^2}}\,dx = -\frac{\sqrt{1-x^2}}{x} + C$

We could have used the substitution $x = \cos\theta$ in Example 3 but with the restriction $0 \le \theta \le \pi$ since this ensures that $\sin\theta \ge 0$.

Example 4   Find the area enclosed by the ellipse

$$\frac{x^2}{25} + \frac{y^2}{4} = 1$$

Solution   Solving the equation of the ellipse for y, we get

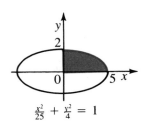

$\dfrac{x^2}{25} + \dfrac{y^2}{4} = 1$

$$\frac{y^2}{4} = 1 - \frac{x^2}{25} = \frac{25 - x^2}{25}$$

$$y^2 = \tfrac{4}{25}(25 - x^2)$$

$$y = \pm\tfrac{2}{5}\sqrt{25 - x^2}$$

The ellipse is symmetric with respect to both axes, so the total area A is four times the area in the first quadrant. The part of the ellipse in the first quadrant is given by

$$y = \tfrac{2}{5}\sqrt{25 - x^2},\ 0 \le x \le 5$$

So $\displaystyle\tfrac{1}{4}A = \int_0^5 \tfrac{2}{5}\sqrt{25 - x^2}\,dx$

$$A = \tfrac{8}{5}\int_0^5 \sqrt{25 - x^2}\,dx$$

To evaluate this integral we substitute $x = 5\sin\theta$. Then $dx = 5\cos\theta\,d\theta$. Also,

$$\sqrt{25 - x^2} = \sqrt{25 - 25\sin^2\theta} = 5\sqrt{1 - \sin^2\theta} = 5\cos\theta$$

We change the limits of integration as follows.

When $x = 0$, $\sin\theta = 0$, so $\theta = 0$.

When $x = 5$, $\sin\theta = 1$, so $\theta = \dfrac{\pi}{2}$.

Thus $\quad A = \frac{8}{5} \int_0^5 \sqrt{25 - x^2}\, dx$

$$= \frac{8}{5} \int_0^{\frac{\pi}{2}} (5 \cos \theta) 5 \cos \theta\, d\theta$$

$$= 40 \int_0^{\frac{\pi}{2}} \cos^2 \theta\, d\theta$$

$$= 40 \int_0^{\frac{\pi}{2}} \tfrac{1}{2}(1 + \cos 2\theta)d\theta$$

$$= 20\left[\theta + \tfrac{1}{2} \sin 2\theta \right]_0^{\frac{\pi}{2}}$$

$$= 20\left[\left(\frac{\pi}{2} + \tfrac{1}{2} \sin \pi\right) - (0 + 0) \right]$$

$$= 10\pi$$

EXERCISE 11.5

B **1.** Evaluate the following integrals.

  (a) $\displaystyle\int \cos^3 x\, dx$

  (b) $\displaystyle\int \sin^3 x \cos^2 x\, dx$

  (c) $\displaystyle\int \sin^2 x \cos^2 x\, dx$

  (d) $\displaystyle\int_0^{\frac{\pi}{2}} \sin^5 x\, dx$

  (e) $\displaystyle\int_0^{\frac{\pi}{2}} \cos^5 x \sin^4 x\, dx$

  (f) $\displaystyle\int_0^{\frac{\pi}{2}} \sin^4 x\, dx$

2. Evaluate each integral.

  (a) $\displaystyle\int x^3\sqrt{1 - x^2}\, dx$

  (b) $\displaystyle\int_0^2 x^2\sqrt{4 - x^2}\, dx$

3. (a) Use the trigonometric substitution $x = \tan \theta$, $-\dfrac{\pi}{2} < \theta < \dfrac{\pi}{2}$, to show that

$$\int_0^1 \frac{x^3}{\sqrt{x^2 + 1}}\, dx = \int_0^{\frac{\pi}{4}} \tan^3 \theta \sec \theta\, d\theta$$

(b) Evaluate $\int_0^{\frac{\pi}{4}} \tan^3 \theta \sec \theta \, d\theta$ by using the identity

$\tan^2 \theta = \sec^2 \theta - 1$ and making the substitution $u = \sec \theta$.

4. Find the area enclosed by the ellipse $\dfrac{x^2}{9} + \dfrac{y^2}{16} = 1$.

5. Evaluate the integral $\int x\sqrt{1 - x^2} \, dx$ by two methods:
    (a) Using the substitution $x = \sin \theta$
    (b) Using the substitution $u = 1 - x^2$

6. Show that the area enclosed by the ellipse $\dfrac{x^2}{a^2} + \dfrac{y^2}{b^2} = 1$ is πab.

11.6 PARTIAL FRACTIONS

We have learned how to add fractions using a common denominator.

$$\frac{2}{x - 1} + \frac{3}{x + 2} = \frac{2(x + 2) + 3(x - 1)}{(x - 1)(x + 2)}$$

$$= \frac{5x + 1}{(x - 1)(x + 2)}$$

A technique of integration is to reverse this process and resolve a fraction into a sum of fractions with simpler denominators, which are easier to integrate.

$$\int \frac{5x + 1}{(x - 1)(x + 2)} \, dx = \int \left(\frac{2}{x - 1} + \frac{3}{x + 2} \right) dx$$

$$= \int \frac{2}{x - 1} \, dx + \int \frac{3}{x + 2} dx$$

$$= 2 \ln |x - 1| + 3 \ln |x + 2| + C$$

The method of reversing this process is illustrated in Example 1.

Example 1   Express $\dfrac{5x + 1}{(x - 1)(x + 2)}$ as the sum of two fractions.

Solution   Let $\dfrac{5x + 1}{(x - 1)(x + 2)} = \dfrac{A}{x - 1} + \dfrac{B}{x + 2}$

Multiplying both sides by the common denominator gives us

$$5x + 1 = A(x + 2) + B(x - 1)$$
$$= Ax + 2A + Bx - B$$
$$= (A + B)x + (2A - B)$$

This is an identity if and only if

$$A + B = 5$$

and $$2A - B = 1$$

Adding the two equations, we get

$$3A = 6$$
$$A = 2$$

Substituting $A = 2$ in the first equation, we have $B = 3$.

Therefore, $$\frac{5x + 1}{(x - 1)(x + 2)} = \frac{2}{x - 1} + \frac{3}{x + 2}$$

This technique of expressing a single fraction as a sum of two or more fractions is called **the method of partial fractions**. The method involves four cases that are distinguished by the type of factors that occur in the denominator. Example 1 demonstrated the technique when the denominator is *the product of distinct linear factors*.

In Example 2 we examine the case when the denominator is *the product of linear factors, some of which are repeated*.

Example 2 (a) Resolve $\dfrac{6x + 7}{(x + 2)^2}$ into partial fractions.

(b) Evaluate $\displaystyle\int \frac{6x + 7}{(x + 2)^2}\,dx$.

Solution (a) Let $$\frac{6x + 7}{(x + 2)^2} = \frac{A}{x + 2} + \frac{B}{(x + 2)^2}$$

Multiplying both sides by the common denominator gives us

$$6x + 7 = A(x + 2) + B$$
$$= Ax + 2A + B$$

Comparing coefficients, we get

$$A = 6$$

and $$2A + B = 7$$

So $$B = -5$$

Therefore, $$\frac{6x + 7}{(x + 2)^2} = \frac{6}{x + 2} + \frac{-5}{(x + 2)^2}$$

Let $u = x + 2$

$$\int \frac{dx}{(x + 2)^2}$$
$$= \int u^{-2} \, du$$
$$= -u^{-1} + C$$
$$= -\frac{1}{x + 2} + C$$

(b)
$$\int \frac{6x + 7}{(x + 2)^2} \, dx = \int \left(\frac{6}{x + 2} + \frac{-5}{(x + 2)^2} \right) dx$$
$$= 6 \int \frac{dx}{x + 2} - 5 \int \frac{dx}{(x + 2)^2}$$
$$= 6 \ln|x + 2| + \frac{5}{x + 2} + C$$

If we wished to express $\dfrac{x^3 - x + 2}{x^2(x + 2)^3}$ as a sum of partial fractions, the initial step would be to let

$$\frac{x^3 - x + 2}{x^2(x + 2)^3} = \frac{A}{x} + \frac{B}{x^2} + \frac{C}{x + 2} + \frac{D}{(x + 2)^2} + \frac{E}{(x + 2)^3}$$

However, we confine our work to simpler examples.

The third case has *non-repeated irreducible quadratic factors* in the denominator.

Example 3   (a)   Resolve $\dfrac{-2x + 4}{(x^2 + 1)(x - 1)^2}$ into partial fractions.

(b)   Evaluate $\displaystyle\int \frac{-2x + 4}{(x^2 + 1)(x - 1)^2} \, dx$.

Solution   (a)   Let $\dfrac{-2x + 4}{(x^2 + 1)(x - 1)^2} = \dfrac{Ax + B}{x^2 + 1} + \dfrac{C}{x - 1} + \dfrac{D}{(x - 1)^2}$

$x^2 + 1$ is irreducible since it cannot be factored.

Notice that when the denominator is an irreducible quadratic the numerator is a function of the form $Ax + B$.

Multiplying both sides by the common denominator gives us

$$-2x + 4 = (Ax + B)(x - 1)^2 + C(x^2 + 1)(x - 1) + D(x^2 + 1)$$
$$= Ax^3 - 2Ax^2 + Ax + Bx^2 - 2Bx + B + Cx^3 - Cx^2 + Cx - C + Dx^2 + D$$
$$= (A + C)x^3 + (-2A + B - C + D)x^2 + (A - 2B + C)x + (B - C + D)$$

Comparing coefficients we get

$$0 = A + C \qquad\qquad ①$$
$$0 = -2A + B - C + D \qquad ②$$
$$-2 = A - 2B + C \qquad\qquad ③$$
$$4 = B - C + D \qquad\qquad ④$$

Subtracting ④ from ②

$$-4 = -2A$$
$$A = 2$$

Substituting $A = 2$ in ①

$$0 = 2 + C$$
$$C = -2$$

Substituting $A = 2$ and $C = -2$ in ③

$$-2 = 2 - 2B - 2$$
$$B = 1$$

Substituting $B = 1$ and $C = -2$ in ④

$$4 = 1 + 2 + D$$
$$D = 1$$

Therefore,

$$\frac{-2x + 4}{(x^2 + 1)(x - 1)^2} = \frac{2x + 1}{x^2 + 1} + \frac{-2}{x - 1} + \frac{1}{(x - 1)^2}$$

$$= \frac{2x}{x^2 + 1} + \frac{1}{x^2 + 1} - \frac{2}{x - 1} + \frac{1}{(x - 1)^2}$$

(b)

$$\int \frac{-2x + 4}{(x^2 + 1)(x - 1)^2} \, dx = \int \frac{2x}{x^2 + 1} \, dx + \int \frac{1}{x^2 + 1} \, dx - \int \frac{2}{x - 1} \, dx + \int \frac{1}{(x - 1)^2} \, dx$$

$$= \ln(x^2 + 1) + \tan^{-1} x - 2 \ln|x - 1| - \frac{1}{x - 1} + C$$

Let $u = x^2 + 1$
$du = 2x \, dx$

$$\int \frac{2x}{x^2 + 1} \, dx$$

$$= \int \frac{du}{u}$$

$$= \ln|u| + C$$

$$= \ln(x^2 + 1) + C$$

A fourth case involves *repeated irreducible quadratic factors* in the denominator. We will not be dealing with these, but the initial step of one such type is presented.

$$\frac{x^2 - x + 1}{(x + 1)(x^2 + 1)^3} = \frac{A}{x + 1} + \frac{Bx + C}{x^2 + 1} + \frac{Dx + E}{(x^2 + 1)^2} + \frac{Fx + G}{(x^2 + 1)^3}$$

In each of our examples, the degree of the numerator has been less than the degree of the denominator. Thus we have been dealing with **proper rational functions**. A theorem in algebra guarantees that every proper rational function can be resolved into partial fractions.

If the degree of the numerator is the same as or greater than that of the denominator, we begin by dividing the numerator by the denominator and proceed from there.

Example 4   Evaluate $\displaystyle\int_3^4 \frac{x + 4}{x - 2} \, dx.$

Solution   Since the degree of the numerator is the same as the degree of the denominator, we divide and get

$$\begin{array}{r} 1 \\ x - 2\overline{)x + 4} \\ \underline{x - 2} \\ 6 \end{array}$$

$$\frac{x + 4}{x - 2} = 1 + \frac{6}{x - 2}$$

Therefore, $$\int_3^4 \frac{x + 4}{x - 2}\,dx = \int_3^4 \left(1 + \frac{6}{x - 2}\right) dx$$

$$= \left[x + 6\,\ln|x - 2|\right]_3^4$$

$$= 4 + 6\ln 2 - (3 + 6\ln 1)$$

$$= 1 + 6\ln 2 \qquad \diamond$$

Example 5   Evaluate $\displaystyle\int \frac{5x^3 - x^2}{x^2 - 1}\,dx.$

Solution   Since the degree of the numerator exceeds the degree of the denominator, we divide and get

$$\begin{array}{r} 5x - 1 \\ x^2 - 1\overline{)5x^3 - x^2} \\ \underline{5x^3 - 5x} \\ - x^2 + 5x \\ \underline{- x^2 + 1} \\ 5x - 1 \end{array}$$

$$\frac{5x^3 - x^2}{x^2 - 1} = 5x - 1 + \frac{5x - 1}{x^2 - 1}$$

We resolve $\dfrac{5x - 1}{x^2 - 1}$ into partial fractions.

Let $$\frac{5x - 1}{(x + 1)(x - 1)} = \frac{A}{x + 1} + \frac{B}{x - 1}$$

Multiplying both sides by the common denominator gives us

$$5x - 1 = A(x - 1) + B(x + 1)$$
$$= Ax - A + Bx + B$$
$$= (A + B)x + (-A + B)$$

Comparing coefficients, we get

$$A + B = 5$$
and $$-A + B = -1$$

Adding the equations

$$2B = 4$$
$$B = 2$$

Substituting $B = 2$ in $A + B = 5$, we get $A = 3$.

Therefore, $$\frac{5x^3 - x^2}{x^2 - 1} = 5x - 1 + \frac{3}{x + 1} + \frac{2}{x - 1}$$

Now, $$\int \frac{5x^3 - x^2}{x^2 - 1}\,dx = 5\int x\,dx - \int dx + \int \frac{3}{x + 1}\,dx + \int \frac{2}{x - 1}\,dx$$

$$= \tfrac{5}{2}x^2 - x + 3\,\ln|x + 1| + 2\,\ln|x - 1| + C \qquad \diamond$$

EXERCISE 11.6

A State the form of the partial fraction decomposition of the given function. Do not determine numerical values.

1. $\dfrac{1}{(x + 2)(x - 3)}$

2. $\dfrac{x + 3}{(x + 2)(x + 5)^2}$

3. $\dfrac{x^2 + x + 1}{(x - 1)(x + 1)^2(x - 2)^3}$

4. $\dfrac{5x}{(x^2 + x + 1)(x - 7)}$

5. $\dfrac{2 - 3x}{(x + 5)(x^2 + 4)(x^2 + 2x + 6)}$

6. $\dfrac{2x - 1}{x^2 - 16}$

7. $\dfrac{x^2 + 1}{(x^2 + 7x + 12)}$

8. $\dfrac{x^3 - 2x^2 + 2}{(x - 5)^3(x^2 + 5x + 10)^2}$

B Evaluate.

9. $\displaystyle\int \dfrac{dx}{x^2 - 1}$

10. $\displaystyle\int_2^5 \dfrac{2t + 3}{t - 1}\, dt$

11. $\displaystyle\int \dfrac{x^3 - 3x^2 + x}{x^2 - 3x + 2}\, dx$

12. $\displaystyle\int \dfrac{t^3}{t^2 + 7t + 12}\, dt$

13. $\displaystyle\int \dfrac{x + 4}{2x - x^2 - x^3}\, dx$

14. $\displaystyle\int \dfrac{dx}{(x - 1)^2(x + 1)}$

15. $\displaystyle\int \dfrac{x^3 - 1}{x^3 + 3x^2}\, dx$

16. $\displaystyle\int_1^4 \dfrac{4}{x^3 + 4x}\, dx$

17. $\displaystyle\int \dfrac{1 - 3x}{x^3 - 1}\, dx$

18. $\displaystyle\int \dfrac{4x^2 + 5x + 4}{(x^2 + 1)(x^2 + 2x + 2)}\, dx$

11.7 VOLUMES OF REVOLUTION

Rotating a plane region about a line produces a solid. For example, a semicircular region rotated about its diameter is a sphere.

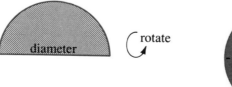
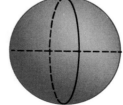

In this section we rotate a plane region about the x-axis and find the volume of the solid that is produced.

Example 1   Find the volume of the solid that is produced when the rectangle in the diagram is rotated about the *x*-axis.

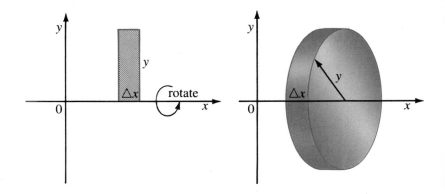

Solution   The solid produced is a cylinder with height Δx and radius *y*.

The volume *V*, of a cylinder with height *h*, and radius *r*, is

$$V = \pi r^2 h$$

Therefore, $V = \pi y^2 \Delta x$

Our method of calculating the volume of a solid that has been generated by rotating a plane region about the *x*-axis parallels the method that we used to calculate the area of a region in Section 10.4. We subdivide the solid into slices of equal thickness and approximate the volume of each slice by the volume of a cylindrical disc. Each cylindrical disc is generated by rotating a rectangle about the *x*-axis.

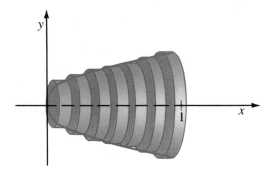

Example 2   Find the volume of the solid that is generated when the region under $y = 2x$ from 0 to 2 is rotated about the x-axis.

Solution   Subdivide the region into n slices of equal thickness $\dfrac{2}{n}$.

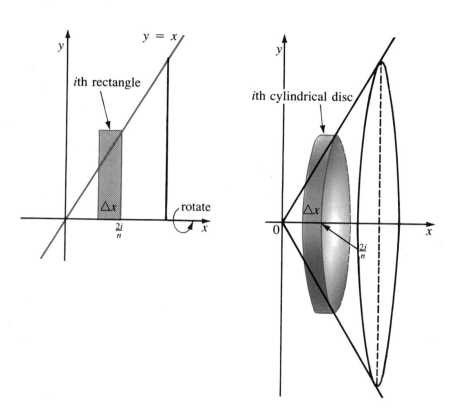

The height of a cylindrical disc is the width of a slice. The ith cylindrical disc has height $\dfrac{2}{n}$ and base radius $f\!\left(\dfrac{2i}{n}\right)$ determined by the right-hand endpoint of the ith slice.

The volume of the ith cylindrical disc is

$$\pi y^2 \Delta x = \pi \left(\frac{2i}{n}\right)^2 \left(\frac{2}{n}\right)$$

$$= \frac{8}{n^3}\pi i^2$$

The sum of the volumes of the n cylindrical discs is

$$\sum_{i=1}^{n} \frac{8}{n^3} \pi i^2 = \frac{8\pi}{n^3} \sum_{i=1}^{n} i^2$$

$$= \frac{8\pi}{n^3} \left[\frac{n(n+1)(2n+1)}{6} \right]$$

$$= \frac{4\pi}{3} \left(1 + \frac{1}{n} \right) \left(2 + \frac{1}{n} \right)$$

In order to find the volume of the solid, we take the limit as n approaches infinity:

$$V = \lim_{n \to \infty} \frac{4\pi}{3} \left(1 + \frac{1}{n} \right) \left(2 + \frac{1}{n} \right)$$

$$= \tfrac{4}{3}\pi(1)(2)$$

$$= \tfrac{8}{3}\pi$$

We develop a formula by calculating the volume of the solid that is generated when the region under $y = f(x)$ from a to b is rotated about the x-axis.

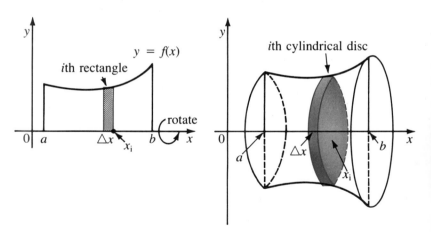

The solid is subdivided into n slices of equal thickness and the volume of each slice is approximated by the volume of a cylindrical disc.

The height of each cylindrical disc is

$$\frac{b - a}{n} = \Delta x$$

The right-hand endpoint of the ith slice is

$$x_i = a + i\Delta x$$

The volume of the ith cylindrical disc is

$$\pi y^2 \Delta x = \pi[f(x_i)]^2 \Delta x$$

The sum of the volumes of the n cylindrical discs is

$$\sum_{i=1}^{n} \pi[f(x_i)]^2 \Delta x$$

and the volume of the region is

$$V = \lim_{n \to \infty} \sum_{i=1}^{n} \pi[f(x_i)]^2 \Delta x = \int_a^b \pi[f(x)]^2 dx$$

Volume of Revolution

$$V = \pi \int_a^b [f(x)]^2 dx$$

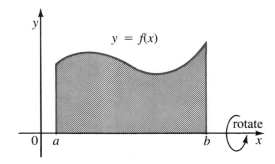

Example 3   Find the volume of the solid that is generated when the region under $y = x^3$ from 1 to 2 is rotated about the x-axis. Include a sketch of the region that is to be rotated and a sketch of the solid.

Solution   First we sketch the region and the solid.

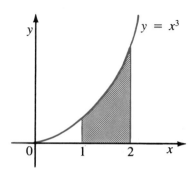
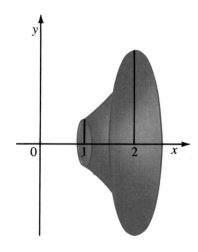

Since $V = \pi \int_a^b [f(x)]^2 dx$

therefore, $V = \pi \int_1^2 x^6 \, dx$

$= \pi \left[\dfrac{x^7}{7} \right]_1^2$

$= \dfrac{128}{7}\pi - \dfrac{1}{7}\pi$

$= \dfrac{127}{7}\pi$

Example 4   Find the volume of the solid that is generated when the region between $y = \sin x$ and $y = \cos x$ from 0 to $\dfrac{\pi}{4}$ is rotated about the x-axis.

Solution   First we sketch the curve and note that $y = \cos x$ is above $y = \sin x$ in the required region. If V_1 is the volume of the solid generated when the region under $y = \cos x$ from 0 to $\dfrac{\pi}{4}$ is rotated about the x-axis and V_2 is the volume of the solid generated when the region under $y = \sin x$ from 0 to $\dfrac{\pi}{4}$ is rotated about the x-axis, then the required volume is $V_1 - V_2$.

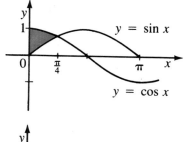

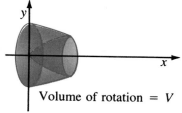

Volume of rotation $= V$

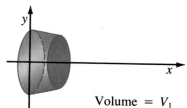

Volume $= V_1$

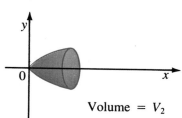

Volume $= V_2$

$$V = V_1 - V_2$$

$$= \pi \int_0^{\frac{\pi}{4}} \cos^2 x \, dx - \pi \int_0^{\frac{\pi}{4}} \sin^2 x \, dx$$

$$= \pi \int_0^{\frac{\pi}{4}} (\cos^2 x - \sin^2 x) dx$$

$$= \pi \int_0^{\frac{\pi}{4}} \cos 2x \, dx$$

$$= \pi \left[\frac{\sin 2x}{2} \right]_0^{\frac{\pi}{4}}$$

$$= \frac{\pi}{2} \left(\sin \frac{\pi}{2} - \sin 0 \right)$$

$$= \frac{\pi}{2}(1 - 0)$$

$$= \frac{\pi}{2}$$

EXERCISE 11.7

B **1.** Find the volume of the solid obtained when the given region is rotated about the x-axis. Include a sketch of the region and the solid.

(a) Under $y = x^2 + 1$ from 1 to 3

(b) Between $y = 2x - x^2$ and the x-axis

(c) Under $y = \dfrac{1}{x}$ from 1 to 4

(d) Between $y = x^2$ and $y^2 = x$

2. Find the volume of the solid obtained when the given region is rotated about the x-axis

   (a) Under $y = \sin^{\frac{3}{2}}x$ from 0 to π

   (b) Bounded by $y = 4 - x^2$ and $y = 3x$ and $x = 0$

   (c) Under $y = \sec x$ from 0 to $\dfrac{\pi}{4}$

   (d) Under $y = 2e^{2x}$ from $\ln 1$ to $\ln 3$

3. Find the volume of the sphere obtained when $x^2 + y^2 = 25$, $y \geq 0$, is rotated about the x-axis.

4. Find the volume of the ellipsoid obtained when $\dfrac{x^2}{16} + \dfrac{y^2}{9} = 1$ is rotated about the x-axis.

5. Use integration to find the volume of a sphere with radius r.

6. Use integration to find the volume of a cone of height h and base radius r.

7. Find the volume of the solid obtained when the region under $y = \sqrt{x} \ln x$ from 1 to 2 is rotated about the x-axis.

8. Find the volume of the solid obtained when the region under $y = \dfrac{x}{x + 1}$ from 0 to 1 is rotated about the x-axis.

C 9. Find the volume of the ellipsoid generated by rotating $\dfrac{x^2}{a^2} + \dfrac{y^2}{b^2} = 1$, $y \geq 0$, about the x-axis. Use the result to find the volume generated in Question 4.

10. Find the volume of the solid obtained by rotating the region bounded by $y = 2x - x^2$, $y = 2x$, and $x = 2$ about the line $y = -1$.

11. Find the volume of the solid obtained when the region in the first quadrant bounded by $y = x^2$, $4y = x^2$, and $y = 1$ is rotated about the y-axis.

11.8 REVIEW EXERCISE

1. Evaluate each integral directly from the definition as a limit of sums.

   (a) $\displaystyle\int_{-1}^{4}(3x + 2)dx$

   (b) $\displaystyle\int_{0}^{1}(x^3 - 2x^2)dx$

2. (a) Evaluate the integral $\displaystyle\int_{-3}^{0}(x^2 + 2x)dx$ as a limit of sums.

   (b) Evaluate the integral in part (a) using the Fundamental Theorem of Calculus.

   (c) Interpret the integral in part (a) as a difference of areas.

3. Evaluate the following indefinite integrals.

   (a) $\displaystyle\int(x^4 - 12x^3 + 6x)dx$

   (b) $\displaystyle\int\sqrt{x}(1 - x + 3x^2)dx$

   (c) $\displaystyle\int(2x + \sec x \tan x)dx$

   (d) $\displaystyle\int\frac{x + 2}{\sqrt[3]{x}}\,dx$

   (e) $\displaystyle\int\frac{\sin x + x \cos x}{x \sin x}\,dx$

   (f) $\displaystyle\int\frac{x}{\sqrt{4 + x^2}}\,dx$

   (g) $\displaystyle\int e^x\sqrt{1 + e^x}\,dx$

   (h) $\displaystyle\int\sec 4x \tan 4x\,dx$

   (i) $\displaystyle\int\sqrt{x}\,\ln x\,dx$

   (j) $\displaystyle\int\frac{1}{x \ln x}\,dx$

   (k) $\displaystyle\int\frac{dx}{x - x^2}$

   (l) $\displaystyle\int\frac{x + 4}{x^3 + 3x^2 - 10x}\,dx$

   (m) $\displaystyle\int xe^{-3x}\,dx$

   (n) $\displaystyle\int\sin^3 x\,dx$

   (o) $\displaystyle\int\frac{x + 4}{(x + 1)^2}\,dx$

   (p) $\displaystyle\int\frac{dx}{x(x^2 + x + 1)}$

   (q) $\displaystyle\int\frac{x^3 + 4x^2}{x^2 + 4x + 3}\,dx$

   (r) $\displaystyle\int\frac{x^3}{x^3 + 4x}\,dx$

   (s) $\displaystyle\int\frac{\sin^{-1} x}{\sqrt{1 - x^2}}\,dx$

   (t) $\displaystyle\int\frac{1}{(9 - x^2)^{\frac{3}{2}}}\,dx$

   (u) $\displaystyle\int\frac{e^x}{1 - e^x}\,dx$

   (v) $\displaystyle\int\frac{e^x}{e^{2x} + 3e^x + 2}\,dx$

4. Evaluate the following definite integrals.

(a) $\int_{-1}^{1} (1 + 4x - x^2) dx$ (b) $\int_{0}^{1} e^{-3x} dx$

(c) $\int_{1}^{3} \frac{1 + 3x}{x^2} dx$ (d) $\int_{0}^{4} \frac{3}{2x + 1} dx$

(e) $\int_{0}^{\frac{\pi}{2}} \cos^3 x \sin^2 x \, dx$ (f) $\int_{0}^{\frac{\pi}{2}} x^2 \sin x \, dx$

(g) $\int_{0}^{1} \frac{x}{x + 1} dx$ (h) $\int_{0}^{3} \sqrt{9 - x^2} \, dx$

5. Find the area of the region bounded by the curves $y = \sin x$ and $y = \sin^2 x$ from $x = 0$ to $x = \pi$.

6. Find the volume of the solid obtained when the given region is rotated about the x-axis. Include a sketch of the region.
   (a) Under $y = \sqrt{x}$ from 0 to 4
   (b) Under $y = \sqrt{\sin x \cos x}$ from 0 to $\dfrac{\pi}{2}$
   (c) Under $y = \dfrac{1}{\sqrt{x}}$ from 1 to 2
   (d) Under $y = e^{-x}$ from 0 to ln 2

7. Find the volume of the solid obtained when the given region is rotated about the x-axis. Include a sketch of the region.
   (a) Between $y = 1$ and $y = 5 - x^2$
   (b) Between $y^2 = 4x$ and $y = x$
   (c) Between $y = \sin x$ and $y = -\cos x$ from $\dfrac{3\pi}{4}$ to π

11.9 CHAPTER 11 TEST

1. (a) State the definition of the definite integral $\int_a^b f(x)dx$.

   (b) Use your definition in part (a) to evaluate $\int_0^3 (x^2 + 4x - 5)dx$.

   (c) State the Fundamental Theorem of Calculus.

   (d) Use the Fundamental Theorem of Calculus to evaluate the integral in part (b).

2. Evaluate the following definite integrals.

   (a) $\int_0^{\frac{\pi}{4}} \sin 4x \, dx$

   (b) $\int_1^2 \frac{1}{\sqrt[3]{x^4}} \, dx$

   (c) $\int_0^{\frac{\pi}{2}} x \sin x \, dx$

   (d) $\int_0^1 \frac{1}{(3x + 2)^2} \, dx$

3. Evaluate the following indefinite integrals.

   (a) $\int x^2 e^{x^3} \, dx$

   (b) $\int \cos^5 x \, dx$

   (c) $\int \frac{\cos \sqrt{x}}{\sqrt{x}} \, dx$

   (d) $\int \sin^2 x \, dx$

   (e) $\int \frac{x^2 + 1}{(x - 1)(x - 2)(x - 3)} \, dx$

   (f) $\int \frac{dx}{x^3 + 3x^2}$

   (g) $\int \frac{x^2}{x^2 + 1} \, dx$

4. Find the volume of the solid obtained when the region under $y = e^{-2x}$ from $-\ln 2$ to $\ln 2$ is rotated about the x-axis.

5. (a) Find the area of the region between the curves $y^2 = 2x$ and $x = 2y$.

   (b) Find the volume of the solid obtained when the region in part (a) is rotated about the x-axis.

PROBLEMS PLUS

Find the volume of the doughnut whose dimensions are shown.

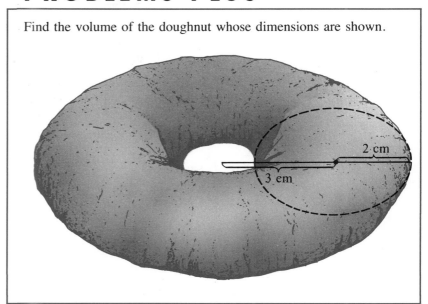

2 cm

3 cm

APPENDIX

The following formula was used in the proof of the Power Rule.

$$x^n - a^n = (x - a)(x^{n-1} + x^{n-2}a + \ldots + xa^{n-2} + a^{n-1})$$

For $n = 2$ or 3 this formula is just the formula for the difference of squares or difference of cubes:

$$x^2 - a^2 = (x - a)(x + a)$$
$$x^3 - a^3 = (x - a)(x^2 + ax + a^2)$$

In general, we can prove it by multiplying out the right side:

$$(x - a)(x^{n-1} + x^{n-2}a + \ldots + xa^{n-2} + a^{n-1})$$
$$= x^n + x^{n-1}a + x^{n-2}a^2 + \ldots + x^2a^{n-2} + xa^{n-1}$$
$$\quad - x^{n-1}a - x^{n-2}a^2 - \ldots - x^2a^{n-2} - xa^{n-1} - a^n$$
$$= x^n - a^n$$

A different proof of the Power Rule can be given using the Binomial Theorem:

$$(a + b)^n = a^n + na^{n-1}b + \binom{n}{2}a^{n-2}b^2 + \ldots + \binom{n}{r}a^{n-r}b^r + \ldots + b^n$$

$$\text{where } \binom{n}{r} = \frac{n!}{r!(n - r)!}$$

(See Section 3.3 in *Finite Mathematics*.)

Alternative Proof of the Power Rule

If $f(x) = x^n$, then $f(x + h) = (x + h)^n$, which we can expand using the Binomial Theorem. Thus

$$\frac{f(x + h) - f(x)}{h} = \frac{(x + h)^n - x^n}{h}$$

$$= \frac{\left[x^n + nx^{n-1}h + \dfrac{n(n - 1)}{2}x^{n-2}h^2 + \ldots + nxh^{n-1} + h^n \right] - x^n}{h}$$

$$= \frac{nx^{n-1}h + \dfrac{n(n - 1)}{2}x^{n-2}h^2 + \ldots + nxh^{n-1} + h^n}{h}$$

$$= nx^{n-1} + \frac{n(n - 1)}{2}x^{n-2}h + \ldots + nxh^{n-2} + h^{n-1}$$

Therefore

$$f'(x) = \lim_{h \to 0} \frac{(x + h)^n - x^n}{h}$$

$$= \lim_{h \to 0} \left[nx^{n-1} + \frac{n(n-1)}{2} x^{n-2}h + \ldots + nxh^{n-2} + h^{n-1} \right]$$

$$= nx^{n-1}$$

because every term, except the first, has h as a factor and so approaches 0.

The following relationship between differentiable functions and continuous functions is needed in the proof of the Product Rule in Section 2.4.

> If f is differentiable at a, then f is continuous at a.

Proof

Since f if differentiable at a, we know that $f'(a)$ exists and we can use the formula

$$f'(a) = \lim_{x \to a} \frac{f(x) - f(a)}{x - a}$$

To verify that f is continuous at a, we have to prove that $\lim_{x \to a} f(x) = f(a)$ or, equivalently, that $\lim_{x \to a} [f(x) - f(a)] = 0$. For $x \neq a$, we can divide and multiply by the quantity $x - a$, so

$$\lim_{x \to a} [f(x) - f(a)] = \lim_{x \to a} \frac{f(x) - f(a)}{x - a} (x - a)$$

$$= \lim_{x \to a} \frac{f(x) - f(a)}{x - a} \lim_{x \to a} (x - a)$$

$$= f'(a)(0)$$

$$= 0$$

Therefore f is continuous at a.

The function $f(x) = |x|$ is continuous at 0, but not differentiable at 0 (see Example 7 in Section 2.1), so the converse of this theorem is false.

ANSWERS

CHAPTER 1 LIMITS AND RATES OF CHANGE

REVIEW AND PREVIEW TO CHAPTER 1

EXERCISE 1

1. (a) $(x - 2)(x + 1)$ (b) $(x - 2)(x - 7)$
  (c) $(x + 3)(x + 4)$ (d) $(2x + 1)(x - 1)$
  (e) $(5x + 3)(x + 2)$ (f) $(3y - 1)(2y - 3)$
  (g) $t(t - 1)(t + 3)$ (h) $x^2(3x + 1)(x + 2)$

2. (a) $(2x + 5)(2x - 5)$
  (b) $(x - 1)(x^2 + x + 1)$
  (c) $(t + 4)(t^2 - 4t + 16)$
  (d) $y(y + 3)(y - 3)$
  (e) $(2c - 3d)(4c^2 + 6cd + 9d^2)$
  (f) $(x^2 + 2)(x^4 - 2x^2 + 4)$
  (g) $(x + 2)(x - 2)(x^2 + 4)$
  (h) $(r + 1)(r - 1)(r^2 + 1)(r^4 + 1)$

3. (a) $(x + 4)(x - 4)(x - 1)$
  (b) $(x - 1)(x + 3)(x - 2)$
  (c) $(x - 2)(x + 3)(x + 4)$
  (d) $(x - 3)(x + 1)(x + 4)$
  (e) $(x + 2)(2x - 1)(2x + 3)$
  (f) $(x + 3)(x - 3)(x - 2)(x - 1)$

4. (a) $x^{\frac{1}{2}}(x - 1)(x + 1)$ (b) $x^{-1}(x + 2)(x + 3)$
  (c) $x^{-\frac{1}{2}}(x + 4)(x - 2)$
  (d) $2x^{\frac{1}{2}}(x - 1)(x^2 + x + 1)$
  (e) $x^{-2}(x + 1)^2$ (f) $(x^2 + 1)^{-\frac{1}{2}}(x^2 + 4)$

EXERCISE 2

1. (a) $\dfrac{1}{\sqrt{x} + 3}$ (b) $-\dfrac{1}{x + \sqrt{x}}$ (c) $\dfrac{x^2 + 4x + 16}{x\sqrt{x} + 8}$

  (d) $\dfrac{2}{\sqrt{2 + h} - \sqrt{2 - h}}$

  (e) $\dfrac{3x + 4}{\sqrt{x^2 + 3x + 4} + x}$

  (f) $\dfrac{2x}{\sqrt{x^2 + x} + \sqrt{x^2 - x}}$

2. (a) $\dfrac{\sqrt{x + 1} + 1}{x}$ (b) $2(\sqrt{x + 2} - \sqrt{x})$
  (c) $x(\sqrt{x^2 + 1} - x)$
  (d) $\frac{1}{2}x^2(\sqrt{x + 1} + \sqrt{x - 1})$

EXERCISE 1.1

1. (a) 4   (b) 3   (c) $\frac{1}{3}$ (d) -3 (e) $-\frac{1}{2}$ (f) $-\frac{1}{2}$

2. $10x + 7y - 5 = 0$ **3.** $f(x) = 2x + 6$

4. (a) increases by 12   (b) decreases by 6

5. (a) decreases by 3   (b) increases by 2

6. $s = 35t$, slope represents speed

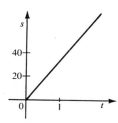

7. (a) (i) 5   (ii) 4.5   (iii) 4.1   (iv) 4.01
  (v) 4.001   (vi) 3   (vii) 3.5   (viii) 3.9
  (ix) 3.99   (x) 3.999   (b) 4
  (c) $4x - y - 1 = 0$
  (d)

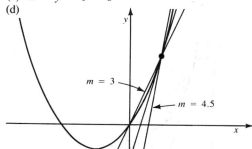

8. (a) (i) 1   (ii) 1.5   (iii) 1.9   (iv) 1.99   (v) 3
  (vi) 2.5   (vii) 2.1   (viii) 2.01   (b) 2
  (c) $2x - y - 4 = 0$
  (d)

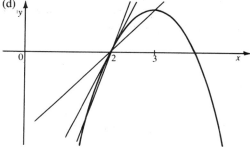

9. (a) (i) 1.75   (ii) 1.1875   (iii) 0.827 5
(iv) 0.757 525   (v) 0.750 75   (vi) 0.25
(vii) 0.4375   (viii) 0.6775   (ix) 0.742 525
(x) 0.749 25   (b) $\frac{3}{4}$ (c) $3x - 4y - 2 = 0$

(d)

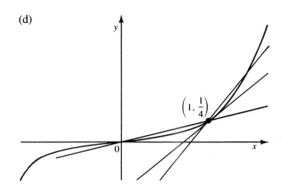

$\left(1, \frac{1}{4}\right)$

10. (a) (i) -1 (ii) -2 (iii) -2.2222 (iv) -2.5
(v) -2.8571 (vi) -3.3333 (vii) -3.6364
(viii) -3.9216 (ix) -4.4444 (x) -4.0816
(b) -4 (c) $4x + y - 4 = 0$

(d)

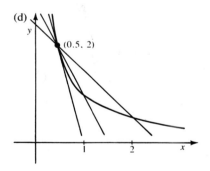

$(0.5, 2)$

11. (a) $T = 20 - 10h$ (h in kilometres)
(b) The slope represents the rate of increase of
temperature as the altitude increases.

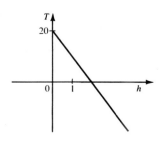

12. (a) $C = \frac{1}{4}d + 300$ (b) $800
(c) cost per kilometre for gas, oil, tires, ...
(d) $300 This is reasonable (insurance, license,
depreciation, ...).
(e) Total cost is fixed expenses plus per
kilometre expenses.

EXERCISE 1.2

1. (a) 1   (b) 0   (c) 1   (d) does not exist
2. (a) 8   (b) π (c) 3   (d) 2   (d) 2   (e) k^6
(f) π
3. (a) -4 (b) 10   (c) 0   (d) 729   (e) -1 (f) $\frac{7}{6}$
(g) $\frac{11}{4}$ (h) $12\sqrt{2}$ (i) 3   (j) 21
4. (a) $-\frac{1}{4}$ (b) -1 (c) 2   (d) $\frac{1}{2}$ (e) $\frac{3}{2}$ (f) $\frac{1}{27}$
(g) 6   (h) $-\frac{1}{4}$
5. (a) 48   (b) -4 (c) -1 (d) 32   (e) $\frac{1}{6}$
(f) $-\frac{1}{4}$
6. (a) does not exist   (b) 0   (c) 4   (d) does not
exist   (e) does not exist   (f) does not exist
(g) $-\frac{2}{27}$ (h) $-\frac{1}{16}$ (i) -1 (j) -2
7. (a) 2.000 000, 2.593 742, 2.704 814,
2.716 924, 2.718 146, 2.718 268, 2.718 280,
2.718 282   (b) 2.718 28
8. (a) 1.0000, 0.7177, 0.6956, 0.6934, 0.6932
(b) 0.693
9. (a) 12   (b) $\frac{1}{2}$ **11.** within 0.000 25
13. $f(x) = \dfrac{1}{x}$, $g(x) = -\dfrac{1}{x}$

EXERCISE 1.3

1. (a) 0   (b) 2   (c) 1   (d) does not exist   (e) 3
(f) 3   (g) 3   (h) 4
2. (a) 2   (b) 2   (c) 1   (d) does not exist   (e) 0
(f) 0   (g) 0   (h) 1
3. (a) continuous   (b) discontinuous
(c) discontinuous   (d) continuous
(e) discontinuous
4. (a) 0   (b) 0   (c) 0   (d) 0   (e) 0   (f) 0   (g) 0
(h) 1   (i) -1 (j) does not exist

5. (a) −1 (b) 1 (c) does not exist

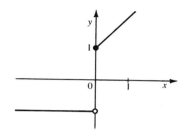

6. (a) 1 (b) 1 (c) 1

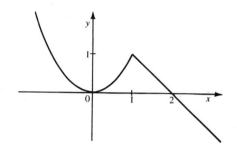

7. (a) 1 (b) −1 (c) does not exist

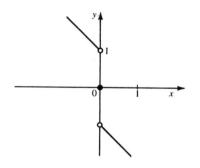

8. (a) (i) −1 (ii) −1 (iii) 1 (iv) 1

(b)

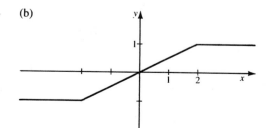

(c) nowhere

9. (a) (i) 0 (ii) −1 (iii) does not exist (iv) 1
(v) 1 (vi) 1

(b)

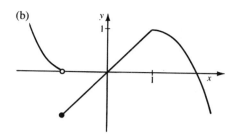

(c) −1

10. (a) 4 (b) 1 (c) −1 (d) 1, 3
11. Discontinuities at $x = 30, 50, 100$.

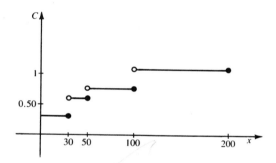

12. Discontinuities at $x = 0.2, 0.3, 0.4, 0.5, \ldots$.

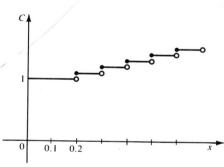

13. Continuous everwhere.

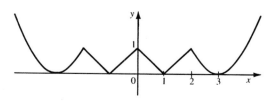

14. $\frac{1}{3}$

EXERCISE 1.4

1. (a) -2 (b) $2x + y - 4 = 0$

(c)

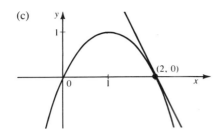

(ii) (a) -2 (b) $2x + y - 1 = 0$

(c)

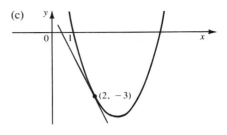

2. (a) 3 (b) $3x - y - 2 = 0$

(c)

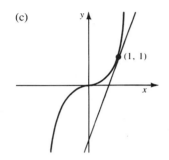

(iii) (a) 0 (b) $y = 1$

(c)

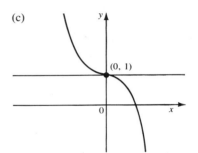

6. (a) (i) -2 (ii) 0 (iii) 4

(b)

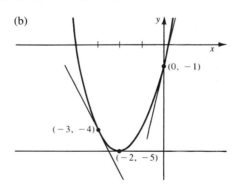

(iv) (a) $-\frac{1}{4}$ (b) $x + 4y - 5 = 0$

(c)

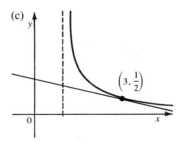

7. (i) (a) 4 (b) $4x - y + 8 = 0$

(c)

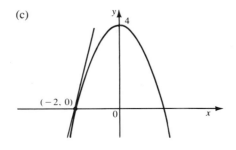

(v) (a) $\frac{1}{6}$ (b) $x - 6y + 12 = 0$

(c)

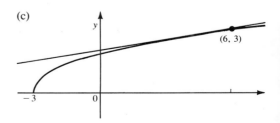

(vi) (a) -8 (b) $8x + y + 6 = 0$

(c)

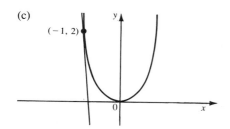

8. (a) $7x + y - 1 = 0$ (b) $x + y = 0$
   (c) $3x + y - 11 = 0$ (d) $x + 2y - 3 = 0$
9. (a) $2a + 1$ (b) $-1, 0, 1, 2, 3$
10. (a) $6a + 2$ (b) $\left(\frac{4}{3}, 8\right)$ 11. $\left(\pm 1, \frac{1}{2}\right)$

EXERCISE 1.5

1. (a) (i) 5.5 m/s   (ii) 7.95 m/s   (iii) 9.91 m/s
   (iv) 10.155 m/s   (v) 10.351 m/s   (b) 10.4 m/s
2. (a) (i) 4 m/s   (ii) 3 m/s   (iii) 2.5 m/s
   (iv) 2.1 m/s   (b) 2 m/s
   (c), (d)

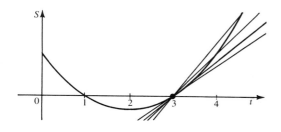

3. $4a + 4$, 8 m/s, 12 m/s, 16 m/s
4. (a) (i) $-0.6°$/min   (ii) $-0.8°$/min
   (iii) $-2.75°$/min   (iv) $-1.8°$/min
   (b) $-1°$/min
5. (a) (i) 14.3 thousand/year
   (ii) 13.7 thousand/year   (iii) 13.0 thousand/year
   (iv) 12.0 thousand/year   (b) 11 thousand/year
6. (a) $-\frac{1}{6}$ (b) $-\frac{2}{9}$

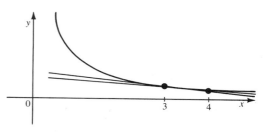

7. (a) (i) 61 mm³/mm   (ii) 49.21 mm³/mm
   (iii) 48.1201 mm³/mm   (b) 48 mm³/mm
8. $\frac{250}{9}$ L/min
9. (a) (i) 47.51 m/s   (ii) 47.93 m/s
   (iii) 48.26 m/s   (iv) 48.30 m/s   (v) 48.33 m/s
   (b) 48.34 m/s   (c) $50 - 1.66t$
   (d) After about 60.24 s   (e) -50 m/s

EXERCISE 1.6

1. (a) 0   (b) 4   (c) does not exist   (d) 3   (e) 0
   (f) 6   (g) does not exist
2. (a) $0, \frac{1}{3}, \frac{2}{5}, \frac{3}{7}, \frac{4}{9}, \frac{5}{11}$ (b) $1, \frac{4}{5}, \frac{6}{10}, \frac{8}{17}, \frac{10}{26}, \frac{12}{37}$
   (c) 2, 8, 24, 64, 160, 384
   (d) $1, -\frac{1}{2}, \frac{1}{3}, -\frac{1}{4}, \frac{1}{5}, -\frac{1}{6}$ (e) $1, \frac{1}{2}, \frac{2}{3}, \frac{3}{5}, \frac{5}{8}, \frac{8}{13}$
   (f) $1, 2, 1, -1, -2, -1$
3. (a) 0   (b) 0   (c) 6   (d) $\frac{1}{3}$ (e) 2   (f) does not
   exist   (g) $\frac{1}{2}$ (h) 1   (i) 0   (j) 0   (k) 0
   (l) does not exist   (m) 0   (n) does not exist
   (o) -2 (p) 0   (q) 0   (r) $-\frac{1}{2}$ (s) 0   (t) does
   not exist   4. $\frac{1}{3}$
5. $2, 1, \frac{8}{9}, 1, \frac{32}{25}, \frac{16}{9}, \frac{128}{49}, 4, \frac{512}{81}, \frac{1024}{100}, 2621.4,$
   $4.5 \times 10^{11}, 128 \times 10^{26}$; does not exist
6. 1, 1.414 214, 1.442 250, 1.414 214, 1.379 730,
   1.348 006, 1.320 469, 1.296 840, 1.276 518,
   1.258 925, 1.081 383, 1.047 129, 1.012 507,
   1.006 932, 1.000 921; 1
8. 2   9. (a) $1, \frac{1}{3}, \frac{3}{5}, \frac{5}{11}, \frac{11}{21}, \frac{21}{43}; \frac{1}{2}$ (b) L, $\frac{1}{2}$

EXERCISE 1.7

1. (a) $\frac{3}{2}$ (b) $\frac{3}{5}$ (c) divergent   (d) $\frac{15}{4}$
   (e) divergent   (f) 180   (g) $\frac{1}{5}$ (h) divergent
2. (a) 8   (b) $-\frac{2}{7}$
3. (a) $\frac{1}{9}$ (b) $\frac{25}{99}$ (c) $\frac{41}{99}$ (d) $\frac{157}{999}$ (e) $\frac{556}{495}$ (f) $\frac{7811}{3330}$
   (g) $\frac{107\,171}{249\,750}$ (h) $\frac{37\,481}{5500}$

4. (a) $|x| < 1$, $\dfrac{1}{1 - x}$ (b) $|x| < 3$, $\dfrac{3}{3 - x}$

(c) $|x| > 1$, $\dfrac{x}{x - 1}$ (d) $3 < x < 5$, $\dfrac{1}{5 - x}$

(e) $|x| < \frac{1}{2}$, $\dfrac{2x}{1 - 2x}$

5. 1, 0.984 375, 0.985 747, 0.985 503, 0.985 567, 0.985 545, 0.985 554, 0.985 550; yes; 0.985 55

6. (a) 0.5, 0.6667, 0.75, 0.8, 0.8333, 0.8571, 0.875, 0.8889, 0.9, 0.9091, 0.9167, 0.9231, 0.9286, 0.9333, 0.9375;   (b) $1 - \dfrac{1}{n + 1}$

(c) 1   (d) 1000   **7.** $\dfrac{\sin \theta}{1 - \sin \theta}$

1.8 REVIEW EXERCISE

1. (a) 1   (b) 0   (c) -1 (d) does not exist   (e) 3
(f) 2   (g) 2   (h) 2

2. (a) discontinuous   (b) continuous
(c) discontinuous

3. (a) 22   (b) -1 (c) -4 (d) 6   (e) $\sqrt{10}$
(f) $\frac{1}{48}$ (g) $\dfrac{\sqrt{2}}{4}$ (h) -6

4. (a) does not exist   (b) $-\frac{2}{5}$ (c) -1 (d) 0
(e) 0   (f) 1   (g) -1 (h) does not exist

5. (a) (i) 0   (ii) 1   (iii) does not exist

(b)

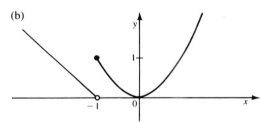

6. (a) (i) 0   (ii) 0   (iii) 0   (iv) 1   (v) 2
(vi) does not exist

(b)

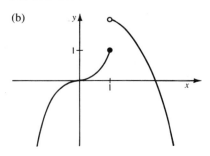

(c) discontinuous at 1

7. $t = 1, 2, 3, 4, 5, \ldots$

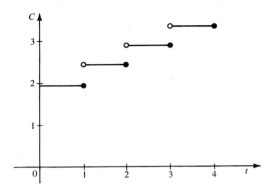

8. (a) (i) 4   (ii) 1.75   (iii) 0.31   (iv) 0.0301
(b) 0   (c) $y = -2$

(d)

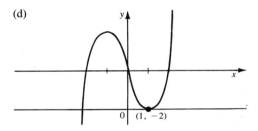

9. $4x + y + 3 = 0$

10. (a) (i) -14.7 m/s   (ii) -10.3 m/s
(b) -9.8 m/s

11. 80π cm²/cm   **12.** (a) 2   (b) $-\frac{2}{3}$ (c) does not exist   (d) 0

13. (a) $\frac{36}{7}$ (b) divergent

14. $\frac{137}{110}$ **15.** $-2 < x < 0$, $-1 - \dfrac{1}{x}$ **16.** 3

1.9 CHAPTER 1 TEST

1. (a) 3   (b) $-\frac{1}{6}$ (c) $-\frac{1}{2}$ **2.** (a) -3 (b) -2
(c) $2x + y - 3 = 0$

(d)

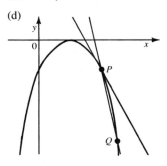

3. (a) (i) 1 (ii) -1 (iii) does not exist

(b)

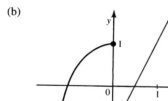

(c) discontinuous at 0

4. (a) 19 m/s (b) 14 m/s **5.** 3 **6.** $\frac{48}{7}$

CHAPTER 2 DERIVATIVES

REVIEW AND PREVIEW TO CHAPTER 2

EXERCISE 1

1. (a) R (b) R (c) $\{x|x \geqslant 5\}$ (d) $\{x|x \leqslant 0\}$
(e) $\{x|-1 \leqslant x \leqslant 1\}$
(f) $\{x|x \geqslant \sqrt{2} \text{ or } x \leqslant -\sqrt{2}\}$
(g) $\{x|x \neq 3\}$ (h) $\{x|x \neq -5, 1\}$ (i) R
(j) $\{t|t > 3 \text{ or } t < 2\}$
(k) $\{x|0 \leqslant x \leqslant 4\}$ (l) $\{x|0 \leqslant x \leqslant 4\}$

EXERCISE 2

1. (a) $(f{\circ}g)(x) = 7 - 6x$, $(g{\circ}f)(x) = 7 - 6x$,
$(f{\circ}f)(x) = 4x - 3$, $(g{\circ}g)(x) = 9x - 8$
(b) $(f{\circ}g)(x) = x^2 + 2x + 1$,
$(g{\circ}f)(x) = x^2 + 1$, $(f{\circ}f)(x) = x^4$,
$(g{\circ}g)(x) = x + 2$
(c) $(f{\circ}g)(x) = -24$, $(g{\circ}f)(x) = 5$,
$(f{\circ}f)(x) = 2x^2 - x^4$, $(g{\circ}g)(x) = 5$
(d) $(f{\circ}g)(x) = \sqrt{x^2 - 4}$, $(g{\circ}f)(x) = x - 4$,
$(f{\circ}f)(x) = \sqrt[4]{x}$, $(g{\circ}g)(x) = x^4 - 8x^2 + 12$
(e) $(f{\circ}g)(x) = \dfrac{3}{x} - 5$, $(g{\circ}f)(x) = \dfrac{1}{3x - 5}$,
$(f{\circ}f)(x) = 9x - 20$, $(g{\circ}g)(x) = x$
(f) $(f{\circ}g)(x) = \dfrac{x + 2}{4}$,
$(g{\circ}f)(x) = \dfrac{2x - 1}{3 - 2x}$, $(f{\circ}f)(x) = \dfrac{x - 1}{x}$,
$(g{\circ}g)(x) = \dfrac{-x - 6}{3x + 2}$ (g) $(f{\circ}g)(x) = \sqrt[4]{1 + x}$,
$(g{\circ}f)(x) = \sqrt{1 + \sqrt{x}}$, $(f{\circ}f)(x) = \sqrt[4]{x}$,
$(g{\circ}g))(x) = \sqrt{1 + \sqrt{1 + x}}$
2. (a) $f(x = x^9$, $g(x) = 2x + 1$
(b) $f(x) = 1 + 2x + 3x^2$, $g(x) = x^2$
(c) $f(x) = \dfrac{1}{x}$, $g(x) = x^2 - 7$
(d) $f(x) = \sqrt{x}$, $g(x) = 6 + x$

EXERCISE 2.1

1. (a) $f(x) = x^2$, $a = 3$ [or $g(x) = (3 + x)^2$,
$a = 0$] (b) $f(x) = x^3$, $a = 2$
(c) $f(x) = \sqrt{x}$, $a = 4$
(d) $f(x) = x^4 + 3x$, $a = 1$
(e) $f(x) = 2^x$, $a = 1$ (f) $f(x) = x^5$, $a = 1$
2. (a) (ii) (b) (i) (c) (iii)
3. (a) $-3, 0, 2, 4$ (b) $-4, -2, 0, 2, 4, 6$
4. 13 **5.** 6 **6.** $-\frac{1}{9}$, $x + 9y - 6 = 0$
7. $3a^2$; 3, 0, 3, 12

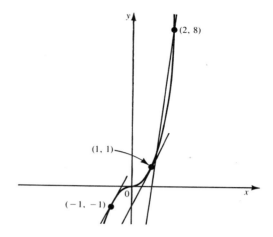

8. (a) $7 - 2a$ (b) $6a^2$ (c) $\dfrac{1}{(1 + a)^2}$ (d) $\dfrac{1}{2\sqrt{a}}$
9. $10a - 2$, 8 m/s, 18 m/s, 28 m/s

10. (a) $f'(x) = 6x + 2$ (b) $f'(x) = 2x - 3x^2$
(c) $f'(x) = 4x^3$ (d) $f'(x) = -\dfrac{1}{(5x - 1)^2}$

11. (a) $f'(x) = \dfrac{1}{\sqrt{2x - 1}}$, $\text{dom}(f) = \{x | x \geqslant \frac{1}{2}\}$,

$\text{dom}(f') = \{x | x > \frac{1}{2}\}$

(b) $g'(x) = -\dfrac{1}{2\sqrt{x^3}}$, $\text{dom}(g) = \text{dom}(g') = \{x | x > 0\}$

(c) $F'(x) = -\dfrac{11}{(4 + x)^2}$, $\text{dom}(F) = \text{dom}(F') = \{x | x \neq -4\}$

(d) $f'(t) = -\dfrac{4t}{(t^2 - 1)^2}$, $\text{dom}(f) = \text{dom}(f') = \{t | t \neq \pm 1\}$

12. (a) -3 (b) $9x^2 + 2$ (c) $1 - \dfrac{1}{x^2}$ (d) $-\dfrac{2}{x^3}$

13.

(a)   (b)

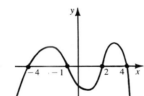

14. (a)

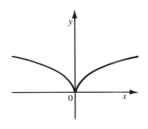

(c) $\dfrac{1}{3\sqrt[3]{a^2}}$

15. (b)

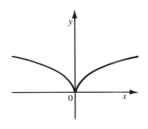

16. (a)

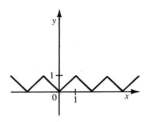

(b) Not differentiable at any integer

EXERCISE 2.2

1. (a) $f'(x) = 0$ (b) $f'(x) = 4x^3$ (c) $y' = 12x^{11}$
(d) $y' = 0$ (e) $f'(x) = 1$ (f) $f'(x) = \pi x^{\pi - 1}$
(g) $f'(x) = 43x^{42}$ (h) $f'(x) = 0$
(i) $g'(x) = -2x^{-3}$ (j) $g'(x) = \frac{3}{2}x^{\frac{1}{2}}$

2. (a) $f'(x) = 96x^{11}$ (b) $f'(x) = -27x^8$
(c) $f'(t) = 4t^{\frac{1}{3}}$ (d) $g'(t) = -6t^{-\frac{7}{4}}$
(e) $y' = -\dfrac{4}{x^5}$ (f) $y' = -\dfrac{4}{x^3}$
(g) $g'(t) = 24t^2$ (h) $h'(y) = \dfrac{2y}{9}$
(i) $f'(x) = \frac{1}{3}x^{-\frac{2}{3}}$ (j) $f'(x) = \dfrac{2}{3}x^{-\frac{1}{3}}$
(k) $y' = -\frac{1}{2}x^{-\frac{3}{2}}$ (l) $y' = -\frac{3}{4}x^{-\frac{5}{4}}$
(m) $y' = \sqrt{6}x^{\sqrt{2} - 1}$ (n) $y' = 12x^{11}$

3. (a) $\frac{2}{3}$ (b) 1.4 (c) -3 (d) $\frac{1}{80}$ (e) $3\sqrt{2}$
(f) $-\frac{2}{3}$

4. (a) $80x - y - 128 = 0$
(b) $x - 3y + 9 = 0$ (c) $x + 25y - 10 = 0$
(d) $x - 12y - 16 = 0$

7. $(4, 48)$ **8.** $(16, 64)$

9. $\left(\frac{1}{2}, -\frac{1}{8}\right)$ **10.** $\left(2, \frac{1}{2}\right), \left(-2, \frac{3}{2}\right)$

11. $(\pm\sqrt{5}, 5)$
$2\sqrt{5}x - y - 5 = 0$
$2\sqrt{5}x + y + 5 = 0$

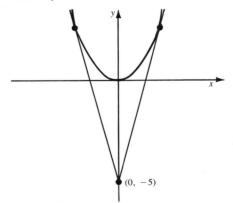

12. $\left(\pm\frac{5}{32}, \frac{25}{128}\right)$

EXERCISE 2.3

1. (a) $f'(x) = 2x + 4$ (b) $f'(x) = 15x^4 - 24x^3$
(c) $g'(x) = 10x^9 + 125x^4$

(d) $g'(x) = 2x + \dfrac{4}{x^3}$

(e) $h'(x) = \dfrac{1}{2\sqrt{x}} - 20x^3$ (f) $h'(x) = 2x + 5$

(g) $y' = \frac{1}{2}x^{-\frac{1}{2}} - \frac{1}{2}x^{-\frac{3}{2}}$ (h) $y' = 5t^4 + 30t^{-6}$

(i) $f'(t) = 3t^2 + 6t + 3$

(j) $F'(x) = \frac{1}{2}x^{-\frac{1}{2}} + \frac{1}{3}x^{-\frac{2}{3}} + \frac{1}{4}x^{-\frac{3}{4}}$

(k) $u'(t) = -\dfrac{b}{t^2} - \dfrac{2c}{t^3}$ (l) $v'(r) = \dfrac{1}{\sqrt{r}} + \frac{9}{2}\sqrt{r}$

2. (a) $f'(x) = 1 + x + x^2 + x^3$,
   $\mathrm{dom}(f) = \mathrm{dom}(f') = \mathbb{R}$

(b) $f'(x) = 4 - \frac{1}{4}x^{-\frac{3}{4}}$,
   $\mathrm{dom}(f) = \{x | x \geqslant 0\}, \mathrm{dom}(f') = \{x | x > 0\}$

(c) $f'(x) = 1 - \dfrac{5\sqrt{10}}{x^6}$,
   $\mathrm{dom}(f) = \mathrm{dom}(f') = \{x | x \neq 0\}$

(d) $f'(x) = \frac{1}{2}x^{-\frac{1}{2}} - x^{-\frac{3}{2}}$,
   $\mathrm{dom}(f) = \mathrm{dom}(f') = \{x | x > 0\}$

3. (a) $2x - y - 2 = 0$ (b) $x - 2y + 7 = 0$
(c) $x + 2y - 12 = 0$ (d) $8x + y + 4 = 0$

4. 20 m/s, 0 m/s, -10 m/s

5. 11 m/s, 27 m/s, 75 m/s   **6.** $(2, -32)$

7. $(-4, 81), (2, -27)$ **9.** $y = 2x, y = -2x$

10. $x + y + 1 = 0, 11x - y - 25 = 0$

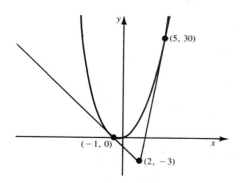

11. $-1 \pm \sqrt{2}$

12. (a) everywhere except at $x = -1, 1$

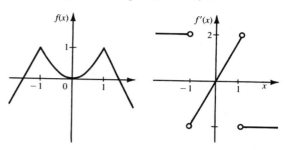

(b)
$$f'(x) = \begin{cases} 2 & \text{if } x < -1 \\ 2x & \text{if } -1 < x < 1 \\ -2 & \text{if } x > 1 \end{cases}$$

13. (a)

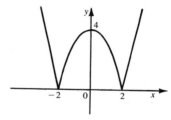

(b) $2, -2$

(c)
$$f'(x) = \begin{cases} 2x & \text{if } x < -2 \\ -2x & \text{if } -2 < x < 2 \\ 2x & \text{if } x > 2 \end{cases}$$

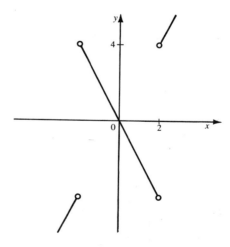

EXERCISE 2.4

1. (a) $f'(x) = (2x - 1)(2x) + 2(x^2 + 1)$
(b) $f'(x) = 3x + (3x - 8)$
(c) $y' = x^2(1 - 6x) + 2x(1 + x - 3x^2)$
(d) $y' = (x^3 + x^2 + 1)(2x) +$
   $(x^2 + 2)(3x^2 + 2x)$

(e) $f'(t) = (t^4 + t^2 - 1)(2t) + (t^2 - 2)(4t^3 + 2t)$

(f) $f'(t) = -\sqrt[3]{t} + \frac{1}{3}t^{-\frac{2}{3}}(1 - t)$

(g) $F'(y) = \sqrt{y}\left[1 - \frac{1}{\sqrt{y}}\right] + (y - 2\sqrt{y} + 2)\frac{1}{2\sqrt{y}}$

(h) $G'(y) = (y - y^2)(2 - \frac{4}{3}y^{\frac{1}{3}}) + (2y - y^{\frac{4}{3}})(1 - 2y)$

2. (a) $y' = 5x^4 + 8x^3 + 9x^2$

(b) $y' = 1 - 12x^{-3}$

(c) $f'(x) = 5x^4 - 3x^2 - 4x$

(d) $f'(x) = -36x^5 - 15x^2$

(e) $f'(t) = 480t^9 + 64t^7 - 90t^2 - 5$

(f) $f'(t) = 3act^2 + 2bct - ad$

(g) $g'(u) = \frac{45}{2}u^{\frac{7}{2}} - \frac{5}{2}u^{\frac{3}{2}} + u^{-\frac{1}{2}}$

(h) $g'(v) = 3v^2 - \frac{5}{2}v^{\frac{3}{2}} + \frac{3}{2}\sqrt{v} - 1$

3. (a) -13 (b) 0   (c) 20   (d) -9 (e) -11
   (f) $-\frac{1}{2}$ 4. 6

5. $x - y + 4 = 0$ 6. -17

7. (a) $g'(x) = xf'(x) + f(x)$

(b) $h'(x) = \sqrt{x}f'(x) + \frac{1}{2\sqrt{x}}f(x)$

(c) $F'(x) = xf'(x) + cx^{c-1}f(x)$

8. (b) $y' = 2(2 + 5x - x^3)(5 - 3x^2)$

9. (b) $y' = \sqrt{x}\,(3x + 5)(12x - 5) + 3\sqrt{x}(6x^2 - 5x + 1) + \frac{1}{2\sqrt{x}}(3x + 5)(6x^2 - 5x + 1)$

10. (b) $y' = 3(1 + x^3 + x^6)^2\frac{d}{dx}(1 + x^3 + x^6) = 3(3x^2 + 6x^5)(1 + x^3 + x^6)^2$

EXERCISE 2.5

1. (a) $f'(x) = \dfrac{2}{(x + 1)^2}$

(b) $f'(x) = \dfrac{-2x^2 + 2x + 2}{(x^2 + 1)^2}$

(c) $g'(x) = \dfrac{-x^2 - 1}{(x^2 + 2x - 1)^2}$ (d) $g'(x) = 1$

(e) $y' = \dfrac{1 - 3x^2}{2\sqrt{x}(x^2 + 1)^2}$

(f) $y' = -\dfrac{2}{\sqrt{x}(\sqrt{x} - 2)^2}$

(g) $f'(t) = \dfrac{-2t^2 - 2t + 11}{(t^2 - 3t + 4)^2}$

(h) $g'(t) = \dfrac{2t^2 - 4t - 4}{(t - 1)^2}$

(i) $f'(x) = \dfrac{-4x^3 + 2x}{(x^4 - 2x^2 + 1)^2}$

(j) $f'(x) = \dfrac{ad - bc}{(cx + d)^2}$ (k) $f'(x) = \dfrac{x^{10} - 60x^5}{(x^5 - 10)^2}$

(l) $f'(x) = \dfrac{1 + 2x - x^2}{x^2(x + 1)^2}$

2. (a) $\{x|x \neq \frac{1}{2}\}, f'(x) = \dfrac{5}{(1 - 2x)^2}$

(b) $\{x|x \neq \pm 1\}, f'(x) = \dfrac{-x^2 - 1}{(x^2 - 1)^2}$

(c) $\{x|x \neq -1, x \neq \frac{3}{2}\},$
$f'(x) = \dfrac{1 - 4x}{(x + 1)^2(2x - 3)^2}$

(d) $\{x|x \neq -3, x \neq 1\},$
$f'(x) = -\dfrac{2(x^2 + x + 4)}{(x^2 + 2x - 3)^2}$

(e) $\{x|x \neq 1, x \neq -1\},$
$f'(x) = \dfrac{-2x^5 - 6x^4 - 2x - 2}{(x^4 - 1)^2}$

(f) $\{x|x \geq 0, x \neq 9\}, f'(x) = \dfrac{3x\sqrt{x} - 12x}{2(\sqrt{x} - 3)^2}$

3. (a) $x + 2y - 8 = 0$ (b) $9x - y - 13 = 0$
   (c) $4x - 25y + 13 = 0$ (d) $x - y - 1 = 0$

4. 7   6. $(0, 0), (-5, 5)$ 7. $\left(3, \frac{3}{2}\right), \left(-1, \frac{1}{2}\right)$

8. (a) $y' = -\dfrac{f'(x)}{[f(x)]^2}$ (b) $y' = \dfrac{xf'(x) - f(x)}{x^2}$

(c) $y' = \dfrac{f(x) - xf'(x)}{[f(x)]^2}$

EXERCISE 2.6

1. (a) $F'(x) = -21(5 - 3x)^6$

(b) $F'(x) = 80x(2x^2 + 1)^{19}$

(c) $G'(x) = \dfrac{9x^2 + 6x}{4\sqrt[4]{x^3 + x^2 - 2}}$

(d) $G'(x) = \dfrac{4x^3 - 1}{2\sqrt{x^4 - x + 1}}$

(e) $y' = \dfrac{2x + 1}{4(x^2 + x)^{\frac{3}{4}}}$

(f) $y' = -\dfrac{3(3 + 8x)}{(1 + 3x + 4x^2)^4}$

(g) $y' = -\dfrac{2(3x^2 + 4x)}{(x^3 + 2x^2 + 1)^3}$

(h) $y' = \dfrac{4x}{(9 - x^2)^{\frac{3}{2}}}$

(i) $y' = \dfrac{6(1 + 2\sqrt{x})^5}{\sqrt{x}}$

(j) $y' = \dfrac{2\sqrt{x} + 1}{4\sqrt{x}\sqrt{x + \sqrt{x}}}$

(k) $y' = 1 - \dfrac{x^4 - 12x^9}{(1 + x^5 - 6x^{10})^{\frac{4}{5}}}$

(l) $y' = 2x + 10x(x^2 - 1)^4$

2. $(4u^3 + 10u)(5x^4 + 4x)$ 3. -117

4. $-\dfrac{2}{9\sqrt{13}}$ 5. $\frac{11}{8}$

6. (a) $F'(x) = \dfrac{2x^2 + 1}{\sqrt{x^2 + 1}}$

(b) $F'(x) = 6(8x + 3)(4x - 1)^4$

(c) $G'(x) = (3 + 16x - 27x^2)(x^2 - 1)^3$

(d) $G'(x) = 2(x^4 - x + 1)(x^2 - 2)^2 \times$
$(7x^5 - 8x^3 - 4x^2 + 3x + 2)$

(e) $F'(x) = \dfrac{x + 3}{(2x + 3)^{\frac{3}{2}}}$

(f) $f'(t) = \dfrac{2(1 + 2t)^4(3t^2 - 6t - 25)}{(3t^2 - 5)^3}$

(g) $g'(x) = \dfrac{-12(x + 2)^2}{(x - 2)^4}$

(h) $h'(t) = \dfrac{10(t^2 + 1)^9(t^2 + 2t - 1)}{(t + 1)^{11}}$

(i) $y' = \dfrac{2x}{(x^2 + 1)^{\frac{3}{2}}\sqrt{x^2 - 1}}$

(j) $y' = \dfrac{4(2x + 3)^2(5x - 12)}{(4x - 7)^{\frac{3}{2}}}$

(k) $y' = \dfrac{3(2x + 1)^4[22x + 1]}{2\sqrt{x}} + \dfrac{2}{\sqrt{4x - 3}}$

(l) $y' = \dfrac{1}{6x^{\frac{2}{3}}\sqrt{1 + \sqrt[3]{x}}}$

(m) $y' = 20(t + \sqrt[3]{t + t^2})^{19}\left(1 + \dfrac{1 + 2t}{3(t + t^2)^{\frac{2}{3}}}\right)$

(n) $y' = \dfrac{1}{2\sqrt{x + \sqrt{x + \sqrt{x}}}}\left(1 + \dfrac{1 + \frac{1}{2\sqrt{x}}}{2\sqrt{x + \sqrt{x}}}\right)$

7. $32x - y - 63 = 0$ 8. $4x - 2y - 7 = 0$

9. 15   10. 14

11. (a) $F'(x) = 4x^3f'(x^4)$ (b) $G'(x) = 4[f(x)]^3f'(x)$

(c) $H'(x) = \dfrac{1}{2\sqrt{x}}f'(\sqrt{x})$

(d) $P'(x) = \dfrac{f'(x)}{2\sqrt{f(x)}}$ (e) $y' = f'(f(x))f'(x)$

(f) $y' = \dfrac{f(x)f'(x)}{\sqrt{1 + [f(x)]^2}}$ (g) $y' = 4xf(x^2)f'(x^2)$

(h) $y' = 3f'(x)[f(x)]^2f'([f(x)]^3)$

12. (b)

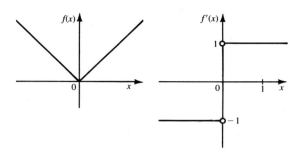

(c) $g'(x) = 2|x|$

EXERCISE 2.7

1. (a) $\dfrac{x}{y}$ (b) $-\dfrac{x^2}{y^2}$ (c) $-\dfrac{y}{x}$ (d) $-\dfrac{y + 2x}{x + 2y}$

(e) $\dfrac{2y - x^2}{y^2 - 2x}$ (f) $\dfrac{2x - 2y^2}{4xy - 3y^2}$ (g) $-\dfrac{\sqrt{y}}{\sqrt{x}}$

(h) $\dfrac{2y}{(x + y)^2 + 2x}$

2. (a) $\frac{1}{4}$ (b) -8 (c) $\frac{7}{8}$ (d) 3 (e) -1 (f) -4

3. (a) $2x - y + 1 = 0$ (b) $4x + y - 9 = 0$

(c) $3x - 16y + 25 = 0$ (d) $x + y = 0$

4. (a) $-\frac{3}{2}$ (c) $3x + 2y - 6\sqrt{2} = 0$

(d)

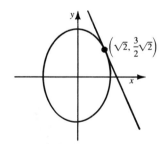

$\left(\sqrt{2}, \frac{3}{2}\sqrt{2}\right)$

5. (a) $3x - 4y - 14 = 0$

(b)

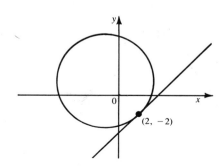

$(2, -2)$

6. (a) $\dfrac{dy}{dx} = \dfrac{x[25 - 4(x^2 + y^2)]}{y[25 + 4(x^2 + y^2)]}$

(b) $9x - 13y + 40 = 0$ (c) $\left(\pm\frac{5}{4}\sqrt{3}, \pm\frac{5}{4} \right)$

7. (a) $\dfrac{dy}{dx} = -\sqrt[3]{\dfrac{y}{x}}$ (b) $2\sqrt{3}x + 2y - \sqrt{3} = 0$

(c) $\left(\dfrac{\sqrt{2}}{4}, -\dfrac{\sqrt{2}}{4} \right)$ and $\left(-\dfrac{\sqrt{2}}{4}, \dfrac{\sqrt{2}}{4} \right)$ **9.** $-\frac{1}{2}$

(b)

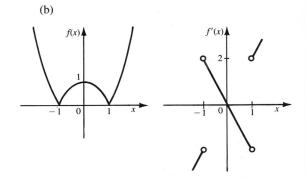

EXERCISE 2.8

1. (a) $f'(x) = 5x^4 - 8x$, $f''(x) = 20x^3 - 8$

(b) $f'(x) = 28x^3 + 36x^2 - 4$,
$f''(x) = 84x^2 + 72x$

(c) $f'(t) = 2 + \dfrac{1}{(t + 1)^2}$; $f''(t) = -\dfrac{2}{(1 + t)^3}$

(d) $g'(t) = -2t^{-\frac{3}{2}}$; $g''(t) = 3t^{-\frac{5}{2}}$

(e) $y' = 16(2x + 1)^7$, $y'' = 224(2x + 1)^6$

(f) $y' = 3t^2 - 3t^{-4}$, $y'' = 6t + 12t^{-5}$

(g) $y' = x(x^2 + 1)^{-\frac{1}{2}}$, $y'' = (x^2 + 1)^{-\frac{3}{2}}$

(h) $y' = -\dfrac{1}{(t - 1)^2}$, $y'' = \dfrac{2}{(t - 1)^3}$

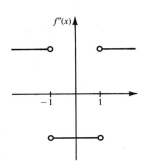

2. (a) $f'''(x) = -6$ (b) $f'''(x) = -\dfrac{210}{x^8}$

(c) $y''' = \dfrac{72}{(4 - x)^5}$ (d) $y''' = 3(1 + 2x)^{-\frac{5}{2}}$

3. $y' = 5x^4 + 4x^3 + 3x^2 + 2x + 1$, $y'' = 20x^3 + 12x^2 + 6x + 2$, $y''' = 60x^2 + 24x + 6$, $y^{(4)} = 120x + 24$, $y^{(5)} = 120$, $y^{(6)} = 0$

4. $\frac{2}{3}$ **5.** $-\frac{405}{131\,072}$ **6.** $n!$

7. (a) $-\dfrac{3x^2}{y^7}$ (b) $-\dfrac{1}{y^3}$ (c) $\dfrac{16xy}{(2x - y^2)^3}$

8. $f(x) = 4x^2 - 2x + 3$

9. (a) $f'' = g''h + 2g'h' + gh''$

(b) $f''' = g'''h + 3g''h' + 3g'h'' + gh'''$

10. (a)
$$f'(x) = \begin{cases} 2x & \text{if } |x| > 1 \\ -2x & \text{if } |x| < 1 \end{cases}$$

$$\mathrm{dom}(f') = \{x | x \neq \pm 1\}$$

$$f''(x) = \begin{cases} 2 & \text{if } |x| > 1 \\ -2 & \text{if } |x| < 1 \end{cases}$$

$$\mathrm{dom}(f'') = \{x | x \neq \pm 1\}$$

2.9 REVIEW EXERCISE

1. (a) $6x - 2$ (b) $3x^2 + 4$ (c) $\dfrac{1}{(1 - x)^2}$

(d) $\dfrac{1}{\sqrt{2x + 1}}$

2. $a = 1$, $f(x) = x^4$

3.

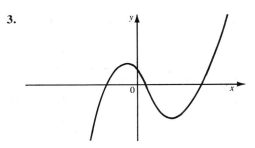

4. (a) $y' = 36x^2 + 8$ (b) $y' = 2(\pi + 1)x^\pi$

(c) $y' = 2 + \dfrac{3}{x^2}$ (d) $y' = \frac{6}{5}\sqrt[5]{x}$

(e) $y' = \dfrac{5}{2\sqrt{x}} - 1$ (f) $y' = \dfrac{3x - 2}{2\sqrt{x}}$

(g) $y' = \dfrac{5}{(1 + 3x)^2}$ (h) $y' = 42x^2(2x^3 - 1)^6$

(i) $f'(x) = \dfrac{-3x^3 - 2x^2 + 2x + 1}{\sqrt{1 - x^2}}$

(j) $g'(x) = \dfrac{-3x^2 + 12x + 1}{(2 - x)^2}$

(k) $h'(x) = \dfrac{-8x^3}{3\sqrt[3]{(2x^4 - 1)^4}}$

(l) $F'(x) = 2(x^4 + 1)^2(-13x^4 + 6x^3 - 1)$

(m) $f'(t) = \dfrac{1 + t}{\sqrt{(1 + 2t)^3}}$ (n) $g'(t) = \dfrac{4(t + 1)^3}{(t + 2)^5}$

(o) $R'(u) = \dfrac{1}{4\sqrt[4]{(u + 1)^3}} + \dfrac{4}{u^3}$

(p) $S'(v) = \dfrac{1 - 10v(v^2 - 8)^4}{2\sqrt{v - (v^2 - 8)^5}}$

(q) $M'(z) = \dfrac{1 - 2z - z^2}{2\sqrt{1 + z}\,\sqrt{(1 + z^2)^3}}$

(r) $F'(y) = \dfrac{3}{(2y + 3)^2}$

5. (a) $f'(x) = \dfrac{-2x^2 + 2x - 10}{(x^2 - 5)^2}$,

$\mathrm{dom}(f) = \mathrm{dom}(f') = \{x | x \neq \pm\sqrt{5}\}$

(b) $f'(x) = \dfrac{2x - 1}{2\sqrt{x^2 - x - 6}}$,

$\mathrm{dom}(f) = \{x | x \geq 3 \text{ or } x \leq -2\}$,

$\mathrm{dom}(f') = \{x | x > 3 \text{ or } x < -2\}$

6. -7

7. (a) $-\dfrac{x^3}{y^3}$ (b) $\dfrac{2xy - 2x}{2y - x^2}$ (c) $\dfrac{3x^2 - 4xy^2}{4x^2y - 3y^2}$

(d) $\dfrac{y - \dfrac{y}{2\sqrt{x - 1}} - \sqrt{y - 1}}{\sqrt{x - 1} + \dfrac{x}{2\sqrt{y - 1}} - x}$

8. (a) $80x^3 - 6x^2 + 6$ (b) $\dfrac{-9}{4\sqrt{(3x + 1)^3}}$

(c) $\dfrac{-4}{(t + 1)^3}$ (d) $-\dfrac{16}{y^3}$

9. (a) $4x + y - 4 = 0$ (b) $2x - y - 6 = 0$

(c) $5\sqrt{2}x + 32y - 14\sqrt{2} = 0$

(d) $13x - 3y + 8 = 0$

(e) $3x - 4y + 14 = 0$

(f) $4x - 5y + 12 = 0$

10. -10 m/s, -20 m/s, -50 m/s

11. $(-1, 11)$ **12.** $(0, -1), (1, 1)$

13. $11x - y - 25 = 0, x + y + 1 = 0$

14. (a) 2   (b) $-\frac{7}{18}$ (c) 10

15. (a) $f'(x) = x^2g'(x) + 2xg(x)$

(b) $f'(x) = \dfrac{2xg'(x) - g(x)}{2x\sqrt{x}}$

(c) $f'(x) = -\dfrac{1}{x^2}g'\!\left(\dfrac{1}{x}\right)$

(d) $f'(x) = \dfrac{g'(\sqrt{x})}{4\sqrt{xg(\sqrt{x})}}$

16. $f''(x) = g'(g(x))g''(x) + g''(g(x))[g'(x)]^2$

17. (a) 1

(b) $f(x) = \begin{cases} 2 - 2x & \text{if } x \leq 0 \\ 2 & \text{if } 0 < x < 1 \\ 1 & \text{if } x > 1 \end{cases}$

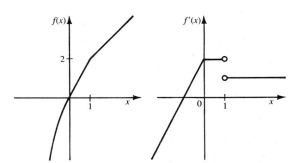

2.10 CHAPTER 2 TEST

1. (a) $f'(x) = \lim\limits_{h \to 0} \dfrac{f(x + h) - f(x)}{h}$

(b) (i) $f'(x) = 2x - 7$ (ii) $f'(x) = \dfrac{-2}{(2x + 1)^2}$

2. (a) $f'(x) = \dfrac{2}{3\sqrt[3]{x}}$ (b) $f'(x) = \dfrac{2x^2 - 2x - 6}{(2x - 1)^2}$

(c) $f'(x) = 2(x^2 - 1)^3(2x + 1)^2 \times$
$(11x^2 + 4x - 3)$
(d) $f'(x) = 7(x + \sqrt{x^4 - 2x + 1})^6 \times$
$\left(1 + \dfrac{2x^3 - 1}{\sqrt{x^4 - 2x + 1}}\right)$

3. (a) $\dfrac{x^2 - y}{x - y^2}$ (b) $4x - 5y + 4 = 0$

4. $y''' = \dfrac{192}{(3 - 2x)^5}$ 5. $(5, 3)$

6. (a) $g'(x) = 6x^5f'(x^6)$ (b) $h'(x) = 6f'(x)[f(x)]^5$
(c) $F'(x) = \dfrac{2xf(x) - x^2f'(x)}{[f(x)]^2}$

CHAPTER 3 APPLICATIONS OF DERIVATIVES

REVIEW AND PREVIEW TO CHAPTER 3
EXERCISE 1

1. $\frac{1}{2}, -\frac{3}{4}$ 2. 2   3. $\frac{800}{13} \doteq 61.5$ km/h

4. 2.4 cm   5. $\frac{4224}{125} \doteq 33.8$ cm

6. $15 + 3\sqrt{37} \doteq 33.25$ h with Bob's hose,
$21 + 3\sqrt{37} \doteq 39.25$ h with Jim's hose

EXERCISE 3.1

1. (a) 0   (b) C   (c) The car was speeding up at A and C, slowing down at B.   (d) The car is stopped.   (e) The car returned to the point at which it started.

2. (a) $v(t) = 12$, 12 m/s, 12 m/s
(b) $v(t) = 16t - 24$, 8 m/s, 40 m/s
(c) $v(t) = 3t^2 - 12t$, -12 m/s, 0 m/s
(d) $v(t) = \dfrac{5}{(1 + t)^2}$, $\frac{5}{9}$ m/s, $\frac{1}{5}$ m/s

3. -24.8 m/s, -34.6 m/s

4. (a) 14.7 m/s, 4.9 m/s, -4.9 m/s, -14.7 m/s
(b) 2.5 s   (c) 30.6 m   (d) at 5 s
(e) -24.5 m/s

5. at 15 min   6. at 3 s

7. (a) -2 m/s, 2 m/s   (b) at 2 s   (c) after 2 s
(d)

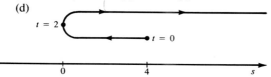

8. (a) at 3 s and 7 s   (b) when $0 \le t < 3$ or $t > 7$
(c)

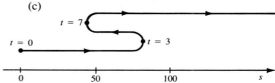

(d) 194 m

9. (a) at 1 s   (b) at $1 + \sqrt{91} \doteq 10.5$ s
(c) -95.4 m/s

EXERCISE 3.2

1. (a) positive   (b) negative   (c) positive
(d) zero   (e) positive

2. (a) velocity increasing, acceleration positive
(b) (i) negative   (ii) positive   (iii) zero
(iv) negative

3. (a) $v = 30$, $a = 0$ (b) $v = 32t + 5$, $a = 32$
(c) $v = 3t^2 + 10t + 1$, $a = 6t + 10$
(d) $v = \dfrac{2t + 1}{2\sqrt{t^2 + t}}$, $a = \dfrac{-1}{4\sqrt{(t^2 + t)^3}}$

4. (a) -9.8 m/s²   (b) 22 m/s²   (c) 20 m/s²
(d) -0.08 m/s²

5. (a) s_0 (b) v_0 (c) g 6. 12 m/s²

7. (a) at 3 s   (b) 0 m, -9 m/s

8. positive when $0 \le t < 1$ or $t > 5$, negative when $1 < t < 5$ 9. (b) $\frac{5}{3}$ s

EXERCISE 3.3

1. 48   **2.** 10π cm²/cm   **3.** $\frac{250}{9}$ L/min

4. (a) 0.488 kg/m (b) 0.5 kg/m   **5.** 7 g/cm

6. 411 bacteria/h   **7.** $\frac{1}{40}$ m³/kPa/m³

8. -0.03 moles/L/min

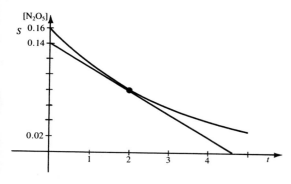

9. -185.2 cm/s/cm

EXERCISE 3.4

1. (a) $C'(x) = 23 + 0.024\,x$ (b) $25.40/item
   (c) $25.41

2. (a) $C'(x) = \frac{1}{10} + \frac{x}{500}$ (b) $1.70/unit
   (c) $1.70

3. (a) $R'(x) = 8000 - 0.06x^2$ (b) $2600/unit
   (c) $2581.92

4. (a) $P(x) = 0.74x - 0.0003x^2 - 23\,000$
   (b) $P'(x) = 0.74 - 0.0006x$ (c) $0.14/pen
   (d) $0.1397

5. (a)

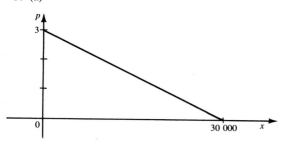

p	0	\$0.50	\$1.00	\$1.50	\$2.00	\$2.50	\$3.00
x	30 000	25 000	20 000	15 000	10 000	5000	0

   (c) $R(x) = \frac{1}{10\,000}(30\,000x - x^2)$

   (d) $R'(x) = \frac{1}{10\,000}(30\,000 - 2x)$ (e) \$2.80

   (f) $P(x) = 2.2x - \dfrac{x^2}{10\,000} - 6000$

   (g) $P'(x) = 2.2 - \dfrac{x}{5000}$ (h) \$0.20

6. (a) $C'(x) = 23 + 0.002x$
   (b) $R'(x) = 100 - 0.02x$
   (c) $P'(x) = 77 - 0.022x$ (d) \$75.90

EXERCISE 3.5

1. -18 **2.** -16 **3.** 4.8 m²/min

4. 3 cm/s   **5.** $5000\pi \doteq 15\,700$ cm²/s

6. $\dfrac{2}{\pi} \doteq 0.64$ m/min   **7.** $\dfrac{1}{64\pi} \doteq 0.005$ cm/min

8. $\dfrac{20}{\sqrt{3}} \doteq 11.5$ cm²/s   **9.** -1.5 cm/min

10. 1 m/s   **11.** $\dfrac{\sqrt{3}}{10} \doteq 0.17$ m/s

12. 90 km/h   **13.** $\dfrac{130}{\sqrt{17}} \doteq 31.5$ km/h

14. $\dfrac{6\sqrt{26}}{13} \doteq 2.35$ m/s   **15.** $240\sqrt{5} \doteq 537$ km/h

16. 5 cm/min   **17.** $\dfrac{8}{15\pi} \doteq 0.17$ m/min

EXERCISE 3.6

1. $-\frac{1}{2}$ **2.** $-2, -\frac{13}{8}$ **3.** (a) 1.521 380

(c)

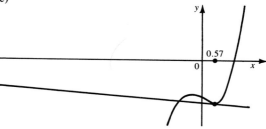

4. (a) 1.556 250 (b) 2.095 366 (c) 1.191 554
5. (a) $-2.330\ 059$, 0.201 640, 2.128 419
   (b) $-0.492\ 689$, 0.508 422, 1.528 643
6. (b) 4.147 288
7. (a) 1.947 294 (b) 1.026 214
8. (a) (1.324 718, 2.324 718)
   (b) (0.682 328, 1.465 571)

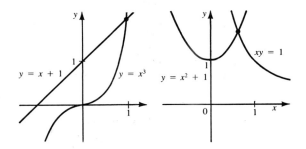

3.7 REVIEW EXERCISE

1. (a) $v(t) = 6t^2 + 8t - 1$, $a(t) = 12t + 8$
   (b) 127 m/s, 56 m/s²
2. (a) at 3 s and 5 s (b) positive when $t > 5$ or $0 \le t < 3$, negative when $3 < t < 5$
   (c) positive when $t > 4$, negative when $0 \le t < 4$
   (d) -3 m/s
   (e)

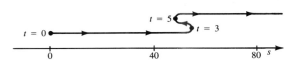

   (f) 112 m
3. (a) 63.34 m/s (b) -1.66 m/s² (c) 78.3 s
   (d) -65 m/s
4. 10   5. (a) 3.05 kg/m (b) 3 kg/m
6. (a) $C'(x) = 16.2 + 0.12x$ (b) \$40.20/unit
   (c) \$40.26/unit
7. (a) $C'(x) = 1.08$ (b) $R(x) = 20x - 0.001x^2$
   (c) $R'(x) = 20 - 0.002x$
   (d) $P(x) = -0.001x^2 + 18.92x - 12\ 500$
   (e) $P'(x) = -0.002x + 18.92$ (f) \$2.92/pizza
8. $\frac{80}{3}$ cm²/min   9. 45 cm³/min
10. $\dfrac{1470}{\sqrt{466}} \doteq 68$ km/h   11. $\frac{4}{5}$
12. $-0.754\ 878$

13. (a)

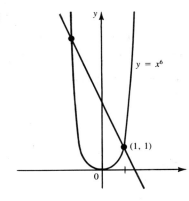

   (b) (1, 1), $(-1.335\ 387, -5.670\ 774)$

3.8 CHAPTER 3 TEST

1. (a) 9 m/s (b) 12 m/s² (c) at 1 s, 3 s
   (d) when $0 \le t < 1$ or $t > 3$ (e) -3 m/s
   (f) 12 m
2. (a) $C'(x) = 122$ (b) $R(x) = 600x - 0.001x^2$
   (c) $R'(x) = 600 - 0.002x$
   (d) $P(x) = -0.001x^2 + 478x - 87\ 000$
   (e) $P'(x) = -0.002x + 478$
3. $\dfrac{32}{81\pi} \doteq 0.13$ cm/s   4. 1.267 168

CUMULATIVE REVIEW FOR CHAPTERS 1 TO 3

1. (a) $\frac{9}{8}$ (b) $\frac{1}{4}$ (c) 0 (d) 12 (e) $-\frac{2}{27}$ (f) $\frac{5}{3}$
   (g) 0 (h) -2
2. (a) (i) 0 (ii) -3 (iii) does not exist (iv) -3
   (v) -3 (vi) -3
   (b)

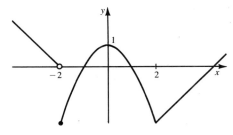

   (c) -2 (d) -2, 2
3. (a) -2 (b) 0   4. (a) divergent (b) 9
5. (a) $6x - 5$ (b) $x - y + 3 = 0$
6. $g'(x) = \dfrac{-1}{2\sqrt{3 - x}}$

7. (a) $f'(x) = 60x^4 - 2x^3 - 4$

(b) $f'(x) = -\dfrac{12}{x^3}$ (c) $g'(x) = \frac{8}{3}x^{\frac{1}{3}} - \frac{2}{3}x^{-\frac{5}{3}}$

(d) $g'(x) = \dfrac{2x(x-3)}{(2x-3)^2}$ (e) $f'(t) = \dfrac{2 - 3t^2}{2\sqrt{2t - t^3}}$

(f) $f'(y) = \dfrac{-20(2-y)^3}{(1+2y)^5}$

(g) $y' = 3(x^3 - 1)^2(10x^3 + 15x^2 - 1)$

(h) $y' = \dfrac{-x^4}{\sqrt[5]{(x^5 + 1)^6}}$ (i) $y' = \dfrac{2\sqrt{x} - 3}{2\sqrt{x^5}}$

(j) $y' = \dfrac{1 - x^2}{2\sqrt{x}\,\sqrt{(1 + x^2)^3}}$

8. $f'(x) = \dfrac{-x}{\sqrt{(x^2 - 1)^3}}$, domain of f = domain of

$f' = \{x \,|\, x < -1 \text{ or } x > 1\}$

9. $\dfrac{dy}{dx} = -\dfrac{2x^3 + 2xy^3}{3x^2y^2 + y}$

10. (a) $y' = \dfrac{1}{(x+2)^2}$, $y'' = \dfrac{-2}{(x+2)^3}$

(b) $y' = \dfrac{2x}{3y^2}$, $y'' = \dfrac{6y^3 - 8x^2}{9y^5}$

11. (a) $x + y - 2 = 0$ (b) $2x - y + 3 = 0$

12. $11x - y + 16 = 0$, $11x - y - 16 = 0$

13. (a) 37   (b) $\frac{43}{16}$ (c) 6

14. (a) $5x^4f'(x^5)$ (b) $5[f(x)]^4f'(x)$

(c) $5x^4f(x) + x^5f'(x)$ (d) $\frac{1}{2}\sqrt{\dfrac{x}{f(x)}}\left(\dfrac{xf'(x) - f(x)}{x^2}\right)$

15. (a) (i) -42.5 m/s   (ii) -38.09 m/s
(iii) -37.65 m/s   (b) -37.6 m/s
(c) -9.8 m/s²

16. (a) -3 m/s, 9 m/s   (b) 12 m/s²
(c) at 1 s, 3 s
(d) positive when $t > 3$ or $0 \le t < 1$,
negative when $1 < t < 3$
(e) positive when $t > 2$, negative when
$0 \le t < 2$ (f) 28 m

17. (a) π m³/m   (b) $\dfrac{5}{18\pi} \doteq 0.088$ m/min

18. $\dfrac{2\sqrt{101}}{25} \doteq 0.8$ m/s

19. $\frac{5}{76}$ m/min $\doteq 6.6$ cm/min   **20.** 2.094 551

CHAPTER 4 EXTREME VALUES

REVIEW AND PREVIEW TO CHAPTER 4
EXERCISE 1
1.

(a) $\{x \,|\, -2 < x < 6\}$

(b) $\{x \,|\, -3 \le x < -2\}$

(c) $\{x \,|\, 1 < x \le 4\}$

(d) $\{x \,|\, -2 \le x \le 1.5\}$

(e) $\{x \,|\, x \ge 3\}$

(f) $\{x \,|\, x < 2\}$

(g) $\{x \,|\, x \le 1\}$

(h) $\left\{x \,\middle|\, x > -\dfrac{3}{2}\right\}$

2.

(a) $(-\infty, 2)$

(b) $(0, 3)$

(c) $[-1, 2)$

(d) $(1, \infty)$

(e) $[-1, 3]$

(f) $(-\infty, -1]$

EXERCISE 2
1. (a) $\left(-\frac{7}{3}, \infty\right)$ (b) $\left(\frac{9}{2}, \infty\right)$ (c) $(-\infty, 2]$

(d) $(4, \infty)$ (e) $(-\infty, 10)$ (f) $(-\infty, 1) \cup (6, \infty)$
(g) $(-4, 3)$ (h) $(0, 3)$ (i) $(-\infty, -3) \cup (3, \infty)$

(j) $[-\sqrt{5}, \sqrt{5}]$ (k) $\left(-1, -\frac{1}{2}\right) \cup (6, \infty)$

(l) $(-\infty, -5) \cup (0, 2)$ (m) $(-\infty, 1)$
(n) $(-3, -2) \cup (3, \infty)$ (o) $[2, \infty)$ (p) $(0, \infty)$

2. (a) $\left(-\frac{1}{2}, \infty\right)$ (b) $(-\infty, -2) \cup (3, \infty)$

(c) $(-\infty, -1) \cup (0, 1)$
(d) $(-\infty, -1) \cup (-1, 0)$

EXERCISE 4.1

1. (a) increases on $(-5, 0)$ and $(2, 5)$, decreases on $(0, 2)$ (b) increases on $(-4, 3)$, decreases on $(-6, -4)$ and $(3, 5)$

2. (a) $\left(-\infty, \frac{1}{2}\right)$ (b) $(0, \infty)$ (c) $(-\infty, -1), (1, \infty)$

(d) $(-\infty, 0), (1, \infty)$ (e) $(-2, 0), (1, \infty)$
(f) $(-\infty, \infty)$

3. (a) $\left(-\frac{2}{3}, 0\right)$ (b) $(-2, 3)$ (c) $(-\infty, -1), (0, 1)$

(d) $(-\infty, -1)$

4. (a) increases on $(3, \infty)$, decreases on $(-\infty, 3)$
(b) increases on $(-\infty, -2), (5, \infty)$, decreases on $(-2, 5)$ (c) increases on $(-1, 0)$, $(1, \infty)$, decreases on $(-\infty, -1), (0, 1)$
(d) increases on $(-1, 2), (3, \infty)$, decreases on $(-\infty, -1), (2, 3)$ (e) increases on $\left(-\infty, \frac{3}{7}\right), (1, \infty)$, decreases on $\left(\frac{3}{7}, 1\right)$

(f) increases on $(-\infty, -1), (-1, \infty)$
(g) increases on $\left(-\infty, \frac{8}{3}\right)$, decreases on $\left(\frac{8}{3}, 4\right)$

(h) increases on $(-3, 0), (3, \infty)$, decreases on $(-\infty, -3), (0, 3)$

5. $\left(\dfrac{-1 - \sqrt{5}}{2}, \dfrac{-1 + \sqrt{5}}{2}\right)$

EXERCISE 4.2

1 (i) (a) $f(7) = 5$ (b) $f(2) = -2$ (c) $f(0) = 2$,
$f(4) = 3$ (d) $f(2) = -2, f(6) = 1$
(ii) (a) $f(4) = 5$ (b) $f(-3) = -2$
(c) $f(1) = 4, f(4) = 5$ (d) $f(2) = 2, f(6) = 1$

2. (a)

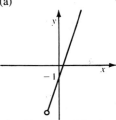

no maximum or minimum

(b)

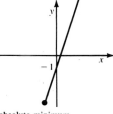

absolute minimum
$g(-1) = -4$, no maximum

(c)

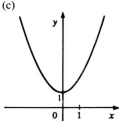

absolute and local minimum
$f(0) = 1$ no maximum

(d)

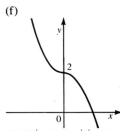

absolute and local minimum
$f(0) = 1$ no maximum

(e)

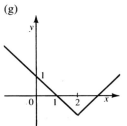

absolute and local minimum
$f(0) = 1$
absolute maximum $f(2) = 5$

(f)

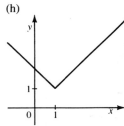

no maximum or minimum

(g)

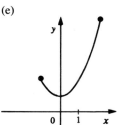

absolute and local minimum
$f(2) = -1$ no maximum

(h)

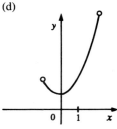

absolute and local minimum
$f(1) = 1$, no maximum

3. (a) $\frac{1}{4}$ (b) ± 1 (c) $-1, 0, 4$ (d) $-1, 2, 3$
(e) $\frac{1}{2}(-1 \pm \sqrt{5})$ (f) none   (g) -6 (h) 0
(i) $0, \frac{1}{4}$ (j) $1, \frac{2}{3}$ (k) -1 (l) ± 1

4. (a) $f(0) = 1, f(2) = -7$ (b) $f(2) = 21$,
$f(-1) = 3$ (c) $f(2) = 4, f(-2) = -28$
(d) $f(-2) = 106, f(3) = -19$
(e) $f(-3) = 79, f(1) = f(-1) = 15$
(f) $f(2) = 58, f(-1) = -5$
(g) $g(4) = 20, g(2) = 12$
(h) $f(1) = 1, f(3) = 3\sqrt[3]{9} - 6$
(i) $f(\pm 6) = 9, f(\pm 3) = 0$
(j) $f(2) = 2, f\left(\frac{1}{2}\right) = -1$

6. -8 7. $a = -3, b = -120$
8. (a) $-1.000, 1.353$ (b) -15.14

EXERCISE 4.3

1. (a) local minimum $f\left(\frac{2}{3}\right) = \frac{35}{3}$

(b) local maximum $f(-2) = 11$, local minimum $f(2) = -21$

(c) local maximum $f(1) = 6$, local minimum $f(-1) = -2$

(d) local minimum $f\left(\frac{3}{4}\right) = -\frac{27}{256}$

2. (a) critical number $\frac{1}{2}$

increases on $\left(-\infty, \frac{1}{2}\right)$

decreases on $\left(\frac{1}{2}, \infty\right)$

local maximum $f\left(\frac{1}{2}\right) = \frac{7}{2}$

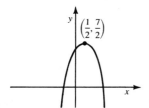

(b) critical numbers 2, 4

increases on $(-\infty, 2)$, $(4, \infty)$

decreases on $(2, 4)$

local maximum $f(2) = 10$

local minimum $f(4) = 6$

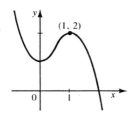

(c) critical numbers 0, 1

increases on $(0, 1)$

decreases on $(-\infty, 0)$, $(1, \infty)$

local maximum $g(1) = 2$

local minimum $g(0) = 1$

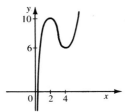

(d) critical numbers 0, 1, 3

increases on $(0, 1)$, $(3, \infty)$

decreases on $(-\infty, 0)$, $(1, 3)$

local maximum $g(1) = 6$

local minima $g(0) = 1$, $g(3) = -26$

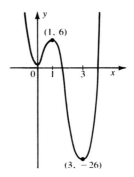

(e) critical numbers -2, 0 2

increases on $(-2, 0)$, $(2, \infty)$

decreases on $(-\infty, -2)$, $(0, 2)$

local maximum $h(0) = 6$

local minima $h(\pm 2) = -10$

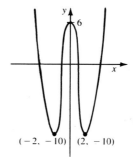

(f) critical numbers -1, 0, 1

increases on $(-\infty, -1)$, $(1, \infty)$

decreases on $(-1, 1)$

local maximum $h(-1) = 2$

local minimum $h(1) = -2$

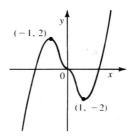

3. (a) local maximum $f\left(\frac{1}{8}\right) = \frac{1}{2}$, local minimum
$f(0) = 0$ (b) local maximum $f(0) = 0$

(c) local maximum $f\left(\frac{8}{3}\right) = \frac{16}{9}\sqrt{3}$

(d) local maximum $f\left(\frac{1}{\sqrt{2}}\right) = \frac{1}{2}$, local minimum
$f\left(-\frac{1}{\sqrt{2}}\right) = -\frac{1}{2}$

4. (a) maximum $f\left(\frac{1}{2}\right) = \frac{109}{4}$
(b) minimum $f(0) = 2$
(c) minimum $g(0) = -1$
(d) minimum $g(1) = \frac{1}{2}$

5.

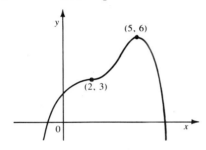

6. local maximum $f(2) = 28$, local minima
$f(0) = 0,\ f(3) = 27$

EXERCISE 4.4

1. 75, −75   **2.** 20, 10   **3.** both 25 cm
5. 20 cm by 20 cm by 10 cm   **6.** 2 m³
7. (a) 100 m by 200 m   (b) 50 m by 300 m
8. $500\sqrt{2}$ m by $750\sqrt{2}$ m   **10.** $\left(-\frac{10}{13}, \frac{2}{13}\right)$
11. $(-2, 2)$.   **12.** $\sqrt[3]{\dfrac{500}{\pi}} \doteq 5.4$ cm
13. (a) all wire for the circle
(b) $\dfrac{160}{4 + \pi} \doteq 22.4$ cm for the square
14. 4 cm²
15. Lay cable underground to a point 1165 m east
of P.
16. $\dfrac{16}{\pi + 4} \doteq 2.24$ m
17. $\frac{16}{41}$ h after noon (about 12:23 p.m.)
18. $\dfrac{4\sqrt{3}}{9}\pi r^3$
19. circular track, radius $\dfrac{1}{2\pi}$ km
20. about 7 m

EXERCISE 4.5

1. (a) \$362.50/item, \$152.50/item   (b) 2000
(c) \$292.50/item
2. (a) \$5.23/unit, \$6.10/unit   (b) 2530
(c) \$5.16/unit
3. 10 000   **4.** 11 000
5. (a) $p(x) = 19 - \dfrac{x}{3000}$ (b) \$9.50
6. (a) $p(x) = 130 - \dfrac{x}{100}$ (b) \$65
7. \$800   **8.** 85

4.6 REVIEW EXERCISE

1. (a) critical numbers $\pm\dfrac{1}{\sqrt{3}}$, increases on
$\left(-\dfrac{1}{\sqrt{3}}, \dfrac{1}{\sqrt{3}}\right)$, decreases on $\left(-\infty, -\dfrac{1}{\sqrt{3}}\right)$,
$\left(\dfrac{1}{\sqrt{3}}, \infty\right)$ (b) no critical number, increases on
$(-\infty, \infty)$ (c) critical numbers $\pm 1, 2$, increases
on $(-1, 1)$, $(2, \infty)$, decreases on $(-\infty, -1)$,
$(1, 2)$ (d) no critical number, decreases on
$\left(-\infty, \frac{1}{2}\right)$, $\left(\frac{1}{2}, \infty\right)$ (e) critical numbers $-2, 0$,
increases on $(-\infty, -2)$, $(0, \infty)$, decreases on
$(-2, -1)$, $(-1, 0)$ (f) critical numbers 0, 2,
increases on $(-\infty, 0)$, $(2, \infty)$, decreases on $(0, 2)$

2. (a) $f(1) = 9, f\left(-\frac{3}{2}\right) = -16$ (b) $f(-3) = 86$,
$f(3) = -22$ (c) $g(4) = 412, g(3) = -216$
(d) $g(5) = -\frac{3}{2}, g(2) = -3$

3. (a) local maximum $f(4) = 215$, local minimum
$f(-3) = -128$ (b) local maximum
$f(0) = 10$, local mimima, $f(\pm 6) = -1286$
(c) local maximum $f(0) = 4$
(d) local maximum $f(-3) = 12$

4. (a) 1, 2, 3   (b) increases on $(1, 2)$, $(3, \infty)$,
decreases on $(-\infty, 1)$, $(2, 3)$
(c) local maximum $f(2) = -8$,
local minima $f(1) = f(3) = -9$
(d)

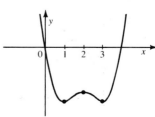

ANSWERS **561**

5. $f\left(-\frac{1}{2}\right) = \frac{4}{3}$ **6.** 240 cm²

7. $\dfrac{40}{1 + \sqrt[3]{2}} \doteq 17.7$ m from dimmer light

8. $2\sqrt{2}, \sqrt{2}$ **9.** $\frac{21}{6}$ km from D

10. (a) 24 495   (b) 444

11. (a) $p(x) = \frac{1}{3}(400 - 2x)$ (b) \$66.67

CHAPTER 5 CURVE SKETCHING

REVIEW AND PREVIEW TO CHAPTER 5
EXERCISE 1

1. (a) x-intercepts $\pm\frac{5}{2}$, y-intercept 25

(b) x-intercepts $-\frac{1}{2}$, 1, y-intercept -1

(c) x-intercepts 1, -3, y-intercept -3

(d) no x-intercept, y-intercept 1

(e) x-intercepts $\dfrac{-2 \pm \sqrt{22}}{3}$, y-intercept -6

(f) x-intercepts 0, $\pm\sqrt{3}$, y-intercept 0

(g) x-intercepts ± 1, y-intercept 1

(h) x-intercepts 0, $-\frac{3}{2}$, 6, y-intercept 0

(i) x-intercept -2, y-intercept 8

(j) x-intercepts ± 2, y-intercept -16

2. x-intercepts 0, ± 3, y-intercept 0

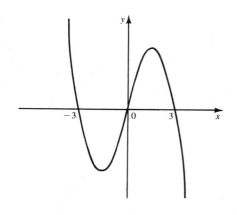

3. 1.53, 0.35, -1.88
EXERCISE 2
1. (a) odd   (b) even   (c) neither   (d) odd
2. (a) even   (b) odd   (c) neither   (d) even
(e) odd   (f) neither   (g) even   (h) odd

4.7 CHAPTER 4 TEST
1. $(-1, 1)$ **2.** $f(1) = 3, f\left(-\frac{1}{3}\right) = \frac{31}{27}$

3. (a) $-2, 0, 2$ (b) increases on $(-2, 0), (2, \infty)$, decreases on $(-\infty, -2), (0, 2)$
(c) local maximum $f(0) = 3$, local minima $f(\pm 2) = -13$

4. A cube with side 10 m
5. 2000   **6.** 90

EXERCISE 5.1
1. (a) $x = -7, x = -3, x = 2, x = 6$
(b) (i) $-\infty$ (ii) ∞ (iii) ∞ (iv) $-\infty$
(v) ∞ (vi) $-\infty$

2. (a) ∞ (b) $-\infty$ (c) ∞ (d) $-\infty$ (e) $-\infty$
(f) ∞ (g) $-\infty$ (h) $-\infty$ (i) ∞ (j) $-\infty$
(k) $-\infty$ (l) $-\infty$

3. (a) $x = -1$ (b) $x = 6$

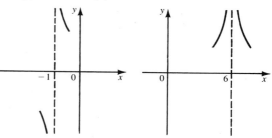

(c) $x = -2$ (d) $x = -1, x = 1$

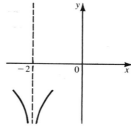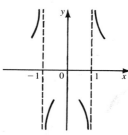

(e) $x = -1, x = 1$ (f) $x = -3, x = -1$

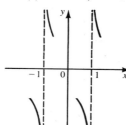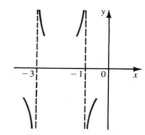

(g) $x = -1$, $x = 0$ (h) $x = -2$, $x = 0$,
$\qquad\qquad\qquad\qquad x = 2$

(e) HA: $y = 0$, VA: $x = -1$, $x = 1$
(f) HA: $y = 2$, VA: $x = -4$, $x = 1$

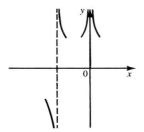
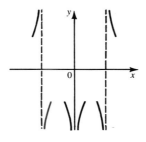

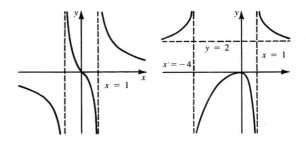

4. $-\infty$ **5.** $|x| < \frac{1}{100}$

(g) HA: $y = 0$, VA: $x = -2$ (h) HA: $y = 1$,
$\qquad\qquad\qquad\qquad\qquad$ VA: $x = -2$

EXERCISE 5.2

Abbreviations: VA, vertical asymptote; HA,
horizontal asymptote

1. (a) HA: $y = 2$, VA: $x = -2$, $x = 1$
$\quad$ (b) HA: $y = -2$, $y = 1$; VA: $x = -1$, $x = 4$

2. (a) 0 (b) 0 (c) 2 (d) 2 (e) $-\frac{1}{5}$ (f) 1

$\quad$ (g) 0 (h) $\frac{1}{2}$ (i) 3 (j) 0

3. (a) $y = -\frac{1}{2}$ (b) $y = 0$ (c) $y = 1$ (d) $y = 1$

4. (a) HA: $y = 0$, VA: $x = -1$ (b) HA: $y = 1$,
$\qquad\qquad\qquad\qquad\qquad\qquad$ VA: $x = -1$

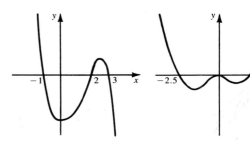

5. (a) ∞ (b) $-\infty$ (c) ∞ (d) $-\infty$ (e) ∞ (f) $-\infty$
6. (a) $-\infty$, ∞ (b) ∞, ∞

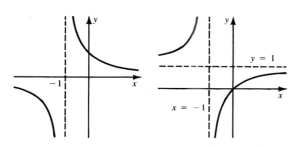

(c) HA: $y = -2$, VA: $x = \frac{3}{2}$
(d) HA: $y = 0$, VA: $x = -1$, $x = 1$

(c) ∞, ∞ $\qquad\qquad$ (d) ∞, $-\infty$

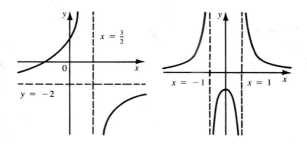

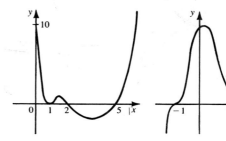

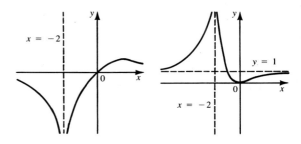

7. $y = 1, y = -1$ **8.** 1   **9.** -3 **10.** $\frac{5}{2}$

11. $-\infty$ **12.** $x > 1000$

EXERCISE 5.3

Abbreviations: CU, concave upward; CD, concave downward; IP, inflection point

1. CU on $(-6, -3)$, $(-1, 1)$, $(1, 3)$, $(10, 13)$,
CD on $(-10, -6)$, $(-3, -1)$, $(3, 7)$, $(7, 10)$,
IP $(-6, -1)$, $(-3, 0)$, $(-1, 2)$, $(3, 1)$, $(10, 2)$

2. (a) CD on $(-\infty, \infty)$ (b) CU on $(-\infty, \infty)$

(c) CU on $\left(-\infty, \frac{1}{3}\right)$, CD on $\left(\frac{1}{3}, \infty\right)$, IP $\left(\frac{1}{3}, \frac{470}{27}\right)$

(d) CU on $(-4, \infty)$, CD on $(-\infty, -4)$,
IP $(-4, 255)$

(e) CU on $(-\infty, 0)$, $(1, \infty)$,
CD on $(0, 1)$, IP $(0, -2)$, $(1, -2)$

(f) CU on $(-\infty, -2)$, $(2, \infty)$, CD on $(-2, 2)$,
IP $(-2, -83)$, $(2, -79)$

(g) CU on $(1, \infty)$, CD on $(-\infty, 1)$

(h) CU on $(-\infty, 5)$, CD on $(5, \infty)$ (i) CU on

$\left(-\infty, -\frac{1}{\sqrt{3}}\right)$, $\left(\frac{1}{\sqrt{3}}, \infty\right)$, CD on $\left(-\frac{1}{\sqrt{3}}, \frac{1}{\sqrt{3}}\right)$,

IP $\left(-\frac{1}{\sqrt{3}}, \frac{3}{4}\right)$, $\left(\frac{1}{\sqrt{3}}, \frac{3}{4}\right)$ (j) CU on

$(-\infty, -\sqrt{6})$, $(0, \sqrt{6})$, CD on $(-\sqrt{6}, 0)$, $(\sqrt{6}, \infty)$, IP $\left(-\sqrt{6}, \frac{5}{(\sqrt{6})^3}\right)$, $\left[\sqrt{6}, -\frac{5}{(\sqrt{6})^3}\right)$ (k) CU

on $(1, \infty)$, CD on $(-\infty, 1)$, IP $(1, 6)$ (l) CU on
$(-1, \infty)$

3. (i) (a) decreasing $(-\infty, \infty)$
(b) none
(c) CU on $(-\infty, -2)$, CD on $(-2, \infty)$
(d) IP $(-2, 14)$
(e)

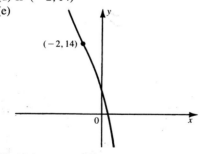

(ii) (a) increasing on $(-2, 0)$, $(2, \infty)$ decreasing
on $(-\infty, -2)$, $(0, 2)$
(b) local maximum $f(0) = 0$
local minima $f(2) = f(-2) = -16$

(c) CU on $\left(-\infty, -\frac{2}{\sqrt{3}}\right)$ and $\left(\frac{2}{\sqrt{3}}, \infty\right)$ CD on

$\left(-\frac{2}{\sqrt{3}}, \frac{2}{\sqrt{3}}\right)$

(d) IP $\left(-\frac{2}{\sqrt{3}}, -\frac{80}{9}\right)$ and $\left(\frac{2}{\sqrt{3}}, -\frac{80}{9}\right)$

(e)

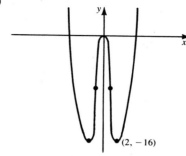

(iii) (a) increasing on $(-\infty, \infty)$
(b) none
(c) CU on $(0, \infty)$, CD on $(-\infty, 0)$
(d) IP $(0, 0)$
(e)

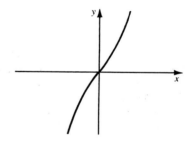

(iv) (a) increasing on $(0, 1)$
decreasing on $(-\infty, 0)$, $(1, \infty)$
(b) local minimum $f(0) = 0$
local maximum $f(1) = 1$
(c) CD on $(-\infty, 0)$, $(0, \infty)$
(d) none
(e)

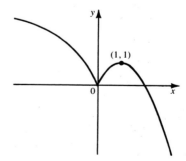

4. $c = -12, d = 117$

6.

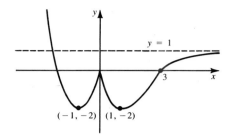

7.

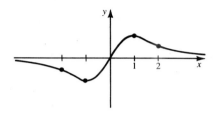

8. $(-0.614, 8.782)$

EXERCISE 5.4

1. (a) local minimum $f\left(\frac{2}{3}\right) = \frac{35}{3}$ (b) local
maximum $f\left(\frac{1}{2}\right) = \frac{7}{2}$ (c) local maximum
$g(-2\sqrt{2}) = 64\sqrt{2} - 17$, local minimum
$g(2\sqrt{2}) = -64\sqrt{2} - 17$ (d) local maximum
$g(1) = 2$, local minimum $g(0) = 1$ (e) local
maximum $h(2) = 10$, local minimum $h(4) = 6$
(f) local minimum $h\left(\frac{3}{4}\right) = -\frac{27}{256}$, no
information on $h(0)$ (g) local maximum
$F(1) = 6$, local minima $F(0) = 1$,
$F(3) = -26$
(h) local maximum $F(1) = 6$, local minimum
$F(-1) = -2$ (i) local maximum $G(0) = 1$,
local minimum $G(2) = -243$, no information
at other critical numbers   (j) local minimum
$G(2) = 12$

2. (a) local maximum $f(0) = 10$, local minima
$f(\sqrt{3}) = f(-\sqrt{3}) = 1$ (b) none
(c) local maximum $g(3) = \frac{1}{6}$,
local minimum $g(-3) = -\frac{1}{6}$
(d) local minimum $f\left(-\frac{3}{2}\right) = -\frac{1}{24}$
(e) local maximum $f(-5) = -5$, local
minimum $f(0) = 0$
(f) local maximum $f(-8) = 4$

3. (a) local maximum $f\left(\frac{1}{\sqrt{3}}\right) = \frac{2\sqrt{3}}{9}$
local minimum $f\left(-\frac{1}{\sqrt{3}}\right) = -\frac{2\sqrt{3}}{9}$

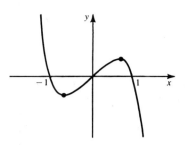

(b) local minimum $f\left(\frac{1}{4}\right) = \frac{229}{256}$

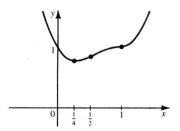

(c) local maxima $f(1) = 38$, $f(-2) = -16$
local minima $f(2) = 16$, $f(-1) = -38$

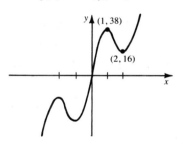

(d) local minimum $f\left(-\frac{20}{3}\right) = -\frac{20\sqrt{30}}{9}$

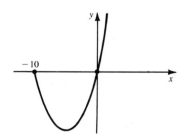

EXERCISE 5.5

1. A. R B. x-intercept 0, y-intercept 0   C. about
the origin   D. none   E. increasing on R
F. none   G. CU on $(-1, 0)$, $(1, \infty)$, CD on
$(-\infty, -1)$, $(0, 1)$, IP $(-1, -38)$, $(1, 38)$, $(0, 0)$

H.

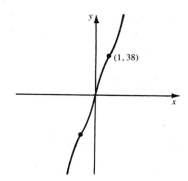

(1, 38)

2. A. R B. x-intercepts ± 1, y-intercept -1
C. about the y-axis   D. none   E. increasing on
$(0, \infty)$, decreasing on $(-\infty, 0)$ F. local
minimum $f(0) = -1$ G. CU on $(-\infty, -1)$,
$\left(-\dfrac{1}{\sqrt{5}}, \dfrac{1}{\sqrt{5}}\right)$, $(1, \infty)$, CD on $\left(-1, -\dfrac{1}{\sqrt{5}}\right)$,
$\left(\dfrac{1}{\sqrt{5}}, 1\right)$, IP $(\pm 1, 0)$, $\left(\pm\dfrac{1}{\sqrt{5}}, -\dfrac{64}{125}\right)$

H.

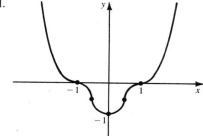

3. A. $(-\infty, -4) \cup (-4, \infty)$ B. y-intercept -1,
x-intercept 4   C. none   D. HA: $y = 1$, VA:
$x = -4$ E. increasing on $(-\infty, -4)$, $(-4, \infty)$
F. none   G. CU on $(-\infty, -4)$, CD on $(-4, \infty)$

H.

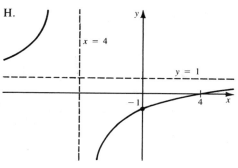

4. A. R B. x-intercept 0, y-intercept 0   C. about
the y-axis   D. HA: $y = 1$ E. increasing on
$(0, \infty)$, decreasing on $(-\infty, 0)$ F. local
minimum $f(0) = 0$ G. CU on $(-1, 1)$, CD on
$(-\infty, -1)$, $(1, \infty)$, IP$\left(\pm 1, \dfrac{1}{4}\right)$

H.

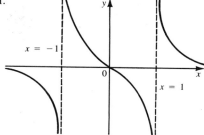

5. A. $(-\infty, -1) \cup (-1, 1) \cup (1, \infty)$
B. y-intercept 0, x-intercept 0   C. About the
origin   D. HA: $y = 0$, VA: $x = \pm 1$
E. decreasing on $(-\infty, -1)$, $(-1, 1)$, $(1, \infty)$
F. none   G. CU on $(-1, 0)$, $(1, \infty)$,
CD on $(-\infty, -1)$, $(0, 1)$, IP $(0, 0)$

H.

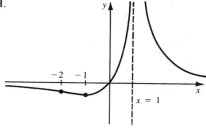

6. A. $(-\infty, 1) \cup (1, \infty)$ B. intercepts 0   C. none
D. HA: $y = 0$, VA: $x = 1$ E. increasing on
$(-1, 1)$, decreasing on $(-\infty, -1)$, $(1, \infty)$
F. $f(-1) = -\dfrac{1}{4}$ is a local minimum
G. CU on $(-2, 1)$, $(1, \infty)$, CD on $(-\infty, -2)$,
IP $\left(-2, -\dfrac{2}{9}\right)$

H.

7. A. $(-\infty, -1) \cup (-1, 0) \cup (0, 1) \cup (1, \infty)$
B. none **C.** about the origin **D. HA:** $y = 0$,
VA: $x = -1$, $x = 0$, $x = 1$ **E.** increases on
$\left(-\sqrt{\frac{1}{3}}, \sqrt{\frac{1}{3}}\right)$, decreases on $\left(-\infty, -\sqrt{\frac{1}{3}}\right)$, $\left(\sqrt{\frac{1}{3}}, \infty\right)$
F. $f\left(-\sqrt{\frac{1}{3}}\right) = \dfrac{3\sqrt{3}}{2}$ is a local minimum,
$f\left(\sqrt{\frac{1}{3}}\right) = \dfrac{3\sqrt{3}}{2}$ is a local maximum.
G. CU on $(-1, 0)$, $(1, \infty)$,
CD on $(-\infty, -1)$, $(0, 1)$

H.

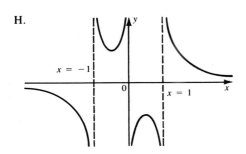

$x = -1$
0
$x = 1$

8. A. $(-\infty, 0) \cup (0, \infty)$ **B.** x-intercepts ± 1
C. about the origin **D. HA:** $y = 0$,
VA: $x = 0$ **E.** increasing on $\left(-\sqrt{3}, \sqrt{3}\right)$,
decreasing on $(-\infty, -\sqrt{3})$, $(\sqrt{3}, \infty)$
F. $f(-\sqrt{3}) = -\dfrac{2\sqrt{3}}{9}$ is a local minimum,
$f(\sqrt{3}) = \dfrac{2\sqrt{3}}{9}$ is a local maximum **G.** CU on
$(-\sqrt{6}, 0)$, $(\sqrt{6}, \infty)$, CD on $(-\infty, -\sqrt{6})$,
$(0, \sqrt{6})$, IP $\left(-\sqrt{6}, -\dfrac{5}{6\sqrt{6}}\right)$, $\left(\sqrt{6}, \dfrac{5}{6\sqrt{6}}\right)$

H.

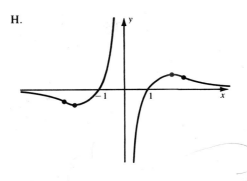

-1
1

9. A. $[-1, 1]$ **B.** y-intercept 0, x-intercepts -1,
0, and 1 **C.** about the origin **D.** none
E. increasing on $\left(-\dfrac{1}{\sqrt{2}}, \dfrac{1}{\sqrt{2}}\right)$, decreasing on
$\left(-1, -\dfrac{1}{\sqrt{2}}\right)$, $\left(\dfrac{1}{\sqrt{2}}, 1\right)$
F. $f\left(-\dfrac{1}{\sqrt{2}}\right) = -\dfrac{1}{2}$ is a local minimum,
$f\left(\dfrac{1}{\sqrt{2}}\right) = \dfrac{1}{2}$ is a local maximum
G. CU on $(-1, 0)$, CD on $(0, 1)$, IP $(0, 0)$

H.

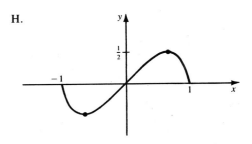

$\frac{1}{2}$
-1
1

10. A. $(-\infty, -2) \cup (2, \infty)$ **B.** none **C.** about the
origin **D. HA:** $y = \pm 1$, **VA:** $x = \pm 2$
E. decreasing on $(-\infty, -2)$, $(2, \infty)$ **F.** none
G. CD on $(-\infty, -2)$, CU on $(2, \infty)$

H.

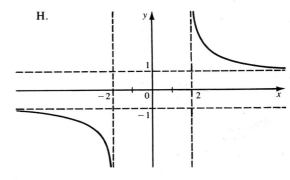

1
-2
0
2
-1

11. A. $[0, \infty)$ **B.** y-intercept 0, x-intercept 0
C. none **D. HA:** $y = 1$ **E.** increasing on
$(0, \infty)$ **F.** none **G.** CD on $(0, \infty)$

H.

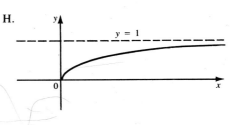

$y = 1$
0

12. A. R **B.** y-intercept 0, x-intercepts -1, 0, 1
C. about the origin   **D.** none   **E.** increases

on $\left(-\infty, -\dfrac{1}{3\sqrt{3}}\right)$, $\left(\dfrac{1}{3\sqrt{3}}, \infty\right)$, f decreases on

$\left(-\dfrac{1}{3\sqrt{3}}, \dfrac{1}{3\sqrt{3}}\right)$,   **F.** $f\left(\dfrac{1}{3\sqrt{3}}\right) = -\dfrac{2\sqrt{3}}{9}$ is a local

minimum, $f\left(-3\dfrac{1}{\sqrt{3}}\right) = \dfrac{2\sqrt{3}}{9}$ is a local maximum

G. CU on $(0, \infty)$, CD on $(-\infty, 0)$, IP $(0, 0)$

H.

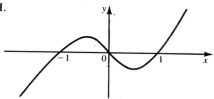

3.

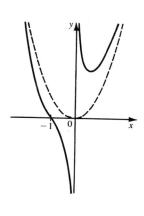

EXERCISE 5.6

1. (a) $y = 2 - x$ (b) $y = x$ (c) $y = 3x + 1$
    (d) $y = 2x - 1$ (e) $y = x + 4$ (f) $y = -x$
2. (a) $y = x$ (b) $y = x - 2$

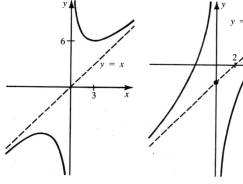

(c) $y = x$ (d) $y = x - 3$

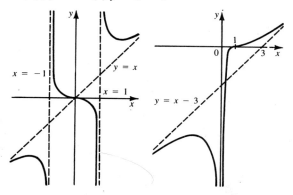

5.7 REVIEW EXERCISE

1. (a) $-\infty$ (b) ∞ (c) $-\infty$ (d) $-\infty$ (e) $-\infty$
    (f) $-\dfrac{1}{5}$ (g) 0   (h) 2   (i) ∞ (j) 1

2. (a) VA: $x = \dfrac{1}{2}$, HA: $y = -3$

   (b) VA: $x = -3$, HA: $y = 0$

   (c) $x = -\dfrac{1}{2}$, $x = 3$, HA: $y = 0$

   (d) VA: $x = 1$, HA: $y = 1$

3. (a) CU on $\left(-\dfrac{4}{5}, \infty\right)$, CD on $\left(-\infty, -\dfrac{4}{5}\right)$,

   IP $\left(-\dfrac{4}{5}, \dfrac{238}{25}\right)$ (b) CU on $\left(-\infty, -\dfrac{1}{2}\right)$, $(1, \infty)$,

   CD on $\left(-\dfrac{1}{2}, 1\right)$, IP $\left(-\dfrac{1}{2}, -\dfrac{209}{16}\right)$ and $(1, -14)$

   (c) CU on $\left(-\dfrac{2}{\sqrt{3}}, \dfrac{2}{\sqrt{3}}\right)$, CD on $\left(-\infty, -\dfrac{2}{\sqrt{3}}\right)$,

   $\left(\dfrac{2}{\sqrt{3}}, \infty\right)$, IP $\left(\pm\dfrac{2}{\sqrt{3}}, \dfrac{1}{4}\right)$ (d) CU on $(0, \infty)$

4. (a) local maximum $f\left(\dfrac{2}{3}\right) = \dfrac{4}{27}$, local minimum

   $f(0) = 0$ (b) local maximum $f(-6) = 324$,
   local minimum $f(1) = -19$ (c) local
   maximum $g(0) = 0$, local minimum $g(2) = 4$
   (d) local maximum $g\left(\dfrac{3}{4}\right) = \dfrac{5}{4}$

5. (a) **A.** R **B.** y-intercept 0, x-intercepts 0, 3
   C. none   **D.** none   **E.** increasing on $(-\infty, 1)$,
   $(3, \infty)$, decreasing on $(1, 3)$ **F.** local maximum
   $f(1) = 4$, local minimum $f(3) = 0$ **G.** CU on
   $(2, \infty)$, CD on $(-\infty, 2)$, IP $(2, 2)$

H.

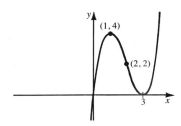

(b) A. R B. y-intercept 0, x-intercepts 0, 1
C. none   D. none   E. increasing on $\left(-\infty, \frac{3}{4}\right)$,
decreasing on $\left(\frac{3}{4}, \infty\right)$ F. local maximum
$f\left(\frac{3}{4}\right) = \frac{27}{256}$ G. CU on $\left(0, \frac{1}{2}\right)$, CD on $(-\infty, 0)$,
$\left(\frac{1}{2}, \infty\right)$, IP $(0, 0)$ and $\left(\frac{1}{2}, \frac{1}{16}\right)$

H.

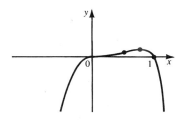

(c) A. $(-\infty, -4) \cup (-4, \infty)$ B. y-intercept $\frac{1}{2}$
C. none   D. HA: $y = 0$, VA: $x = -4$
E. decreasing on $(-\infty, -4)$, $(-4, \infty)$ F. none
G. CU on $(-4, \infty)$, CD on $(-\infty, -4)$

H.

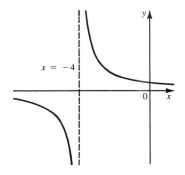

(d) A. R B. y-intercept 1, x-intercepts ± 1
C. about the y-axis   D. HA: $y = -1$
E. increasing on $(-\infty, 0)$, decreasing on $(0, \infty)$
F. local maximum $f(0) = 1$
G. CU on $\left(-\infty, -\dfrac{1}{\sqrt{3}}\right)$, $\left(\dfrac{1}{\sqrt{3}}, \infty\right)$,
CD on $\left(-\dfrac{1}{\sqrt{3}}, \dfrac{1}{\sqrt{3}}\right)$, IP $\left(\pm\dfrac{1}{\sqrt{3}}, \dfrac{1}{2}\right)$

H.

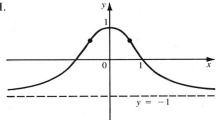

(e) A. $(-\infty, -1) \cup (-1, 1) \cup (1, \infty)$
B. y-intercept 1   C. about the y-axis
D. HA: $y = -1$, VA: $x = -1$, $x = 1$
E. increasing on $(0, 1)$, $(1, \infty)$, decreasing on
$(-\infty, -1)$, $(-1, 0)$ F. local minimum $f(0) = 1$
G. CU on $(-1, 1)$, CD on $(-\infty, -1)$ and $(1, \infty)$

H.

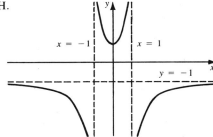

(f) A. R B. y-intercept 0, x-intercepts 0, 4
C. none   D. none   E. increasing on $\left(-\infty, \frac{4}{3}\right)$,
$(4, \infty)$, decreasing on $\left(\frac{4}{3}, 4\right)$ F. local minimum
$f(4) = 0$, local maximum $f\left(\frac{4}{3}\right) = \frac{4}{3}\sqrt[3]{4}$

G. CU on $(-\infty, 0)$, CD on $(0, 4)$, $(4, \infty)$,
IP $(0, 0)$

H.

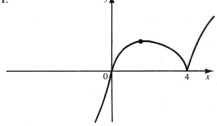

6.

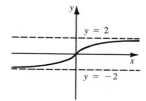

7.

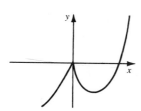

(e)

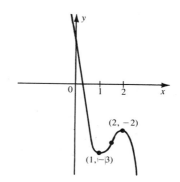

5. (a) $(-\infty, -3) \cup (-3, 3) \cup (3, \infty)$
(b) intercepts 0 (c) about the origin
(d) VA: $x = 3, x = -3$, HA: $y = 0$
(e) decreasing on $(-\infty, -3), (-3, 3), (3, \infty)$
(f) none (g) CU on $(-3, 0), (3, \infty)$, CD on
$(-\infty, -3), (0, 3)$, IP $(0, 0)$

5.8 CHAPTER 5 TEST

1. (a) 3 (b) ∞ **2.** VA: $x = -\frac{5}{3}$, HA: $y = -\frac{2}{3}$

3. (a) CU on $(2, \infty)$, CD on $(-\infty, 2)$, IP $\left(2, \frac{2}{9}\right)$

4. (a) increasing on $(1, 2)$, decreasing on $(-\infty, 1)$,
$(2, \infty)$ (b) local maximum $f(2) = -2$, local
minimum $f(1) = -3$ (c) CU on $\left(-\infty, \frac{3}{2}\right)$,
CD on $\left(\frac{3}{2}, \infty\right)$ (d) IP $\left(\frac{3}{2}, -\frac{5}{2}\right)$

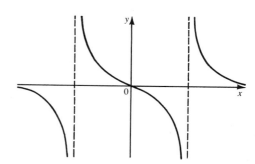

CHAPTER 6 TRIGONOMETRIC FUNCTIONS

REVIEW AND PREVIEW TO CHAPTER 6

EXERCISE 1

1. (a) 30° (b) $-270°$ (c) 225° (d) 540°
(e) 229° (f) $-43°$ (g) $-688°$

2. (a) 0.79 (b) 5.50 (c) 3.67 (d) 9.95
(e) 0.03 (f) -0.49 (g) 10.5

3. (a) 25 (b) 1.2   **4.** 25.46

EXERCISE 2

1. $\sin \theta = \frac{4}{5}$, $\cos \theta = \frac{3}{5}$, $\tan \theta = \frac{4}{3}$, $\csc \theta = \frac{5}{4}$,
$\sec \theta = \frac{5}{3}$, $\cot \theta = \frac{3}{4}$

2. $\sin \theta = \frac{-1}{\sqrt{5}}$, $\cos \theta = \frac{-2}{\sqrt{5}}$, $\tan \theta = \frac{1}{2}$

3. $\csc \theta = -\frac{13}{12}$, $\sec \theta = \frac{13}{5}$, $\cot \theta = -\frac{5}{12}$

4. $\cos \theta = \frac{2\sqrt{2}}{3}$, $\tan \theta = \frac{1}{2\sqrt{2}}$

5. $\csc \theta = \frac{2}{\sqrt{3}}$, $\cot \theta = -\frac{1}{\sqrt{3}}$

6. $\cos \theta = \frac{3}{\sqrt{34}}$, $\csc \theta = -\frac{\sqrt{34}}{5}$

7. $\sec \theta = -\frac{13}{5}$, $\sin \theta = -\frac{12}{13}$

EXERCISE 3

1.

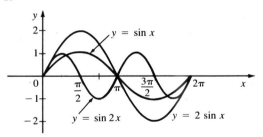

2.

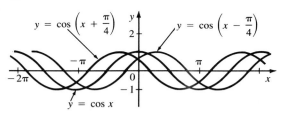

3.

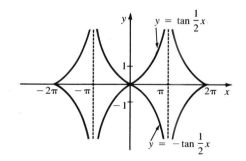

EXERCISE 4

1. (a) 0 (b) $\dfrac{2 + 2\sqrt{3}}{\sqrt{3}}$ (c) $\frac{3}{4}$ d) 4 (e) $3 - \sqrt{2}$

(f) $\sqrt{2} - \frac{2}{3}$

EXERCISE 6.1

1. (a) $\frac{1}{2}$ (b) $\dfrac{1}{\sqrt{2}}$ (c) $\sqrt{3}$ (d) 1 (e) $-\dfrac{\sqrt{3}}{2}$

(f) $-\dfrac{1}{\sqrt{2}}$ (g) $-\dfrac{1}{\sqrt{3}}$ (h) $\dfrac{1}{\sqrt{2}}$

2. (a) $\dfrac{\sqrt{3}}{2}$ (b) $\frac{1}{2}$ (c) $\dfrac{\sqrt{3}}{2}$ (d) $\sqrt{3}$ (e) $-\dfrac{1}{\sqrt{3}}$

(f) $\dfrac{1}{\sqrt{2}}$

3. (a) 0 (b) $2 \tan x$ (c) 0 (d) $\sin x$ (e) 0

4. (a) csc x, $-$sec x, $-$cot x (b) sec x, $-$ csc x,

$\dfrac{1}{-\cot x}$ (c) $-$csc x, $-$sec x, cot x

(d) $-$sec x, csc x, $-\dfrac{1}{\cot x}$

5. (a) $-\sin x$ (b) $\sin x$ (c) $-\tan x$

6. (a) -2 (b) $-\dfrac{2}{\sqrt{3}}$ (c) $-\sqrt{3}$ (d) $-\sqrt{2}$

(e) $-\sqrt{2}$ (f) 1

7. (a) $-\sin x - \cos^2 x$ (b) $\csc^2 x$

EXERCISE 6.2

1. (a) cos $3a$ (b) cos $3x$ (c) sin 3 (d) sin $3m$
(e) tan $5a$ (f) $-\tan 2$ (g) cos $2x$ (h) sin $2a$
(i) tan $2x$ (j) 1

2. (a) $\dfrac{\sqrt{3} - 1}{2\sqrt{2}}$ (b) $\dfrac{-1 - \sqrt{3}}{2\sqrt{2}}$ (c) $-\dfrac{1 + \sqrt{3}}{1 - \sqrt{3}}$

(d) $\dfrac{\sqrt{3} + 1}{1 - \sqrt{3}}$ (e) $\dfrac{\sqrt{3} + 1}{2\sqrt{2}}$ (f) $\dfrac{\sqrt{3} + 1}{2\sqrt{2}}$

3. (a) $\dfrac{1 - \sqrt{3}}{2\sqrt{2}}$ (b) $\dfrac{\sqrt{3} - 1}{2\sqrt{2}}$ (c) $\dfrac{1 - \sqrt{3}}{1 + \sqrt{3}}$

4. (a) $\frac{16}{65}$ (b) $\frac{33}{65}$ (c) $\frac{56}{33}$

5. (a) $-\frac{16}{65}$ (b) $-\frac{33}{65}$ (c) $\frac{56}{33}$

6. (a) $\frac{1}{2}$ (b) $\frac{1}{2}$ (c) $\dfrac{\sqrt{3} - 1}{\sqrt{3} + 1}$ (d) $\dfrac{1 + \sqrt{3}}{2\sqrt{2}}$

12. (a) 2 sin 40° cos 20° (b) 2 sin 20° (c) cos 20°

(d) 2 cos $4x$ sin $2x$ (e) $\dfrac{2}{\sqrt{2}}$ cos 85°

(f) -2 sin $3x$ sin x

13. (a) $\sqrt{3}$ (b) $\dfrac{-4}{1 - \tan^2 x}$ (c) cot $\dfrac{x}{2}$

14. $\dfrac{15}{\sqrt{21} - 4\sqrt{2}}$

15. $\dfrac{\csc x \csc y \sec x \sec y}{\sec x \csc y + \csc x \sec y}$

16. sin x cos y cos z + cos x sin y cos z + cos x
cos y sin z − sin x sin y sin z

17. $\dfrac{-6\sqrt{10} + 8\sqrt{3} - 2\sqrt{30} - 1}{60}$

20. $2 \pm \sqrt{3}$

21. (a) 0 (b) 4 sin x (c) 0

EXERCISE 6.3

1. (a) $\cos^2 2x - \sin^2 2x$ or $1 - 2\sin^2 2x$ or
$2\cos^2 2x - 1$ (b) 2 sin $\frac{3}{2}x$ cos $\frac{3}{2}x$

(c) $\dfrac{2 \tan 3x}{1 - \tan^2 3x}$ (d) 2 sin $\frac{1}{4}x$ cos $\frac{1}{4}x$

(e) $\cos^2 \frac{1}{3}x - \sin^2 \frac{1}{3}x$ (f) $\dfrac{-2 \tan \frac{7}{2}x}{1 - \tan^2 \frac{7}{2}x}$

2. (a) $\sin 6\theta$ (b) $3 \sin 2\theta$ (c) $\frac{1}{4} \sin \theta$ (d) $\cos 3\theta$

(e) $\cos \dfrac{\theta}{2}$ (f) $\cos 7\theta$ (g) $-4 \cos 4\theta$ (h) $\sin x$

3. $\sin 2\theta = -\frac{24}{25}$, $\cos 2\theta = \frac{7}{25}$, 4th quadrant

4. $\sin 2\theta = \frac{120}{169}$, $\cos 2\theta = -\frac{119}{169}$, 2nd quadrant

5. $\dfrac{8\sqrt{5}}{81}$

6. $\csc 2\theta = \dfrac{25}{-4\sqrt{21}}$, $\sec 2\theta = \dfrac{25}{-17}$

7. $\frac{4}{3}$ **8.** $\frac{24}{7}$

9. (a) $3 \sin \theta - 4 \sin^3 \theta$ (b) $4 \cos^3 \theta - 3 \cos \theta$

(c) $\dfrac{3 \tan \theta - \tan^3 \theta}{1 - 3 \tan^2 \theta}$

(d) $8 \cos^4 \theta - 8 \cos^2 \theta + 1$

10. (a) $\sqrt{\dfrac{\sqrt{2} + 1}{2\sqrt{2}}}$ (b) $-\sqrt{\dfrac{\sqrt{2} - 1}{2\sqrt{2}}}$

(c) $-1 + \sqrt{2}$ (d) $-\sqrt{\dfrac{\sqrt{2} - 1}{2\sqrt{2}}}$

(e) $\sqrt{\dfrac{\frac{1 + \sqrt{2}}{2\sqrt{2}} + 1}{2}}$ (f) $\dfrac{-1 + \sqrt{4 + 2\sqrt{2}}}{1 + \sqrt{2}}$

11. (a) $\pm\sqrt{\dfrac{1 - \cos \theta}{2}}$ (b) $\pm\sqrt{\dfrac{1 + \cos \theta}{2}}$

(c) $\pm\sqrt{\dfrac{1 - \cos \theta}{1 + \cos \theta}}$

12. (a) $\dfrac{5}{\sqrt{26}}$ (b) $-\dfrac{1}{\sqrt{26}}$ (c) -5

13. (a) $\dfrac{2 \tan \theta}{1 + \tan^2 \theta}$ (b) $\dfrac{1 - \tan^2 \theta}{1 + \tan^2 \theta}$ **14.** $\tan x$

15. $\tan x$ **16.** $\cos 2x$ **17.** $-\frac{5}{9}$ **18.** $\dfrac{\sqrt{3}}{2}$

20. 1   **21.** $\dfrac{5 \pm \sqrt{5}}{8}$ **22.** $\dfrac{1}{\sqrt{2}} \sin \theta$

EXERCISE 6.5

1. (a) $\dfrac{\pi}{3}, \dfrac{2\pi}{3}$ (b) $\dfrac{\pi}{3}, \dfrac{5\pi}{3}$ (c) $\frac{3}{4}\pi, \frac{7}{4}\pi$ (d) $\dfrac{2\pi}{3}, \dfrac{4\pi}{3}$

(e) $\dfrac{7\pi}{6}, \dfrac{11\pi}{6}$ (f) $\dfrac{\pi}{3}, \dfrac{2\pi}{3}, \dfrac{4\pi}{3}, \dfrac{5\pi}{3}$

2. (a) $-\dfrac{3\pi}{4}$ (b) $-\dfrac{3\pi}{4}, -\pi, 0$ (c) $-\dfrac{\pi}{2}$

(d) $-\dfrac{2\pi}{3}, -\dfrac{\pi}{3}$ (e) $-\dfrac{5\pi}{6}, -\dfrac{\pi}{6}$ (f) $-\dfrac{\pi}{2}$

3. (a) $0, \dfrac{\pi}{4}, \pi$ (b) $-\pi, -\dfrac{2\pi}{3}, -\dfrac{\pi}{3}, 0$

(c) $\dfrac{\pi}{3}, \dfrac{5\pi}{3}$ (d) $-\pi, -\dfrac{3\pi}{4}, 0, \dfrac{3\pi}{4}, \pi$

(e) $-2\pi, -\pi, 0, \pi, 2\pi$ (f) $-\dfrac{11\pi}{6}, -\dfrac{7\pi}{6}$

4. (a) $-\pi, 0, \pi$ (b) $-\dfrac{\pi}{2}, \dfrac{\pi}{6}, \dfrac{\pi}{2}$ (c) $\dfrac{\pi}{8}$ (d) $\dfrac{\pi}{24}$,

$\dfrac{5\pi}{24}$ (e) $-\dfrac{\pi}{8}, 0, \dfrac{3\pi}{8}$ (f) $-\dfrac{3\pi}{4}, -\dfrac{\pi}{4}, \dfrac{\pi}{4}, \dfrac{3\pi}{4}$

5. $-2\pi, -\dfrac{11\pi}{6}, -\dfrac{7\pi}{6}, -\pi, 0, \dfrac{\pi}{6}, \dfrac{5\pi}{6}, \pi, 2\pi$

6. $\sin x = \pm \frac{4}{5}$, $\cos x = \pm\frac{3}{5}$ or $\sin x = \pm\frac{3}{5}$,

$\cos x = \pm\frac{4}{5}$

7. (a) 0   (b) 0.7391   (c) 0   (d) ± 1.17 (e) 0, 1

(f) ± 1.165 **8.** $p^2 + q^2$

6.6 REVIEW EXERCISE

1. (a) $-\frac{33}{65}$ (b) $\frac{63}{16}$ (c) $\frac{2047}{4225}$

2. (a) $\dfrac{-\sqrt{3} + 1}{2\sqrt{2}}$ (b) $\dfrac{-\sqrt{3} - 1}{2\sqrt{2}}$ (c) $\dfrac{\sqrt{3} + 1}{\sqrt{3} - 1}$

(d) $\dfrac{\sqrt{3} - 1}{2\sqrt{2}}$ (e) $\dfrac{\sqrt{3} - 1}{2\sqrt{2}}$ (f) $\dfrac{\sqrt{3} + 1}{\sqrt{3} - 1}$

3. (a) $-\frac{24}{25}$ (b) $\frac{7}{25}$ (c) $-\frac{24}{7}$

4. (a) $\frac{1}{9}$ (b) $4\sqrt{5}$ (c) $\sqrt{\dfrac{3 - \sqrt{5}}{6}}$

5. (a) $\sqrt{\dfrac{\sqrt{2} + 1}{2\sqrt{2}}}$ (b) $\sqrt{\dfrac{1 + \sqrt{2}}{2\sqrt{2}}}$

(c) $\dfrac{-1 + \sqrt{4 + 2\sqrt{2}}}{1 + \sqrt{2}}$

6. (a) $\dfrac{\sqrt{3}}{2}$ (b) $\dfrac{\sqrt{3}}{2}$ (c) $-\sqrt{3}$

7. (a) $\frac{1}{2}$ (b) $-\dfrac{1}{\sqrt{2}}$ (c) -1

9. (a) $0, \dfrac{\pi}{2}, \pi$ (b) $-\pi, -\dfrac{\pi}{2}, 0, \pi$

(c) $0, \dfrac{\pi}{2}, \dfrac{3\pi}{2}, 2\pi$ (d) $-\dfrac{3\pi}{2}, \dfrac{\pi}{2}$ (e) $\pm\dfrac{\pi}{2}$

(f) $0, \pm\dfrac{\pi}{2}, \pm\pi, \pm\dfrac{3\pi}{2}, \pm 2\pi$

(g) $0, \dfrac{\pi}{2}, \pi$ (h) $-\dfrac{4\pi}{3}, -\dfrac{\pi}{3}$

10. (a) $\dfrac{25\sqrt{2}}{31}$ (b) $\dfrac{25\sqrt{2}}{31}$

11. $1 - 8 \sin^2 3a + 8 \sin^4 3a$ and
$8 \cos^4 3a - 8 \cos^2 3a + 1$

13. $2 \sin\left(x + \dfrac{\pi}{6}\right)$

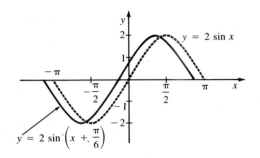

$y = 2 \sin x$

$y = 2 \sin\left(x + \dfrac{\pi}{6}\right)$

14. $2 \cos\left(x + \dfrac{4\pi}{3}\right)$

16. (a) $\dfrac{-1 + \sqrt{5}}{4}$ (b) $\sqrt{\dfrac{5 + \sqrt{5}}{8}}$

18. $\dfrac{ab - 1}{a - b}$

6.7 CHAPTER 6 TEST

1. (a) $\dfrac{\sqrt{3} + 1}{2\sqrt{2}}$ (b) $\sqrt{\dfrac{\sqrt{2} + 1}{2\sqrt{2}}}$ (c) 1

  (d) $\dfrac{\sqrt{2} + 1}{\sqrt{2}}$ (e) 1 **2.** $-\dfrac{2016}{4225}$ **3.** $-\dfrac{24}{7}$

4. $-\dfrac{1}{2}$ **6.** (a) $-\dfrac{7\pi}{24}, -\dfrac{\pi}{8}, \dfrac{5\pi}{24}, \dfrac{3\pi}{8}$ (b) $\dfrac{\pi}{2}$

7. $\dfrac{\tan a + \tan b - \tan c + \tan a \tan b \tan c}{1 - \tan a \tan b + \tan a \tan c + \tan b \tan c}$

CHAPTER 7 DERIVATIVES OF TRIGONOMETRIC FUNCTIONS

REVIEW AND PREVIEW TO CHAPTER 7

EXERCISE 1

1. (a) 25 cm   (b) 1.2   (c) 100 cm²   (d) $\dfrac{100\pi}{3}$ cm²

2. $a = \dfrac{\pi}{3}$ cm and $\theta = \dfrac{\pi}{18}$

EXERCISE 2

1. (a) $x = y^2$ is not a function
   (b) $x = y^2 - 2y$ is not a function

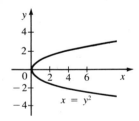

$x = y^2$

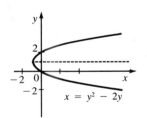

$x = y^2 - 2y$

  (c) $y = x^2 + x$ is a function
  (d) $x + 2y = 3$ is a function

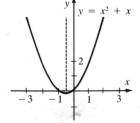

$y = x^2 + x$

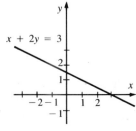

$x + 2y = 3$

(e) $2x + 5y < 1$ is not a function
(f) $3y - x \geq 6$ is not a function

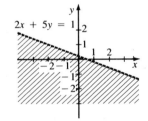

$2x + 5y = 1$

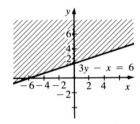

$3y - x = 6$

(g) $x = \dfrac{2 - y}{7}$ is a function

(h) $x^2 + y^2 + 2x = 0$ is not a function

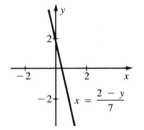

$x = \dfrac{2 - y}{7}$

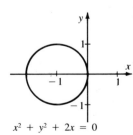

$x^2 + y^2 + 2x = 0$

2. (a) $1 - 1$ (b) not $1 - 1$ (c) $1 - 1$
   (d) $1 - 1$ (e) not $1 - 1$ (f) not $1 - 1$
   (g) $1 - 1$ (h) not $1 - 1$ (i) $1 - 1$
   (j) $1 - 1$

3. (a) $y = 2x + 7$ (b) $y = 36 - 5x$

(c) $y = \sqrt[3]{\dfrac{x + 6}{5}}$ (d) $y = x^2, x \geq 0$

(e) $y = x^2 + 3, x \geq 0$ (f) $y = \dfrac{1}{x - 1}$

(g) $y = \dfrac{1}{x} - 1$

(h) $y = \dfrac{1 - x}{1 + x}$ (i) $y = \dfrac{2x + 1}{4 - 3x}$

(j) $y = \dfrac{\pi}{x + 3}$ (k) $y = x^{\frac{1}{4}}$

(l) $y = \sqrt{\dfrac{x}{3}} + 1$ (m) $y = \sqrt{x^2 - 9}$

(n) $y = -\sqrt{25 - x^2}, x \geq 0$

4. (a) $f^{-1}(x) = \dfrac{x - 1}{2}$ (b) $f^{-1}(x) = \sqrt{x - 2}$

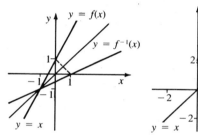

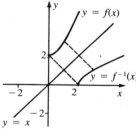

(c) $f^{-1}(x) = x^{\frac{1}{3}}$ (d) $f^{-1}(x) = -\dfrac{1}{x}$

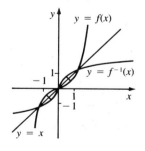

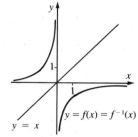

EXERCISE 7.1

1. 2.999 999 955   **2.** 0.666 666 672

3. 0.296 296 304   **4.** 0.998   **5.** 0.000 049 9

6. 0.841 470 978   **7.** 3   **8.** $\dfrac{a}{b}$ **9.** $\dfrac{8}{27}$

10. 0   **11.** 1   **12.** $\dfrac{\sqrt{3} - 1}{2}$ **13.** $\dfrac{2\sqrt{2}}{3\pi}$

14. 0   **15.** 0   **16.** $\dfrac{1}{\pi}$ **17.** $\dfrac{1}{2}$ **18.** 9

19. $\sqrt{\dfrac{1}{2}}$ **20.** 0   **21.** 0   **22.** $\dfrac{1}{4}$ **23.** $\dfrac{1}{8}$

24. $\dfrac{1}{4}$ **25.** 2   **26.** 2   **27.** 1   **28.** 2

29. 1   **30.** -1 **31.** 2   **32.** 1   **33.** 0

34. 0   **35.** 0   **36.** $\dfrac{1}{2}$ **37.** 2   **38.** sin 1

39. (a) 0.334 672 085, 0.333 346 6, 0.333 33, 0.333   (b) Appears to be approaching 0.3   (c) 0.3, -10, -1000. The correct value of this limit is $\dfrac{1}{3}$. Eventually all calculators will give incorrect values. Different calculators will give different incorrect values. Because of loss of significant digits in the process of rounding off, when two numbers that are very close together are subtracted, this type of error is likely to occur.

40. Limit does not exist. Left-hand limit $= -1$ and right-hand limit $= 1$.

41. $\dfrac{1}{2}$ **42.** -1 **43.** cos a **44.** $-\sin a$

EXERCISE 7.2

1. (a) $-4 \sin 4x$ (b) $3 \cos(3x + 2\pi)$

(c) $-16x \cos(-2x^2 - 3)$ (d) $\sin(4 + 2x)$

(e) $2x \cos x^2$ (f) $2x \sin x^2$ (g) $\dfrac{-6x^2 \cos x^3}{\sin^3 x^3}$

(h) $-4x(x^2 - 2) \sin(x^2 - 2)^2$

(i) $\dfrac{12 \cos (2 - x)^{-1} \sin^3(2 - x)^{-1}}{(2 - x)^2}$

(j) $\cos x - x \sin x$ (k) $\dfrac{\sin x - x \cos x}{\sin^2 x}$

(l) $\dfrac{1}{1 + \cos x}$ (m) $-6 \sin 2x(1 + \cos^2 x)^5$

(n) $-\dfrac{1}{x^2} \cos \dfrac{1}{x}$ (o) $-\sin x \cos(\cos x)$

(p) $-3 \cos x \sin(\sin x) \cos^2(\sin x)$

(q) $\dfrac{1}{x} \sin \dfrac{1}{x} + \cos \dfrac{1}{x}$

(r) $\dfrac{\sin x(2 \cos^2 x + \sin^2 x)}{\cos^2 x}$

(s) $\dfrac{\cos x - \cos x \sin 2x + 2 \cos 2x + 2 \sin x \cos 2x}{(1 - \sin 2x)^2}$

(t) $3 \sin x \cos x(\sin x - \cos x)$

(u) $\sin 2 \left(\dfrac{1 - \sqrt{x}}{1 + \sqrt{x}}\right)\left(\dfrac{1}{\sqrt{x}(1 + \sqrt{x})^2}\right)$

2. (a) $\dfrac{-2 \sin 2x}{\cos y}$ (b) $\dfrac{\cos y - \cos(x + y)}{x \sin y + \cos(x + y)}$

(c) $\dfrac{1 - \sin x}{1 + \cos y}$ (d) $\dfrac{\sin x \cos(\cos x)}{\cos y \sin(\sin y}$ (e) -1

(f) $\dfrac{\cos x - 2 \sin 2x - 2y}{2x}$

3. (a) $6\sqrt{3}x - 6y - \pi\sqrt{3} + 6 = 0$
   (b) $4x - 2y + 2 - \pi = 0$
   (c) $3\sqrt{3}x - y + 1 - \pi\sqrt{3} = 0$
   (d) $4x + y - 1 - \pi = 0$
   (e) $6\sqrt{3}x + 12y - 12 - \pi\sqrt{3} = 0$
   (f) $y = 1$

4. (a) critical numbers $\pm\pi, \pm\dfrac{\pi}{2}, 0$;

   increasing on $\left(-\pi, -\dfrac{\pi}{2}\right)$ and $\left(0, \dfrac{\pi}{2}\right)$,

   decreasing on $\left(-\dfrac{\pi}{2}, 0\right)$ and $\left(\dfrac{\pi}{2}, \pi\right)$;

   local maximums $f\left(-\dfrac{\pi}{2}\right) = 1, f\left(\dfrac{\pi}{2}\right) = 1$;

   local minimum $f(0) = 0$.

   (b) critical numbers $-\dfrac{\pi}{4}, \dfrac{3\pi}{4}$;

   increasing on $\left(-\pi, -\dfrac{\pi}{4}\right)$ or $\left(\dfrac{3\pi}{4}, \pi\right)$;

   decreasing on $\left(-\dfrac{\pi}{4}, \dfrac{3\pi}{4}\right)$;

   local maximum $f\left(-\dfrac{\pi}{4}\right) = \dfrac{2}{\sqrt{2}}$;

   local minimum $f\left(\dfrac{3\pi}{4}\right) = -\dfrac{2}{\sqrt{2}}$

5. (a) concave down on $\left(0, \dfrac{\pi}{2}\right)$ or $\left(3.394, \dfrac{3\pi}{2}\right)$ or

   $(6.030, 2\pi)$; concave up on $\left(\dfrac{\pi}{2}, 3.394\right)$ or

   $\left(\dfrac{3\pi}{2}, 6.030\right)$; points of inflection $\left(\dfrac{\pi}{2}, 0\right)$,

   $(3.394, -1.453)$, $\left(\dfrac{3\pi}{2}, 0\right)$, and $(6.030, 1.451)$

   (b) concave down on $\left(-\dfrac{3\pi}{4}, -\dfrac{\pi}{4}\right)$ or $\left(\dfrac{\pi}{4}, \dfrac{3\pi}{4}\right)$;

   concave up on $\left(-\pi, -\dfrac{3\pi}{4}\right)$ or $\left(-\dfrac{\pi}{4}, \dfrac{\pi}{4}\right)$

   or $\left(\dfrac{3\pi}{4}, \pi\right)$;

   points of inflection $\left(-\dfrac{3\pi}{4}, 1\right)$, $\left(-\dfrac{\pi}{4}, 1\right)$,

   $\left(\dfrac{\pi}{4}, 1\right)$ and $\left(\dfrac{3\pi}{4}, 1\right)$.

6. (a) A. $[0, 2\pi]$ B. y-intercept $= 0$, x-intercept
   $= 0$ C. none   D. none   E. always increasing
   F. minimum $f(0) = 0$, maximum $f(2\pi) = 2\pi$
   G. CD on $(0, \pi)$ and CU on $(\pi, 2\pi)$; IP (π, π)

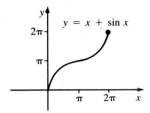
$y = x + \sin x$

(b) A. $(0, \pi)$ B. y-intercept 0, x-intercepts 0, $\dfrac{\pi}{2}$

C. none   D. none   E. increasing on $(0, 0.86)$,
decreasing on $(0.86, \pi)$ F. local maximum
$f(0.86) = 0.56$, minimums $f(0) = 0$ and
$f(\pi) = -\pi$ G. CD on $(0, 2.29)$ and CU on
$(2.29, \pi)$; IP $(2.29, -1.51)$

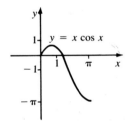
$y = x \cos x$

7. $5\sqrt{3}$

8. (a) 0.739 085   (b) 0.704 576   (c) 1.895 494

9. $\dfrac{d}{dx} \tan x = \sec^2 x$, $\dfrac{d}{dx} \csc x = -\csc x \cot x$

10. $\dfrac{\cos^2 y \cos x + \sin^2 x \sin y}{\cos^3 y}$

11. (a) $(\cos x - 1) \cot(x - \sin x) \csc(x - \sin x)$
    (b) $\dfrac{\cos \sqrt{x}}{4\sqrt{x} \sin \sqrt{x}}$ (c) $\dfrac{\cos x - x \sin x}{3\sqrt[3]{x^2 \cos^2 x}}$
    (d) $\sin x[\sin(\cos x)][\cos(\cos x)][3 \cos (\cos x) - 2]$
    (e) $\dfrac{-\sin x \cos x[\sin(\sin^2 x)]}{\sqrt{\cos(\sin^2 x)}}$

12. $2x - y = 0$ 13. $\dfrac{\sin x + y \sec^2(xy) + 1}{\cos y - x \sec^2(xy)}$

EXERCISE 7.3
1. (a) $6 \sec^2 2x$ (b) $-3 \csc^2 9x$

(c) $3 \sec \dfrac{x}{4} \tan \dfrac{x}{4}$ (d) $-2 \csc 8x \cot 8x$

(e) $2x \sec^2 x^2$ (f) $2 \tan x \sec^2 x$

(g) $\dfrac{\sec \sqrt[3]{x} \tan \sqrt[3]{x}}{3\sqrt[3]{x^2}}$ (h) $x \csc x(2 - x \cot x)$

(i) $12(1 - 2x) \csc^2(1 - 2x)^2 \cot^2(1 - 2x)^2$

(j) 0   (k) $\dfrac{-3 \sec 2x \tan 2x}{\sqrt{(\sec 2x - 1)^5}}$ (l) $x(x \cos x + 2$

$\sin x)$ (m) $3\sqrt{x} + 2x \csc^2 x - 2 \cot x$

(n) $\sec^2 x[\cos(\tan x)]$ (o) -2

$\sin x[\tan(\cos x)][\sec^2(\cos x)]$

(p) $\dfrac{6(2x - 1) \sec^2(x^2 - x)^{-2}}{(x^2 - x)^3 \tan^4(x^2 - x)^{-2}}$

2. (a) $\dfrac{\sec^2 x}{1 - \sec y \tan y}$ (b) $-\dfrac{2 \sec^2 2x}{\sin 3y}$

(c) $-\dfrac{\csc^2 x + \csc^2(x + y)}{\csc^2(x + y) + \csc^2 y}$

(d) $-\dfrac{y \csc(xy) \cot(xy)}{2y + x \csc(xy)\cot(xy)}$

(e) $\dfrac{2xy^2 + y \sec\left(\dfrac{x}{y}\right) \tan\left(\dfrac{x}{y}\right)}{x \sec\left(\dfrac{x}{y}\right) \tan\left(\dfrac{x}{y}\right)}$

(f) $\dfrac{2x}{2y - \sec^2 y[\cos(\tan y)]}$

3. (a) $4x + y - 1 - \pi = 0$

(b) $3\sqrt{3}x - 6y - \sqrt{3}\pi + 3 = 0$

(c) $4y + 8\sqrt{2}x + 4\sqrt{2} + \pi\sqrt{2} = 0$

(d) $4\sqrt{2}x - 2y - 3\sqrt{2}\pi = 0$

4. No critical numbers exist and $y' > 0$

5. (a) $x = \pi$

(b) $x = -\dfrac{\pi}{2}$, $x = \dfrac{\pi}{2}$, and $x = \dfrac{3\pi}{2}$

6. No critical numbers; always increasing

7. CU on $\left(-\dfrac{\pi}{2}, 0\right)$ or $\left(\dfrac{\pi}{2}, \pi\right)$;

CD on $\left(0, \dfrac{\pi}{2}\right)$ or $\left(\pi, \dfrac{3\pi}{2}\right)$

8. A. $\left(-\dfrac{\pi}{2}, \dfrac{\pi}{2}\right)$ B. y-intercept is 0,

x-intercept is 0   C. y-axis   D. $x = \pm\dfrac{\pi}{2}$

E. increasing on $\left(0, \dfrac{\pi}{2}\right)$, decreasing on $\left(-\dfrac{\pi}{2}, 0\right)$

F. minimum $f(0) = 0$ G. CU on $\left(-\dfrac{\pi}{2}, \dfrac{\pi}{2}\right)$

H.

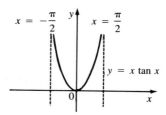

10. $\dfrac{\pi}{4}, \dfrac{3\pi}{4}, \dfrac{5\pi}{4}, \dfrac{7\pi}{4}$ **11.** $\pm\dfrac{1}{2}$

12. $\dfrac{3 \sec^{\frac{3}{2}}(\sqrt[4]{x}) \tan(\sqrt[4]{x})}{8(\sqrt[4]{x^3})}$

13. $\dfrac{dy}{dx} = -2x, \dfrac{d^2y}{dx^2} = -2$

EXERCISE 7.4

1. (a) local minimum $f\left(\dfrac{\pi}{3}\right) = -0.685$; local

maximum $f\left(\dfrac{5\pi}{3}\right) \doteq 6.968$ (b) none   (c) local

minima $f\left(\dfrac{\pi}{4}\right), f\left(\dfrac{3\pi}{4}\right), f\left(\dfrac{5\pi}{4}\right), f\left(\dfrac{7\pi}{4}\right) = \dfrac{1}{2}$; local

maxima $f(0), f\left(\dfrac{\pi}{2}\right), f(\pi), f\left(\dfrac{3\pi}{2}\right), f(2\pi) = 1$

(d) local minimum $f(0) = 1$; local maxima

$f\left(-\dfrac{\pi}{2}\right) = f\left(\dfrac{\pi}{2}\right) \doteq 1.571$

2. (a) abs min $= -\dfrac{3\sqrt{3}}{2}$; abs max $= \dfrac{3\sqrt{3}}{2}$

(b) abs min $= -2$; abs max $= 1$

3. $\dfrac{\pi}{4}$ **4.** $\dfrac{\pi}{2}$ **5.** $\dfrac{\pi}{3}$ **6.** 0.588 00

7. 0.588 00   **8.** 25 m/h   **9.** 0.02 m/s

10. 33 708 m/min and 11 624 m/min

11. 0.727 m²/min   **12.** $\dfrac{\sqrt{2}}{5}$ rad/s

13. 0.05 rad/s   **14.** 0.128 rad/s   **15.** $\dfrac{\pi}{3}$

16. 24.5 m²   **18.** 125 m

EXERCISE 7.5

1. (a) $\dfrac{\pi}{6}$ (b) $\dfrac{2\pi}{3}$ (c) $-\dfrac{\pi}{4}$ (d) $-\dfrac{\pi}{4}$ (e) $\dfrac{\pi}{4}$

(f) $\dfrac{\pi}{6}$

2. (a) $\dfrac{12}{\sqrt{313}}$ (b) $\dfrac{3}{5}$ (c) $-2\sqrt{2}$ (d) $\dfrac{\sqrt{15}}{8}$

(e) $\dfrac{5}{\sqrt{74}}$ (f) -2

3. (a) $\dfrac{\sqrt{3}}{2}$ (b) $\dfrac{3\pi}{7}$ (c) $\dfrac{\pi}{4}$ (d) $\dfrac{\sqrt{2}}{2}$ (e) $\dfrac{7\pi}{8}$

(f) $\dfrac{\pi}{4}$ (g) $\sqrt{3}$ (h) $-\dfrac{\pi}{6}$ (i) $-\dfrac{\pi}{6}$

4. (a) $\sqrt{1-x^2}$ (b) $\sqrt{1-x^2}$ (c) $\dfrac{x}{\sqrt{1-x^2}}$

(d) $\dfrac{\sqrt{1-x^2}}{x}$ (e) $\dfrac{x}{\sqrt{1+x^2}}$ (f) $\dfrac{1}{\sqrt{1+x^2}}$

(g) $1-2x^2$

5. (a) $\dfrac{24}{25}$ (b) $\dfrac{119}{169}$ (c) $\dfrac{\sqrt{5}+4\sqrt{2}}{9}$

(d) $\dfrac{\sqrt{7}-3\sqrt{15}}{16}$

6. (a) $[0,2]$ (b) $[-1,1]$ (c) $[-\sqrt{2},\sqrt{2}]$
(d) $[-1,1]$ (e) $[-\sqrt{5},-\sqrt{3}]\cup[\sqrt{3},\sqrt{5}]$
(f) $[1,2]$

7. (a) $-\dfrac{\pi}{2}$ (b) $\dfrac{\pi}{2}$ (c) $-\dfrac{\pi}{2}$ (d) $-\dfrac{\pi}{2}$

11. (a)   (b)

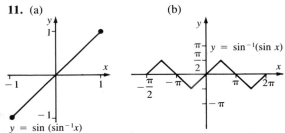

$y = \sin(\sin^{-1}x)$ $y = \sin^{-1}(\sin x)$

EXERCISE 7.6

1. (a) $\dfrac{1}{\sqrt{-x^2-2x}}$ (b) $\dfrac{-2x}{\sqrt{1-x^4}}$ (c) $\dfrac{3}{1+9x^2}$

(d) $\dfrac{2\sin^{-1}x}{\sqrt{1-x^2}}$ (e) $\dfrac{-3x^2}{\sqrt{4-x^6}}$

(f) $1 + 2x\tan^{-1}x$

(g) $\dfrac{-1}{\sqrt{(2-2x)(2x-1)}}$ (h) $\dfrac{\cos x}{2-\cos^2 x}$

(i) $\dfrac{-1}{\sqrt{2}\sin x(\sin x + 1)}$ (j) $\dfrac{\cos^{-1}x - \sin^{-1}x}{(\cos^{-1}x)^2\sqrt{1-x^2}}$

(k) $\dfrac{-1}{(1+x^2)(\tan^{-1}x)^2}$ (l) $\dfrac{4x}{(\cos^{-1}x^2)^3\sqrt{1-x^4}}$

(m) 0 (n) $\dfrac{x^2-1}{x^2\sqrt{1-x^2}}$ (o) $\dfrac{x^2}{\sqrt{(1-x^2)^3}}$

(p) $\dfrac{|x|+x}{|x|\sqrt{1-x^2}}$ (q) $\dfrac{2x\cos(\sin^{-1}x^2)}{\sqrt{1-x^4}}$

(r) $\dfrac{1}{(1+x^2)\sqrt{1-(\tan^{-1}x)^2}}$

(s) $\dfrac{2|x|}{\sqrt{x^2-4}} + 2x\cos^{-1}\left(\dfrac{2}{x}\right)$ **2.** $\dfrac{2+\pi}{4}$

3. $\pi x - 6y + 12\sqrt{3} = 0$ **4.** $3\pi^3$

5. $\dfrac{1-y^2\cos x - x^2y^2\cos x}{(1+x^2)(1+2y\sin x)}$ **6.** 12

7. (a) $y' = -1,\ \sin x > 0$
$\qquad y' = 1,\ \sin x < 0$

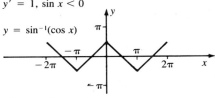

$y = \sin^{-1}(\cos x)$

(b) $y' = 1,\ \sin x > 0$
$\qquad y' = -1,\ \sin x < 0$

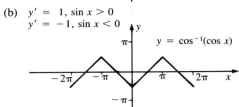

$y = \cos^{-1}(\cos x)$

(c) $y' = 1,\ \cos x > 0$
$\qquad y' = -1,\ \cos < 0$

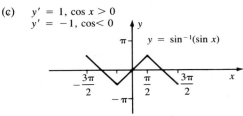

$y = \sin^{-1}(\sin x)$

(d) $y' = -2,\ \sin 2x > 0$
$\qquad y' = 2,\ \sin 2x < 0$

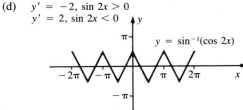

$y = \sin^{-1}(\cos 2x)$

7.7 REVIEW EXERCISE

1. (a) $\dfrac{1}{2}$ (b) 1 (c) $\dfrac{3}{5}$ (d) 0 (e) 1 (f) 1 (g) 0

(h) 2 (i) 1

2. (a) $12\tan^3 3x\sec^2 3x$ (b) $\dfrac{\cos x - 2}{(1 - 2\cos x)^2}$

(c) $2x\sec x^2\tan x^2$

(d) $\dfrac{-2\cot 2x[2(1+x^2)\csc^2 2x + x\cot 2x]}{(1+x^2)^2}$

(e) $-3x^2\csc(x^3+1)\cot(x^3+1)$

(f) $\dfrac{\sec\sqrt{x}\,\tan\sqrt{x}}{\sqrt{x}}$ (g) $\dfrac{\tan x + x\sec^2 x}{3\sqrt[3]{x^2}\tan^2 x}$

(h) $-\sec^2 x\,\sin(2\tan x)$

(i) $\dfrac{(\cos x - 1)[\cos(x - \sin x)]}{\sin^2(x - \sin x)}$

3. (a) $\dfrac{-\sin(x - y)}{1 - \sin(x - y)}$

(b) $\dfrac{\cos(x - y) + \cos(x + y)}{\cos(x - y) - \cos(x + y)}$ (c) $-\dfrac{\sec^2(x + y)}{y^2}$

(d) $-\dfrac{y\cos x + \sin(x + y)}{\sin x + \sin(x + y)}$ (e) $-\dfrac{y}{x}$

(f) $\dfrac{1 + \csc(x - y)\cot(x - y) - \sec(x + y)\tan(x + y)}{\csc(x - y)\cot(x - y) + \sec(x + y)\tan(x + y)}$

4. $\left(\dfrac{\pi}{4}, \dfrac{2}{\sqrt{2}}\right)$ and $\left(\dfrac{5\pi}{4}, -\dfrac{2}{\sqrt{2}}\right)$

5. $12x - 3y + 3\sqrt{3} - 4\pi = 0$

6. $\dfrac{2}{6 - \pi}$ **7.** $\frac{25}{36}\pi$ cm/s^2

8. increasing 90 cm^2/min   **9.** 512π km/min

11. $60°$ **12.** fold $6\sqrt{2}$ cm of the 12 cm side
or 6 cm of the 8 cm side   **13.** $-\frac{3}{20}$ rad/min

14. (a) A. $[0, 2\pi]$ B. y-intercept 3, x-intercepts $\dfrac{\pi}{2}$,

$\dfrac{3\pi}{2}$ C. none   D. none   E. decreasing on

$(0, \pi)$; increasing on $(\pi, 2\pi)$ F. local minimum
$f(\pi) = -1$, maxima $f(0) = 3$ and $f(2\pi) = 3$

G. CD on $\left(0, \dfrac{\pi}{3}\right)$, $\left(\dfrac{5\pi}{3}, 2\pi\right)$, CU on $\left(\dfrac{\pi}{3}, \dfrac{5\pi}{3}\right)$,

Points of inflection $\left(\dfrac{\pi}{3}, 1.25\right)$, $\left(\dfrac{5\pi}{3}, 1.25\right)$

H.

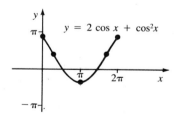

$y = 2\cos x + \cos^2 x$

(b) A. $[-\pi, \pi]$ B. y-intercept 0, x-intercept 0
C. origin   D. none   E. increasing on

$\left(-\pi, -\dfrac{2\pi}{3}\right)$, $\left(-\dfrac{\pi}{3}, \dfrac{\pi}{3}\right)$, $\left(\dfrac{2\pi}{3}, \pi\right)$;

decreasing on $\left(-\dfrac{2\pi}{3}, -\dfrac{\pi}{3}\right)$, $\left(\dfrac{\pi}{3}, \dfrac{2\pi}{3}\right)$

F. local maxima: $f\left(-\dfrac{2\pi}{3}\right) \doteq -1.2$, $f\left(\dfrac{\pi}{3}\right) \doteq 1.9$,

local minima: $f\left(-\dfrac{\pi}{3}\right) \doteq -1.9$, $f\left(\dfrac{2\pi}{3}\right) \doteq 1.2$

G. CD on $\left(-\pi, -\dfrac{\pi}{2}\right)$, $\left(0, \dfrac{\pi}{2}\right)$;

CU on $\left(-\dfrac{\pi}{2}, 0\right)$, $\left(\dfrac{\pi}{2}, \pi\right)$.

Points of inflection $\left(-\dfrac{\pi}{2}, -\dfrac{\pi}{2}\right)$, $(0, 0)$, $\left(\dfrac{\pi}{2}, \dfrac{\pi}{2}\right)$

H.

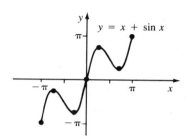

$y = x + \sin x$

15. $(-0.739\,08, 0.739\,08)$

16. (a) $\dfrac{\pi}{6}$ (b) $\dfrac{\pi}{4}$ (c) $-\dfrac{\pi}{3}$ (d) $\dfrac{\sqrt{3}}{2}$ (e) $\frac{4}{5}$ (f) $\frac{1}{2}$

(g) $\dfrac{\pi}{4}$ (h) $\dfrac{\pi}{6}, \dfrac{\pi}{6}$ (j) $\dfrac{\pi}{3}$ (k) $\dfrac{\pi}{3}$ (l) $\dfrac{2\pi}{3}$

17. (a) $\dfrac{2x}{\sqrt{1 - x^4}}$ (b) $\dfrac{x^3}{\sqrt{9 - x^2}} + 3x^2\sin^{-1}\left(\dfrac{x}{3}\right)$

(c) $\dfrac{-1}{2\sqrt{x(1 - x)}}$ (d) $\dfrac{x^2}{1 + x^2}$ (e) $\dfrac{|x + 1|}{(x + 1)^2\sqrt{x}}$

(f) $\dfrac{\sin 2x}{1 + \sin^4 x}$ (g) $\dfrac{|x|}{x^2\sqrt{x^2 - 1}}$

(h) $\dfrac{1}{\sqrt{(1 - x^2)[1 - (\sin^{-1} x)^2]}}$

(i) $\dfrac{1}{(1 + x^2)[1 + (\tan^{-1} x)^2]}$

18. (a) $-\dfrac{\pi}{2}$ (b) $\dfrac{\pi}{2}$

19. (a) $\dfrac{(1 + y^2)(3x^2 + \sin y)}{x\cos y(1 + y^2) + 1}$

(b) $\dfrac{-y\sqrt{1 - (x + y)^2} - \sqrt{1 - x^2 y^2}}{x\sqrt{1 - (x + y)^2} + \sqrt{1 - x^2 y^2}}$

7.8 CHAPTER 7 TEST

1. (a) 2   (b) $\frac{1}{2}$

2. (a) $\dfrac{-24x^2\sin(x^3 - 2)^{-4}\cos(x^3 - 2)^{-4}}{(x^3 - 2)^5}$

(b) $-3\sin x\cos^2 x\,\sec^2(\cos^3 x)$

(c) $\dfrac{-\csc x(\cot x - 1)}{(1 + \cot x)^2}$

(d) $\dfrac{-2\cot 2x[2(1+x^2)\csc^2 2x + x\cot 2x]}{(1+x^2)^2}$

(e) $-4\sec^2 x\tan x$ (f) $\dfrac{4(3\sin^2 x - 1)}{\cos^2 x\sin^3 2x}$

3. $\dfrac{y - \cos y + y\sin x}{-x\sin y + \cos x - x}$ 4. $-\dfrac{24}{25}$

5. (a) $\dfrac{1}{\sqrt{4-x^2}}$ (b) $\dfrac{1}{x^2+1}$ (c) ± 1

6. (a) $-\dfrac{\pi}{2}, \dfrac{\pi}{6}, \dfrac{\pi}{2}, \dfrac{5\pi}{6}$ (b) increasing on

$\left(-\dfrac{\pi}{2},\dfrac{\pi}{6}\right), \left(\dfrac{\pi}{2},\dfrac{5\pi}{6}\right),$

decreasing on $\left(-\pi, -\dfrac{\pi}{2}\right), \left(\dfrac{\pi}{6},\dfrac{\pi}{2}\right), \left(\dfrac{5\pi}{6},\pi\right)$

(c) abs min $= -3$; abs max $= 1.5$

7. $\dfrac{3}{25}$ rad/s counter-clockwise   9. $n = 4i, i \in N$

CUMULATIVE REVIEW FOR CHAPTERS 4 TO 7

1. (a) $-\infty$ (b) 1   (c) ∞ (d) $-\infty$ (e) 2   (f) ∞

   (g) $-\infty$ (h) $\dfrac{5}{8}$ (i) 3   (j) -1 2. $\dfrac{5}{13}$

3. (a) 0   (b) undefined   (c) $\dfrac{\sqrt{3}-1}{\sqrt{3}+1}$

   (d) $\sqrt{\dfrac{1+\sqrt{2}}{2\sqrt{2}}}$ (e) $-\dfrac{1}{2\sqrt{2}}$ (f) $\dfrac{\sqrt{2}-1}{\sqrt{2}}$

5. (a) $-\dfrac{3\pi}{2}, -\dfrac{5\pi}{6}, -\dfrac{\pi}{6}, \dfrac{\pi}{2}, \dfrac{7\pi}{6}, \dfrac{11\pi}{6}$

   (b) $0, \dfrac{\pi}{4}, \dfrac{\pi}{2}, \pi, \dfrac{5\pi}{4}, \dfrac{3\pi}{2}, 2\pi$ (c) $\dfrac{\pi}{2}$

   (d) $\dfrac{5\pi}{24}, \dfrac{11\pi}{24}$

6. (a) $\dfrac{\pi}{6}$ (b) $-\sqrt{3}$ (c) $-\dfrac{\pi}{6}$

7. (a) $\dfrac{(1-x)\cos x + (1+x)\sin x}{(\sin x + \cos x)^2}$ (b) $\dfrac{-\sin 2x}{\sqrt{\cos 2x}}$

   (c) $\dfrac{ax\cos ax - \sin ax}{bx^2}$

   (d) $2\csc x\cot x\sin(2\csc x)$

   (e) $\dfrac{2\sec 2x(\sec 2x - 2\csc 2x)}{(1-\cot 2x)^2}$

   (f) $-\dfrac{\csc x(x\cot x + 2)}{x^3}$

   (g) $\dfrac{\cos(x-y) + y\sin x}{\cos(x-y) + \cos x}$

   (h) $\dfrac{\tan x\sec^2 x}{\tan y\sec^2 y}$

   (i) $-\cos x\sin(\sin x)\sec^2[\cos(\sin x)]$

   (j) $\dfrac{x^2}{\sqrt{4-x^2}} + 2x\sin^{-1}\dfrac{x}{2}$

(k) $\dfrac{|x-1|}{(x-1)^2\sqrt{1-2x}}$ (l) $\dfrac{1}{2\sqrt{x}(1+x)}$

8. (a) local maximum $f\left(\dfrac{1}{2}\right) = \dfrac{1}{4}$,

   local minimum $f(1) = 0$

   (b) local maximum, $f(-\sqrt{3}) = \dfrac{-3\sqrt{3}}{2}$, local minimum

   $f(\sqrt{3}) = \dfrac{3\sqrt{3}}{2}$ (c) local minimum

   $f\left(-\dfrac{\pi}{4}\right) = -\sqrt{2}$ (d) local maxima

   $f\left(-\dfrac{5\pi}{6}\right) = f\left(\dfrac{7\pi}{6}\right) = -\sqrt{3}$, local minima

   $f\left(-\dfrac{\pi}{6}\right) = f\left(\dfrac{11\pi}{6}\right) = \sqrt{3}$

9. (a) $f\left(\dfrac{9}{2}\right) = \dfrac{97}{8}, f(3) = 2$ (b) $f\left(\dfrac{\pi}{2}\right) = 3$,

   $f(0) = f(\pi) = 0$

10. $\left(\dfrac{2\pi}{3}, \dfrac{4\pi}{3}\right)$

11. (a) A. R B. y-intercept 0, x-intercepts 0, $\pm\sqrt{2}$ C. about the y-axis   D. none
    E. increasing on $(-\infty, -1)$, $(0, 1)$, decreasing on $(-1, 0)$, $(1, \infty)$ F. local maximum $f(-1) = f(1) = 1$, local minimum $f(0) = 0$
    G. CU on $\left(-\dfrac{1}{\sqrt{3}}, \dfrac{1}{\sqrt{3}}\right)$, CD on $\left(-\infty, -\dfrac{1}{\sqrt{3}}\right)$, $\left(\dfrac{1}{\sqrt{3}}, \infty\right)$; IP $\left(\pm\dfrac{1}{\sqrt{3}}, \dfrac{5}{9}\right)$
    H.

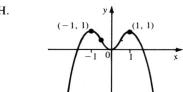

(b) A. $[-1, \infty)$ B. y-intercept 0, x-intercepts -1, 0
    C. none   D. none   E. increasing on $\left(-\dfrac{2}{3}, \infty\right)$,
    decreasing on $\left(-1, -\dfrac{2}{3}\right)$ F. local minimum
    $f\left(-\dfrac{2}{3}\right) = -\dfrac{2\sqrt{3}}{9}$ G. CU on $(-1, \infty)$
    H.

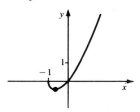

(c) A. $(-\infty, -1) \cup (-1, 1) \cup (1, \infty)$
B. intercepts 0   C. about y-axis   D. VA:
$x = \pm 1$, HA: $y = 1$ E.. increasing on
$(-\infty, -1)$, $(-1, 0)$, decreasing on $(0, 1)$,
$(1, \infty)$ F. local maximum $f(0) = 0$
G. CU on $(-\infty, -1)$, $(1, \infty)$, CD on $(-1, 1)$

H.

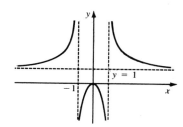

(d) A. $\left[-\dfrac{\pi}{2}, \dfrac{\pi}{2}\right]$ B. y-intercept $= 1$,
x-intercept $\doteq 0.51$ C. none   D. none
E. increasing on $\left(-\dfrac{5\pi}{12}, -\dfrac{\pi}{12}\right)$, decreasing
on $\left(-\dfrac{\pi}{2}, -\dfrac{5\pi}{12}\right)$, $\left(-\dfrac{\pi}{12}, \dfrac{\pi}{2}\right)$ F. local minimum
$f\left(-\dfrac{5\pi}{12}\right) \doteq 0.44$, local maximum $f\left(-\dfrac{\pi}{12}\right) \doteq$
1.13   G. CU on $\left(-\dfrac{\pi}{2}, -\dfrac{\pi}{4}\right)$, $\left(\dfrac{\pi}{4}, \dfrac{\pi}{2}\right)$, CD on

$\left(-\dfrac{\pi}{4}, \dfrac{\pi}{4}\right)$; IP $\left(-\dfrac{\pi}{4}, \dfrac{\pi}{4}\right)$ and $\left(\dfrac{\pi}{4}, -\dfrac{\pi}{4}\right)$

H.

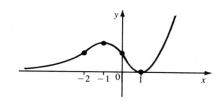

$y = \cos 2x - x$

12.

13. $\frac{1}{40}$ rad/sec   14. $(2, \pm 2)$ 15. 2 rad

16. (a) $p(x) = 560 - \frac{1}{5}x$ (b) \$280

CHAPTER 8 EXPONENTIAL AND LOGARITHMIC FUNCTIONS

REVIEW AND PREVIEW TO CHAPTER 8
EXERCISE 1

1. -243 (b) $\frac{1}{64}$ (c) $\frac{625}{8}$ (d) $-\frac{8}{9}$ (e) 6
   (f) -4 (g) 25   (h) $\frac{1}{2187}$

2. (a) 2^7 (b) 2^{18} (c) 2^{36} (d) 2^{-2} (e) $2^{-\frac{3}{2}}$
   (f) $2^{\frac{1}{2}}$ (g) $2^{\frac{5}{2}}$ (h) 2^0

3. (a) $6x^7 y^5$ (b) $8s^9 t^3$ (c) $16x^{10}$ (d) $\dfrac{a^2}{b}$ (e) $64r^7 s$

   (f) $\dfrac{8v^7}{9}$ (g) $\dfrac{x^3}{y}$ (h) $\dfrac{d^7}{c^6}$ (i) $\dfrac{(a+b)^2}{ab}$ (j) $\dfrac{y^{\frac{8}{3}}}{z^2}$

   (k) $\dfrac{3t^{\frac{25}{6}}}{s^{\frac{1}{2}}}$ (l) $\dfrac{a^{\frac{9}{2}}x}{b^{10}y^{\frac{19}{3}}}$

EXERCISE 2

1. (a) $2^6 = 64$ (b) $5^0 = 1$ (c) $10^{-2} = 0.01$
   (d) $8^{\frac{2}{3}} = 4$ (e) $8^3 = 512$ (f) $2^{-4} = \frac{1}{16}$
   (g) $a^c = b$ (h) $r^w = v$

2. (a) $\log_2 8 = 3$ (b) $\log_{10} 100\,000 = 5$
   (c) $\log_{10} 0.0001 = -4$ (d) $\log_{81} 9 = \frac{1}{2}$
   (e) $\log_4 0.125 = -\frac{3}{2}$ (f) $\log_6 \frac{1}{6} = -1$
   (g) $\log_r t = s$ (h) $\log_{10} n = m$

3. (a) 4   (b) 5   (c) 3   (d) 17   (e) 1   (f) 0
   (g) -3 (h) $\frac{3}{2}$ (i) $-\frac{2}{3}$ (j) $\frac{1}{4}$

4. (a) 1024   (b) 625   (c) $\frac{95}{3}$ (d) -25
   (e) $1 - \log_2 3$ (f) $\frac{1}{2}(1 + \log_3 5)$
   (g) 43 046 721   (h) $\log_5(\log_{10} 3)$

EXERCISE 3

1. (a) $\log_2 x + \log_2(x - 1)$ (b) $\log_5 x - \log_5 2$
   (c) $\log_2 A + 2\log_2 B$ (d) $\frac{1}{4}\log_6 17$
   (e) $\log_3 x + \frac{1}{2}\log_3 y$ (f) $10\log_2 x + 10\log_2 y$

(g) $\frac{1}{3}\log_5(x^2 + 1)$ (h) $2\log_b x - \log_b y - 3\log_b z$ (i) $3\log_{10}x + 4\log_{10}y - 6\log_{10}z$

(j) $2\log_{10}a - 4\log_{10}b - \frac{1}{2}\log_{10}c$

2. (a) $\frac{3}{2}$ (b) 4   (c) 1   (d) $-\frac{1}{2}$ (e) 3   (f) 2

3. (a) $\log_{10}(6\sqrt{7})$ (b) $\log_2\left(\dfrac{AB}{C^2}\right)$ (c) $\log_5(x + 1)$

(d) $\log_2\left[\dfrac{x^4(x - 1)}{\sqrt[3]{x^2 + 1}}\right]$ (e) $\log_5\left(y\sqrt{\dfrac{x}{z^3}}\right)$

(f) $\log_a\left(\dfrac{bd^c}{s^r}\right)$

EXERCISE 8.1

1. (a)

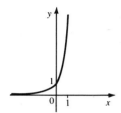

(b)

(c)

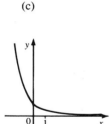

(d)

2.

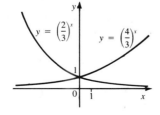

3.

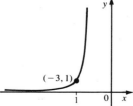

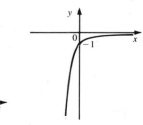

4. (a) domain R, range $(-\infty, 0)$ HA: $y = 0$

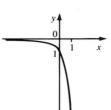

(b) domain R, range $(0, \infty)$ HA: $y = 0$

(c) domain R, range $(-5, \infty)$ HA: $y = -5$

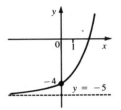

(d) domain R, range $(0, \infty)$ HA: $y = 0$

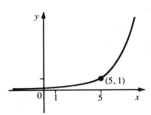

(e) domain R, range $(3, \infty)$ HA: $y = 3$

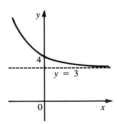

(f) domain R, range $(-\infty, 4)$ HA: $y = 4$

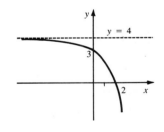

(g) domain R, range $(0, \infty)$ HA: $y = 0$

(h) domain R, range $(-\infty, 0)$ HA: $y = 0$

(i) domain R,
   range $(0, \infty)$
   HA: $y = 0$

(j) domain R,
   range $(1, \infty)$
   HA: $y = 1$

(b)

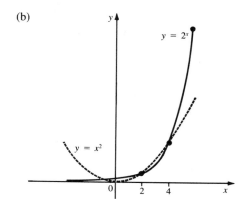

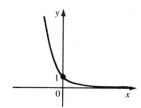

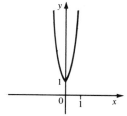

8. (a) $y = 10^{|x|}$ (b) $y = 10^{-|x|}$

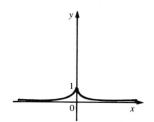

(k) domain R,
   range $(-\infty, 5)$
   HA: $y = 5$

(l) domain R,
   range $(-\infty, 4)$
   HA: $y = 4$

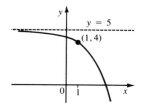

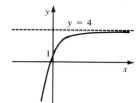

EXERCISE 8.2

1. (a) $2e^x$ (b) e^{4x} (c) e^{2x+1} (d) 1
   (e) $e^{2x} - 5e^{5x}$ (f) $6e^{5x}$

2. (a) $y = 5^x$

5. (a) 0   (b) 0   (c) ∞ (d) 0   (e) ∞ (f) 0   (g) 0
   (h) 1   (i) 0   (j) 0

6. (a)

x	x^2	2^x
0	0	1
1	1	2
2	4	4
3	9	8
4	16	16
5	25	32
6	36	64
7	49	128
.8	64	256
9	81	512
10	100	1 024
15	225	32 768
20	400	1 048 576

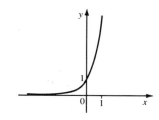

(b)

h	$\dfrac{5^h - 1}{h}$
0.1	1.746 189
0.01	1.622 459
0.001	1.610 734
0.0001	1.609 567

Slope of secant line

(c) 1.61   (d) The slope of the tangent line to $y = 5^x$ at $(0, 1)$.

3. (a) 0.99   (b) 1.03

4. (a) $y' = -2e^{-x}$ (b) $y' = x^3e^x(4 + x)$
(c) $y' = e^{2x}(2 \sin 3x + 3 \cos 3x)$
(d) $y' = \dfrac{e^{\sqrt{x}}}{2\sqrt{x}}$ (e) $y' = (\sec^2 x)e^{\tan x}$

(f) $y' = (e^x) \sec^2(e^x)$ (g) $y' = \dfrac{e^x}{x^2}(x - 1)$

(h) $y' = \dfrac{e^x(1 + e^{2x})}{(1 - e^{2x})^2}$

(i) $y' = 2x \cos(x^2)e^{\sin(x^2)}$
(j) $y' = e^{\cot 4x}(1 - 4x \csc^2 4x)$
(k) $y' = -200e^{-10x}(1 + 5e^{-10x})^3$

(l) $y' = \dfrac{1 - 2xe^{1 - x^2}}{2\sqrt{x + e^{1 - x^2}}}$

5. $x - y + 1 = 0$ **6.** $\dfrac{2 - ye^{xy}}{xe^{xy} - 1}$ **7.** 64

8. increasing on $(0,2)$, decreasing on $(-\infty, 0)$, $(2, \infty)$ **9.** e

10. (a) $-\dfrac{1}{e}$ (b) CU on $(-2, \infty)$, CD on $(-\infty, -2)$
(c) $(-2, -2e^{-2})$

11. (a) 0   (b) ∞ (c) 0

12. (a) $y = e^x$

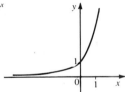

(b) (i) $y = e^{-x}$

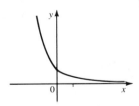

(ii) $y = 1 - e^x$

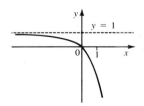

13. (a) A. R   B. y-intercept 0   C. about the origin
D. none   E. increasing on $(-\infty, \infty)$ F. none
G. CU on $(0, \infty)$, CD on $(-\infty, 0)$, IP $(0, 0)$

H.

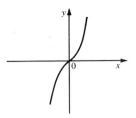

(b) A. $(-\infty, 0) \cup (0, \infty)$ B. none   C. about
the y-axis   D. HA: $y = 1$, VA: $x = 0$
E. increases on $(-\infty, 0)$, decreases on $(0, \infty)$
F. none   G. CU on $(-\infty, 0)$, $(0, \infty)$, no IP

H.

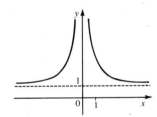

14. (a)

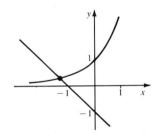

(b) $-1.278\ 465$

15. A. $(-\infty, 0) \cup (0, \infty)$ B. none   C. none
D. HA: $y = 1$, VA: $x = 0$ E. increasing on
$(-\infty, 0)$, $(0, \infty)$ F. none   G. CU on $(-\infty, 0)$,
$\left(0, \frac{1}{2}\right)$ CD on $\left(\frac{1}{2}, \infty\right)$, IP $\left(\frac{1}{2}, e^{-2}\right)$

H.

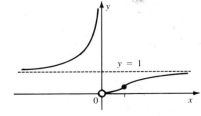

16. $f^{(1\,000\,000)}(x) = e^{-x}(x - 1\,000\,000)$

EXERCISE 8.3

1.

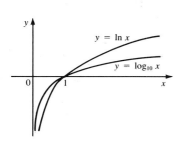

2. (a) domain $(4, \infty)$, **(b)** domain $(0, \infty)$,
   range R   range R
   asymptote $x = 4$ asymptote $x = 0$

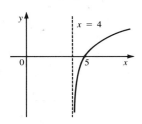

(c) domain $(-\infty, 0)$, **(d)** domain $(-2, \infty)$,
   range R   range R
   asymptote $x = 0$ asymptote $x = -2$

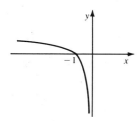
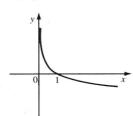

(e) domain $(0, \infty)$, **(f)** domain $(1, \infty)$,
   range R   range R
   asymptote $x = 0$ asymptote $x = 1$

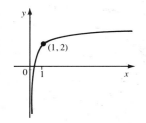
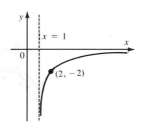

(g) domain $(0, \infty)$, **(h)** domain $(-\infty, 0)$,
   range R   range R
   asymptote $x = 0$ asymptote $x = 0$

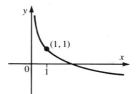
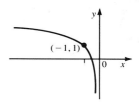

(i) domain $(0, \infty)$, **(j)** domain $(-\infty, 0) \cup (0, \infty)$,
   range $[0, \infty)$ range R
   asymptote $x = 0$ asymptote $x = 0$

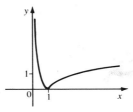
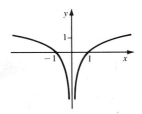

3. (a) 5 **(b)** 2 **(c)** 2 **(d)** 32 **(e)** $\frac{1}{2}$ **(f)** 0

4. (a) ln 4 **(b)** e^6 **(c)** $\frac{1}{2}(e + 1)$
   (d) $\frac{1}{3}(\ln 10 - 5)$ **(e)** -5 **(f)** 28
   (g) e^{e^2} **(h)** ln(ln 5)

5. (a) 19.085 537 **(b)** 0.693 147
   (c) $-0.139\,483$ **(d)** 6.584 963

6. (a) $\ln[\sqrt[3]{x}(3x - 5)^2]$ **(b)** $\ln\left(\dfrac{x^2(x^2 + 1)^3}{\sqrt{x^2 - 1}}\right)$

7. (a) $\left(-\frac{2}{5}, \infty\right)$ **(b)** $\left(-\infty, \frac{10}{3}\right)$
   (c) $(-\infty, -1) \cup (1, \infty)$ **(d)** $(0, 1)$ **(e)** $(0, 2)$
   (f) $[2, 10)$

8. dom$(f) = (-\infty, 0) \cup (0, \infty)$, dom$(g) = (0, \infty)$

9. (a) $-\infty$ **(b)** ∞ **(c)** $-\infty$ **(d)** $-\infty$

10. (a) 2.807 355 **(b)** 0.430 677 **(c)** 2.182 658
   (d) 2.523 658

12. $\log_2 7$

13. (a) $P(t) = M - Ce^{-kt}$

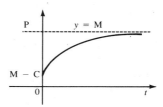

(b) $t = -\dfrac{1}{k}\ln\left(\dfrac{M-P}{C}\right)$

14. $\log_4 17$ **15.** (a) $(1, \infty)$ (b) $f^{-1}(x) = 10^{2^x}$

16. (a) (e, ∞) (b) $f^{-1}(x) = e^{e^{e^x}}$ **17.** $\log_2 3$

18. 64

EXERCISE 8.4

1. (a) $f'(x) = x(2\ln x + 1)$

(b) $f'(x) = \dfrac{1}{2x\sqrt{\ln x}}$ (c) $g'(x) = \dfrac{3x^2}{x^3 + 1}$

(d) $g'(x) = \dfrac{1}{x}$ (e) $y' = \dfrac{1}{x}\cos(\ln x)$

(f) $y' = \cot x$ (g) $y' = \dfrac{1 - 3\ln x}{x^4}$

(h) $y' = 3(x + \ln x)^2\left(1 + \dfrac{1}{x}\right)$

(i) $y' = \dfrac{2}{2x + 1}$

(j) $y' = -\dfrac{2}{x^2 - 1}$ (k) $y' = \dfrac{3}{2x(2x + 3)}$

(l) $y' = \dfrac{1}{x(x^2 + 1)}$ (m) $y' = \sec x$

(n) $y' = \dfrac{-3\sec^2[\ln(1 - 3x)]}{1 - 3x}$

2. (a) $f'(x) = \dfrac{1}{x\ln x}$ (b) $(1, \infty), (1, \infty)$

3. (a) $f'(x) = \dfrac{2x}{(x^2 + 1)\ln 2}$

(b) $g'(x) = \log_{10} x + \dfrac{1}{\ln 10}$

(c) $F'(x) = \dfrac{3}{(3x - 8)\ln 5}$

(d) $G'(x) = \dfrac{1 - \ln x - \ln 3}{(\ln 3)\,x^2}$

4. (a) $y' = 3x^2 + 3^x\ln 3$

(b) $y' = (4x^3 - 1)(\ln 2)\,2^{x^4 - x}$

(c) $y' = \tfrac{1}{2}5^{\sqrt{x}}(\sqrt{x}\ln 5 + 2)$

(d) $y' = \pi(\sec^2\pi x)\ln 10[10^{\tan \pi x}]$

5. (a) $x - y - 2 = 0$ (b) $x - y - 1 = 0$

(c) $10(\ln 10)\,x - y - 10(\ln 10 - 1) = 0$

(d) $x - 100(\ln 10)\,y + 100(2\ln 10 - 1) = 0$

6. $\dfrac{1}{x + y - 1}$ **7.** (a) $-\dfrac{1}{e}$ (b) $(0, \infty)$

8. (a) local maximum $f(e^{-2}) = 4e^{-2}$, local

minimum $f(1) = 0$ (b) $\left(\dfrac{1}{e}, \dfrac{1}{e}\right)$

9. (a) A. $(-3, 3)$ B. y-intercept $\ln 9$, x-intercepts $\pm 2\sqrt{2}$ C. about the y-axis

D. VA: $x = 3$, $x = -3$

E. increasing on $(-3, 0)$, decreasing on $(0, 3)$

F. local maximum $f(0) = \ln 9$

G. CD on $(-3, 3)$

H.

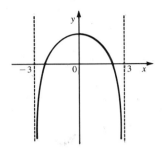

(b) A. $(0, \infty)$ C. none   D. VA: $x = 0$

E. increasing on $(0, \infty)$ F. none

G. CD on $(0, \infty)$

H.

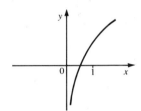

(c) A. $(0, \infty)$ B. x-intercept 1   C. none

D. VA: $x = 0$ E. increasing on $(1, \infty)$,

decreasing on $(0, 1)$ F. local minimum $f(1) = 0$

G. CU on $(0, e)$, CD on (e, ∞), IP $(e, 1)$

H.

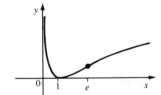

(d) A. $\{x \mid (4n - 1)\dfrac{\pi}{2} < x < (4n + 1)\dfrac{\pi}{2}, n \in I\}$

B. x-intercepts $2n\pi$, $n \in I$, y-intercept 0

C. about the y-axis; period 2π

D. VA: $x = (2n + 1)\dfrac{\pi}{2}$, $n \in I$

E. increasing on $\left((4n - 1)\dfrac{\pi}{2}, 2n\pi\right)$,

decreasing on $\left(2n\pi, (4n + 1)\dfrac{\pi}{2}\right)$

F. local maxima $f(2n\pi) = 0$

G. CD on $\left((4n - 1)\dfrac{\pi}{2}, (4n + 1)\dfrac{\pi}{2}\right)$

H.

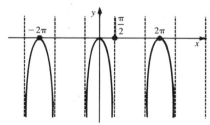

10. (a)

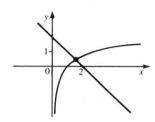

(b) 1.557 146

12. e^3

EXERCISE 8.5

1. (a) $(1000)\,10^{\frac{t}{2}}$ (b) 316 228   (c) 364 071
bacteria/h   (d) after 2 h 21 min

2. (a) $(400)3^t$ (b) $\dfrac{\ln 2}{\ln 3}$ h $\doteq$ 37.5 min

3. (a) $(500)2^{3t}$ (b) 8.389×10^9
(c) $\dfrac{\ln 12}{3 \ln 2}$ h $\doteq$ 1 h 11 m

4. (a) 2500   (b) $(2500)\,16^t$ (c) 13 863 bacteria/h
(d) $\dfrac{\ln 60}{4 \ln 2}$ h $\doteq$ 1 h 28 min

5. (a) 334 580   (b) 602 559

6. (a) (i) 6.6 billion   (ii) 47 billion   (b) 2103

7. (a) $(100)\,2^{-\frac{t}{4.5 \times 10^9}}$ (b) 99.999 846 mg
(c) 1.540×10^{-8}mg/a

8. (a) $(2)\,2^{-\frac{t}{15}}$ (b) $2^{\frac{4}{3}} \doteq 1.587$ g   (c) 0.073 g/h
(d) $\dfrac{15 \ln 5}{\ln 2} \doteq 34.8$ h

9. (a) 9.972 mg   (b) 128 643 a

10. (a) 5 d   (b) 19% of original mass

11. (a) $1345.60   (b) $1368.57   (c) $1374.22
(d) $1376.45   (e) $1377.03   (f) $1377.13

12. (a) $14 641.00   (b) $14 774.55
(c) $14 893.54   (d) $14 917.43
(e) $14 918.21   (f) $14 918.25

13. (a) is better   **14.** $\dfrac{\ln 2}{0.085} \doteq$ 8 a, 56 d

15. (a) $Ce^{-0.0005t}$ (b) 2000 ln 2 $\doteq$ 1386 s

16. 2100 a

EXERCISE 8.6

1. (a) $y' = (x^2 + 1)^2(x^2 + x + 1)^3 \times$
$\left[\dfrac{4x}{x^2 + 1} + \dfrac{6x + 3}{x^2 + x + 1}\right]$

(b) $y' = (x - 1)^4(2x + 3)^5(x^2 - 2x + 3)^3$
$\times \left[\dfrac{4}{x - 1} + \dfrac{10}{2x + 3} + \dfrac{6x - 6}{x^2 - 2x + 3}\right]$

(c) $y' = e^{x^2}x^3(x^2 + 8)^4\left[2x + \dfrac{3}{x} + \dfrac{8x}{x^2 + 8}\right]$

(d) $y' = \dfrac{(x + 1)^3}{(x + 2)^5(x + 3)^7} \times$
$\left[\dfrac{3}{x + 1} - \dfrac{5}{x + 2} - \dfrac{7}{x + 3}\right]$

(e) $y' = \dfrac{x\sqrt{x + 1}}{(x + 2)(x^3 + 1)} \times$
$\left[\dfrac{1}{x} + \dfrac{1}{2(x + 1)} - \dfrac{1}{x + 2} - \dfrac{3x^2}{x^3 + 1}\right]$

(f) $y' = \sqrt{\dfrac{x^2 + 1}{x^2 + 4}}\left[\dfrac{x}{x^2 + 1} - \dfrac{x}{x^2 + 4}\right]$

2. (a) $y' = x^{x^2}(2x \ln x + x)$

(b) $y' = x^{\sqrt{x}\,-\frac{1}{2}}\left(\dfrac{1}{2} \ln x + 1\right)$

(c) $y' = x^{\cos x}\left[-(\sin x) \ln x + \dfrac{\cos x}{x}\right]$

(d) $y' = (\cos x)^x[\ln(\cos x) - x \tan x]$

(e) $y' = (\ln x)^x\left[\ln(\ln x) + \dfrac{1}{\ln x}\right]$

(f) $y' = (\cos x)^{\sin x}[(\cos x) \ln(\cos x) -$
$(\sin x) \tan x]$

3. $(4 \ln 2 + 4)x - y - 4(2 \ln 2 + 1) = 0$

4. (a) 0, 0   (b) $-2x^{-1 - \ln x}(\ln x)$
(c) increasing on (0, 1), decreasing on $(1, \infty)$
(d) $f(1) = 1$
(e) CU on $\left(0, \dfrac{1}{e}\right)$, $(\sqrt{e}, \infty)$, CD on $\left(\sqrt{e}, \dfrac{1}{\sqrt[4]{e}}\right)$
(f)

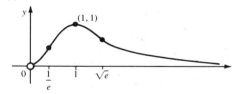

8.7 REVIEW EXERCISE

1. (a) (b)

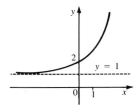

(c) (d)

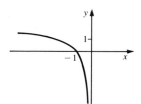

(e) (f)

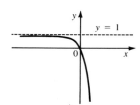

2. (a) 1 (b) $-\infty$ (c) ∞ (d) 0 (e) ∞ (f) $-\infty$

3. (a) $(-2, \infty)$, R, $x = -2$
(b) R, $(1, \infty)$, $y = 1$
(c) R, $(-\infty, 10)$, $y = 10$
(d) $\left(-\infty, \tfrac{1}{2}\right)$, R, $x = \tfrac{1}{2}$

4. (a) 0 (b) 10 (c) 8 (d) -1

5. (a) $\sqrt{e} \doteq 1.648\ 721$
(b) $\ln 7 \doteq 1.945\ 910$
(c) $\tfrac{1}{3}(5 - \ln 2) \doteq 1.435\ 618$
(d) $\tfrac{1}{4}(e^4 - 7) \doteq 11.899\ 538$

6. (a) $\ln\left[\dfrac{x^2(1 + x)^3}{(2 + x)^4}\right]$ (b) $\ln\left(\dfrac{\sqrt{x}}{(x^2 + x + 1)^2}\right)$

7. (a) $f'(x) = \dfrac{2x}{x^2 + 1}$
(b) $f'(x) = 3x^2 e^{x^3}$
(c) $f'(x) = \dfrac{e^x}{2\sqrt{x}}(1 + 2x)$

(d) $f'(x) = \dfrac{1 - 2 \ln x}{x^3}$
(e) $y' = 4x^3 - 4^x \ln 4$
(f) $y' = \dfrac{-11}{(2x + 3)(4x - 5)}$
(g) $y' = 2e^{2x} \cos (e^{2x})$
(h) $y' = (2 \cos x)e^{2 \sin x}$
(i) $y' = \dfrac{3x^2 - 1}{(\ln 10)(1 - x + x^3)}$
(j) $y' = e^x\left(\ln x + \dfrac{1}{x}\right)$
(k) $y' = \dfrac{2e^{x^2}}{x^3}(x^2 - 1)$
(l) $y' = \dfrac{2(\ln x)^3}{x\sqrt{1 + (\ln x)^4}}$

8. (a) $(\ln 2)x - y + 1 = 0$ (b) $x - y - 1 = 0$

9. -3

10. (a) $y' = x^5 e^x \sqrt{x^2 - x + 1} \times$
$\left[\dfrac{5}{x} + 1 + \dfrac{2x - 1}{2(x^2 - x + 1)}\right]$
(b) $y' = \dfrac{\sqrt{x}^x}{2}(\ln x + 1)$

11. increases on $\left(\tfrac{1}{2}, \infty\right)$, decreases on $\left(0, \tfrac{1}{2}\right)$

12. $g(0) = 1$

13. (a) A. R B. y-intercept 2 C. none
D. none E. increasing on $\left(\tfrac{1}{3} \ln 2, \infty\right)$,
decreasing on $\left(-\infty, \tfrac{1}{3} \ln 2\right)$
F. local minimum $f\left(\tfrac{1}{3} \ln 2\right) = \tfrac{3}{2}\sqrt[3]{2}$
G. CU on $(-\infty, \infty)$
H.

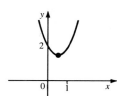

(b) A. R B. intercepts 0 C. about y-axis
D. none E. increasing on $(0, \infty)$, decreasing on
$(-\infty, 0)$ F. local minimum $f(0) = 0$
G. CU on $(-1, 1)$, CD on $(-\infty, -1)$,
$(1, \infty)$, IP $(\pm 1, \ln 2)$
H.

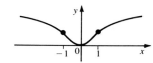

14. (a) 6.546 984

15. (a) $800(3)^{\frac{t}{2}}$ (b) 21 600   (c) 11 865 bacteria/h

(d) $\dfrac{2 \ln 25}{\ln 3} \doteq 5$ h, 51 min

16. (a) $(1.2)^{\frac{t}{10}}$ (b) $(1.2)^{2.4} \doteq 1.549$ g   (c) 38 h

17. (a) $15(2)^{\frac{-t}{26.8}}$ (b) 3.178 g   (c) 0.082 193 g/min

(d) $\dfrac{26.8(\ln 15)}{\ln 2} \doteq 105$ min

18. (a) (i) $6298.56   (ii) $6326.60   (iii) $6356.08

(iv) $6356.25   (b) $\dfrac{\ln 1.6}{0.08} \doteq 5.9$ a

8.8 CHAPTER 8 TEST

1.

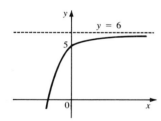

2. R, $(-\infty, 6)$, $y = 6$

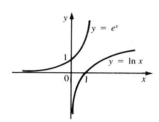

3. (a) $-\infty$ (b) 0   **4.** $\frac{1}{9}$ **5** $\frac{1}{2}(1 - \ln 5)$

6. (a) $y' = \dfrac{x^2(3x^2 + 2)}{x^3 + 2x - 1} + 2x \ln(x^3 + 2x - 1)$

(b) $y' = \dfrac{2e^{4x}}{(x^2 + 1)^2}(2x^2 - x + 2)$

(c) $y' = \dfrac{1}{2\sqrt{x}}(\sec^2 \sqrt{x})e^{\tan\sqrt{x}}$ (d) $y' = \dfrac{\ln 2}{x^2} 2^{-\frac{1}{x}}$

(e) $y' = x^{x^3+2}(3 \ln x + 1)$

7. (a) $(1000)7^t$ (b) 343 000   (c) 667 447

bacteria/h   (d) $\dfrac{\ln 10}{\ln 7}$ h $\doteq 1$ h, 11 min

8. $\dfrac{\ln 2}{0.09} \doteq 7.7$ a

9. A. $(-3, 3)$ B. y-intercept $2 \ln 3$, x-intercepts $\pm 2\sqrt{2}$ C. about the y-axis   D. VA: $x = \pm 3$ E. decreasing on $(0, 3)$, increasing on $(-3, 0)$ F. maximum $f(0) = 2 \ln 3$ G. CD on $(-3, 3)$

H.

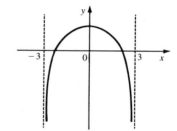

CHAPTER 9 DIFFERENTIAL EQUATIONS

REVIEW AND PREVIEW TO CHAPTER 9

EXERCISE 1

1. (a) $F'(x) = 16x^9 - 9x^4 + 3x$

(b) $F'(x) = 3.9x^{0.5} - 7.03x^{0.9}$

(c) $F'(x) = -\dfrac{3}{x} + \dfrac{5}{x^2}$

(d) $F'(x) = \dfrac{2}{2x + 7} + \dfrac{1}{2\sqrt{x - 3}}$

(e) $F'(x) = -\dfrac{12}{x^3} + \dfrac{5}{x^2} + \dfrac{6}{x}$

(f) $F'(x) = \sin 2x + 2 \cos x$

(g) $F'(x) = 21 \cos 3x + 77 \sin 7x$

(h) $F'(x) = -4 \cos(x + 2) - 15 \sin(3x - 7)$

(i) $F'(x) = e^{2x} + e^{-3x} + e^{4x}$

(j) $F'(x) = -40e^{8x} - 12e^{-6x}$

(k) $F'(x) = \dfrac{1}{2\sqrt{x}} - \dfrac{1}{2\sqrt{1 - x}}$

(l) $F'(x) = \dfrac{1}{x} - \dfrac{1}{1 - x}$

(m) $F'(x) = \dfrac{4}{x} + \dfrac{5}{1 - x}$

(n) $F'(x) = 4xe^{x^2} - 12xe^{2x^2}$

(o) $F'(x) = \cos^2 x - \sin^2 x(= \cos 2x)$

(p) $F'(x) = \dfrac{x}{\sqrt{x^2 + 1}}$

(q) $F'(x) = \dfrac{3(x^2 + 2)}{x^3 + 6x + 7}$

(r) $F'(x) = -\tan x$

EXERCISE 2

2. (a) $-16y$ (b) $-y$ (c) $-2y$ (d) $-ky$

EXERCISE 9.1

1. (a) $F(x) = x^2 + x + C$
   (b) $F(x) = x^4 - 11x + C$
   (c) $F(x) = 1.6x^{10} - 1.8x^5 + 1.5x^2 + C$
   (d) $F(x) = \frac{1}{8}x^8 + \frac{1}{6}x^6 + \frac{1}{4}x^4 + \frac{1}{2}x^2 + C$

2. (a) $F(x) = -\dfrac{1}{3x^6} + \frac{1}{12}x^6 + C$

   (b) $F(x) = \frac{2}{3}x^{\frac{3}{2}} + \frac{3}{4}x^{\frac{4}{3}} + C$

   (c) $F(x) = -3 \ln x - \dfrac{5}{x} + C$

   (d) $F(x) = -\frac{1}{6}x^{-6} - \frac{1}{4}x^{-4} - \frac{1}{2}x^{-2} + \ln x + C$

3. (a) $F(x) = \ln|x| + C$

   (b) $F(x) = -\dfrac{1}{x^2} + \dfrac{3}{x} + C$

   (c) $F(x) = -\frac{2}{3}(-x)^{\frac{3}{2}} + C$

   (d) $F(x) = -\dfrac{1}{3x^3} + \frac{1}{4}x^4 - \dfrac{1}{x} + C$

4. (a) $F(x) = -\frac{1}{2}\cos 2x + 2 \sin x + C$

   (b) $F(x) = -\frac{3}{5}\sin 5x - 8 \cos x + C$

   (c) $F(x) = 7 \sin x + \cos 11x + C$
   (d) $F(x) = -4 \sin(x + 2) + C$

5. (a) $F(x) = e^x - e^{-x} + C$
   (b) $F(x) = e^x + e^{-x} + C$
   (c) $F(x) = 2e^{2x} + 2e^{-3x} + C$
   (d) $F(x) = e^x + \frac{1}{2}e^{-2x} + \frac{1}{3}e^{3x} + C$

6. (a) $F(x) = \frac{2}{3}\left(x^{\frac{3}{2}} + (1 - x)^{\frac{3}{2}}\right) + C$
   (b) $F(x) = \ln(x - x^2) + C$
   (c) $F(x) = 2(\sqrt{x} - \sqrt{1 - x}) + C$
   (d) $F(x) = 4 \ln x - 5 \ln(1 - x) + C$

7. (a) $F(x) = \frac{1}{2}e^{x^2} + C$ (b) $F(x) = \frac{1}{3}\sin^3 x + C$
   (c) $F(x) = \ln(x^2 + 1) + C$
   (d) $F(x) = \sqrt{x^2 + 1} + C$

8. (a) $F(x) = \arctan x + C$
   (b) $F(x) = \ln \cos x + C$
   (c) $F(x) = \sec x + C$ (d) $F(x) = \frac{1}{2}x^2 + C$

EXERCISE 9.2

1. (a) $y = 2x^2 - 3x$ (b) $y = 2x^2 - 3x - 1$
   (c) $y = 2x^2 - 3x - 3$ (d) $y = 2x^2 - 3x - 9$
2. (a) $s = 4.9t^2$ (b) $s = 0.25t^4 - 0.5t^2$
   (c) $s = 1 - \cos t$ (d) $s = 10(e^{0.1t} - 1)$

3. (a) $F(x) = x^3 - \frac{3}{2}x^2 + 6x - 13$
   (b) $F(x) = (2x)^{\frac{3}{2}} - 5$
   (c) $F(x) = 4e^{\frac{x}{2}} + 3 - 4e$
   (d) $F(x) = \frac{2}{3}(x^{1.5} + (4 - x)^{1.5}) + 3 - \dfrac{8\sqrt{2}}{3}$

4. (a) $y = \sin x - \cos x + 1$ (b) $y = e^x - e^{-x}$
   (c) $y = 2(\sqrt{x + 1} - 1)$
   (d) $y = 0.25x^4 + 0.5x^2$

5. (a) $F(x) = \frac{1}{2}(x^2 + 1)$ (b) $F(x) = \frac{1}{4}(x^4 + 3)$
   (c) $F(x) = -\frac{1}{6}(x^6 + 5)$ (d) $F(x) = -x$

6. $y = e^x + 4$ 7. $F(x) = \frac{1}{3}(2 - x^3)$

8. (a) $s = \frac{1}{2}(1 + \sin 2t)$

   (b) $s = 0.5t - 0.25 \sin 2t - \dfrac{\pi}{4}$

EXERCISE 9.3

1. (a) 2 m (b) 4 m (c) 8 m
2. The canister lands with a velocity of 99 m/s, so it probably will not burst.
3. 2.9 s   4. 4.6 s   5. 2.5 km
6. (a) 400 m (b) 55 m/s (c) About 13.6 s
7. $\frac{1}{9.8}(v_0 + \sqrt{v_0^2 + 19.6\,h_0})$ seconds

EXERCISE 9.4

1. $1366.84   2. 43 a   3. 11.5 a
4. (a) 0.45 s (b) 2.1 s   5. 22.5°C
6. 19 min   7. 23°C

8. (a) $\dfrac{dA}{dt} = k(M - A)$ (b) $A = M(1 - e^{-kt})$
   (c) 29 min

9. $I = \dfrac{E}{R}(1 - e^{-\frac{Rt}{L}})$

EXERCISE 9.5

1. (a) 50.5 kg (b) 173 min
2. (a) 75.9 kg (b) 69 min
3. (a) 41.2 kg (b) 195 min
4. (a) 38.5 kg
5. (a) $A = 30(1 - e^{-0.36t})$ (b) After two minutes
   (c) 10 min
6. (a) $M = 80 + 15e^{-0.0016t}$ (b) 80 kg (c) 433 d
7. $\dfrac{g}{k}$ metres per second
8. $A = cV + (A_0 - cV)e^{-\frac{rt}{v}}$

EXERCISE 9.6

1. (a) $P = \dfrac{6000}{1 + 19e^{-0.75t}}$ (b) 3100   (c) 5.8 a

2. 7.4 h

3. (a) 16 d   (b) About 800

4. (a) 27.2 million   (b) 23.9 million   (c) 1987

5. 185, 620, 1650, 2910, 3640, and 3980.

6.

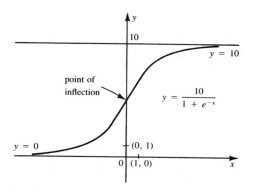

EXERCISE 9.7

1. (a) $s = 0$ (b) $s = \cos 2t$
   (c) $s = -\cos 2t + \sin 2t$
   (d) $s = 3 \cos 2t - 2.5 \sin 2t$

2. (a) $y = A \cos x + B \sin x$
   (b) $y = A \cos 3x + B \sin 3x$
   (c) $y = A \cos 1.5x + B \sin 1.5x$
   (d) $y = A \cos \sqrt{2}x + B \sin \sqrt{2}x$

3. (a) $f(x) = \cos x - 2 \sin x$
   (b) $f(x) = \cos 2x - \sin 2x$
   (c) $f(x) = \cos 1.5x - \dfrac{2}{1.5} \sin 1.5\, x$
   (d) $f(x) = \cos \sqrt{2}x - \sqrt{2} \sin \sqrt{2}x$

4. (a) $s = -0.1 \cos \sqrt{40}t$
   (b) $s = 0.18 \cos \sqrt{40}t$
   (c) $s = -0.40 \cos \sqrt{40}t$
   (d) $s = 0.39 \cos \sqrt{40}t$

5. (a) $s = -0.26 \cos \sqrt{40}t + \dfrac{1}{\sqrt{40}} \sin \sqrt{40}t$

   (b) $s = -0.26 \cos \sqrt{40}t - \dfrac{2}{\sqrt{40}} \sin \sqrt{40}t$

   (c) $s = -0.26 \cos \sqrt{40}t + \dfrac{3.7}{\sqrt{40}} \sin \sqrt{40}t$

   (d) $s = -0.26 \cos \sqrt{40}t - \dfrac{4.1}{\sqrt{40}} \sin \sqrt{40}t$

6. (a) $\sqrt{2}$ (b) 2   (c) 5   (d) $\sqrt{5}$ **7.** 0.44 m

9.8 REVIEW EXERCISE

1. (a) $F(x) = 1.5x^2 - \pi x + C$
   (b) $F(x) = -e \cos x + \sqrt{2} \sin x + C$
   (c) $F(x) = 2\sqrt{2}\, e^{\sqrt{2}x} + \dfrac{1}{7\pi}e^{-\pi x} + C$
   (d) $F(x) = \ln(x^4 + 1) + C$

2. (a) $F(x) = 0.1 \ln x - \sqrt{2}x^{-1} + C$
   (b) $F(x) = 1.6\, x^{2.5} - \dfrac{3}{3.7}x^{3.7} + C$
   (c) $F(x) = \frac{2}{3}(1 + \sqrt{2} + \sqrt{3})x^{\frac{3}{2}} + C$
   (d) $F(x) = e^{\frac{1}{x}} + C$

3. (a) $F(x) = \frac{2}{3}x^3 - \frac{3}{2}x^2 + \frac{37}{6}$
   (b) $F(x) = e^x + \frac{1}{2}e^{-2x} + 4 - e^{-1} - \frac{1}{2}e^2$
   (c) $F(x) = -\cos x - \sin x + 4 + \cos 1 - \sin 1$
   (d) $F(x) = \frac{1}{3}[(3 + 2x)^{1.5} + 11]$

4. 103 s   **5.** (a) 560 m   (b) 63.4 m/s   (c) 19 s

6. 22°C   **7.** (a) 52 kg   (b) 23 min

8. (a) $P = \dfrac{420}{1 + 20e^{-2.5t}}$ (b) 415   (c) 30 h

9. (a) $y = -0.6 \sin 5x$
   (b) $y = 2 \cos 5x + 0.2 \sin 5x$
   (c) $y = \cos 5x$
   (d) $y = 3 \cos 5x + 0.6 \sin 5x$

10. (a) $s = \dfrac{4}{\sqrt{3}} \sin \sqrt{3}t$ (b) $\dfrac{4}{\sqrt{3}}$

9.9 CHAPTER 9 TEST

1. (b) $F(x) = \frac{1}{3}x^3 - 3e^{-x} - 4 \cos x + C$

2. $F(x) = \frac{1}{3}(2\sqrt{2}x^{\frac{3}{2}} + 18x - 29)$ **3.** 6.5 s

4. 3 min   **5.** 4.6 min

6. If N is the number who have heard the rumour
   after t days, then $N = \dfrac{1500}{1 + 249e^{-1.8t}}$

7. $y = 2 \cos\left(\dfrac{2x}{3}\right) - 4.5 \sin\left(\dfrac{2x}{3}\right)$

CHAPTER 10 AREA

REVIEW AND PREVIEW TO CHAPTER 10

EXERCISE 1

1. (a) $\dfrac{\pi}{8}(1 + \sqrt{3})$ (b) $\dfrac{\pi}{4}$ (c) $\dfrac{3}{4}$

EXERCISE 2

1. (a) $(1^2 + 1) + (2^2 + 1) + (3^2 + 1) +$
$(4^2 + 1) + (5^2 + 1) = 60$

(b) $\dfrac{1}{4}f(1) + \dfrac{1}{2}f(2) + \dfrac{3}{4}f(3) + f(4)$

(c) $\dfrac{3}{n}f\left(1 + \dfrac{3}{4}\right) + \dfrac{3}{n}f\left(1 + \dfrac{6}{4}\right) + \dfrac{3}{n}f\left(1 + \dfrac{9}{4}\right) +$
$\ldots + \dfrac{3}{n}f\left(1 + \dfrac{3n}{4}\right)$

2. (a) $\displaystyle\sum_{i=1}^{6}(3i - 2)$ (b) $\displaystyle\sum_{i=1}^{7}(-1)^{i-1}$ (c) $\displaystyle\sum_{i=1}^{n}x^i$

(d) $\displaystyle\sum_{i=1}^{6}\dfrac{i}{6}f\left(\dfrac{i}{6}\right)$ (e) $\displaystyle\sum_{i=1}^{n}\dfrac{i}{n}f\left(\dfrac{2i-2}{n}\right)$

3. (a) $\displaystyle\sum_{i=1}^{n}i^2 + 4\sum_{i=1}^{n}i + 4n$ (b) $3\displaystyle\sum_{i=1}^{20}i^2 - 12\sum_{i=1}^{20}i$

(c) $2\displaystyle\sum_{i=1}^{n}i^3 - 3\sum_{i=1}^{n}i^2 + 5\sum_{i=1}^{n}i - 12n$

EXERCISE 3

1. (a) $n(2n + 1)$ (b) $\dfrac{1}{2}(3^n - 1)$ (c) $n^2(n + 1)$

(d) $\dfrac{n}{2}(n^3 + 2n^2 + 4n - 1)$ (e) 270

(f) 24 821 640

EXERCISE 10.1

1. (a) $\dfrac{76}{3}$ (b) $\dfrac{45}{64}$

(c) $\dfrac{50}{3}$

(d) 1

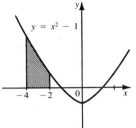

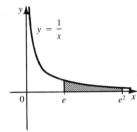

(e) 2

(f) $\dfrac{16}{3}$

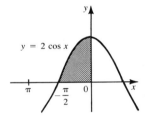

(g) 2

(h) $1 + \sqrt{3}$

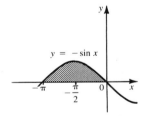

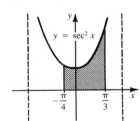

(i) $\dfrac{e^6 - 1}{e^4}$

(j) 20

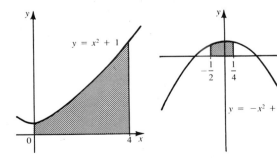

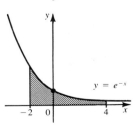

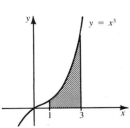

(k) 10.5

(l) $\dfrac{e^2 - 1}{e^2}$

(c) 6.75

(d) $\frac{4}{15}$

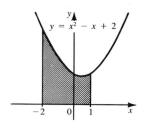

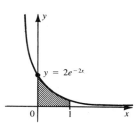

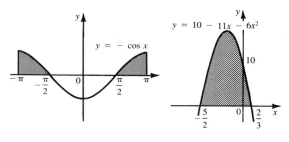

(m) $-2\sqrt{\dfrac{\sqrt{2} - 1}{2\sqrt{2}}} + 2$ (n) $\dfrac{3(1 + \sqrt{2})}{2\sqrt{2}}$

(e) 2

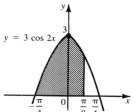

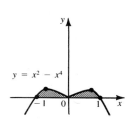

(o) $\frac{10}{11}$

(p) 309.3

(g) 108

(h) $\frac{125}{6}$

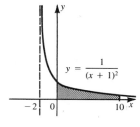

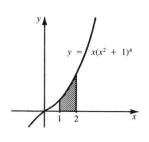

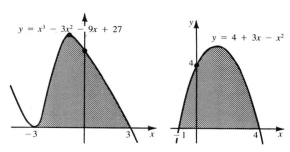

2. (a) $10\frac{2}{3}$

(b) 36

3. (a) ln 2

(b) ln 3

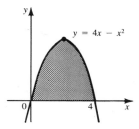

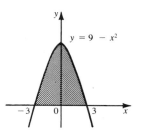

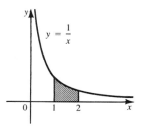

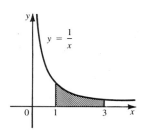

(c) $\ln e = 1$

(d) $\ln n$

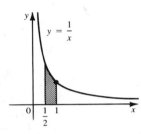

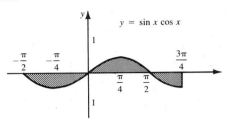

7. 1.25

4. (a) $\ln 2$

(b) $\ln 3$

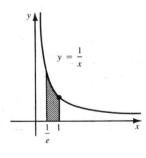

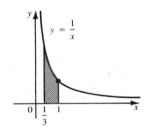

EXERCISE 10.2

1. (a) $\frac{50}{3}$

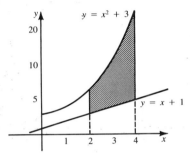

(b) $\frac{8}{3}$

(c) $\ln e = 1$

(d) $\ln 10$

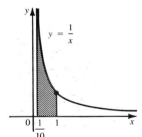

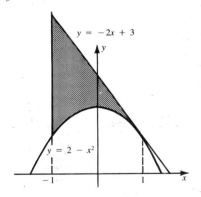

(c) $\frac{4}{3}$

5. 2

6. $11\frac{1}{3}$

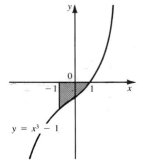

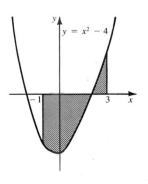

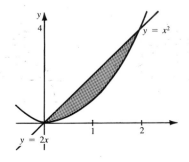

(d) $\frac{32}{3}$

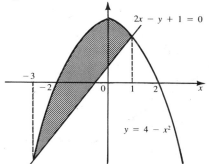

$2x - y + 1 = 0$

-3 -2 0 1 2 x

$y = 4 - x^2$

(h) $\frac{1}{12}$

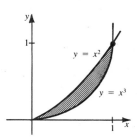

$y = x^2$

$y = x^3$

(i) 8

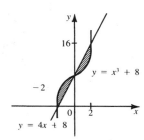

16

-2

$y = x^3 + 8$

0 2 x

$y = 4x + 8$

(e) 32

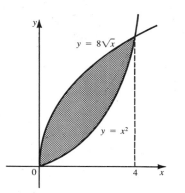

4

$y = 2x^2 - 8$

-2 2 x

$y = 4 - x^2$

(j) $\frac{4}{3}$

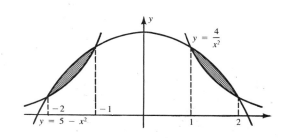

$y = \frac{4}{x^2}$

-2 -1 1 2

$y = 5 - x^2$

(f) $\frac{64}{3}$

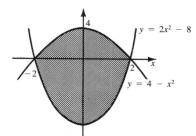

$y = 8\sqrt{x}$

$y = x^2$

0 4 x

(k) $\frac{16}{3}$

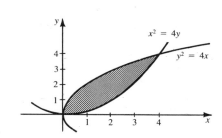

$x^2 = 4y$

$y^2 = 4x$

4

3

2

1

1 2 3 4 x

(g) $\frac{9}{2}$

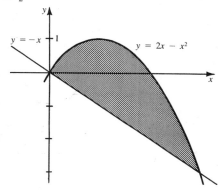

$y = -x$ 1

$y = 2x - x^2$

(l) $\frac{1}{2}$

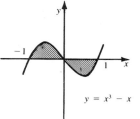

-1

1 x

$y = x^3 - x$

(m) 66

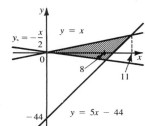

$y = -\frac{x}{2}$ $y = x$

0

8 11

-44 $y = 5x - 44$

(n) $\frac{20}{3}$

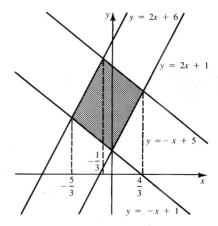

(r) $\ln 3 + \ln 2 - \frac{5}{8}$

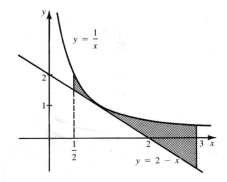

(o) $4\sqrt{2}$

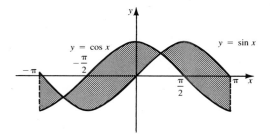

(s) $\frac{3\sqrt{3}}{2}$

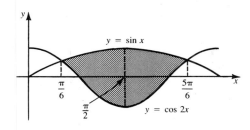

(p) $\dfrac{32 - \pi^2 + 8\pi}{32}$ (q) $\frac{8}{3}$

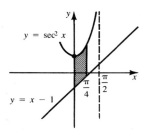

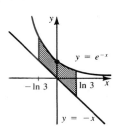

(t) $\frac{16}{3}$

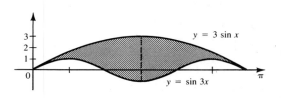

2. (a) $\frac{4}{3}$ (b) $\frac{7}{3}$

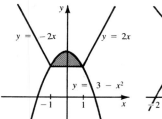

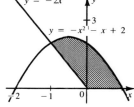

(c) $\dfrac{\pi}{4} + \tan^{-1} 2 + \ln \frac{2}{5}$

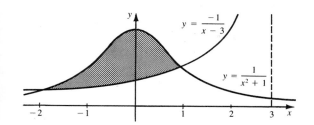

3. (a) ln 2

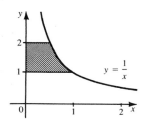

(b) $\dfrac{4\sqrt{3}}{9}$

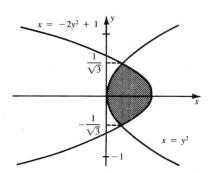

(c) 18

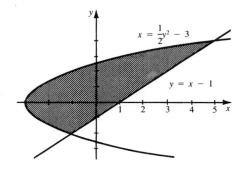

EXERCISE 10.3

1. (a) ln 1.5   (b) ln 2   (c) ln 3   (d) ln 4

2. (a)   (b)

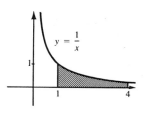
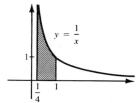

(c)   (d)

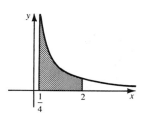
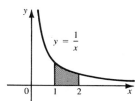

(e)   (f)

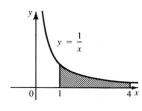
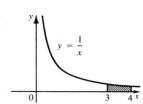

(g)   (h)

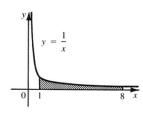
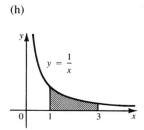

(i)

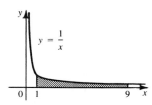

5. (a) $x + 36y - 12 = 0$ (b) Area of the trapezoid determined by the tangent in (a).

6. (b) Area of the trapezoid with vertices $(3, 0)$, $(6, 0)$, $\left(6, \frac{1}{6}\right)$, $\left(3, \frac{1}{3}\right)$

7. (b) Area of the trapezoid with vertices $(18, 0)$, $(36, 0)$, $\left(36, \frac{1}{36}\right)$, $\left(18, \frac{1}{18}\right)$

(c) 10

(d) $\frac{23}{12}$

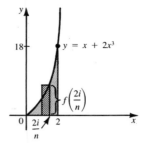

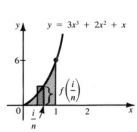

EXERCISE 10.4

1. (a) 24 (b) 28

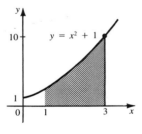

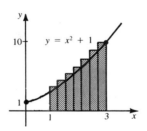

4. (a) $\frac{70}{3}$ (b) $\frac{75}{2}$

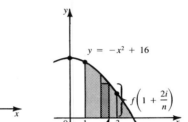

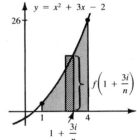

2. (a) $\frac{32}{3}$ (b) 11.48

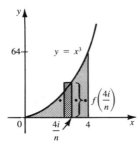

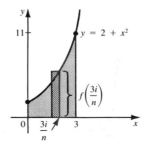

(c) 30 (d) $\frac{52}{3}$

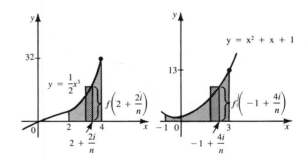

3. (a) 64 (b) 15

5. $\frac{\pi}{6}(1 + \sqrt{3})$

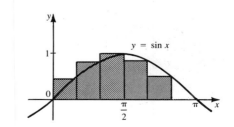

6. (a) $\frac{14}{3}$

(c) $\frac{2\pi}{3} + \sqrt{3}$ (d) $\frac{\pi^3}{12} + 2\sqrt{2}$

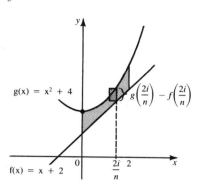

$g(x) = x^2 + 4$

$g\left(\frac{2i}{n}\right) - f\left(\frac{2i}{n}\right)$

$f(x) = x + 2$

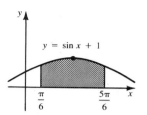

$y = \sin x + 1$

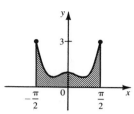

(e) $3e^2 - 5$ (f) $\ln 2 - \frac{1}{2}$

(b) $\frac{81}{2}$

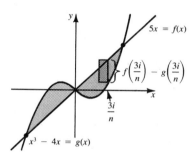

$5x = f(x)$

$f\left(\frac{3i}{n}\right) - g\left(\frac{3i}{n}\right)$

$x^3 - 4x = g(x)$

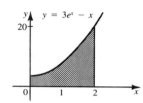

$y = 3e^x - x$

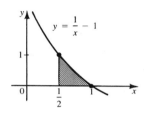

$y = \frac{1}{x} - 1$

2. (a) $\frac{32}{3}$ (b) $\frac{1}{20}$

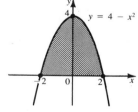

$y = 4 - x^2$

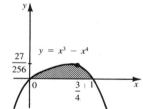

$y = x^3 - x^4$

$\frac{27}{256}$

EXERCISE 10.5

1. (a) (i) 6.521 610   (ii) 6.322 986
(b) $e^2 - 1 \doteq 6.389\ 056$
2. (a) (i) 1.657 458   (ii) 1.732 039
(b) $\cos\frac{\pi}{4} - \cos\pi \doteq 1.707\ 107$
3. 40.862 771   **4.** 0.343 793   **5.** 1.116 667
6. 0.329 675

(c) $\frac{343}{6}$

EXERCISE 10.6

1. (a) $\frac{4}{9}$ (b) $\frac{9}{16}$

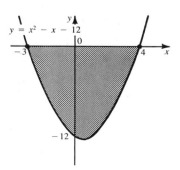

$y = x^2 - x - 12$

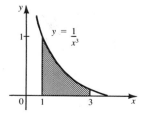

$y = \frac{1}{x^3}$

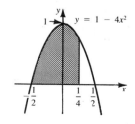

$y = 1 - 4x^2$

3. (a) $\frac{34}{3}$ (b) 6   **5.** (a)   (b)

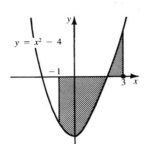

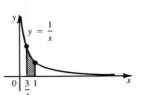

6. (a) ln 3   (b) trapezoid with vertices $(4, 0)$, $(12, 0)$ $\left(12, \frac{1}{12}\right)$, $\left(4, \frac{1}{4}\right)$ and area $\doteq 1.333\ 333$

(c) $\frac{17}{4}$ (d) 3

8. (a) $\frac{4}{3}$ (b) 18   (c) $393\frac{1}{3}$

9. (a) 0.789 219   (b) 2.866 105

10. 37.326 155

11. 2.166 253 if the height is determined by the midpoint of the base

12. (a) $\frac{1}{6}$ (b) $\frac{1}{4}$

13. (a) $\frac{32}{3}$ (b) $2\sqrt[3]{2}$

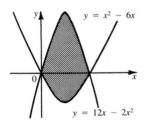

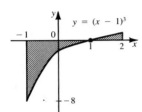

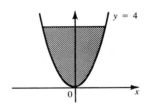

4. (a) 108   (b) $\frac{4}{3}$

10.7 CHAPTER 10 TEST

1. 6   **2.** $\frac{64}{3}$

(c) $\dfrac{9\sqrt{3}}{4}$ (d) $6 - \ln 16$

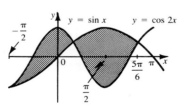

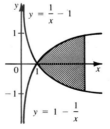

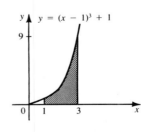

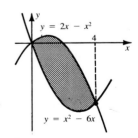

3. 8

4. $\frac{128}{15}$

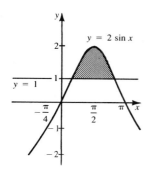

5. $4\sqrt{3} - \sqrt{2} - 1 - \dfrac{5\pi}{12}$

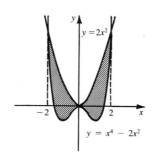

6. (a) ln 2.5   (b) the area of the trapezoid with vertices $(2, 0)$, $(5, 0)$, $\left(5, \frac{1}{5}\right)$, $\left(2, \frac{1}{2}\right)$ is 1.05

7. 18   **8.** 0.537 607   **9.** 77.177 154

10. $\frac{95}{6}$

CUMULATIVE REVIEW FOR CHAPTERS 8 TO 10

1. (a)

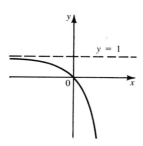

(b) R, $(-\infty, 1)$, $y = 1$

2. (a)

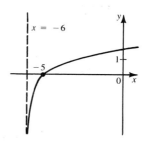

(b) $(-6, \infty)$, R, $x = -6$

3. (a) 1   (b) $-\infty$ **4.** (a) 2   (b) 9

5. (a) $\frac{1}{2}(\ln 20 - 1) \doteq 0.997\ 866$

(b) $1 - \dfrac{1}{e^2} \doteq 0.864\ 665$

6. (a) $y' = -(3 + 4x)e^{3-4x}$

(b) $y' = \dfrac{2x^2 - (x^2 + 1)\ln(x^2 + 1)}{x^2(x^2 + 1)}$

(c) $y' = \dfrac{2xe^{x^2}}{1 + e^{x^2}}$ (d) $y' = -\dfrac{10^{-\sqrt{x}}\ln 10}{2\sqrt{x}}$

(e) $y' = \frac{1}{2}\left(\dfrac{1}{x} + \dfrac{3x^2}{1 - x^3}\right)$

(f) $y' = x^{\tan x}\left(\sec^2 x \ln x + \dfrac{\tan x}{x}\right)$

7. (a) $g'(x) = e^{f(x)}f'(x)$ (b) $h'(x) = f'(e^x)e^x$

8. $3x - y = 3(\ln 3 - 1)$

9. (a) increasing on $(-1, \infty)$, decreasing on $(-\infty, -1)$ (b) minimum $f(-1) = -\frac{1}{e}$

(c) CU on $(-2, \infty)$, CD on $(-\infty, -2)$, IP $(-2, -2e^{-2})$

10. (a) $F(x) = 3x^4 - 3x^3 + 4x^2 + 31x + C$

(b) $F(x) = -2\cos 2x + \frac{5}{3}\sin(3x + 1) + C$

(c) $F(x) = -\frac{2}{3}e^{3x} - \frac{1}{12}e^{-4x} + C$

11. (a) $F(x) = \sqrt{2}\ln(x + 1) - \sqrt{3}\ln x + c$

(b) $F(x) = \frac{2}{3}(\sqrt{2} + \sqrt{5} + \sqrt{8})x^{\frac{3}{2}} + C$

12. (a) $F(x) = x^3 + x^2 - 9$

(b) $F(x) = 2\sqrt{x} - \frac{1}{2}x^2 + 5 - 2\sqrt{2}$

(c) $F(x) = \frac{3}{4}(e^{4x} - e^8) + 3$ **13.** 3.9 s

14. (a) $1200\left(\frac{10}{3}\right)^t$ (b) 44 444

(c) 53 510 bacteria/h   (c) 1.76 h

15. (a) $(50)e^{-\frac{\ln 2}{19.7}t}$ (b) 0.73 g   (c) 0.026 g/min
(d) 1 h, 51 min

16. 11 min   **17.** 4.53 kg

18. two years and eleven months

19. $s = 1.7 \cos 1.2t + 1.5 \sin 1.2t$

20. (a) $\frac{2\pi}{5}s$ (b) 0.75 m/s

21. (a) $\frac{164}{3}$ (b) $\ln \frac{5}{3}$

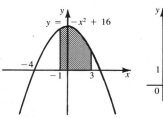

(c) $\dfrac{e^7 - 1}{e^7}$

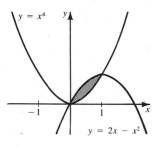

22. (a) $\frac{7}{15}$ (b) $\frac{9}{2}$

(c) $\dfrac{8}{\sqrt{2}}$

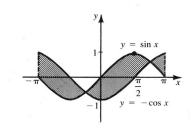

(d) 2   (e) $\frac{157}{12}$

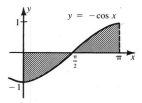

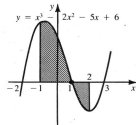

23. (a) $\frac{1}{2}ma^2$ (b) $\frac{4}{3}$ **24.** 161.601 142

25. 1.860 176

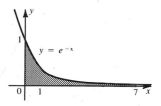

CHAPTER 11 INTEGRALS

REVIEW AND PREVIEW TO CHAPTER 11

EXERCISE 1
1. (a) $2000\,\pi$ cm³   (b) $1080\,\pi$ cm³
   (c) $2.4\,\pi$ cm³   (d) $3906.25\,\pi$ cm³
   (e) $317.25\,\pi$ cm³   (f) $960\,\pi$ cm³

EXERCISE 11.1
1. (a) $\frac{16}{3}$ (b) 7.5

(c) 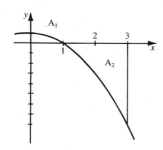   (d)

2. (a) -5 (b) 1   (c) $\frac{1}{4}$ (d) 3

3. (a) -6 (b) 2

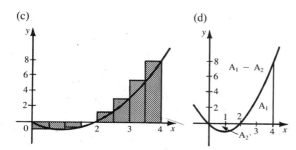

4. $\frac{1}{3}(b^3 - a^3)$

5. (a)

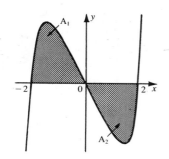

(b) 0   (c) $A_1 = A_2$

EXERCISE 11.2

1. (a) 26   (b) 30   (c) -3 (d) $\frac{7}{3}$ (e) $\frac{27}{4}$ (f) 1.01
   (g) $\frac{1}{6}$ (h) $\frac{17}{6}$ (i) $\frac{4}{9}$ (j) 9   (k) $\frac{11}{8}$ + ln 2
   (l) 2 + ln 4   (m) $\dfrac{48\ 128}{33}$ (n) π^2 + 1
   (o) $\dfrac{2}{\sqrt{3}} - 1$ (p) $\frac{1}{2}(3\sqrt{2} - 1) - \sqrt{3}$

2. (a) $\frac{1}{6}x^6 - \frac{1}{2}x^4 + 4x + C$ (b) $\frac{2}{7}x^{\frac{7}{2}} + C$
   (c) $\frac{1}{2}t^2 + 2 \ln|t| + C$
   (d) $x + \frac{4}{3}x^{\frac{3}{2}} + \frac{1}{2}x^2 + C$ (e) $\frac{4}{7}x^{\frac{7}{4}} - \frac{20}{3}x^{\frac{3}{4}} + C$
   (f) $\sin\theta - \cos\theta + C$ (g) $x^5 + 2\csc x + C$
   (h) $x - 2\cot x + C$

3. (a) $e - 1$ (b) $\dfrac{3}{2\ln 2}$ (c) $\dfrac{\pi}{6}$ (d) π
   (e) $2 + \frac{3}{2}\pi$ (f) $-2e^{-\pi}$

4. The function is not continuous on $[-2, 1]$, so the Fundamental Theorem does not apply.

EXERCISE 11.3

1. (a) $u = x^2$ (b) $u = \ln x$ (c) $u = 5x$
   (d) $u = \sin x$

2. (a) $-\frac{1}{22}(1 - x^2)^{11} + C$ (b) $\frac{1}{5}e^{5x} + C$
   (c) $\frac{2}{3}(x - 1)^{\frac{3}{2}} + C$ (d) $\frac{1}{2}\ln|x^2 + 2x - 6| + C$

3. (a) $\frac{1}{18}(x^2 + 4)^9 + C$ (b) $\frac{2}{9}(x^3 + 2)^{\frac{3}{2}} + C$
   (c) $\frac{1}{11}(x + 6)^{11} + C$ (d) $-\dfrac{1}{3(3x - 1)} + C$
   (e) $\frac{1}{3}\tan 3x + C$ (f) $\frac{1}{16}(1 + 2x^4)^2 + C$
   (g) $\frac{1}{3}\sin^3 x + C$ (h) $\frac{2}{3}(\ln x)^{\frac{3}{2}} + C$
   (i) $\frac{1}{3}e^{t^3} + C$ (j) $-\ln|1 - x| + C$
   (k) $-\dfrac{1}{2(x^3 - 2x + 1)^2} + C$
   (l) $-2\cos\sqrt{x} + C$ (m) $-e^{3-x} + C$
   (n) $-e^{\cos x} + C$ (o) $\frac{2}{3}(1 + \tan x)^{\frac{3}{2}} + C$
   (p) $-\frac{1}{2}\cos(x^2) + C$ (q) $\cos(\cos x) + C$
   (r) $\frac{1}{2}(\tan^{-1} x)^2 + C$

4. (a) $\frac{1}{2}(e^3 - e)$ (b) $\frac{266}{3993}$ (c) $\frac{8}{3}$ (d) $\dfrac{2}{\pi}$ (e) $\frac{3}{2}$
   (f) 2.1   (g) $\frac{665}{6}$ (h) $\frac{1}{6}(e^{20} - e^5)$

5. (a) $\ln|\sec x| + C$ (b) $\ln|\sin x| + C$

6. $\frac{1}{6}(41\sqrt{41} - 1)$ **7.** 2   **8.** $\frac{1}{2}(e^2 - 3) + \dfrac{1}{e}$

9. (a) $2 \ln (\sqrt{x} + 1) + C$
(b) $x + 2 - \ln|x + 2| + C$

EXERCISE 11.4

1. (a) $x \sin x + \cos x + C$ (b) $\frac{1}{2}xe^{2x} - \frac{1}{4}e^{2x} + C$

(c) $\frac{1}{2}x^2 \ln x - \frac{1}{4}x^2 + C$

(d) $t \tan t - \ln|\sec t| + C$

(e) $(x^2 - 2x + 2)e^x + C$

(f) $\left(\frac{17}{16} - \frac{3}{4}x\right)e^{-4x} + C$

(g) $x \tan^{-1} x - \frac{1}{2} \ln(x^2 + 1) + C$

(h) $\dfrac{e^x}{x + 1} + C$

2. (a) π (b) $1 - \dfrac{2}{e}$ (c) $\frac{32}{5} \ln 2 - \frac{31}{25}$ (d) 4π

3. (b) $6 - 2e$ **4.** $2e^{\sqrt{x}}(\sqrt{x} - 1) + C$

5. $\frac{1}{9}(1 - 7e^{-6})$ **6.** $5 \ln 5 - 4$

7. $\frac{1}{2}e^x(\sin x - \cos x) + C$

EXERCISE 11.5

1. (a) $\sin x - \frac{1}{3} \sin^3 x + C$

(b) $\frac{1}{5} \cos^5 x - \frac{1}{3} \cos^3 x + C$

(c) $\frac{1}{8}(x - \frac{1}{4} \sin 4x) + C$

(d) $\frac{8}{15}$ (e) $\frac{8}{315}$ (f) $\dfrac{3\pi}{16}$

2. (a) $\frac{1}{5}(1 - x^2)^{\frac{5}{2}} - \frac{1}{3}(1 - x^2)^{\frac{3}{2}} + C$ (b) π

3. (b) $\frac{1}{3}(2 - \sqrt{2})$ **4.** 12π

5. $-\frac{1}{3}(1 - x^2)^{\frac{3}{2}} + C$

EXERCISE 11.6

1. $\dfrac{A}{x + 2} + \dfrac{B}{x - 3}$

2. $\dfrac{A}{x + 2} + \dfrac{B}{x + 5} + \dfrac{C}{(x + 5)^2}$

3. $\dfrac{A}{x - 1} + \dfrac{B}{x + 1} + \dfrac{C}{(x + 1)^2} + \dfrac{D}{x - 2} + $
$\dfrac{E}{(x - 2)^2} + \dfrac{F}{(x - 2)^3}$

4. $\dfrac{Ax + B}{x^2 + x + 1} + \dfrac{C}{x - 7}$

5. $\dfrac{A}{x + 5} + \dfrac{Bx + C}{x^2 + 4} + \dfrac{Dx + E}{x^2 + 2x + 6}$

6. $\dfrac{A}{x - 4} + \dfrac{B}{x + 4}$

7. $1 - \left(\dfrac{A}{x + 3} + \dfrac{B}{x + 4}\right)$

8. $\dfrac{A}{x - 5} + \dfrac{B}{(x - 5)^2} + \dfrac{C}{(x - 5)^3} + \dfrac{Dx + E}{x^2 + 5x + 10}$
$+ \dfrac{Fx + G}{(x^2 + 5x + 10)^2}$

9. $\ln \sqrt{\dfrac{x - 1}{x + 1}} + C$ **10.** $6 + 5 \ln 4$

11. $\frac{1}{2}x^2 - 2 \ln|x - 2| + \ln|x - 1| + C$

12. $\frac{1}{2}t^2 - 27 \ln|t + 3| + 64 \ln|t + 4| + C$

13. $2 \ln|x| - \frac{1}{3} \ln|2 + x| - \frac{5}{3} \ln|1 - x| + C$

14. $-\frac{1}{4} \ln|x - 1| - \dfrac{1}{2(x - 1)} + \frac{1}{4} \ln|x + 1| + K$

15. $x - \frac{1}{9} \ln|x| + \dfrac{1}{3x} + \frac{28}{9} \ln|x + 3| + K$

16. $\ln 2$

17. $-\frac{2}{3} \ln|x - 1| + \frac{1}{3} \ln|x^2 + x + 1| - $
$\dfrac{4}{\sqrt{3}} \tan^{-1} \dfrac{2x + 1}{\sqrt{3}} + C$

18. $\frac{1}{2} \ln(x^2 + 1) + 2 \tan^{-1} x - \frac{1}{2} \ln(x^2 + 2x + 2) + $
$\tan^{-1}(x + 1) + K$

EXERCISE 11.7

1. (a) $\dfrac{1016}{15} \pi$

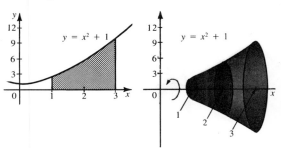

(b) $\frac{16}{15}\pi$

2. (a) $\frac{4}{3}\pi$ (b) $\frac{158}{15}\pi$

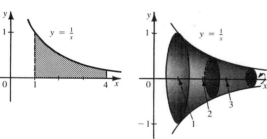

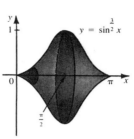

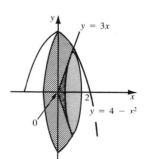

(c) $\frac{3}{4}\pi$

(c) π (d) 320π

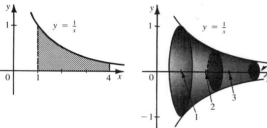

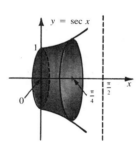

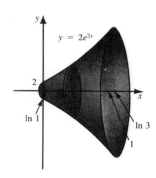

(d) $\frac{3}{10}\pi$

3. $\frac{500}{3}\pi$ **4.** 48π **5.** $\frac{4}{3}\pi r^3$ **6.** $\frac{1}{3}\pi r^2 h$

7. $\left(2\ln 2 - \frac{3}{4}\right)\pi$ **8.** $\left(\frac{3}{2} - \ln 4\right)\pi$

9. $\frac{4}{3}\pi ab^2$ **10.** $\frac{224}{15}\pi$ **11.** $\frac{3}{2}\pi$

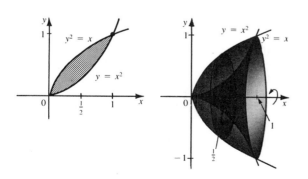

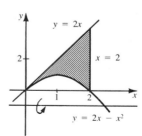

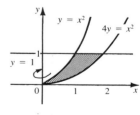

11.8 REVIEW EXERCISE

1. (a) 32.5   (b) $-\frac{5}{12}$ **2.** 0

3. (a) $\frac{1}{5}x^5 - 3x^4 + 3x^2 + C$

(b) $\frac{2}{3}x^{\frac{3}{2}} - \frac{2}{5}x^{\frac{5}{2}} + \frac{6}{7}x^{\frac{7}{2}} + C$

(c) $x^2 + \sec x + C$ (d) $\frac{3}{5}x^{\frac{5}{3}} + 3x^{\frac{2}{3}} + C$

(e) $\ln|x| + \ln|\sin x| + C$ (f) $\sqrt{4 + x^2} + C$

(g) $\frac{2}{3}(1 + e^x)^{\frac{3}{2}} + C$ (h) $\frac{1}{4}\sec 4x + C$

(i) $\frac{2}{3}x^{\frac{3}{2}} \ln x - \frac{4}{9}x^{\frac{3}{2}} + C$ (j) $\ln|\ln x| + C$

(k) $\ln\left|\dfrac{x}{1-x}\right| + C$ (l) $-\frac{2}{5}\ln|x| - \frac{1}{35}\ln$
$|x + 5| + \frac{3}{7}\ln|x - 2| + C$

(m) $-\frac{1}{9}e^{-3x}(3x + 1) + C$

(n) $-\cos x + \frac{1}{3}\cos^3 x + C$

(o) $\ln|x + 1| - \dfrac{3}{x+1} + C$

(p) $\ln \dfrac{|x|}{\sqrt{x^2 + x + 1}} - \dfrac{1}{\sqrt{3}}\tan^{-1}\left(\dfrac{2x+1}{\sqrt{3}}\right) + C$

(q) $\frac{1}{2}x^2 + \frac{3}{2}\ln|x + 1| - \frac{9}{2}\ln|x + 3| + C$

(r) $x - 2\tan^{-1}\left(\dfrac{x}{2}\right) + C$ (s) $\frac{1}{2}(\sin^{-1}x)^2 + C$

(t) $\dfrac{x}{9\sqrt{9 - x^2}} + C$ (u) $-\ln|1 - e^x| + C$

(v) $\ln(e^x + 1) - \ln(e^x + 2) + C$

4. (a) $\frac{4}{3}$ (b) $\frac{1}{3}(1 - e^{-3})$ (c) $\frac{2}{3} + 3\ln 3$ (d) $3\ln 3$

(e) $\frac{2}{15}$ (f) $\pi - 2$ (g) $1 - \ln 2$ (h) $\dfrac{9\pi}{4}$

5. $2 - \dfrac{\pi}{2}$

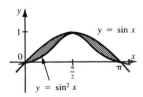

6. (a) 8π

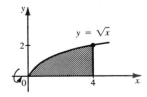

(b) $\dfrac{\pi}{2}$ (c) $\pi \ln 2$

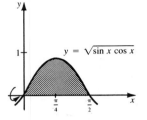

(d) $\dfrac{3}{8}\pi$ **7.** (a) $\dfrac{832}{15}\pi$

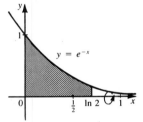

(b) $\frac{32}{3}\pi$ (c) $\dfrac{\pi}{2}$

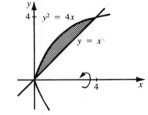

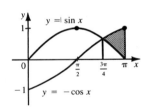

11.9 CHAPTER 11 TEST

1. (b) 12   **2.** (a) $\frac{1}{2}$ (b) $3\left(1 - \dfrac{1}{\sqrt[3]{2}}\right)$

(c) 1   (d) $\frac{1}{10}$

3. (a) $\frac{1}{3}e^{x^3} + C$ (b) $\sin x - \frac{2}{3}\sin^3 x + \frac{1}{5}\sin^5 x + C$

(c) $2\sin\sqrt{x} + C$ (d) $\frac{1}{2}x - \frac{1}{4}\sin 2x + C$

(e) $\ln|x - 1| - 5\ln|x - 2| + 5\ln$
$|x - 3| + C$

(f) $-\frac{1}{9}\ln|x| - \dfrac{1}{3x} + \frac{1}{9}\ln|x + 3| + C$

(g) $x - \tan^{-1}x + C$ **4.** $\dfrac{255}{64}\pi$

5. (a) $\frac{16}{3}$ (b) $\frac{64}{3}\pi$

INDEX